ANIMAL BEHAVIOUR

A Synthesis of Ethology and
Comparative Psychology

ANIMAL BEHAVIOUR

A Synthesis of Ethology and Comparative Psychology

Robert A. Hinde
Cambridge University

McGraw-Hill Book Company
New York · St. Louis · San Francisco
Toronto · London · Sydney

Preface

The obsolescence of the old distinctions between the biological sciences is nowhere more evident than in the study of animal behaviour. The problems it raises not only provide a meeting ground for psychologists, zoologists, physiologists, anatomists, geneticists, ecologists and many others—they demand their cooperation. As a result of this, the subject of animal behaviour cannot be rigidly circumscribed: its students both contribute to and depend on the traditional disciplines of biology.

In this book I have attempted to survey the area where psychology, physiology, and ethology overlap. The term ethology is applied particularly to the work of students who, although differing widely in the problems they tackle, the level of analysis at which they work, the methods they use and the theoretical interpretations (if any) they adopt, share certain orienting attitudes which are, perhaps, more important as unifying factors than any particular theoretical scheme. Many of these attitudes are a consequence of the zoological training of the early ethologists. They felt, for instance, that the description and classification of behaviour is a necessary preliminary to its analysis; that the behaviour of an animal cannot be properly studied without some knowledge of the environment to which its species has become adapted in evolution; and that questions about the evolution and biological function of behaviour are, in principle, as valid and important as those about its immediate causation.

In practice it is not profitable to make a rigid distinction between their interests and those of many physiologists and psychologists. In studying causation, ethologists have sought explanations in physiological terms; and there have long been comparative psychologists interested in the problems with which ethologists are concerned. More recently the mutual benefit to be gained from a marriage of the ethological approach with the detailed analyses made by those psychologists especially concerned with learning has become apparent. It is for these reasons that, although there will always, rightly, be some who continue in the traditions of classical comparative psychology and others who will pursue classical ethology, the term ethology is now often extended to cover the whole area of common interest.

Because the common ground involves, primarily, questions about the causation and development of behaviour in the individual, these have been my main concern: the evolution and function of behaviour, although the principal interest of the early ethologists such as Heinroth, Whitman, Craig and Lorenz, are considered more briefly. While believing that the student of the causation of behaviour must work towards physiological explanations, limitations of space and my own competence have prohibited, with few exceptions, detailed discussion of neurophysiological mechanisms. At the other extreme, I have touched only briefly on social organization, dominance hierarchies, and other consequences of individual behaviour for the group. I have limited myself to those aspects of the study of learning for which ethologists' observations have a special relevance, and I have omitted any discussion of the genetics of behaviour. Where it seemed relevant, I have attempted to show how my subject matter is related to these other fields and to provide one or two recent key references for those who wish to follow them.

Within these limits I have drawn my material primarily from studies of vertebrate behaviour, to some extent from studies of arthropods and molluscs, but hardly at all from forms lower than these: the wider the range of species discussed, the greater the diversity of the mechanisms which underlie their behaviour and, therefore, the more superficial the generalizations that can be made.

To achieve a wholly satisfactory classification of the material has proved an impossible task: such traditional categories as motivation and perception, or maturation and learning, can be artificial, and constrain nature. Nevertheless, a book must be divided into chapters, so I have had to resort to frequent cross-references. The chapters are grouped into four sections. The first is concerned with general questions of method and theory. The immediate causation of behaviour is considered in Section 2, and its development in the individual in Section 3. Questions of the evolution and function of behaviour are discussed more briefly in Section 4.

It would have been impossible for me to have completed this book without the help of numerous friends and colleagues. I would like especially to thank W. H. Thorpe, Director of the Sub-department of Animal Behaviour at Cambridge; it has been my good fortune to work with him for the last fifteen years, and I am happy to have this opportunity to acknowledge my debt to him. He read the manuscript in full, and it has benefited greatly from his criticisms. The book was originally planned as a joint one with N. Tinbergen, but extraneous circumstances made a collaborative project impossible. He has nevertheless read part of the manuscript, and I am greatly indebted to him for his comments on it, and also for the many discussions we have had and for all I have learnt from him. Yvette Spencer-Booth read a complete draft of the manuscript. Her attention to points of logic and exposition and her hard-headed constructive criticism forced me to re-think many issues, and led to the elimination of many errors and inconsistencies: I am very grateful to her. In my attempts to bring together the studies of ethologists and comparative psychologists I have been helped by four American colleagues. Joan Stevenson read critically the whole manuscript, making many suggestions for its improvement on both major issues and points of detail, and introducing me to material with which

I had previously been unfamiliar: I profited greatly from discussions with her. F. A. Beach, Frances Clayton and J. S. Rosenblatt each read a number of chapters and, by their comments and suggestions, helped to reduce their shortcomings. I also received much help from others who read and commented on parts of the manuscript—P. Bateson, P. Bertelson, J. M. Cullen, G. Horn, J. S. Kennedy, Barbara Lade, H. W. Lissmann, C. J. Pennycuick, M. Richards, and a number of other colleagues. The final draft owed much to the care with which my wife amended earlier and clumsier versions. I am grateful to Yvette Spencer-Booth for a number of figures, and to Elizabeth Steel for some of the diagrams. Finally, I would like to acknowledge my debt to Moira Bruce for the care with which she looked after the preparation of the manuscript and helped in checking references and proofs.

Contents

SECTION 1

Aims and Methods

1

Introduction

1.1. The Network of Events

The moment we start to observe behaviour, we begin to abstract. In the first place, while observing one aspect of behaviour, such as nest-building, we select some activities, but neglect others which are going on simultaneously. Yet the extent to which the different but simultaneous activities interact with each other is an open problem: if we are interested in the nest-building of a canary we may be able to neglect respiration, but if the building of the bubble nest of the air-breathing fish *Betta splendens* is under study, we cannot.

Second, we must confine our observations to a finite span of time. Yet each activity we study is related to events which immediately preceded it in time— electrical and chemical changes in nerve fibres, for instance, or activity in endocrine glands. These events may also be related to concurrent activities other than the one under observation. Furthermore, they occur in structures which have a developmental history extending further into the past.

Moving forward in time, the activity selected for study will have consequences reflected in changes in the organism, its environment, or both. Some of these consequences will influence the subsequent behaviour of the organism, and some will not: in either case, some will be of no significance, while others will affect its chances of surviving and reproducing in the environment in which it lives. These significant consequences, through the mechanisms of inheritance and natural selection, may influence the behaviour of future members of the species.

All this is not merely a way of saying that behaviour is complicated. Only when we see that behaviour involves a complex nexus of events in time, and that its study involves both the selection of an interval of time, and also selection from among the events occurring within that interval, can we even formulate the problems which it poses. Conversely, the problems we choose will determine the way in which we describe behaviour, what we select for analysis or measurement, and what we ignore or reject.

1.2. The Problems

The study of behaviour involves three main kinds of problem, theoretically separate but, in practice, interrelated.

First, the events selected for study must be related to other events or conditions which immediately precede them. This can be called "causal analysis": provided we are sufficiently sophisticated to bear in mind that temporal correlations may be of more than one kind, we need not be chary of using the word "cause" in its everyday sense.

For instance, if we find that a Great Tit consistently responds aggressively to its mirror image, we can be sure that visual stimuli are important. We may also find that the response occurs only if the animal is in a certain hormonal condition: internal and external factors are both involved. If we analyse the aggressive behaviour further, we find it consists of particular patterns of muscular contraction, and we may even hope to identify particular patterns of activity in the central nervous system: this represents a further stage of causal analysis. The causal study of behaviour thus leads to the study of sense organs, effectors, endocrine glands and the whole of the neuromuscular machinery. A complete understanding of the complicated systems underlying behaviour requires analysis at every level of complexity—not only the patterns of behaviour of the whole animal, but also the functioning of its sense organs and effectors, and the nervous mechanisms which relate them. The general methods used at each level are similar in principle but, of course, differ in detail.

Since the interval over which we make our causal analysis has a finite length, the earlier events may affect the later ones: the consequences of behaviour can become causes. Furthermore, the consequences of behaviour, through changes in the environment or within the organism itself, influence the probability that the same behaviour will be repeated during later intervals of time. The problems of cause and consequence are thus closely linked.

As an animal develops, its behaviour changes. The ontogeny of behaviour thus presents a second group of problems—how does the behaviour change? To what extent do the changes depend on environmental influences? How do such influences produce their effects? The behaviour we study in any one interval of time is influenced by the developmental processes which have given rise to the dynamic structure the animal has at that time, and influences its structure in the future: problems of ontogeny are thus closely linked to those of causation. Indeed, the distinction between "developmental" changes and the changes which occur from moment to moment is in some degree arbitrary, though in general it is convenient to distinguish between long-term more or less irreversible changes and those which are seasonal or of shorter duration.

The consequences of the activity under study may affect the organism's chances of survival or reproduction. Since individuals differ in their behaviour, natural selection can operate. Here, therefore, lies a third group of interrelated problems: which consequences of each pattern of behaviour provide material for the action of natural selection? How did the behaviour differences between species arise? What have been the nature and course of the evolutionary changes in the behaviour of each species? How does behaviour affect the formation of new species?

Questions about evolution usually refer to events in the past, and, thus, an experimental approach is nearly always impossible. Nevertheless, the comparative study of existing species has permitted considerable progress (*see* Section 4).

1.3. The Aims

These then are the problems with which we are concerned. What precisely can be achieved? In the case of causal analysis, at present we are beginning to understand a few types of behaviour in the repertoire of a handful of species at one level of analysis. About the behaviour of the great majority of species we know nothing. Except for certain limited aspects of behaviour, it would be presumptuous for us to think we could devise principles applicable to all organisms which were not mere truisms. Thus we must first limit our goals, attempting to elucidate unifying principles or generalizations applicable within a specified range. These may be relatively superficial and applicable to a wide range of phenomena or species, or else intensive and concerned only with one aspect of the behaviour of one animal. Most work lies somewhere in between these two extremes; but because generalizations made on the basis of one can be partially tested by information obtained with the other, both approaches are necessary and complementary to each other.

The extent of the validity of any statement is, of course, inversely related to the degree of precision with which it is stated: every generalization must thus be accompanied by a qualification which defines its scope. For instance, the statement, "In the breeding season most birds defend territories from other individuals of the same species and sex" is true for most male passerine birds but not, for example, for the Emperor Penguin (*Aptenodytes forsteri*). The statement, "Courtship displays depend on conflicting tendencies to behave in incompatible ways" is useful descriptively for many birds and fishes, but probably not for frogs and toads. The statement, "Chaffinch song attracts females but repels males" is true in the breeding season but not outside. More quantitative statements may be valid only for one strain of one species reared in a particular laboratory with one kind of pre-experimental treatment. Generalizations about behaviour and statements about the range of their validity must go hand in hand.

1.4. The Comparative Approach

At some stage it becomes necessary to make statements valid for more than one species: these must be based on comparative study of a number of species. But the comparative method has to be used cautiously: apparently close similarities between species may prove to be merely parallel evolutionary adaptations to a similar environment, and rest on quite different causal bases. Just as the wings of pterodactyls, birds, and bats evolved independently and have entailed different modifications to the primitive fore-limb, so also do the de-husking of seeds by tits (*Parus* spp.) and cardueline finches involve quite different movements. In order to assess the validity and depth of generalizations, it is therefore useful to choose first, for comparison, species believed on other grounds to be closely related phylogenetically, and only then proceed to the more distantly related ones (Chapters 27 and 28).

Pursued in this way, a comparative approach does more than permit generalization. Even in the initial stage of selective description, knowledge of the behaviour of one species may be helpful in the study of a related one. The present writer would certainly never have noticed the occasional pivoting movements made by Greenfinches (*Chloris chloris*) if he had not already been familiar with the highly ritualized and thus conspicuous pivoting display of the related Goldfinch (*Carduelis carduelis*) (Hinde, 1955/1956). Many complex behaviour patterns which have been elaborated after a long evolutionary history may be more easily understood if studied first in a relatively primitive and uncomplicated form. Such comparison is also the only method available for investigating the evolution of behaviour—the origin of many display postures would be quite obscure if it were not possible to observe them in a less ritualized form in related species (Lorenz, 1935, 1950, 1951).

The differences revealed by comparative study may be as interesting and important as the similarities: both will provide new theoretical insight into problems of causation, function, and evolution. Such differences must, however, be considered in relation to the biology of the species: for example, measures of "intelligence" obtained by applying the same test to widely differing species are meaningless unless this is done (Baerends, 1941; Tinbergen, 1951).

1.5. Levels of Analysis—Behaviour and Physiology

The material with which we start is usually at the behaviour level. If prediction of behaviour, given the antecedent conditions, was the sole aim, there might be no need to reduce to a physiological level: reference to underlying mechanisms could be unnecessary. But even if the complete prediction of behaviour were possible, we should still have advanced only one stage towards its full understanding: a further stage would be reached if the organization of behaviour could be understood in terms of the physiological organization which it reflects. Thus hypotheses must be judged not only at the behaviour level, but also in terms of their compatibility with lower ones.

Indeed, a theoretical system which by its nature cannot be related to physiological data is unlikely to have a wide validity even at the behaviour level. To take a parallel from physics, Toulmin (1953) has pointed out that it is a "great virtue of a good model that it does suggest further questions, taking us beyond the phenomena from which we began, and tempts us to formulate hypotheses which turn out to be experimentally fertile". Thus the Greek antenna-model of sight, and the models of thermal and gravitational phenomena as the effects of caloric and gravitational fluids, prompted unprofitable questions; on the other hand, "the model of light as a substance in motion is a good model, not only because it provides us with an easily intelligible interpretation of the diagrams of geometrical optics, but also because it . . . leads us to speculate about light-particles or light-waves as the things which travel, or are propagated: these speculations have borne fruit". Of course, just as an explanation of shadow-casting in terms of the wave theory of light tends to be laborious, prediction of behaviour via all the physiological intermediaries would be hopelessly cumbersome. But a behaviour model should be at least compatible with, and, if possible, translatable into, a physiological one. Analysis down to a physiological level is therefore a desirable, but not at present usually attainable, aim.

"Physiologizing" is, however, more than a long-term aim. Physiology is a valuable source of information for the behaviour student. A fertile psychology cannot afford to ignore physiological data that may suggest useful concepts: psychologists who deny themselves such data may be neglecting an important source of evidence on which to base their predictions of behaviour. It is proper, therefore, to aim at an analysis of behaviour into units which the physiologist will be able to handle: that analysis can be guided by a consideration of present physiological knowledge (Hebb, 1955).

The student who aims to pursue his analysis from the behavioural level to the physiological one is exposed to a special danger—concepts useful at one stage in the analysis may be misleading at another. A classic example of this— and we shall meet others later—is the concept of "drive", "urge" or "tendency", which is useful at an initial behavioural level of analysis but can become a handicap at a physiological one. The concepts used must be appropriate to the task in hand, and their limitations recognized.

1.6. Use of Models
The crossing of the bridge between behaviour and physiology can often be facilitated by the use of models. Those used in this book are "functional schemata, constructed in order to illustrate definite causal relationships", and "are quite abstract, although the consequences they predict are concrete and experimentally verifiable" (von Holst, 1954). They serve merely to indicate the job which the physiological machinery must be doing, and to provide the physiologist with an indication of what he must look for (*see also* Hinde, 1956a, 1960).

1.7. Summary
1. The study of behaviour involves selection from a complex nexus of events in time.

2. The study of behaviour involves three main kinds of problem—its immediate causation, its ontogeny, and its functional and evolutionary aspects.
3. In the present state of knowledge, it is advisable for the student of behaviour to pursue limited goals, attempting to elucidate principles applicable over a specified range. Superficial generalizations of wide validity and precise ones of limited scope are complementary to each other, and both are necessary.
4. Comparative study is necessary before generalizations applicable to more than one species can be made. It is also essential for studies of the evolution of behaviour.
5. The analysis of behaviour can be aided by physiological data, and the student of behaviour should attempt to devise hypotheses compatible with the physiological information available.
6. The analysis of behaviour can be aided by the use of models which indicate the nature of the causal relationships involved.

2

The Description and Classification of Behaviour

The importance of the initial descriptive phase in the study of behaviour has often been neglected, especially by those who have modelled their methods on those of classical physics. The earlier physicists dealt largely with everyday events—falling apples, floating boats, rainbows, melting ice—which were already familiar to them and to their colleagues. In biology, by contrast, the work of generations of taxonomists and systematists was necessary before progress could be made. The task of the taxonomist of species is to sort out the almost unlimited diversity of individuals in nature into easily recognizable groups, to describe those groups in terms of their significant characters, and to define the differences between them. Similarly, a complex stream of behaviour must be described and broken down into units suitable for study, which then must be classified into groups for ease of reference. No two of these units will be absolutely identical in all of their properties, and classifying them into groups requires emphasis on particular common properties (MacCorquodale *et al.*, 1954).

2.1. Methods of Description

In practice, there are two methods of describing behaviour. One involves reference ultimately to the strength, degree and patterning of muscular contractions (or glandular activity, or change in some other physiological property). The other involves reference not to these changes, but to their consequences. This is not a distinction between types of behaviour, as the "molecular" *v.* "molar" distinction is often used by learning theorists, but between criteria for describing behaviour: it is of the utmost importance since the whole character of the subsequent analysis may be influenced by which type of description is chosen.

The first method is often limited to patterns of limb or body movement, as a complete description would not only be impracticable, but also unnecessarily refined and cumbersome. Terms such as "knee jerk", "positive supporting reaction", "sleeping posture" are of this type. Of course, the degree of precision required in description depends on the nature of the analysis undertaken.

In classifying on the basis of such descriptions, we are grouping together similar spatio-temporal patterns of muscular contraction, though the classification will depend only on selected characteristics, others being ignored. The choice of the characteristics employed should, of course, have an objective justification, but it may take cognisance of the fact that variability in motor patterns is not necessarily paralleled by a similar variability of mechanisms; just as, although pecking at a piece of food could involve an infinite variety of motor patterns, it involves localization in only three dimensions. In addition, the criteria may vary greatly in complexity. Thus the crouching of a bird could be characterized merely by a certain degree of bending in the tarsal joint. "Tail-flicks" are more complicated, involving a temporal pattern of contractions in a number of different muscles. Courtship displays, to take an even more complicated case, may consist of the simultaneous or sequential occurrence of several such spatio-temporal patterns. In such cases the selection of criteria is further complicated by the disappearance of some components when the response is given at low intensity. The usual practice here is to describe low and high intensity forms and indicate the intermediate variations, a method roughly comparable to that used by taxonomists when the characteristics of a species change gradually over its area of distribution, but often leading to the description only of rare extreme cases.

The second method for the description of behaviour may be called "description by consequence". "Picking up nest material", "pressing down the lever", or "approaching" do not refer to particular patterns of muscular contraction, but cover all patterns which lead (or could lead, and there is room for ambiguity here) to the specified result. Descriptions like this are normally used when the behaviour involves orientation to objects in the environment, and when the motor patterns, though leading to a constant result, are themselves diverse. They thus tend to be used especially for "appetitive" or searching behaviour.

There are two advantages in this kind of description. First, a brief description may cover a multitude of motor patterns, each of which in itself is variable —for instance "approaching" covers hopping, walking, flying, sidling, etc.: they therefore provide an essential shorthand. Often the number of smaller groups, characterized by physical description, into which it is possible to divide each behaviour class characterized by consequence, is large. Sometimes, however, their number is surprisingly limited. Thus the Herring Gull (*Larus argentatus*) uses only one method for retrieving eggs which have rolled out of its nest—it puts its beak beyond them and tries to manoeuvre them back under its breast. In spite of the inefficiency of this technique, the bird never attempts to use its apparently more suitable webbed feet or wings (Tinbergen, 1953).

A second advantage of descriptions by consequence is that they often call attention to essential features of the behaviour that may not appear in physical descriptions, such as orientation with respect to the environment, or responsiveness to external stimuli. An animal's behaviour may change radically (e.g.

from one type of appetitive behaviour to another) with little change in the motor pattern; or, alternatively, a radical change in the patterns of muscular contraction (e.g. from flying to walking) may be, for some purposes, of little significance. Description by consequence is thus often essential for a full understanding of the behaviour.

There are, however, also dangers in descriptions of this type. First, the manner in which categories of behaviour are described may have important effects on subsequent hypotheses; whether, for instance, we say "entering the goal box" or "escaping from the alley".

Second, as stressed by MacCorquodale and Meehl (1954), such descriptiods are susceptible to overinterpretation. The statement, "the rat learned to press the lever" can be interpreted as pure description, but can also be overinterpreted to imply reciprocal relations between the various behaviour classes by which the lever could be depressed, such that a decrease in frequency of one is followed by a compensatory increase in another. This may be so, but does not necessarily follow from the initial descriptive statement. As we have seen in the case of the egg-rolling response, the number of alternative response classes which can be used in bringing about a given consequence may be surprisingly limited.

Whichever type of description is used, it inevitably involves the rejection of some of the data and a selection (arbitrary, intuitive, or rational) of the features to be studied—as soon as we move away from the initial cinematographic record of the behaviour we are neglecting information. Just because description and classification involve rejection of data and the selection of criteria, there are always the dangers that the essential data are rejected and that the units used are irrelevant, too small or too large for the task in hand. For instance, descriptions of reproductive behaviour in terms of "maternal behaviour", "sexual behaviour", etc. are inadequate for a proper analysis of the stimuli controlling them (Tinbergen, 1951). Similarly, the understanding of the apparently "insightful" tool-using behaviour of primates is greatly facilitated by examination of its components (Schiller, 1957).

On the other hand, insufficient rejection of data may lead to a hopelessly confusing mass of detail, and divert attention from the essentials of the problem. Thus, any attempt to describe precisely the patterns of muscular contraction involved when a fighting bird strikes its adversary with its beak would be difficult because of the variations in the initial posture and relative positions of the combatants—it is more useful to describe the behaviour in terms of consequence.

The two types of description are thus not always alternative. Description in terms of muscular contraction is unsuitable in some cases because of the complexity of the data it provides, and in others because the data cannot be subdivided into classes with an objective validity. In other cases, description by consequence is equally unsuitable. Sometimes—as in the threat and courtship postures of birds, which involve both a relatively stereotyped motor pattern and an orientation with respect to the environment—both must be used.

2.2. Classification of Behaviour Types

The isolation of instances of behaviour allows us to associate them with each other by virtue of common characteristics and, thus, to recognize them as examples of the "same" type of behaviour. These types may be defined either as involving movements whose form varies only within prescribed limits, or in terms of a common effect. Mere enumeration of such types is, however, almost valueless unless they are further classified into groups. Classification requires criteria, and, in principle, the number of criteria that could be chosen is infinite. They could, for example, depend on common features in the form of the movement, or on the oxygen consumption needed for its performance, or on the consequences which the behaviour has. In practice we choose criteria suitable for the particular problem we are concerned with: three kinds which have been especially valuable must be mentioned.

1. *Causal Classification*

The types of behaviour shown by an animal can be grouped together according to the causal factors on which they depend, activities which share causal factors being classified together. Thus, all activities whose frequency or intensity is significantly increased by male sex hormone can be grouped together as male sexual behaviour. All activities similarly influenced by the stimulus situation "rival male" can be described as "agonistic behaviour". This type of classification is essential for an understanding of the behaviour of the whole animal, and it works well in practice. There are, however, some difficulties. Two methods are used to assess whether patterns of behaviour share a causal factor. One is to administer it and see whether both types of behaviour increase in frequency. The other, useful when the factor itself has not been isolated, is to investigate the temporal correlations between the appearances of various activities: two activities which consistently appear together are likely to be related causally (*see* pp. 291-3). But in either case, a positive result does not necessarily mean a direct effect of any factor on both patterns (pp. 293-4). Nor does the non-occurrence of a pattern when a factor is administered mean that the factor is without influence on it—additional ones may be necessary before the behaviour appears (*see* Hanson, 1955, for a discussion of the pitfalls involved in thinking in terms of simple causal chains).

2. *Functional Classification*

Activities can also be classified according to the adaptive (in an evolutionary sense) consequences they serve. "Threat", "courtship", "hunting" refer to categories of this type. Such terms correspond to words such as "legs" or "eyes" in morphology. A structure is classed as a leg because of its function, and there is no implication that the legs of, for example, arthropods and vertebrates are related either embryologically, i.e. causally, or phylogenetically. A similar structure which has a different function is given a different name; for instance "maxilliped".

In practice, when any one species is being considered, a functional classification of behaviour very often corresponds to a causal one: considered from the point of view of evolution, this is not hard to understand—the mechanisms which underlie adaptive behaviour need be far less complex if functionally related activities share causal factors than if the various causal factors are distributed at random among the functional groups. It is for this reason that functional-sounding terms, like "sexual behaviour" and "parental behaviour", are sometimes used to refer to categories which are also defined in causal terms. But although the functional classification is a good guide to the causal, this is not always the case, and in many animals it is quite unjustifiable to talk about "reproductive behaviour" when implying a causal category, since sexual and parental behaviour depend on different causal factors. Causal analysis must precede causal classification if functional and causal categories are not to be confused. Further, as Tinbergen (1952, 1953, 1963) has shown, the same functional category, courtship, may rest on quite different causal bases in different animals, so that great care is necessary in generalizing from species to species.

Functional categories are often used to include behaviour patterns from unrelated species. "Territorial behaviour" and "migratory behaviour" are cases in point. Such a procedure is quite justifiable so long as the categories are used in discussions of function only. Here care is again necessary, for almost identical behaviour elements may have dissimilar functions in different species.

3. *Historical Classification*
Two quite distinct systems must be recognized:

(*a*) *Classification according to source.* Here patterns of behaviour believed to have a common historical origin are grouped together. This is much used in the study of the evolution of behaviour, especially the evolution of "fixed action patterns". The basic criterion for grouping together is then similarity in the pattern of muscular contraction, but, as in the systematics of organisms, due allowance must be made for possibilities of convergence, divergence, etc. (Chapter 27).

(*b*) *Classification according to method of acquisition.* Here behaviour classes are grouped not according to their historical source but according to the nature of intervening changes which have occurred; for instance, "learned," "ritualized".

The Independence of the Classificatory Systems
Although the classificatory systems discussed in the previous section are basi-

cally independent of each other, possibilities of confusion constantly arise. Just because, for reasons we have already seen, functional and causal categories often overlap, the temptation to confuse them may be severe. This is particularly dangerous when the functional categories are nothing more than descriptive generalizations. Reference to "self-preservative" as opposed to "reproductive" instincts, for instance, both confuses functional and causal categories and implies something causally in common between, for example, feeding and preening. Similarly, although some authors have grouped together activities such as scratching, stretching and shaking as "comfort movements", Weidmann (1958) has shown that they occur independently of each other.

2.3. Summary

1. Behaviour may be described and categorized in terms of spatio-temporal patterns of muscular contraction, or in terms of the consequences of the behaviour.
2. Types of behaviour can be classified according to a theoretically unlimited number of systems. Three useful ones depend on common causal factors, common functional consequences, and common historical (ontogenetic or evolutionary) source or method of acquisition. Classificatory systems based on different types of criteria must be treated as independent.

SECTION 2

The Study of Causation

3

The Control of Movement

We have already seen that the movements shown by animals can be described in two ways: in terms of the spatio-temporal patterns of muscular contraction involved, or in terms of their consequences. Our main concern in this chapter is with the means by which the patterning of movements are controlled. Any movement involves a number of muscles contracting in particular relationships with each other: is the temporal patterning of their contractions determined from the start in the central nervous system, or is it adjusted by peripheral stimuli received as a consequence of earlier phases of the movement? In those cases in which the movement is specified more appropriately in terms of its environmental consequences than as a particular sequence of muscular contractions, environmental stimuli are likely to play a part in its control. When the movement itself is more stereotyped, however, the question is an open one, for even if environmental stimuli play no part, proprioceptive feedback may yet control the sequence and extent of muscular contractions.

There are, thus, three possible sources for the patterning of complex movements: environmental stimuli (and, in the case of movements directed towards the animal's own body, we must include here some stimuli from its own body surface), proprioceptive stimuli, and coordinating mechanisms within the central nervous system itself. In any particular case the pattern is likely to be derived from more than one of these sources, and our first task is to separate their effects.

3.1. Fixed Action Patterns

There are some movements whose form seems to be independent of environmental stimuli, even though they may be elicited by such stimuli in the first instance. A female canary uses a special weaving movement to push loose strands of material into the cup of its nest. If the bird is given neither a nest site nor nest-material, this movement may be performed on the floor of the cage and without nest-material; its form then differs little if at all from when it is performed in its normal functional context, so stimuli from the nest-cup or nest-material can play little part in its control. The soliciting posture of a female Chaffinch, which includes flexion of the legs, withdrawal of the head, raising of the tail and rapid vibration of the wings, is remarkably constant in

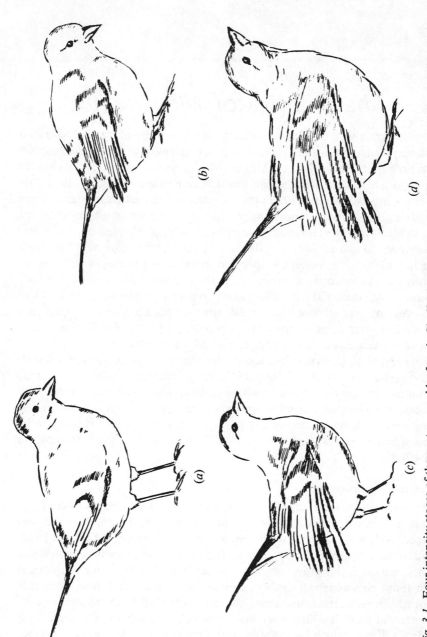

Fig. 3.1. Four intensity stages of the posture used by female Chaffinches in soliciting for copulation. (*From a drawing by Yvette Spencer-Booth.*)

form: although it involves most of the muscles in the body, the relations between their contractions vary little, and they are thus presumably independent of immediate environmental control (Fig. 3.1).

Such movements are often referred to as Fixed Action Patterns (F.A.Ps). Each one, although it may consist of a quite complicated spatio-temporal pattern of muscular contractions, cannot be split into successive responses which depend on qualitatively different external stimuli (Lorenz, 1935, 1937; Tinbergen, 1942). Since such movements depend on external factors only for their elicitation, they vary in degree of completeness, but not in the relationships between their parts. The soliciting posture of the female Chaffinch may involve any degree of leg-flexion, tail-raising or wing-shivering, but a given degree of one is always combined with an approximately constant degree of the others. In other cases even such intensity differences are almost absent: the duration of the "head-throw" display of the Goldeneye Duck is remarkably constant, having a mean duration of 1·29 seconds and a standard deviation of

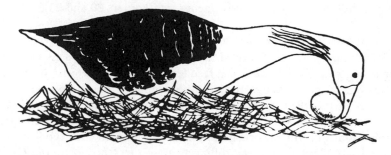

Fig. 3.2. Grey-lag Goose retrieving an egg. (*After Tinbergen, 1951.*)

only $\pm 0·08$ second (Dane *et al.*, 1959). Such extreme constancy, we shall see later (Chapters 16 and 27), is especially characteristic of "signal" movements used in intra-specific communication.

Each animal has a repertoire of these fixed action patterns, and only a limited ability for developing new ones. The limitation may be set by the availability of the effectors and the mechanics of the body: there are some sounds which the vocal apparatus of a song bird cannot produce, and hippopotami just cannot walk on two legs. Beyond this, however, limitations are imposed by the nature of the nervous system. Thus, as we have seen, the Herring Gull and many other ground-nesting birds have a special movement for retrieving eggs which roll out of the nest: they stand up, place the bill beyond the egg, and then roll the egg back into the nest, moving the bill from side to side to prevent the egg from slipping away (Fig. 3.2). The whole act is clumsy, for the egg frequently rolls away from the narrow ventral side of the bill, and it would seem much more efficient to use one of the wings or feet. Nevertheless, no bird has ever been known to develop a new movement for retrieving eggs (Lorenz *et al.*, 1939; Tinbergen, 1953).

Any particular movement of this type may be characteristic of a genus or higher systematic category, a species, or merely one individual. All passerine birds and their relatives, as well as the plovers, scratch their heads by bringing a foot over the partly lowered wing of the same side, whereas nearly all other birds bring the foot under the wing (Wickler, 1961a, b); and the neonates of nearly all primate species use special movements of the head in searching for the nipple (e.g. Prechtl, 1958; Hinde, Rowell *et al.*, 1964). As we shall see later (Chapter 27), in such cases the pattern of movement can be used as an indicator of phylogenetic relationship in exactly the same way as a morphological structure. On the other hand, the lateral courtship display of the male Chaffinch is given by that species alone, other finches having different displays, and the song of each kind of song-bird is limited to that species alone. Finally, particular individuals may develop stereotyped movements of their own: these are especially evident in captive animals, which often develop tics as a result of the impoverished conditions of confinement (*see* Chapters 20 and 23).

3.2. Orientation of Fixed Action Patterns with Respect to the Environment

By definition, the form of a fixed action pattern is independent of environmental control. Nevertheless, we frequently observe patterns of muscular contraction which, although recognizably similar from one occasion to the next, are yet modified by stimuli from the environment. The modifications usually serve to orient the movement, and it is often possible to separate the stimuli responsible for the orientation from those which elicit the fixed action pattern itself. Thus, in the egg-rolling response (*see* p. 19) by the Grey-lag Goose, the side-to-side movements of the beak are continuously governed by stimuli from the irregular movements of the egg. If the egg is removed, or if it is replaced by a cylinder which rolls in a regular fashion, these lateral movements cease. On the other hand the movement of the bill towards the breast, once elicited, is independent of further stimuli from the egg; if the egg is removed once the movement has started, it nevertheless goes through to completion in the normal way. It is thus only the movement of the bill towards the breast which, once elicited, is independent of further external stimuli and constitutes the fixed action pattern (Lorenz *et al.*, 1939).

Similarly the alarm call, given by Chaffinches when a flying predator appears, elicits flying to cover in other members of the species. The direction of the flight, however, is determined by stimuli from suitable cover in the neighbourhood—the alarm call merely elicits it (Marler, 1956b). A comparable case has been analysed in some detail by Baerends (1957a). The alarm response of the young of the mouthbreeding Cichlid *Tilapia mosambica* is released by the approach of a large object or by turbulence in the water. The direction in which they swim, however, is determined by stimuli normally provided by the female. Some experiments to determine the nature of these stimuli are illustrated in Fig. 3.3. The fry direct themselves towards the lower parts of a dummy object, and to dark patches on it, and push themselves repeatedly into holes on the surface. As a consequence most of them find their way into the female's mouth.

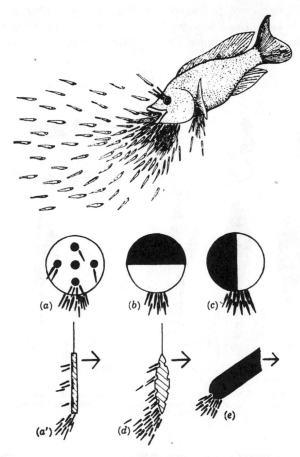

Fig. 3.3. Some model experiments on the stimulus directing the approach of young towards the female of the mouthbreeding *Tilapia mosambica.* (*After Baerends, 1957a.*)

Models *a, b,* and *c* are flat discs (cross-section, *a'*), *d* is a disc with pits, *e* is a black-painted test-tube with an opening in the bottom. The underside of the object is attractive (*a, b, c, d, e*) but not because it is the darkest part (*b, c*). In addition, black spots attract the young (*a, a'*), while hollows are found by constant pushing against the surface of the model (*d, e*).

In these cases the fixed action pattern is related in a constant fashion to environmental stimuli, but many fixed action patterns can be oriented in two or more ways. The male Guppy (*Lebistes reticulatus*) uses a "sigmoid posture" in courting the female. This movement appears at two points in courtship: first, when the male is "leading" the female away from the school, when his body is aligned with hers; and again in the "checking" phase, when the male orients his body at right angles to the female and just in front of her, thereby stopping further forward movement (Fig. 3.4). The fixed action pattern is the same in both cases, only the orientation differing (Baerends *et al.*, 1955).

Of course, it is not possible to separate eliciting from orienting stimuli in all stereotyped movements. In some, an orientation component is entirely lacking:

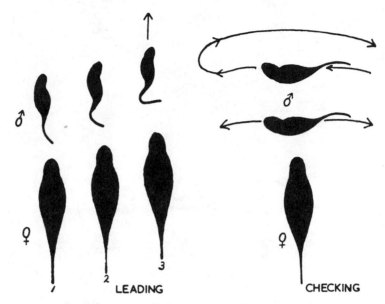

LEADING   CHECKING

Fig. 3.4. The sigmoid posture of the male Guppy (*Lebistes reticulatus*). (*After Baerends et al. 1955.*)

In those on the left the male's body is oriented away from the female: this position is used in leading the female. The transverse orientation, shown on the right, is used in checking her.

swallowing and ejaculation are examples. In other cases the roles of the stimuli which elicit and orient the movement may be too closely interwoven to be separated. We shall return to consider the problem of the integration of such movements later in this chapter. First, however, we must consider the relative roles of central and peripheral factors in the control of some fixed action patterns.

3.3. Co-ordination of Movement Patterns

Central Patterning

Some complicated movements can be elicited by a wide range of external stimuli, or by crude electrical stimulation applied to parts of the central nervous system (e.g. Hess, 1943; Huber, 1955; Sheer, 1961; von Holst *et al.*, 1963). In such cases the form of the movement cannot be dictated by the eliciting stimuli. At the extremes, two possibilities are open. The sequence in which the muscles contract could be determined solely by the properties of central nervous mechanisms underlying the movement, so that, once initiated, the movement is independent of sensory stimuli, internal or external to the animal. Alternatively, the muscles contracting later in the sequence could be activated by feedback effects from those contracting earlier: in this case the form of the movement would be continually under sensory control. Even fixed action patterns, in which the sequence of muscular contractions, once elicited, is by definition independent of external control, could depend on proprioceptive feedback.

In either case the first phase of the response must be centrally determined: the alternative possibility that these stereotyped movements always begin with a random movement which is corrected proprioceptively can be dismissed (Horridge, 1961). The fundamental issue is, thus, whether or not their continuance depends on the afferent effects of their own earlier phases. In order to tackle this problem experimentally it is necessary to compare the form of the movement, or of the impulses in the motor nerves, under two conditions: when the sensory stimulation from the earlier phases of the movement is available to the central nervous system, and when it is not. For obvious reasons, rhythmic movements lend themselves especially to analyses of this sort: the question then becomes, "Does the rhythmic pattern persist in the absence of feedback from the periphery?"

One of the simplest and best analysed cases concerns the cardiac ganglion of decapod crustacea, which contains only nine neurones. The electrical impulses in the efferent nerve consist of a regular sequence of intermittent patterned bursts, each containing large and small spikes separated by silent periods. This pattern continues even when the ganglion is isolated from outside influences. Although occasional variants occur, the detailed sequence of the impulses which constitute each burst is remarkably constant—the order of the first few spikes often remaining the same for over 3,500 bursts. Since afferent influences are excluded, this patterning must be a consequence of the structure of the central nervous mechanism itself (Maynard, 1955; Hagiwara, 1961).

A similar conclusion has been reached for the sound-producing mechanism of the cicada *Graptopsaltria nigrofuscata* (Hagiwara *et al.*, 1956). This involves contractions in two main sound muscles, one on each side of the body, which are each innervated by a single efferent nerve fibre from the mesothoracic ganglion. When the sensory nerves leading from the hair sensillae to the ganglion are stimulated, the electrical response of the sound muscles consists of a series of spikes. As the intensity of the stimulus is increased, the frequency of these spikes remains constant at about 100/second, but the length of each series increases to 10 or more. If the electrical discharges of the two muscles are recorded simultaneously, it is found that each spike in one muscle occurs half way between two spikes in the other. Thus, a simple stimulus on the sensory side results, without feedback control, in a pattern of alternate responses in the two muscles at 100/second: this patterning must originate in the ganglion. Hagiwara and Watanabe have been able to suggest how this happens. Since the effect of an antidromic impulse on the motor neurone does not change the patterning of the reflex discharge, the motor rhythm must originate in the pre-motor neurone. Furthermore, internuncial neurones have been found which, on stimulation of the sensory nerves, gave repetitive spikes at 200/second. They thus suggest that the rhythm in the two muscles depends on a common pace-maker which fires at twice the frequency of the motor neurones and activates the two sides alternately. On this view the alternation between the two sides would be due to some form of mutual inhibition. Sound production by crickets is more complex, involving feedback from the musculature: it has been analysed in detail by Huber (1960).

In a similar manner, Horridge (1961) has studied the sequence of motor impulses from the cerebral ganglion of the bivalve mollusc *Mya*, which normally brings about retraction of the mantle and closure of the shell. Single impulses in a preganglionic (sensory) axon can induce a sequence of motor impulses from the ganglion in which up to ten motor axons can be individually identified, the patterning of the impulses being similar (but not identical) in successive repetitions. The sequence is unchanged when all other nerves of the cerebral ganglion are severed and when the motor nerve is cut beyond the recording electrodes: the sequence thus does not depend on proprioceptive feedback from the movement which it causes. Traditionally, a patterned output of this type is ascribed to patterned connections between the internuncial neurones, but Horridge points out that the neuropile consists of a tangled mass of small fibres in which specific connections between cells seem to be absent. He therefore suggests that the internuncial and motor neurones respond differentially to a transmitter substance liberated in the neuropile by the preganglionic fibre.

In these cases it has been shown that the patterning in the output of a single ganglion can arise within the ganglion independently of any sort of feedback from the earlier stages of the movement. Complete central patterning of this type has not yet been established with certainty for any complex movement in vertebrates. Although Weiss (1941a, b) claimed that complete deafferentation did not affect the swimming of tadpoles, later work on other species (*see* p. 29) suggests that this study should be repeated. However, the evidence is highly suggestive in the case of reflex swallowing in mammals (Doty *et al.* 1956). The initial phase of swallowing is a complicated activity in which motor neurones scattered from mesencephalic to third cervical levels are integrated to produce a coordinated pattern of contraction among about twenty different muscles. The

sequence of contraction in some of these muscles in the dog is illustrated in
Fig. 3.5. The temporal pattern, duration and amplitude of the contractions is
independent of the means used to elicit swallowing, whether this be electrical
stimulation of the superior laryngeal nerve at frequencies ranging from 3 to
100/second, stimulation of the pharynx with a cotton swab, or rapid injection
of water into the mouth: the patterning thus arises within the mechanism of

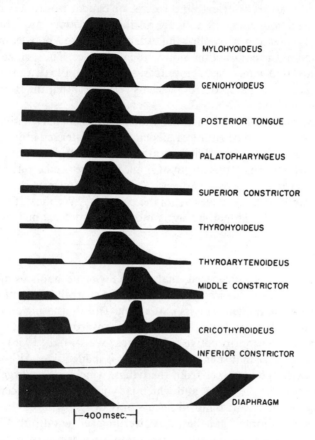

Fig. 3.5. Schematic summary of electromyographic activity in deglutition
for unanaesthetized dog. (*From Doty and Bosma, 1956.*)
      Height of line indicates intensity of action in each muscle.

swallowing itself. Once swallowing is elicited, its coordination could be due to
the patterning of internuncial neurones in the brain stem, to collateral linkages
between motor neurones arranged in such a manner that the firing of one leads
sequentially to the firing of another, or to the activation of those motor
neurones which fire later in the sequence by afferents from muscles which contracted earlier. Sequential linkages between motor neurones are rendered

unlikely as a sole explanation by the observation that pontine section of the brain stem, which excludes the action of the mylohyoideus muscle, does not modify the course of swallowing. There is also considerable evidence against control by proprioceptive feedback: a wide variety of treatments likely to upset any such feedback, including strychnine, moderate asphyxia, cocainization of the pharynx, excision or procainization of participating muscles, fixation of the hyoid mass at extreme rostral or caudal positions, and varying degrees of traction upon the tongue, all fail to produce any change in the temporal organization of swallowing except for minor changes in amplitude and duration of the contraction in individual muscles. Thus, since deglutition can be elicited by a wide range of inputs (*see also* Doty, 1951), and in view of the evidence against feedback control, it seems very likely that the coordination of the movement is entirely central.

Although the number of cases in which patterned nervous discharge or movement is known to be entirely independent of patterned input are few, this should not be taken to mean that central patterning is the exception. Rather, as Bullock (1961) stresses, "the output of single neurones and groups of neurones is normally probably always patterned". Usually, however, the central patterning is modified by feedback from the periphery. We must, therefore, now turn to cases where the patterning is modified or determined by peripheral factors.

Peripheral Influences

In the first case to be considered, that of the flight mechanisms of the locust, peripheral feedback influences the frequency of a centrally determined rhythm, but has little or no influence on its patterning. The alternating contractions of the musculature used in the upward and downward beats of the wings was earlier ascribed to proprioceptive reflex loops (Weis-Fogh, 1956), but there is now strong evidence that such an explanation is inadequate. Although there is a sensory discharge in nerves from the wings, which comes largely from the stretch-receptors of the hinge, and which is synchronized with certain phases of the wing-beat cycle, its removal results only in a slowing of the rhythmical output from the thoracic ganglia: the patterning of the output still resembles that occurring in flight. Even after the main sensory nerves from the wings are cut, a normal flight-inducing stimulus, or electric stimulation of the nerve cord, can produce a pattern of wing movements similar to those occurring in flight. Furthermore, the influence of the input on the frequency of the discharge from the central ganglia is phase-independent: various types of evidence indicate that there is a number of pacemakers, potentially independent, which are coupled into a dominant frequency which depends on the quantity of the input.

The advantages of such a mechanism over a chain-reflex system can be seen as follows. When the wing speed is such as to produce maximum efficiency, the downstroke muscles begin to shorten just as the wings reach the top position, and vice versa. When the central output has a higher frequency, the up-beat is not over when the downstroke command arrives at the wing muscles. The downstroke muscles thus help to slow the end of the up-beat. Such a muscular brake at the ends of the strokes permits a higher wing-beat frequency. If the rhythm was controlled by chain reflexes, the contractions of the muscle groups would be fixed relative to each other, and this method of adjusting frequency would not be possible (Wilson, 1961, 1964; Wilson and Gettrup, 1963; Wilson and Weis-Fogh, 1963; Weis-Fogh, 1964).

In other cases, an external stimulus may reset a rhythm which is otherwise endogenous. An example of this, taken from the control of respiration in an aeschnid dragonfly nymph, is shown in Fig. 3.6. In the species concerned the nymph respires by moving water across its gills, which are situated in the modified rectum. The expiratory phase is aided by the contraction of the abdominal respiratory dorso-ventral muscles, which receive bursts of impulses, one per respiratory cycle, from the second lateral nerve roots. The pattern of such bursts is shown at A, where the upper trace shows the expiratory bursts

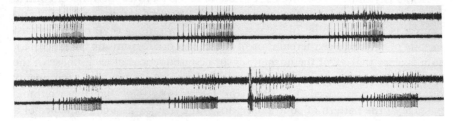

Fig. 3.6. Discharges, in motor roots of abdominal ganglia of aeschnid dragonfly nymph, which control respiratory movements. (*Mills and Hughes, personal communication.*)

   A. Normal rhythm. *B.* An extra burst is elicited by stimulation.

in the second root of the fifth abdominal ganglion, and the lower trace shows the bursts in the corresponding root of the seventh ganglion. Stimulation of the first root of, say, the seventh ganglion between two such bursts produces an additional burst, which is followed by further rhythmical bursts at the normal interval after the extra burst: the rhythm is thus displaced in phase with respect to the original one (*B* in Fig. 3.6) (Mills *et al.*, personal communication).

A more intimate relationship between external and internal factors is seen in the swimmeret movements of the crayfish (*Procambarus clarkii*), where both inflow from peripheral proprioceptors and intrinsic properties of the central ganglia have a role in coordination (Hughes *et al.*, 1960). Rhythmic discharges, corresponding to the movements of the swimmerets, can be recorded from the first root of each segment in the abdominal nerve cord, and persist when the nerve cord is isolated except for one intact first root. When the cord is completely isolated, intermittent bursts still occur, but their pattern, frequency and phase relationships sometimes differ from those found before isolation was completed. In spite of possible differences, these intermittent bursts are almost certainly related to those producing normal movements of the swimmerets, for they resemble those which occur sometimes under normal conditions when the swimmerets are not well coordinated, and in later experiments by Ikeda and Wiersma (1964) appeared to be identical with them. Furthermore, they do not occur in the other nerve roots, which do not innervate these appendages. It thus seems that bursts of motor activity can occur in the isolated ganglion, but proprioceptive input is usually necessary for the production of the normal rhythmical bursts. However, stimulation of certain fibres in the circumoesophageal commissure produces highly specific movements of the swimmerets. The discharges which are responsible for these persist even when the abdominal cord is totally isolated from the periphery. Thus such a "centrally driven" rhythm is independent of rhythmical reafferent stimulation from the swimmerets, though sensory stimuli from head and thorax may normally be important.

In the rhythmic locomotory movements of vertebrates, peripheral control is normally essential, but the integration of central patterning and peripheral control is usually subtle. In Teleost fishes the swimming rhythm may persist in spite of extensive deafferentation of the spinal cord region (von Holst, 1935a), so it is clear that all of the normal sensory consequences of each phase of the movement are not necessary for its continuation. As a result of experiments on partially narcotized Teleosts, von Holst proposed that the rhythmic passage of the pattern of contraction down the trunk was a consequence of a rhythm generated centrally by cells in the anterior region of the spinal cord and medulla: under partial urethane anaesthesia the respiratory, fin and tail movements appear to have a common rhythm, but when sensory regulation is possible, separate rhythms are differentiated. In his view, therefore, the rhythm was in the first place independent of afferent inflow, though it could be influenced by it.

However, careful studies of dogfish (*Scyllium canicula, Acanthias vulgaris*) by Lissmann (1946a, b) have shown that in these species sensory input into the spinal cord does in fact play an essential role in the maintenance of the rhythm itself. Swimming can be analysed into the adoption of an undulatory posture, and the propagation of this posture down the body. The static undulatory posture is produced as a reflex in which the spinal cord acts as an entity—in other words the *static* patterning of contraction and relaxation of the trunk musculature is centrally determined. This finding is in agreement with the earlier work of von Holst (1935a, b) on the eel, and of Gray and Sand (1936a, b) on the dogfish. The latter authors cut all nerves to the musculature of about twelve segments of a dogfish and clamped the denervated region rigidly: the swimming movements of the anterior and posterior regions were nevertheless perfectly coordinated. The coordination of the locomotory posture across the denervated region is thus central.

The passage of the static posture down the trunk is, however, another matter. In the first place, weak stimulation of the body during swimming results in modification to the swimming stroke in progress, the precise nature of the modification depending on the site of the stimulus and the phase of the swimming stroke at which it is given. Since the swimming rhythm which emerges

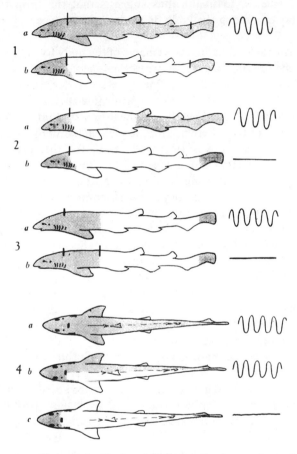

Fig. 3.7. The effect of deafferentation upon the locomotory rhythm of spinal dogfish. (*After Lissmann, 1946a.*)

The white regions represent the desensitized areas of the body. The level of spinal transection is indicated by a thick line. The presence or absence of a locomotor rhythm is indicated on the right.

after such a stimulus is out of phase with that which preceded it, the change cannot be interpreted as a temporary modification superimposed on a basic pattern, but must involve a fundamental change in the swimming rhythm (cf. Fig. 3.6). Secondly, persistence of the locomotory rhythm depends on afferent excitation: it is abolished by severance of the dorsal roots. It is, however, not necessary for all the sensory roots to be intact—deafferentation of half of the body (anterior or posterior, left or right) still leaves a preparation which shows persistent swimming. With extensive deafferentation rhythmical swimming movements may occur, but do not persist for long. With nearly complete deafferentation, exteroceptive stimulation induces a static posture, but no rhythmic movements. Lissmann thus suggests that the propagation of the reflex static posture along the body depends on proprioceptive reflexes (Fig. 3.7).

In the dogfish, the undulatory movements of the body form the basis of loco-motion, and the fins show little in the way of independent rhythmic movement. In most Teleosts, by contrast, the fins have some degree of independence. Medullary preparations of the Teleost *Labrus* show rhythmical fin movements which may persist for days. Each fin can beat in a rhythm of its own, but, in addition, rhythms of the different fins influence each other ("relative coordin-ation"). Two main principles are involved. In the first place, two fins or sets of fins, initially beating with independent rhythms, may gradually fall into step, the periodicity of one being dominant to that of the other. This is known as the "magnet effect", the frequency of one rhythm attracting that of the other. Second, the amplitude of one of two fins which are beating out of phase with each other may be increased or decreased according to whether it coincides with a beat of the other fin. This "superposition" effect is found also in deaffer-entated spinal fish, and so appears to be independent of peripheral stimuli (*see* von Holst, 1935a, b, c; 1936, 1939, 1948).

A similar type of relationship is found in the coordination of head and leg movements in walking chickens. As the chicken advances, its head moves backwards and forwards relative to the body. The head movement is in either relative or absolute coordination with the leg rhythm, the latter being domin-ant. In addition, the head movement is elicited by the shifting of the retinal image which accompanies forward locomotion: it is probable that the back-ward movement of the head is adjusted to the forward speed of the body so that the shifting of the retinal image is minimized over short periods of time. If chicks are fitted with ground-glass spectacles, so that shifting of the retinal image is prevented, the head still nods in a regular manner (Bangert, 1960).

In tetrapods the limbs move in an orderly diagonal sequence, in absolute coordination with each other—left front, right hind, right front, left hind. Each phase of the walking rhythm must involve a characteristic proprioceptive discharge: the question therefore arises, to what extent is this necessary for the rhythmical sequence of limb movement? The walking of the toad has been subjected to particularly detailed analysis. The early experiments suggested that the proprioceptors played only a minor part in coordination, for the normal ambulatory rhythm continues when some of the limbs are deafferen-tated. However Gray and Lissmann (1946a, b) showed that the presence of one, but only one, intact spinal nerve is essential for the continuation of rhythmical locomotory movements. So long as one spinal nerve remains intact, even if it supplies only the muscles of the back or the pelvis, the diagonal pattern of iimb movement continues, but this pattern is never found unless there is one segment which contains intact both sensory and motor nerves. It is thus clear that afferent input from an intact segment is necessary for continued locomotion. This could be acting in two ways. On the one hand, the rhythmical movements of the limbs could be the result of a rhythmicity originating centrally but requiring a certain threshold level of not necessarily rhythmical impulses from the periphery. Alternatively, the locomotory rhythm could depend on the sensory input also being rhythmical. The first of these possibilities is rendered improbable by the behaviour of a preparation in which the motor nerves to three of the limbs and the dorsal musculature were severed. Under these circumstances stimulation of the deafferentated limbs produced rhythmical movements in the intact limb. Thus, absence of the normal proprioceptive consequences of walking from three of the limbs had practically no influence on the ease with which rhythmic stepping could be induced in the intact limb. But if the fourth limb was then deafferentated, all rhythmical response disappeared: stimulation of the other limbs induced only a monophasic response and rhythmicity was absent however intense the stimulation (Fig. 3.8). Further experiments showed that proprioceptive impulses from each limb influence the posture in all remaining limbs, producing postures characteristic of specific phases of the ambulatory pattern.

Swimming movements, unlike those of terrestrial locomotion, persist in spinally deafferentated toads, but only so long as the labyrinths are intact. There is suggestive evidence that the acceleration produced by the swimming stroke excites the labyrinths and thereby produces further strokes (Gray and Lissmann, 1947).

In view of these results Gray and Lissmann regard the earlier view that amphibian locomotion is centrally coordinated as unproven, and emphasize the role of patterned peripheral impulses from all parts of the body in contributing to a general pattern of excitation which, in turn, elicits a pattern of response from the musculature as a whole (Gray, 1950). The peripheral control is thus not merely a matter of local reflexes—sensory input from each limb has some influence on the posture of all the limbs. Not all workers agree with this view. Thus Weiss (1950) believes in the essential importance of central factors in coordination on the basis of experiments in which amphibian limbs were transplanted into abnormal positions. For instance, both forelimbs were reversed, so that their morphologically anterior sides were directed towards the tail. In the normal position, the abductor of the forelimb lies in front and is stretched forward when the body is moving forwards: it could be this which initiates the swinging forward of the limb for the next step. If the front limb is reversed, the abductor is not stretched when the body moves forwards. Nevertheless, it contracts at the same point in the locomotory sequence as it

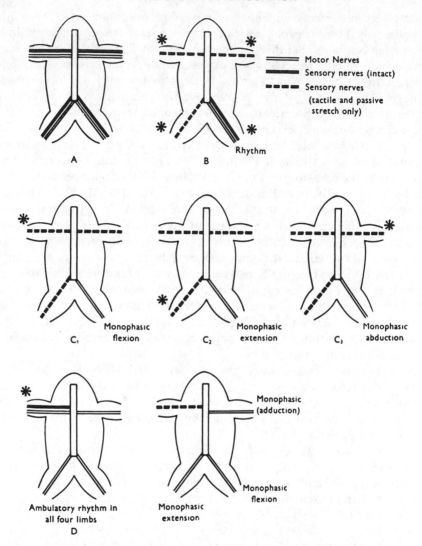

═══ Motor Nerves
━━━ Sensory nerves (intact)
▬ ▬ ▬ Sensory nerves
(tactile and passive
stretch only)

A

B   Rhythm

C₁   Monophasic
flexion

C₂   Monophasic
extension

C₃   Monophasic
abduction

D   Monophasic
extension

Ambulatory rhythm in
all four limbs   Monophasic
extension

Monophasic
(adduction)

Monophasic
flexion

Fig. 3.8. Diagram illustrating the dependence of an ambulatory rhythm on an intact nerve supply to one or more spinal segments. (*After Gray, 1950.*)

(Motor nerves; sensory nerves, together with sensory supply from passive stretch receptors; sensory nerves from tension receptors.) The site of an external stimulus is shown by an asterisk. In all cases, the back has been completely denervated.
A: The nerve supply to all four limbs is intact and the animal walks normally. *B*: Only the right hindlimb has an intact supply; the motor nerves to the other three limbs have been cut. A stimulus applied to any limb elicits an ambulatory rhythm in the right hindlimb. *C*: As in *B*, but the right hindlimb has been deafferentated. The response of the right hindlimb to a stimulus is then monophasic, and its nature depends on the site of the stimulus. *D*: The left forelimb is intact, the remaining three limbs being deafferentated. A stimulus applied to the left forelimb elicits a coordinated ambulatory rhythm in all four limbs. *E*: As in *D*, but the motor nerves of the left forelimb have been cut. A stimulus applied to the left forelimb elicits a characteristic but monophasic response in each of the others.

would have done if the limb had been in its normal position. This results, of course, in the reversed limb moving backwards when the normal limb would have moved forwards. Weiss regards this as proving that the coordination patterns are determined centrally. His argument, however, seems to neglect the role of the inter-member reflexes demonstrated in Gray and Lissmann's experiments, which could be overriding the intra-member ones in this case.

Turning to invertebrates for a moment, Gray and Lissmann's emphasis on the importance of inter-member reflexes finds some parallel in studies of insect walking. If one or two legs of a cockroach are removed, adjustments take place in the position and locomotory rhythm of those remaining, making effective locomotion still possible. The number of different adjustments which are possible is considerable (Fig. 3.9), and it is improbable that they arise from previously latent central nervous mechanisms adapted to meet such contingencies. Hughes (1957) thus considered the new rhythms to be due to the operation of the same reflex mechanisms which produce coordinated movements in the normal insect—intersegmental and intrasegmental reflexes, coordination between the thoracic ganglia, overall effects from the supra- and suboesophageal ganglia, and so on. In particular, Hughes suggests there is a mechanism for comparing the forces on the tarsi of the two sides and adjusting the posture until they are equalized (*see also* Hughes, 1958).

Recently Wilson (1966) has shown that the apparently diverse locomotor patterns of both intact and operated insects can be described in terms of a simple model. The legs of each side move in a sequence of constant length R_3, R_2, R_1 .... R_3, R_2, R_1 (*see* Hughes, 1957). At lowest frequencies of leg movement the sequences of the two sides alternate, thus:

$$R_3, R_2, R_1 \ldots \ldots \ldots \ldots R_3, R_2, R_1 \ldots \ldots \ldots$$
$$L_3, L_2, L_1 \ldots \ldots \ldots \ldots L_3, L_2, L_1$$

The intervals between the successive sequences of each side are, however, variable, so that at higher frequencies the sequences of the two sides overlap, e.g.:

$$R_3, R_2, R_1 \ldots R_3, R_2, R_1 \ldots \ldots$$
$$L_2, L_1 \ldots \ldots L_3, L_2, L_1 \ldots \ldots L_3$$

With further reduction of the intersequence interval, the third leg on each side may be moved synchronously with the first leg: this is actually the best-known insect walking pattern. In some cases the third leg may move even before the first one (Wendler, 1964).

Not only does the model describe nearly all walking patterns of intact insects, but also the results of amputation experiments. The gaits of amputees are speeded up (but leg-deficient) gaits of intact insects. It is thus unnecessary to postulate plasticity consequent upon adaptive reflex actions.

Although proprioceptive reflexes are important in intrasegmental control, the intersegmental reflexes are always exactly in or out of phase with the

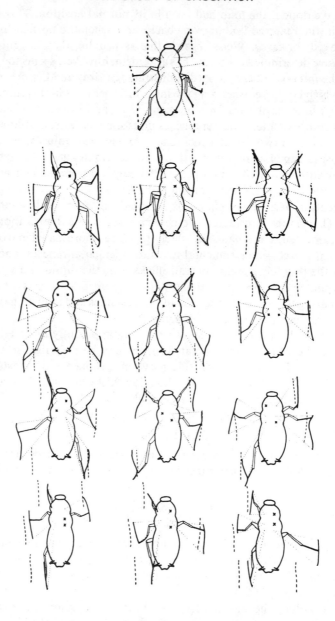

Fig. 3.9. Diagrams show the changes in stride position which occur when different legs are amputated from a cockroach. (*After Hughes, 1957.*)

Amputation of a leg is indicated by a cross on the thorax corresponding to its position. The positions occupied by the strides of the remaining legs in a normal insect are shown by interrupted lines, and their altered position following these operations is shown by continuous lines. Dotted lines indicate the angular movement of these legs, which are drawn for one phase of the cycle.

moved leg. Thus they cannot account for the continuous variation shown in the phase relations between the legs. Wilson suggests that the leg movements of each segment depend on coupled oscillators with different inherent frequencies, the metathoracic being the fastest (cf. Chapter 14 and Ikeda *et al.*, 1964, on the crayfish). If the coupling is sufficiently strong, the three will operate at the same frequency, but the slower ones lag in phase, producing the sequential timing of the legs. The phase lag would increase as the frequency of the whole system increases, thus giving rise to the various frequency dependent patterns. A mechanism involving the superimposition of some reflex control on coupled (endogenous) segmental oscillators could, Wilson suggests, account both for the data on gaits in intact and amputated insects, and for the information on the reflex patterns. The apparent plasticity shown by spiders in their ability to build normal webs after amputation of one or two legs (Szlep, 1952) deserves comparable analysis.

In mammals, deafferentation of even a single limb usually results in the failure of that limb to show locomotory activity, though the other limbs may move normally (Lassek *et al.*, 1953). Furthermore, cortical stimulation elicits only monophasic responses from deafferentated limbs, even when the intact limbs show rhythmical movements. Most rhythmical movements thus require an intact sensory input. Since severance of the sensory nerves to the distal portions of a cat's limbs does not prevent walking, it would seem that the essential feedback comes from the proprioceptors in the proximal sections (Sherrington, 1910).

Although proprioceptive feedback may be essential for rhythmic limb movement, central integrative processes also play a role. Thus an alternating rhythm of contraction and relaxation can be produced in the deafferentated tibialis anticus and gastrocnemius of a decerebrated cat (Graham-Brown, 1911). Sherrington (1913) produced rhythmical and alternating contractions of the deafferentated extensor muscles of the two knees by simultaneous stimulation of right and left peroneal nerves. Some elements of central patterning are thus certainly possible. Such cases do not necessarily require the postulation of a very complex central mechanism—alternate flexion and extension could, for instance, result from mutual inhibition between the mechanisms underlying extension and flexion, or from activity in each mechanism leading to fatigue, which is subject to recovery with time (e.g. Gray, 1950). Furthermore, such rhythmical movements as do persist in deafferentated limbs could depend in large part on sensory input elsewhere, as discussed above for amphibians. Indeed, in some cases a proper balance between postural flexor and extensor influences may be necessary for the rhythmic movements to appear; in the labyrinthectomized and decerebrate cat, ventroflexion of the head elicits flexion of the forelimbs, dorsiflexion elicits extension, but an intermediate position, approximating to the normal posture, gives rhythmic movements (Pollack *et al.*, 1931).

So far we have been primarily concerned with rhythmical locomotory movements, chiefly because it is for these that most information is available. It is unfortunate that none of the complicated fixed action patterns used by lower vertebrates in display have yet been analysed from this point of view, since many of them show remarkable constancy of form and might seem not to require feedback control. It must be remembered, however, that the precise patterning of muscular contraction required in each case will vary with the initial posture. Great Tits, for instance, may use a recognizable "head-up" threat posture (see p. 249) whether perched on a twig, a vertical trunk, or the horizontal ground. The patterning of muscular contraction is thus not rigidly fixed, and could be controlled by a system which produces closer and closer approximation to a required pattern of sensory feedback. This argument, however, would be less applicable to stereotyped vocal signals, and there is indeed some evidence that these are more or less independent of feedback. If Blackbirds are artificially deafened at 18 days of age, the song develops with only slight differences from normal birds (Messmer et al., 1956; see also Chapter 20). That there are some differences indicates that auditory feedback plays a role in the monitoring of the sound: that the difference is not more extensive indicates either that the role of feedback stimulation is a minor one, or that the feedback is proprioceptive and not auditory. We shall see later that the control of human speech is quite a different matter.

When we come to consider the non-locomotory movements of mammals, there are few exceptions to the general rule that deafferentation of a limb results in an almost total disappearance of complex movements. One exception is the scratch reflex of the dog which, although involving a rhythmic pattern of contraction in about nineteen muscles, can be elicited by simple stimulation from the deafferentated hind limb, the rhythm of the movement being independent of the frequency of stimulation (Sherrington, 1931). Mott et al. (1895) described the behaviour of a monkey with a completely deafferentated forelimb. The limb was never used for "voluntary" or skilled movements, but was used under duress; for instance when recovering from anaesthesia, or when held so that it was struggling with its whole body. The evidence thus suggests that only the more elementary and crude arm movements do not require proprioceptors in the same limb. However, in carnivores, simple instrumental acts, established by conditioning procedures, may persist after deafferentation of the limb (Gorska and Jankowska, 1961; Gorska et al., 1961). Lashley (1917) made a case for the independence from proprioceptive control of some skilled movements in man on rather different grounds: he suggested that some skilled movements, such as those of a pianist's fingers, are made so quickly that there would be no time for peripheral adjustment. The case here depends on the size of the units of movement considered: it remains possible that the playing of a short sequence of notes can be independent of feedback, while the chaining together of successive sequences can not. The extent of the role of central patterning in these non-locomotory movements of mammals thus remains problematical: what is clear is that sensory feedback is of primary importance.

In the more elementary cases we have considered the feedback control could act largely in the manner of a chain reflex, proprioceptive stimuli from the earlier phases of the movement eliciting the later ones. That it is not usually as simple as this is revealed for instance by Gray and Lissmann's studies of dogfish and amphibian locomotion—the sensory control is exerted not through a series of independent local reflexes, but through a central mechanism such that altered input from one part may produce changes in all or nearly all the musculature relevant to the response. In fact, the mechanisms of sensory control can be far more subtle even than this. In man, degeneration of the sensory nerves leads to a marked disturbance of all movements. The gait, for instance, is clumsy, the feet being raised too high and stamped down too hard. If sensory information is absent, accurate movement is impossible, especially if the movement is made slowly. Thus, the proprioceptive information is being used not to trigger the next phase of the movement, but to grade the movement itself—to control muscle contractions which are in progress. The mechanism by which this is achieved is considered in the next section.

3.4. The Control of Graded Muscular Contractions

Among the proprioceptors serving mammalian striped muscle are muscle spindles which lie parallel to the muscle fibres and share their attachments. In human subjects these do not convey information about the position of the limb, a function which is discharged by sense organs in the joints and skin (Merton, 1964). They do, however, respond to changes in the length of the muscle: extension gives rise to afferent impulses which excite the muscle's own motor-neurones. They can thus act to maintain the length of the muscle constant: in the "stretch-reflex", extension of the spindle causes an increased excitation of the motor neurone and thus contraction of the muscle. There is in fact a self-correcting system here: extension of the muscle sets in course a sequence of events which leads to a reduction in its length. In the language of the control engineer, the spindle provides negative feedback in a closed-loop system (Fig. 3.10).

Graded voluntary movement depends on the fact that the equilibrium length of the muscle spindles is adjustable. The ends of the spindles are contractile, receiving a motor supply (the γ efferents) from the spinal cord. When the ends of a spindle contract, the sensory part will discharge at the same rate as it would otherwise have done at a longer muscle length. Thus, if the γ efferents cause the ends of the spindle to contract, the sensory portion will be stretched, its rate of discharge will increase, and the muscle stretch reflex will be set off. The muscle will shorten until the increased rate of discharge from the spindle is offset. It will be noticed that the sensory portion of the spindle is not, in fact, responding to the absolute length of the muscle but to the difference between the length of the spindle and the length of the muscle. Whether the muscle contracts or relaxes depends in part on the state of contraction of the spindle.

In subsequent chapters we shall have frequent occasion to refer to feedback control of this sort, and it will be convenient to have a general term for the required or optimal stimulation received when the effector organ is in its

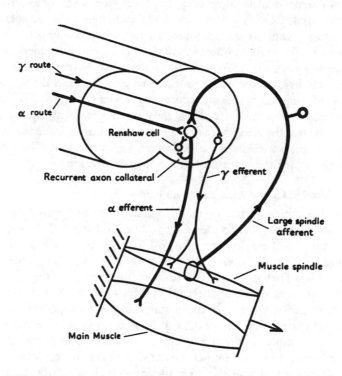

Fig. 3.10. The mechanisms underlying the stretch reflex and involved in the control of graded muscular contractions. (*After Hammond, Merton and Sutton, 1956.*)

equilibrium position. A precise English word is hard to find, though such terms as "goal", "target value", or "equilibrium position" are all useful in some contexts. The German term "Sollwert" (literally the "should be value") has a wider applicability. In the present context the Sollwert is achieved when the lengths of muscle and muscle spindle bear a certain relation to each other, but the term might equally be applied to the setting on the thermostat controlling a heating system, or that on the governor controlling a steam engine.

The muscle can thus be caused to contract in two ways: either through the γ efferents and servo-mechanism, or directly. In human subjects either method may be used, depending for instance on previous instructions and the speed of movement required (Hammond *et al.*, 1956).

Another complication is that even the direct route of muscular excitation is subject to servo-control. Collaterals from the motor neurones run back into the central horn of the spinal cord, to form synapses with the small "Renshaw" cells. When these are excited, they inhibit the motor neurones in the area. The "Renshaw" cells thus form part of a negative feedback circuit which probably serves to stabilize the discharge of the motor neurones (Holmgren *et al.*, 1954).

Furthermore, striped muscles are also influenced by the tension receptors (the Golgi tension organs), impulses from which tend to inhibit the motor neurones (Granit, 1955a). The precise role these play in the control of muscular contraction is still not clear (review by Merton, 1964).

3.5. Skilled Movements

There is no sharp dividing line between the more- or less-stereotyped movements discussed earlier in this chapter, and the individually-acquired skilled movements of man and other higher mammalian species. However, studies of skilled movements demonstrate a complexity of feedback control through a variety of sensory modalities which exceeds, but is nevertheless almost a logical sequence to, the simpler cases discussed earlier in this chapter. Although they have been studied mostly in man, the mechanisms which have been revealed are undoubtedly variations on mechanisms existing but not yet studied in other animals.

The importance of feedback in the control of skilled movements becomes apparent only when it is cut off or upset. This can most easily be done with exteroceptive feedback. Deutsch (1960) studied the attempts made by singers to sustain a steady note. In practice, the note achieved was rarely steady, but subject to small oscillations. By a device which amplified the volume of the voice and delayed its reception by the singer, Deutsch verified the hypothesis that the relative constancy of the note depends on small corrections for error. The singer starts to correct only when he hears his voice straying from the Sollwert, and corrects again when he finds that the initial correction has led him into the opposite error (*see also* Miller *et al.*, 1941).

As we talk, our words are constantly monitored by our ears, and interference with this feedback produces gross distortions of speech. If the speaker is prevented from hearing his own words as he says them, but allowed to do so after a brief delay, his speech rapidly becomes incoherent, with widely fluctuating frequencies and amplitude, and jumbled words. He is, as it were, trying to monitor by a feedback which is no longer appropriate.

It is evident that such monitoring mechanisms must be of considerable complexity. The disturbance to speech at any instant is a consequence of a discrepancy between feedback assumed to come from what has just been said and the feedback which should have been produced. K.U. Smith (1962) emphasizes that the disturbance caused by delayed feedback is not a simple function of length of delay, but varies between individuals, and with the nature of the task.

Interference with the feedback through other sensory modalities produces comparable disturbances. If a subject is asked to write, but instead of seeing his hand directly sees it projected on a television screen, there is no disturbance in his performance so long as the angle of the camera corresponds with that of his own eyes. But if the position of the camera is altered so that the picture that he sees shows him his hand from an angle quite different from that at which he normally sees it when writing, his performance is confused. Delayed feedback causes similar confusion in human operators required to track a target by turning a control. This occurs even when the delay is shorter than their own reaction time. Such results suggest to Smith (1962) that monitoring is a continuous process and cannot be accounted for in terms of unit responses linked into chains—though such a view seems to suggest an approach less likely to be fertile than analytical attempts to disentangle the feedback loops involved (e.g. Chase *et al.*, 1961).

The complexity which must exist in the mechanisms controlling skilled movements is immediately apparent when one considers how the detailed patterning of contractions must depend on the initial posture. One way of conceptualizing the processes involved is to imagine the movements as being made with reference to a "body schema", an organized consequence of past and current sensations stored in some way in the brain (Head, 1920). This concept has been critically discussed by Oldfield *et al.* (1942a, b): it finds an echo in some more recent work on the control of skilled movement which will be discussed in Chapter 21.

Because skilled movements are made with respect to an initial posture, the feedback systems at the spinal cord/muscle level, discussed in the previous section, can form only one part of the total control system. Proprioceptive reflexes from muscles and labyrinth would be too slow for many purposes, and central activation of the proprioceptive reflexes in anticipation of the strains imposed by the directive components must occur. Postural support must thus be under the continuous control of higher mechanisms. Presumably interlocking control systems with positive and negative feedback are operating at different levels in the nervous system (Jung *et al.*, 1960), complex interreactions between the sensory-motor cortex, cerebellum and brain-stem being involved. The cerebellum, for instance, appears to play a part in comparing an actual movement, as indicated by proprioceptors, with a Sollwert received from the cerebral cortex. We have thus not only a Sollwert, related to reafferent stimulation, at the level of the individual muscle, but also similar systems of control at higher levels, the movement being adjusted at each one (e.g. Lashley, 1952). Some of the possible mechanisms concerned are discussed by Ruch (1951).

As yet, practically nothing is known of how these higher level control systems might work, but some aspects of the functioning of the mammalian cerebral cortex are at least compatible with multiple control of this sort. For instance, the classical picture of discrete sensory and motor areas of the cortex is now clearly inaccurate: in primates somatic afferents reach the pre-central region (generally known as the "motor area"), as well as the post-central "sensory area", and the pyramidal tract seems to originate from post-central areas as well as the entire pre-central area. This close relationship between sensory and motor pathways is clearly compatible with feedback control. Similarly, eye movements can be elicited by stimulation in the "visual sensory" cortex, ear movements from the "auditory" cortex, and so on. Removal of the pre-central cortex leads to a disturbance of organized pathways of movement, not in terms of the final solution of the problem presented but in terms of increased awkwardness and clumsiness (Pribram, 1958). To go to the other extreme, it seems that *Octopus* can never learn to make skilled movements with its arms because it cannot use proprioceptive information about the position of its arms. Presumably, with such flexible arms, the mechanism necessary for it to be able to do so would have to be impossibly complicated (Wells, 1962b).

3.6. Conclusion

This chapter has been concerned with the means by which the patterning of movements are controlled. Our principal question has been this: are the sequences of muscular contractions involved in particular movements predetermined from the start in the central nervous system, or are the later phases of the movement adjusted by peripheral stimuli received during the earlier stages? Central patterning certainly occurs in some cases. In others, input from the periphery plays a part in controlling the rhythmicity, phasing, strength or sequence of the muscular contractions. This input may act in a variety of ways: for instance it may control intra-member or inter-member reflexes, or it may feed into a control system which makes finely graded contraction possible. In mammals, feedback control plays an essential role in nearly all movements: furthermore, the control may be extremely complex, consisting of a number of interlocking systems.

Thus, as we shall find repeatedly in later chapters, generalizations of universal applicability are hard to find. In the present instance, unifying principles are most likely to come from evolutionary and functional considerations, for the nature and extent of peripheral control is likely to vary between species, and with the function of the movement. We might, for instance, expect peripheral control to be more important in locomotion over a rough terrestrial environment than in swimming, in movements involving manipulation of objects than in stereotyped signal movements, and in animals whose motor patterns are modifiable than in those where they are more stereotyped. As yet, however, too few species have been studied to provide a sound basis for such hypotheses.

3.7. Summary

1. The patterning of complex movements could be determined from the start in the central nervous system, or could be adjusted by peripheral (proprioceptive or exteroceptive) stimuli received as a result of the earlier phases of the movement. This chapter is largely concerned with experiments aimed at assessing the relative effects of central and peripheral factors.
2. Each individual and species has a repertoire of "fixed action patterns"—movements whose patterning does not depend on external stimulation, though it may depend on proprioceptive sources of input.
3. Some, but by no means all, fixed action patterns are oriented with respect to the environment. In some such cases the stimuli responsible for the orientation can be distinguished from those responsible for elicitation of the movement in the first instance.
4. The beating of the lobster heart and sound production by a cicada are examples of movements whose patterning is independent of peripheral control. Swallowing, in vertebrates, may be another.
5. Feedback stimulation resulting from earlier phases of the movement influences the frequency of the beats in the flying of locusts, and may reset the respiratory rhythm of aeschnid nymphs. Peripheral input is essential for the locomotory rhythms of lower vertebrates.
6. In mammals deafferentation of a limb results in the failure of that limb to take part in any but the crudest movements.
7. The feedback provided by the muscle spindles provides a mechanism for the control of graded muscular movements.
8. Skilled movements in man (and presumably also many other vertebrates) depend not only on feedback stimulation from exteroceptors and proprioceptors, but also on control systems operating at a number of higher levels.

4

The Effective Stimuli

In his "Stroll through the worlds of animals and men" von Uexküll (1934) described how the mated female tick climbs to the tip of a bush, clinging at such a height that she can drop off on to mammals that run beneath her. She clings there, perhaps for months, without response to the sounds, smells and other changes about her, until one particular stimulus acts as a signal for her to release her grip. This stimulus is the smell of butyric acid, a product of mammalian skin glands, and thus an indication of the proximity of a potential blood meal. Out of the hundreds of stimuli in its environment to which it might respond, the tick selects only this one, "Like a gourmet who picks the raisins out of the cake", as von Uexküll puts it.

Stimulus selection of this sort plays a part in all behaviour. At every moment an animal's sense organs are being bombarded by physical energy in many forms. To this chiaroscuro it responds selectively: some configurations of energy-change influence its behaviour, others do not. Selection from among the energy changes to which the animal is subjected evidently occurs. Furthermore, since some stimuli influence one type of behaviour and others another, there must be an optimal stimulus situation for each type of behaviour— *Tubifex* worms stimulate a male Stickleback to feed, green algae stimulate it to build, another male stimulates it to fight, and a female stimulates it to court. The importance of this selection has been emphasized by many workers (e.g. Lorenz, 1935; Russell, 1943; Tinbergen, 1948, 1951; Broadbent, 1958): in this chapter we shall consider experiments which demonstrate its occurrence, tell us which environmental changes influence the animal's behaviour, and indicate the optimum stimulus situation for eliciting each response.

First, however, we must consider the meaning of the word "stimulus", for it has been used in a number of different ways in the study of behaviour, and this has sometimes caused confusion (Verplanck, 1954). In particular, the word may refer to a part, or to a change in a part of the environment; or it may be confined to something which elicits an observable response. While it would be an abuse of language to label as a stimulus a physical change to which the animal is actually known to be insensitive, it will become apparent during the course of later chapters that the distinction between producing a response and not producing one is not absolute. An environmental change may, for instance, affect the nervous system but have no immediate effect on behaviour, or its effect may vary with the state of the organism or with the coincidence of other environmental influences. In this book, therefore, the use of the word "stimulus" need not necessarily imply an identifiable response on the part of the organism. On the other hand, the word will be anchored to the physical world, and will not be used to refer to hypothetical events postulated to account for changes in behaviour, as is often the case when the term "internal stimuli" is used.

4.1. Selective Responsiveness to Stimulation

The technique for assessing the effectiveness of a physical character in influencing a given pattern of behaviour consists basically of comparing the responses of the animal to two situations which differ by that character: if the responses differ, then the character is significant. The word "responses" is, of course, used loosely here with intention. It is always necessary to select one or more characteristics for measurement—for instance, frequency, latency or intensity. These may not be closely correlated with each other, and it is thus advisable to measure several in order to assess the effect of the stimulus (pp. 141–4).

In practice, we often start by comparing the naturally occurring situations which do and do not affect the response: this enables us to form an hypothesis about the nature of the effective stimuli. Thus, the observation that a foraging Cabbage White Butterfly (*Pieris* sp.) visits a series of blue flowers, and occasionally interrupts these visits by fluttering round the blue cover of a note book, suggests that it responds to the blue colour. In practice, also, we usually narrow down the possible sensory modalities before investigating the characters (or stimulus parameters) which are important within any one. This procedure may be made unnecessary by field observations of the type just cited, or by simple experiments. If we find that Great Tits will attack their image in a mirror, we can conclude that visual stimuli alone are sufficient for eliciting this response. In other cases, surgical interference may be necessary to delimit the sensory modalities—we can for instance sever the olfactory nerve of a bird and see whether this affects its response to food (Portmann, 1961 and references cited), or assess the response of a female rat to her litter when deprived of various senses (Beach *et al.*, 1956a).

Within each sensory modality we can identify the characters of the total stimulus situation relevant to a particular response by systematically varying the situation and assessing the effect on the response. For instance male Three-spined Sticklebacks establish territories in spring and behave aggressively to other males who intrude on them. Intruding females, however, are less often attacked and may be courted. At this time of year the male Stickleback has a red belly, and the female has not: by using models, ter Pelkwijk and Tinbergen (1937) showed that this red belly plays a very important role in eliciting attack from the territory owner. Some of the models they used, though only crude imitations of a Stickleback, were painted red underneath, while others were very similar to a Stickleback but lacked the red belly (Fig. 4.1). The former group of models was attacked much more vigorously than the latter, indicating that the "red belly underneath" was of primary importance in eliciting attack, while the other morphological characters were of minor influence. Behavioural

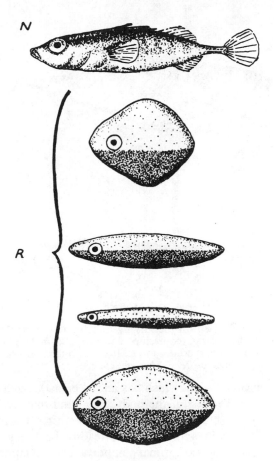

Fig. 4.1. Models used for identifying the stimulus characters important in eliciting the aggressive behaviour of the male Three-spined Stickleback. The four lower models have a red belly which is absent in the upper one. (*After Tinbergen, 1951.*)

characters also play a part, however, since a dummy is more likely to elicit attack if presented in the head-down posture adopted by a threatening male than if presented horizontally. Similarly, ter Pelkwijk and Tinbergen isolated two features of special importance in eliciting the first phase of the courtship sequence normally given by territory owners to gravid females—the swollen belly of the female and the rather upright position in which she swims in the water (Figs. 4.2 and 4.3).

Lack (1939), investigating the characters of an adult (European) Robin (*Erithacus rubecula*) which elicit threat from a territory owner, placed three types of stimulus object in the territories of wild Robins—a stuffed adult

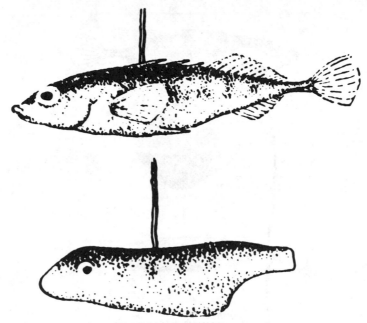

Fig. 4.2. Two models used for identifying the stimulus characters important in eliciting the zig-zag courtship dance of the male Three-spined Stickleback. The lower and cruder model has a swollen abdomen which is absent in the upper one. (*After Tinbergen, 1951.*)

Robin, a stuffed juvenile Robin (which has no red breast), and a bunch of red breast feathers lacking the rest of the body. He found that territory-owning males would threaten the bunch of red breast feathers almost as readily as they would a stuffed adult Robin, and much more readily than the stuffed juvenile Robin: the red breast is thus of primary importance in eliciting threatening behaviour.

The detailed studies of Tinbergen and Perdeck (1950) on the begging of gull chicks provide further examples. After hatching, gull chicks peck at the tips of the parent's bill. The parent regurgitates food on to the ground, picks some of it up in its bill tip and holds it near the young. In the course of its pecking, the young gets hold of some of the food and swallows it. The Herring Gull, on which the original experiments were performed, has a yellow bill with a red patch near the end of the lower mandible. The importance of the various stimulus characters of the adult's bill in eliciting pecking was studied by using series of cardboard models—within each series the models varied in only one stimulus character. Figure 4.4 shows such a series, the bars indicating the number of responses elicited by each model in a balanced series of tests. The experiments showed that the greatest response was obtained from models which were fairly low, near the chick, moving, long and thin, pointing downwards, and with a

Fig. 4.3. Dead tench (*Tinca vulgaris*) of Stickleback size presented in the posture adopted by a female Stickleback carrying eggs when entering a male's territory. (*After Tinbergen, 1951.*)

red patch contrasting with the bill near the tip. In this case, therefore, quite a number of stimulus characteristics were shown to be important. Others, however, were not: neither the colour of the bill nor the colour of the head were found to influence the response.

Some further examples are summarized in Table 4.1. In each case some features of the natural object have been shown to be of major importance in eliciting a particular response, while others have, at most, a minor effect. Thus, even in the absence of any precise definition of "a stimulus character", we can say that some responses are elicited by very few stimulus characters, others by many, but selection apparently always occurs. When a response depends much more on some characters than others, these charycters are usually referred to

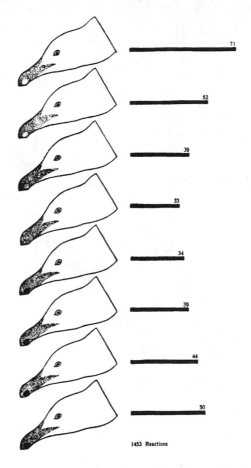

Fig. 4.4. A series of cardboard models of Herring Gulls' heads with grey bills and spots of varying shade. (*After Tinbergen, 1951.*)

as "sign stimuli" (Russell, 1943). This term has usually been used to refer to characters whose effectiveness is more or less specific to one response, although the experimental methods described so far in this section provide no evidence on this point (Schneirla, 1952, 1956; Lehrman, 1953): this matter is discussed later (pp. 62–3).

Since relational properties are usually important, few sign stimuli can

TABLE 4.1

Some studies indicating differential responsiveness to aspects of the natural stimulus object for species-characteristic responses.

Species	Response	Characters of Major Importance	Characters of Minor Importance	Reference
Silk-worm	Male's approach to female	Specific smell of female	Other smells Visual characters	Butenandt, 1955
Water-beetle (*Dytiscus*)	Prey-catching	Chemical and tactile stimuli	Visual stimuli	Tinbergen, 1951
Grayling Butterfly (*Eumenis semele*)	Sexual pursuit by male	Dark shade Type of movement Distance	Shape	Tinbergen *et al.*, 1943
Fritillary Butterfly (*Argynnis paphia*)	Male sexual pursuit	Colour Speed of flicker Size	Black patterning Shape	Magnus, 1958
Mantis	Prey-catching	Distance Type of movement	Size, shape, direction, colour, smell	Rilling *et al.*, 1959
Honey-Bee worker	Food-begging	Head carrying specific scent Tactile stimuli from antennae	Body Colour and shape of head	Free, 1956
Honey-Bee worker	Stinging	Dark colour Sting venom odour Human sweat odour Movement	General bee odour	Free, 1961
Char (*Salmo alpinus*)	Attack Nest-site selection	Red colour Visual stimuli from gravel	Size, shape Tactile stimuli from gravel	Fabricius and Gustafson, 1954

TABLE 4.1 (*continued*)

Species	Response	Characters of Major Importance	Characters of Minor Importance	Reference
Darter (*Etheostoma blennioides*)	Egg-laying	Texture	Smell Colour	Winn, 1957
Cichlid fish (*Apistogramma* sp.)	Approach to parent by young	Movement Colour	Form Size	Kuenzer *et al.*, 1962 (*see also* Kühme, 1962)
Domestic hen	Maternal protection of chicks	Distress call	Visual characters	Brückner, 1933
Domestic fowl	Mounting	Crouching posture	Male and female characters	Fisher *et al.*, 1956–7. (*See also* Carbaugh *et al.*, 1962)
Brewer Blackbird (*Euphagus cyanocephalus*)	Male mating behaviour	Posture Head and/or tail above horizontal Colour of fore-parts	Eye colour Colour of posterior region Wings	Howell *et al.*, 1952
Bullfinch (*Pyrrhula pyrrhula*)	Anxiety responses	Visual texture Convex surface Coloured surface	Specific outline of predator	Kramer *et al.*, 1951
Herring Gull	Egg-rolling	Speckling, size, colour	Shape	Baerends, 1957b, 1959b
Turkeys	Fleeing from a winged predator	Relation between speed and size	Shape	Schleidt, 1961 Müller, 1961
White mouse	Retrieving of young by inexperienced female	Cries of young	Visual and olfactory characteristics of drowned young	Noirot, 1964c, in press

readily be specified quantitatively along a single physical scale. Thus, in
Tinbergen's experiments on the stimuli releasing aggressive responses from
male Sticklebacks, the red patch was found to be more effective when on the
lower side of the model than when on the upper (*see also* Baerends, 1957a).
An even more interesting case concerns the release of fleeing responses in turkeys by a flying predator. Lorenz and Tinbergen found that this response could
be elicited by a relatively simple moving model, as shown in Fig. 4.5. In birds
which had lived in the open and become accustomed to the other birds in the
area, the model elicited a fleeing response if moved with the short end in front
("hawk model") but not if pulled the other way ("goose model") (Tinbergen,

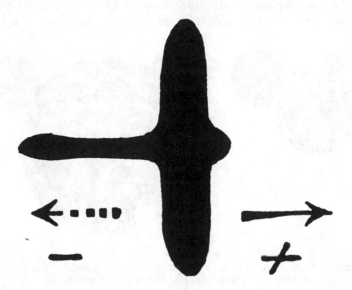

Fig. 4.5. Cardboard model used to elicit escape reactions from young
turkeys. It was effective when moved to the right but not when moved to
the left. (*After Tinbergen, 1951.*)

1948). Since this case has been a rather controversial one, it is as well to stress
that at this point we are concerned only with the occurrence of differential
responsiveness to the two models: its development is discussed later (pp. 363–4).
    Tinbergen and Kuenen's (1939) study of the stimuli eliciting gaping from
nestling thrushes (*Turdus merula*) provides another example of the importance
of relational characters. After about 8 days from hatching, the response is both
released and directed by visual stimuli, the nestling's gape being directed
towards the head of the parent. In Fig. 4.6, gaping was directed towards the
smaller of the two heads of the smaller model, but to the larger head of the
larger model. It thus seems that the head is characterized not by absolute size,
but by its size relative to that of the body.

Relational properties are not the only ones which may make the important features of the stimulus situation difficult to define. We shall see later (pp. 65–6) that the organism may respond to both first and higher order variables, gradients of physical variables and rates of change of gradients. Wherever relational or higher-order properties are involved, an attempt to isolate simple physical variables in the stimulus situation can be only a first step. Such difficulties in specifying the important features of the stimulus situation make it all the more important to remember that the "characters" of the stimulus situation studied are artificial abstractions made by the experimenter: the animal may abstract differently.

There is another point about the technique of such experiments which must be emphasized here. The strength of the response to any stimulus situation varies

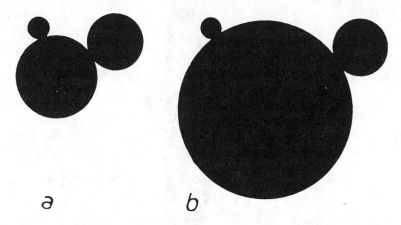

Fig. 4.6. Cardboard models used to release gaping responses from nestling thrushes. Further explanation in text. (*After Tinbergen, 1951.*)

with the internal state of the responding animals: a male Stickleback behaves aggressively only during a certain season of the year, and then only when on its territory. Even there its tendency to show aggressive behaviour varies with the stage of the breeding cycle. Not only does the strength of the response to a particular stimulus situation change, but so also does the difference between the response strengths to two models. Thus the models shown in Fig. 4.1 would be equally ineffective in eliciting attack from a male in winter condition, and all might elicit an immediate and maximal response from a male at the peak of his aggressiveness. The skill of the experimenter lies in selecting animals in an intermediate state in which the differences between the models will show up to best advantage. It goes without saying that the experimenter should also design his experiments to equalize the effects of the preceding tests between groups. In man, such effects can be important (Welford *et al.*, 1950) and complex (Helson, 1948), and comparable effects occur in animals (Chapter 13).

If, as a result of experiments of this type, we are able to specify the characters of a natural object which elicit a particular response, it may be possible to construct a model in which some of these sign stimuli are exaggerated relative to the natural object. We then have a "super-normal" stimulus object. Thus the egg-rolling response of the Oyster Catcher (*Haematopus ostralegus*), whereby eggs lying outside the nest are retrieved, is elicited more readily by an egg several times the normal size than by a normal egg (Tinbergen, 1948). Similarly, the pecking response of a newly hatched Herring Gull can be elicited even more effectively by a red knitting needle with three white bands near the tip, than by a three-dimensional plaster head. The needle combines, in an exaggerated form, just those characters, such as the contrasting red/white border and others specified on p. 47, which are important in eliciting the response (Tinbergen, 1953).

Most of the experiments cited so far have been concerned with visual stimuli, but similar principles apply to all other modalities. To cite but two recent examples, Wilson (1962) found that a number of different responses in Fire-ant workers (*Solenopsis saevissima*) could be elicited by chemical substances removed from the bodies of other individuals. His experiments demonstrated considerable specificity in the chemical stimulus for each response. In the auditory sphere, Stout (1963) demonstrated that specific sounds influence the aggressive and courtship behaviour of a Cyprinid fish. Furthermore, many responses can be evoked by cues acting through different senses. The begging of the young of both gulls and passerine birds can, at a certain stage, be elicited by either visual or auditory stimuli (Tinbergen *et al.*, 1950; Tinbergen *et al.*, 1939), and Beach *et al.* (1956b) showed that the maternal behaviour of experienced rats could be elicited through several sensory modalities. Of course, the finding that a response is influenced through more than one sensory modality provides no evidence for supposing that selection is not occurring within each of them (cf. Lashley, 1938a).

Where a response is influenced by stimulus characters acting through more than one sensory modality, or by more than one stimulus character in any one modality, their effects supplement each other. In the case of the Grayling Butterfly (*see* p. 87), the male's sexual pursuit is influenced by the type of movement shown by the model, by the darkness of its colour, and by its distance. Deficiencies in any one of the stimulus characters can be compensated for by increasing one of the others: a pale model close by is as effective as a dark model at a distance. This fact has been referred to as the Law of Stimulus Summation (Seitz, 1940/41, 1943; Lorenz, 1939) or Heterogeneous Summation (Tinbergen, 1951), though, of course, the effect of combining a number of sign stimuli is not necessarily simply additive in an arithmetical sense.

In all the examples cited so far, the sign stimuli important for a particular response have been more or less the same for all members of a species—all territory-owning male Sticklebacks respond aggressively to models with red bellies, all newly-hatched Herring Gull chicks peck at models which have the characters indicated on p. 47. Indeed, the experimental method used in nearly all these studies consisted of presenting models successively to large numbers of individuals and determining statistically which models produced the strongest responses. This method can give information only about stimulus characters effective in eliciting the response from the population, and clear-cut results are to be expected only if the individuals comprising the population behave similarly. In most of the experiments we have been considering so far, similarity between individuals was ensured because responsiveness to the particular features of the stimulus situation was little influenced by such differences in experience as occurred within the group of animals tested.

The use of this experimental method has led to the view that dependence on a few sign stimuli is characteristic only of responses common to a whole species (Tinbergen, 1951), a view which is certainly incorrect. The cartoonist's art is in itself a demonstration that our recognition of other individuals depends on some features much more than others, though his skill depends in part on picking out features which have a similar high significance for all who see the picture. Where individuals each respond to different features of the whole, selection from among all possible stimulus characters is more difficult to demonstrate, but nevertheless occurs. Some examples will be discussed later (e.g. Chapters 5 and 6).

Conclusion

These results have been obtained by one basic method—the animal is presented with stimulus situations differing in known physical characters, and a difference in response indicates that these characters are significant for the response in question. The method shows that for each type of behaviour some stimulus characters are important, while others are, at most, of minor significance: stimulus selection or filtering of the potential sensory input always occurs. Of course, some of the stimulus characters found to be important for one response may also be so for others: their specificity can be assessed only by studying different responses (*see* Chapters 5 and 6).

Such experiments show that some aspects of the total stimulus situation are of more importance than others, but they cannot prove that any aspects are of no importance. In fact, territory-owning Robins do sometimes threaten juvenile Robins, and male Sticklebacks sometimes attack models without a red belly (Tinbergen, 1951). A negative experimental result is evidence but not proof that the character is without influence on the response being tested, and further experiments may or may not support such a hypothesis. If the character does appear to be ineffective for one response, it may yet have an influence on others. If it is ineffective for all responses, one possibility is that the animal's sense organs are not responsive to it. Before proceeding further, therefore, some methods used for assessing the potentialities of sense organs must be discussed.

4.2. Limitations of Sensory Equipment

No organism is equipped with sense organs suitable for detecting all possible physical changes in the environment. This is obvious enough, but sensory capacities diverge so widely that the characteristics of an object to which an animal responds may be quite different from those by which we recognize that object ourselves.

The most direct techniques for studying the ability of a sense organ to detect changes in the environment involve recording from the sense receptors or the sensory nerves themselves. In this way Sand (1937) established that the lateral line canals of rays were sensitive to movements in the water; and Autrum *et al.* (1950) showed that some ommatidia in a bee's eye could distinguish polarized light from non-polarized light of the same intensity (*see* review by Carthy, 1961).

Recording from single fibres indicates that many sensory cells are normally sensitive to more than one form of energy: single units in the cat's lingual nerve can be activated by mechanical or thermal stimuli to the tongue (Hensel *et al.*, 1951), and single units in the lobster statocyst are sensitive to both position and acceleration. At the other extreme, some receptor cells have a highly specific sensitivity. For instance, a blowfly (*Phormia regina*) drinks if the solution touched by its mouth-parts contains sugars, but other solutes inhibit drinking. On the tips of the labellar hair are two neurones, one of which responds to sugar and the other to salts, acids and alcohols. It thus seems likely that the former is concerned with ingestion, and the latter with avoidance (Hodgson *et al.*, 1956; Hodgson, 1957). In this case, therefore, specificity in responsiveness of the organism may depend on specificity in the sense receptors: other examples are given by Liesenfeld (1956) and in a review by Marler (1961). Such limitation of sensitivity is to be regarded as specialized (in an evolutionary sense), a broader range of sensitivity being the primitive condition.

Partly because sense cells may be sensitive to more than one form of energy, the use of physiological methods for investigating the limitations of sense organs can be misleading from a behavioural point of view. A change in the pattern of nerve impulses passing along the optic nerve is produced by a blow on the eyeball, but must not be taken as indicating that the eye is normally a mechanoreceptor. Further, even when physiological techniques indicate that the sense organ itself is responsive to a certain dimension of the stimulus, we cannot be certain that variation in that feature can influence behaviour: although electrical recording from the cat's retina clearly indicates the presence of colour vision, behavioural confirmation has been obtained only with difficulty (Sechzer *et al.*, 1964).

For the study of behaviour, therefore, a behavioural method of assessing sensitivity is often a necessary complement to an apparently more precise physiological one. Often, a direct behavioural response to change in one dimension of a stimulus can be used to indicate the sensitivity of the organism.

Examples of this are to be found in studies showing that various arthropods respond to the plane of polarization of light (Fig. 4.7): if the plane is rotated, the animal changes its direction of movement (e.g. Bainbridge *et al.*, 1957, and references cited). Similarly, if a male moth responds to a place where the female has been sitting, he must be sensitive to some chemical indicator of her recent presence (Butenandt, 1955).

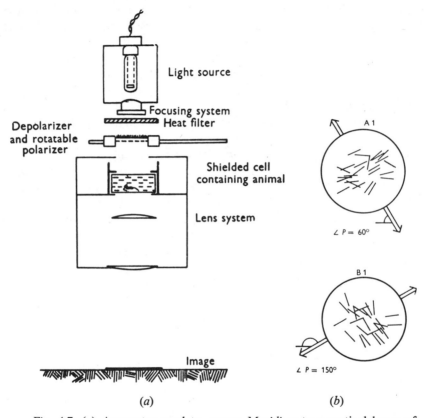

(a)   (b)

Fig. 4.7. (*a*) Apparatus used to expose *Mysidium* to a vertical beam of polarized light and record the resultant swimming orientation, with (*b*) the data obtained on two sample runs. (*After Bainbridge and Waterman, 1957.*)

Such a method can, however, be used only where the stimulus change in question already regularly elicits an identifiable response. A method of wider applicability involves a conditioning technique—if an animal can learn to respond differently to two stimulus situations, it must be able to distinguish them. A recent example of this method is the demonstration that certain fishes (*Gymnarchus, Gymnotus*, etc.) are sensitive to changes in the electric field surrounding them (Lissmann, 1958). Preliminary experiments showed that they responded by jerking or avoidance responses whenever they approached loops of wire placed in the water, and accordingly conditioning trials were undertaken. In the definitive experiments fish were trained to respond to the presence of a magnet placed behind a screen outside the aquarium. The apparatus is shown in Fig. 4.8. One fish was trained to accept food when the magnet was present and to refuse it for 30 sec when it was not, mild punishment being administered in the latter case for an incorrect response. The other fish was trained in the opposite way. The final tests were carried out in complete darkness to avoid any subconscious optical signals from the experimenter (*see also* Lissmann *et al.*, 1958).

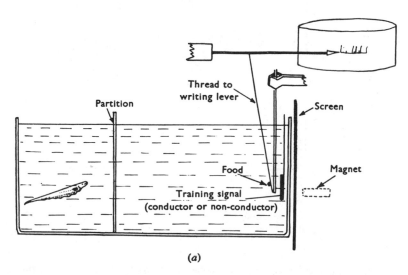

(*a*)

Fig. 4.8. Arrangement for training electric fishes to respond to conductors and non-conductors or to a stationary magnet outside its tank. (*After Lissmann, 1958.*)

Recently, operant conditioning (*see* pp. 403–4) techniques have proved of special value in this field. For instance the sensitivity of the pigeon to lights of different wavelengths has been studied by training birds to peck on one response key when a stimulus patch of a given wavelength is visible, and on another when it is not. These pecks control the intensity of the patch, reducing it in the former case and increasing it in the latter. The intensity of the patch thus oscillates up and down across the pigeon's threshold (Blough, 1957).

Conditioning methods can be used to determine the range of any physical variable to which the organism is sensitive, and also the fineness of the discriminations of which it is capable. The method has also been used to provide suggestive evidence that animals are not sensitive to certain physical variables.

Blinded Octopuses can readily be trained to discriminate between pairs of objects differing in texture: the technique involves rewarding the animal with a piece of fish for passing one of the objects to its mouth and punishing it with an electric shock for taking the other. Even after prolonged training, however, Octopuses fail to discriminate between similar objects differing only in weight (Fig. 4.9). Since the conditions of the experiments were identical in the two

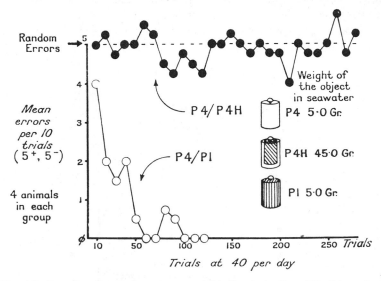

Fig. 4.9. Results of experiments on weight discrimination (●, *P4* against *P4H*) and textural discrimination (○, *P4* against *P1*) in *Octopus*. (*After Wells, 1962b.*)

cases, this "can hardly mean otherwise than that *Octopus* is incapable of recognizing objects by their weight" (Wells, 1961). Wells has emphasized that such results do not show that *Octopus* does not respond in any way to differences in weight—it clearly does, because it adjusts the muscle tension in its arms to allow for the weights of the things which it handles. Rather it seems that in *Octopus*, as in vertebrates (Merton, 1964), there are two mechano-sensory systems, one concerned solely with the local adjustment of muscle tension and the other sending information to higher parts of the nervous system which can be used in learning: the latter does not discriminate weight differences (Wells, 1964b).

Some of these examples show that an organism may be responsive to some types of change in a given form of physical energy, but not to others. The human eye is sensitive only to a certain range of light wavelengths, and to these only above a certain intensity, but within that range of wavelengths it has considerable powers of discrimination which are lacking in many other vertebrates. All vertebrates, however, seem to lack the ability to respond differentially to the plane of polarization of the light. As another example, many insects have auditory organs, but these are, on the whole, very insensitive to changes in the frequency of the incident sound. Recordings from the auditory nerve show marked changes related to amplitude variations in the sound, but little change when the frequency is varied. The information contained in the latter is thus lost (Pumphrey, 1940; Haskell, 1956).

Even when we know the general nature of the stimuli to which an organism responds, we may not be able to specify the dimensions along which these stimuli should be assessed. Thus, *Octopus* makes tactile discriminations between objects held by the suckers on its arms merely by the proportion of sense organs excited in the area of the arm in contact with the object (Figs. 4.9 and 4.10).

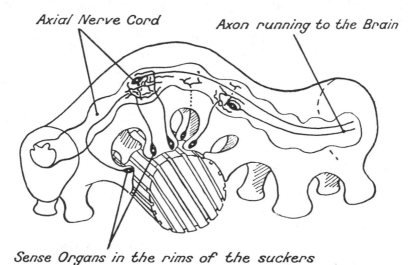

Fig. 4.10. Diagram of the arm of an octopus touching a cylinder of the type labelled *P*1 in Fig. 4.9. The proportion of the sense organs in contact will depend on the proportion of the surface of the object that is cut away to form grooves into which the suckers cannot penetrate. (*After Wells, 1962b.*)

They thus fail to distinguish between cylinders having longitudinal grooves and ones with transverse grooves, provided the same amount of surface is cut out in each case—a result rather surprising to the human observer, who can readily detect the differences by feel (Wells, 1962b).

The results of studies of the extent to which *Octopus* can distinguish between shapes held in its arms is also rather unexpected. Proprioceptive information about the bending of the arms is apparently not available: instead the animal uses only information about the degree of distortion imposed on the suckers by contact with the surface. This was shown by assessing the response to composite cylinders built up from narrower rods: these caused bending of the arm similar to that produced by a cylinder of the size of the whole, but sucker distortion similar to that produced by cylinders the size of the components. They were treated as being the diameter of the components. Further, since Octopuses, trained to reject the smaller and take the larger of two cylinders, without further training also reject the rougher and accept the smoother of two objects of similar size, it seems that differences of texture and surface curvature are measured in the same way: in principle it should be possible to discover a texture which is equivalent to any shape as far as *Octopus* is concerned (Wells, 1964a, b).

The response of noctuid moths to ultrasonic frequencies similar to those emitted by free-flying bats provides another example of the way in which, even within a modality in which an organism seems to be sensorily well equipped, its behavioural responsiveness may be determined by the limitations of its sensory equipment. Electrical recording suggested that the acoustic information received by the moths could enable them to make a rough determination of the position of a bat 20-100 feet away. These studies also predicted that, at closer distances, the intensity of an average bat cry would saturate the sense organs, there would be no differential response from the two sides, and the directional information would be lost. Observations under field conditions confirmed this view: low intensity ultrasonic sounds caused the moths to fly away from the source, but high intensity sounds caused a wide variety of manoeuvres which were non-directional except that they carried the insects towards the ground (Roeder, 1962a, 1964).

That an organism's sensory equipment plays a role in determining which of the stimuli to which it is exposed will influence behaviour is, of course, a statement of the obvious, though it is not hard to find cases where such sensory filtering has been wrongly ascribed to more central processes. In the next chapter we shall consider other mechanisms by which the stimuli impinging on an organism are filtered.

4.3. Summary

1. Animals respond selectively to the changes in physical energy to which they are exposed.
2. For any type of behaviour, such selection can be demonstrated by comparing the responses of an animal to stimulus situations differing in known characters. In every case some stimulus characters are found to be significant, others of, at most, minor importance.
3. The effective stimulus characters or "sign stimuli" cannot always be readily specified along a single physical scale: relational properties may be important.
4. In assessing the effectiveness of a stimulus character, animals in an appropriate motivational state must be used.
5. Once the stimulus characters effective for a given response have been isolated, they can be combined in an exaggerated form in a "supernormal" stimulus object.
6. The effects of different stimulus characters relevant to the same response supplement each other.

7. Stimulus selection occurs in all responses, those characteristic of particular individuals as well as those characteristic of a species.
8. The changes in physical energy to which an organism can respond are controlled in part by the limitations of its sensory equipment. These can be studied by both physiological and behavioural techniques.

5

Selective Response to Stimulation— Sensory/Perceptual Mechanisms

We have seen that not all the energy changes to which an organism is exposed influence its behaviour, and that selection from the potential sensory input is due in part to limitations in the capabilities of the sense organs. However, conditioning experiments show that most animals are capable of responding to, or discriminating between, stimuli which had no influence before training started: thus, further stimulus selection or filtering of the sensory input must occur.

We can distinguish two types of selection from among the stimuli to which the sense organs are responsive as follows. As we have seen (p. 44), if we elicit the same response by stimuli differing in known ways, a comparison between the response strengths indicates whether or not the difference between the stimuli is significant for the response in question. By repeating this procedure we can draw up a list of stimulus characters significant for that response. If we do this for more than one type of behaviour, we find that some characters are important in one context but not in others, while some are effective for all, or nearly all, responses that we test. In the first case, the effectiveness of the character has some degree of response-specificity, while in the second it does not. In Sticklebacks, for instance, the character "red underneath" increases the effectiveness only of models eliciting territorial aggression, but moving models are more effective than stationary ones in producing both sexual and aggressive responses. In such cases as the latter, where the effect is not response-specific, it is likely to be related to aspects of the sensory/perceptual mechanisms common to diverse types of behaviour. Similarly, in our own species, some stimulus configurations catch our attention more readily than others: in a visual field, for example, circular forms are more conspicuous than those with irregular outlines, and regularly arranged elements more conspicuous than irregular ones. Stimuli that are louder, brighter, or more intense tend to be more effective for a wide range of responses.

That the effectiveness of a character may be valid for behaviour other than the response tested has sometimes been overlooked (Schneirla, 1952, 1956; Lehrman, 1953). Thus many of the stimulus characters which Tinbergen *et al.*

(1950) found to be effective in eliciting the pecking response of Herring Gull chicks (p. 47) owe their effectiveness to properties of the sensory/perceptual mechanisms common to all visual responses. Movement and contrast are obvious examples, and the greater effectiveness of a vertically oriented beak may be related to a greater conspicuousness of radial, as compared with

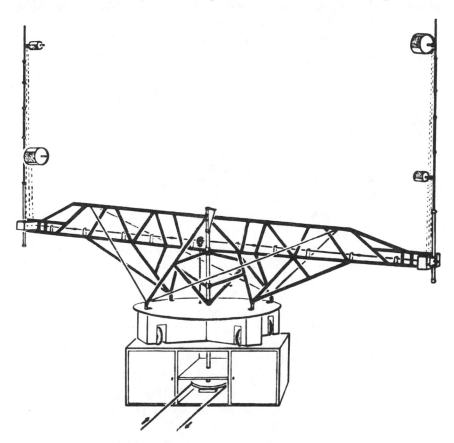

Fig. 5.1. Apparatus used to investigate the stimulus characters eliciting courtship pursuit flight from males of the Fritillary Butterfly *Argynnis paphia*. Both horizontal arm and the small cylinders rotate. (*After Magnus, 1955.*)

tangential, movement of an image over the retina (Tinbergen, 1955; Weidmann *et al.*, 1958; Marler, 1961; Hailman, 1962). Similarly, from a detailed study of the pecking responses of young Arctic Terns (*Sterna macrura*), Quine *et al.* (1964) argued that some of the characters owed their effectiveness to properties of the sensory/perceptual mechanisms, while others were specific to the feeding situation.

In some cases the effectiveness of a character can be ascribed to properties of the sensory/perceptual mechanisms not by assessing its influence on other responses, but by a direct study of those mechanisms themselves. In studying the stimuli eliciting the courtship approach of male Fritillary Butterflies (*Argynnis paphia*), Magnus (1958) used the revolving model shown in Fig. 5.1. Three stimulus characters influenced responsiveness—colour, size (within limits), and the rapidity of the revolution of the drum. The special effectiveness of a particular orange colour which corresponds to that of the female is presumably specific to this particular response. The increase in effectiveness with size, however, is presumably related to the number of ommatidia stimulated. That the importance of the rapid alternation of stimuli is also related to sensory/perceptual mechanisms is suggested by Magnus's finding that the model becomes less effective if the rate is increased above 125 presentations per second. This corresponds reasonably well to the flicker fusion frequency of 150 as determined electrophysiologically. Similarly Vogel (1957), studying the courtship of male houseflies, found that the attractiveness of models increased up to 270 presentations per second; the flicker fusion frequency for a related species has been determined as 265/second (Autrum, 1950).

The problem of why some patterns of energy distribution are more effective than others for a wide range of behaviour has been studied more in the context of human than animal perception. With human subjects the use of verbal instructions can eliminate the elaborate pre-training necessary for animal experiments and thus avoids many of their inherent difficulties (e.g. Koffka, 1935; Gibson, 1950; Vernon, 1952; Teuber, 1960). Although the perceptual world of animals is often very different from our own (von Uexküll, 1934), the principles which emerge from the study of human perception are often highly relevant to the study of perception in animals. Here discussion is limited to three problems, all concerned with the relation between the physical properties of the stimulus and its effectiveness in controlling behaviour, which are of special relevance to work on animal behaviour. The first is by nature of a caveat: quantitative variations in a stimulus along a simple physical dimension may produce complex changes in its effect on the organism. The second concerns the abilities of animals to discriminate shapes, and emphasizes the danger of premature generalizations as to the patterns of stimulation which an animal can or cannot distinguish. The third, the perception of movement, indicates that the mechanisms which determine the effectiveness of a given stimulus may be considerably more complicated than appears at first sight. Finally, some physiological correlates of perceptual phenomena will be considered.

5.1. Physical Scales and the Perceived Stimulus

One of the lessons to be learnt from the study of human perception is that physical measurements and subjective measurements along a given stimulus dimension do not coincide. For many stimuli the subjective magnitude ψ

increases as a function of physical magnitude ϕ above the threshold ϕ_0 raised to a power n. That is,

$$\psi = k(\phi - \phi_0)^n$$

and log ψ plotted against log $(\phi - \phi_0)$ gives a straight line with gradient n. However, the relationship of the physical scale to the subjective scale varies between the sensory modalities. The gradient is only 0·33 for brightness, but increases for loudness, smell, vibration, taste, temperature, and heaviness up to a value of 3·5 for electric shock. In other words a large increase in physical intensity is necessary to double the subjective intensity of a light, but only a small increase in physical intensity is necessary to double the subjective intensity of an electric shock (Stevens, 1958, 1961). Although human subjects have been used for most of this work, comparable results have been obtained with animals. For instance, Herrnstein *et al.* (1962) found that pigeons increased their rate of pecking as a power function of the luminance of the response key. Thus, no particular relationship, good for all stimuli and all modalities, between the intensity of a stimulus and its consequences in the central nervous system can be assumed.

Indeed we cannot even assign the subjective sensory qualities like hue, brightness and loudness, to particular physical dimensions. Hue may depend on the intensity as well as the wavelength of the incident light: with certain exceptions, the perceived hue of all wavebands changes as the intensity of the light is increased. Although this reservation applies primarily to film colours (i.e. colours not obviously belonging to a surface), it could have important consequences for the conduct of experiments aimed at identifying the stimuli relevant for particular responses: the hues of a given series of models could appear to be slightly different on bright and dull days. Similarly, subjective brightness and saturation (or vividness) also depend on both wavelength and intensity of stimulation; while the pitch, loudness, volume and density of a sound all depend on both its intensity and its frequency. The perceptual dimensions do not correspond completely to physical dimensions, so that it is not possible to produce variation along a single perceptual dimension by variation along a single physical one while other factors are kept constant. Indeed, the response to stimulation can have more dimensions than the stimulus itself, the additional ones arising in part from the properties of the sense organ (for further discussion *see* Boring, 1935).

A further complication is that the characteristics of the stimuli on which human perception depends may be more complex than those which have usually been studied by sensory physiologists. The stimulation from the environment usually acts on a sense organ, not just a single receptor cell, so that gradients, ratios and changes in the pattern of stimulation can function as essential components for discrimination of the situation. For instance, an important visual characteristic of a receding surface is the density of its stimulus elements.

In Fig. 5.2 the receding surface *AB* yields a retinal image *ab* in which there is a gradient of texture from coarse to fine, whereas the frontal surface *BC* yields no such gradient. There is considerable evidence that the gradient of texture in *AB* provides one of the means whereby the observer can detect that it is receding. Furthermore, along *AB* the texture changes at a constant rate: if *AB* were curved or discontinuous, however, the rate of change of texture would not be constant. Such higher order variables are probably among the means by which we detect curvature, discontinuities in surfaces, and so on (Gibson, 1950).

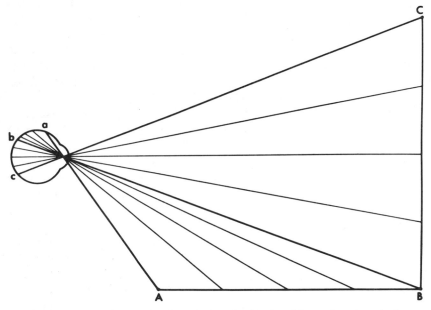

Fig. 5.2. The optical projection of a longitudinal and frontal surface. (*After Gibson, 1950.*)

We see, then, that both with simple stimulus dimensions and with more complex patterned stimulus configurations, physical measurements of stimuli may give a quite misleading impression of their potential effectiveness for influencing behaviour.

5.2. Form Discrimination

The response elicited from an organism depends not merely on the total amount of stimulation, but on its patterning—patterning in either space or time or both. We must, therefore, ask not only what patterns of stimulation are likely to elicit what responses, but also what patterns the organism is capable of discriminating, and by what criteria they are discriminated. Equally, we may ask the obverse of this—by what properties are patterns of stimulation classified by the organism as similar?

Nearly all attempts to answer these questions for animals have depended on two methods. In order to assess the ability of an organism to differentiate between two patterns of stimulation, the conditioning method already discussed on pp. 56–60 is used. The animal is trained to respond differentially to two patterns, and some characteristics of the learning score (e.g. number of errors, or number of trials to reach a given criterion of correct choices, number of

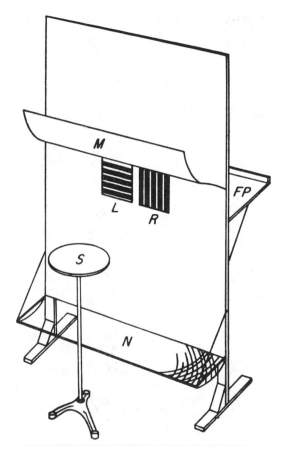

Fig. 5.3. The jumping stand as used by Lashley for testing pattern discrimination by rats. (*After Lashley, 1930.*)

errors in a specified series of trials, etc.) are used as criteria of the difficulty of the task. Secondly, once an animal has been taught to discriminate between two patterns, the extent to which new stimuli are "equivalent" to the original ones can be assessed. If substitution of the new stimulus patterns for the original ones results in no change in, for example, error scores, then the new situation can be regarded as equivalent to the old one: if the precision of the discrimination is reduced, a measure of the extent to which the patterns are not equivalent is thereby provided. A series of such tests then provides information about the dimensions in terms of which the original patterns were discriminated. Both these methods provide information on the abilities of organisms to classify patterns and on the criteria by which they do so: they can also be used to analyse the steps involved.

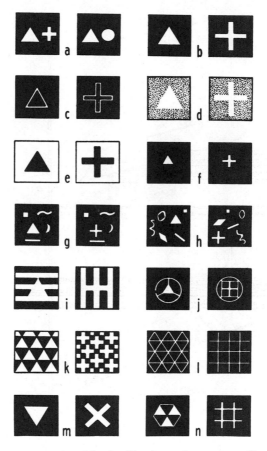

Fig. 5.4. Some patterns used by Lashley in testing pattern discrimination in rats. (*After Lashley, 1938b.*)

Such methods could be applied to stimulation received through any sensory modality and patterned in either space or time. In practice, the bulk of the work has been confined to the visual discrimination of shape by animals The apparatus used by Lashley (1930) for this purpose is shown in Fig. 5.3. The screen had two holes $5\frac{1}{2}$ in. sq. (*L* and *R*), which could be closed with heavy cards, on which the patterns to be discriminated were drawn. The rats were trained to jump from the stand *S* towards one of the cards. The positive card would fall backwards when the rat jumped against it, allowing the animal to reach the feeding platform *FP*. The negative card was fixed, so that if the animal jumped that way, it fell into the net *N*. Some patterns used by Lashley are shown in Fig. 5.4.

Another apparatus widely used at the present time for primates is the Wisconsin general test apparatus (e.g. Harlow *et al.*, 1962). The monkey is confined in a suitable cage, and the stimulus objects are presented on a horizontal tray to one side of the cage (Fig. 5.5). The objects are placed over small depressions in the tray, where suitable rewards can be hidden. The monkey is trained to reach out and displace one of the objects: if it selects an object which

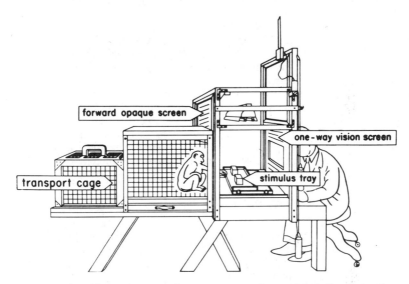

Fig. 5.5. The Wisconsin general test apparatus for studying discrimination in primates. (*After Harlow and Harlow, 1962.*)

covers a depression containing food, it can eat the food. The apparatus is provided with a device by which the tray can be withdrawn from the animal's reach after it has made a choice. There is usually, also, an opaque screen which can be lowered to prevent the monkey seeing the tray while it is being baited, and a one-way vision screen to conceal the experimenter.

With other species, rather different testing techniques have been used. For instance, *Octopus* can be trained by introducing the shapes one at a time into its tank: the animal is rewarded with food for attacking one of the shapes and punished with electric shock for attacking the other (Young, 1961). Recently, operant methods comparable to that described on p. 57 have proved invaluable for some species. Other methods are described by Sutherland (1961).

The literature on shape discrimination in vertebrates and cephalopods has recently been reviewed by Sutherland (loc. cit., 1963)*. Some of his conclusions can be summarized as follows:

1. *Discrimination of Shapes differing in Orientation*

(*a*) *Rectangles and Lines.* For a number of species—chimpanzee, dog, rat, various fish and *Octopus*—discrimination between horizontal and vertical lines, and between horizontal and vertical rectangles, is easy; but for some of these species at least, discrimination between opposite oblique striations is difficult or impossible. Cats perform well in oblique discriminations.

(*b*) *Triangles.* Dogs, rats and gudgeon learn to discriminate between upright and inverted triangles, but transfer tests suggest that, while dogs respond to the whole figure, rats respond primarily to the lower part and gudgeon to the apex (but *see* Matthews, 1964).

(*c*) *Mirror Images and 180° Rotations.* Macaques, rats and *Octopus* discriminate more easily between figures which are an up-down inversion of each other (e.g. ⊓ and ⊔), than left-right inversions (e.g. ⊏ and ⊐). There is no evidence that figures which differ only by inversions are more difficult to discriminate than figures with genuine form differences but of comparable complexity.

Although many pairs of mirror images can thus be readily discriminated by a number of species, some such discriminations are difficult, at any rate for rats and *Octopus*. Sutherland has shown that the vertical and horizontal projections (calculated by summing the total vertical and horizontal projections at each point along the two axes) of such shapes are similar (Fig. 5.6, *d, e, f*), and suggested that differences in the distribution of horizontal and vertical projections may be necessary for discrimination (*see* pp. 73, 85).

2. *Discrimination of Shapes Differing in Form*

(*a*) *Triangles and Circles.* Macaques, cats, rats, chickens, crows and *Octopus* discriminate readily between a circle and a triangle. Monkeys and cats, but not rats, show considerable transfer of training when the triangle is rotated.

(*b*) *Triangles and Squares.* Chimpanzees, macaques, rats, pigeons, various fish and octopuses make this discrimination easily.

(*c*) *Squares and Circles.* Sheep, cats, crows, chickens, frogs, various fish and octopuses make this discrimination. For rats, it is easier if the square has its sides oblique (i.e. a diamond shape) than if they are horizontal and vertical. This may be because rats discriminate primarily on the base of the figure.

(*d*) *Crosses, and other shapes.* Rats, hens and various fishes can discriminate between crosses and squares, diamonds, rectangles, triangles, etc. (Tree squirrels (*Sciurus*) discriminate random shapes more readily as the number of sides is increased from 4 to 7 (Michels *et al.*, 1962).)

3. *The Properties by which Shapes are Discriminated*

Transfer of training experiments have provided considerable data about the properties of the shapes which are discriminated:

* See also Meng (1957) for the toad *Bufo bufo*; Giebel (1958) for Equidae; Saxena (1960) for trout; Michels *et al.* (1962) for Tree Squirrels (*Sciurus spp.*); Zimmermann (1962) for infant Rhesus monkeys; Stichmann (1962) for chickens; Parriss *et al.* (1962) and Mackintosh *et al.* (1963) and refs. cited for *Octopus*; Mackintosh and Sutherland (1963) for Goldfish; Matthews (1964) for various tropical fish.

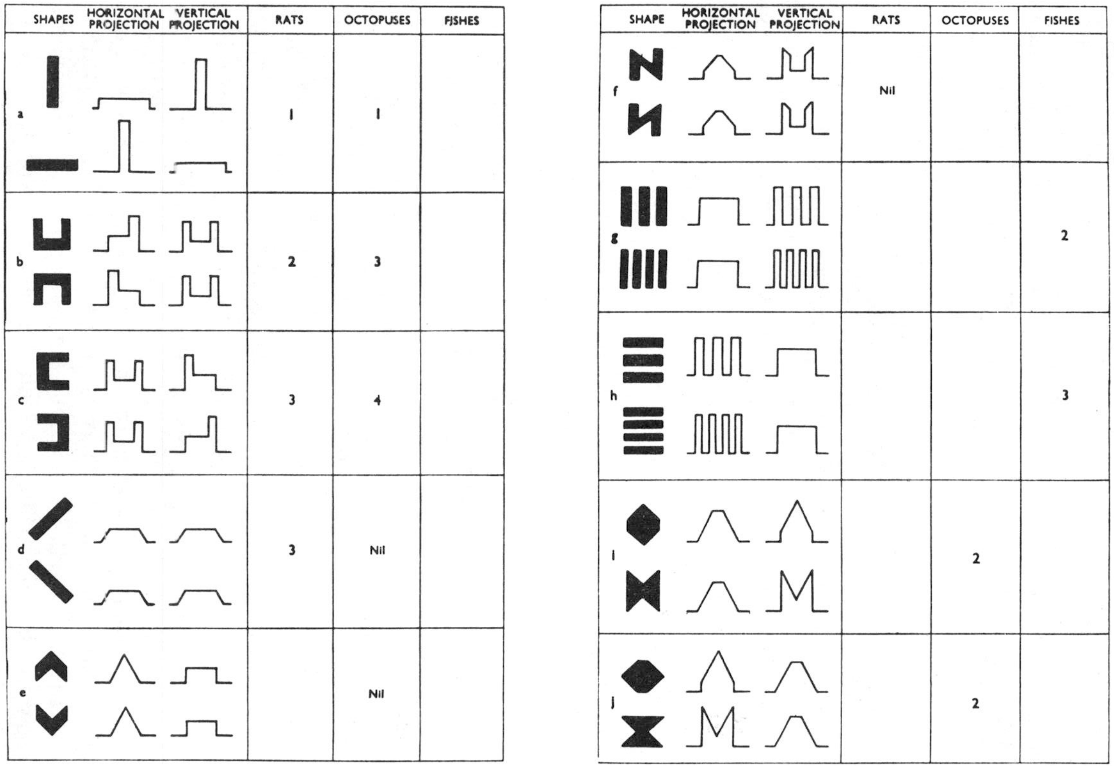

Fig. 5.6. The relation between the abilities of animals to learn visual discriminations and the horizontal and vertical projections of the figures. (*After Sutherland, 1961.*)

1, 2, 3, 4 and nil indicate decreasing degrees of discriminability.

(a) *Size.* A wide range of species show good generalization when the sizes of the figures they have learnt to discriminate are altered. This indicates that the shapes are analysed in terms of relative properties which remain constant even when size changes.

(b) *Outlines.* Many species show good generalization from solid to outline figures, or vice versa. This shows that the original discrimination was not based solely on differences in area, brightness, or distribution of brightness. Transfer from solid shapes to dotted outlines is moderately good in monkeys and hens, but poor in Minnows and Sticklebacks, though the results obtained depend on the size and frequency of the dots. If the dots are placed only at the corners of the shape, transfer is nearly always poor, though it is better if angles rather than dots are placed at the corners. Comparable results are obtained if the sides are present but the angles omitted.

(c) *Background.* Macaques generalize readily when the background of the figures is changed in size and/or shape, but data for other animals are scarce.

(d) *Relative Brightness for Figure and Background.* Reversal of brightness relations between figure and background has produced equivocal results, some experiments reporting good transfer, and others little. Species differences play a role here, for some animals (e.g. macaques), tend to identify stimuli by colour or brightness in preference to shape when the two are in conflict. For fishes, the dominance of colour seems to be less marked.

(e) *Parts of Figure.* If a discrimination has been learnt in terms of part of a figure only, generalization should occur when that part only is exposed or when the rest of the figure is distorted. This has been shown to occur in some species. Thus, on a Lashley jumping-stand, rats tend to discriminate in terms of the lower half of the figure; while in other types of experiments chickens and fish have been shown to rely on those features which most differentiate the two figures, wherever these occur on them.

(f) *Rotation.* Primates, some carnivores and octopuses have been shown to generalize when the triangle on which they have been trained was rotated (cf. 1 (b) above). (In addition, in an operant situation, a pigeon's rate of pecking decreased systematically as an isosceles triangle was rotated away from the training position (Reynolds, 1961).) For other species there is little evidence of transfer of training when the original figure is rotated. The only certain case in the rat is transference from H v + to ⊥ v ×. In fishes and rats it seems that generalization occurs only if the original shapes differ in the degree to which they are open or closed, i.e. in jaggedness. This suggests that they can discriminate in terms of this property.

In spite of the many experiments that have been conducted, statements of general validity about shape discrimination in animals are hard to make. It is clear that most simple discriminations are readily learnt by the standard laboratory mammals, though there are some surprising failures. For the most part, the results obtained from vertebrates and cephalopods are similar. For instance, 3–4 year old children, just like octopuses, confuse oblique lines oriented in opposite directions although, like octopuses, they can readily discriminate vertical from horizontal lines. Similar results are obtained with U shapes in various orientations (Rudel *et al.*, 1963). Similarities in perceptual abilities might be expected on other grounds, for the devices which have been evolved to camouflage shape depend on similar principles over a wide range of species (Cott, 1940).

In spite of these overall similarities there are also clearly some quite marked differences in ability for shape discrimination, even among the vertebrates. Differences are even more marked in the extent to which generalization occurs when the figures are rotated or distorted in various ways, and in the extent to which the whole or part of the figure is used. Unfortunately, detailed comparisons are difficult because of the differences in animals and techniques used: one study designed deliberately to investigate interspecies differences showed that squirrels and raccoons used the various parameters from the stimulus objects differently (Hitchcock *et al.*, 1963).

As mentioned on p. 70, Sutherland (1957) suggested that many of the results on shape discrimination in *Octopus* can be understood on the assumption that the animals analyse shape by counting the horizontal extents at each point on the vertical axis and their vertical extent at each point on the horizontal axis (Fig. 5.6). This hypothesis accounts for many of the experimental findings, though Sutherland (1962b) subsequently modified it with some additional suggestions; for instance that open and closed forms are differentiated by the height and width of the peaks on the horizontal and vertical projections, the horizontal being more important than the vertical. Other views on the mechanisms underlying shape discrimination are given by Dodwell (1961, 1962), and by Deutsch (1962).

Relatively little work has been done on form perception in invertebrates other than cephalopods. Some evidence suggests that even the higher arthropods do not use form vision in some contexts in which they might be expected to do so. For instance, in training experiments in which food is used as a reward, bees learn only with great difficulty to distinguish the simple geometric shapes, such as circle, square and triangle, which are easily distinguished by most vertebrates. In fact, a number of lines of evidence indicate that, in the feeding situation, bees show a marked preference for figures which have a long outline with respect to their surface area (e.g. Wolf *et al.*, 1937; von Frisch, 1953). Thus bees visit flowers and artificial figures more, the richer the contour that they possess, and can readily discriminate figures which are broken up into black and white areas from geometrical shapes. They show a preference for divided figures, and cannot be trained to visit a less sub-divided figure for food in preference to a more divided one (Zerrahn, 1933; Hertz, 1929, 1930, 1931, 1935). Presumably, a figure with an uneven outline provides numerous changes of stimulation in the individual ommatidia as the bee passes over them, and it is to this "flicker" effect that they owe their effectiveness. Flicker is undoubtedly also important in many other contexts—for instance in the courtship responses of many insects (*see* Table 4.1, pp. 49–50).

However, in some cases bees have been taught discriminations which appear to be based on patterning (Hertz, 1933, 1935), and bees and other arthropods certainly use form vision in other contexts, for instance in locating their nests. Tinbergen *et al.* (1938) placed movable landmarks (twigs, pine cones etc.) near the nests of the hunting wasp *Philanthus triangulum*. When the wasp had had an opportunity to learn the landmarks, some of them were moved and the extent to which the wasp was disoriented assessed. It was apparent that the wasp was responding not to particular landmarks but to the pattern of them all (*see* Chapter 7). An ability to discriminate forms is similarly demonstrated by Drees's (1952) analysis of the stimuli eliciting courtship or hunting in spiders, and by the ability of dragonfly adults (*Aeschna*) to discriminate almost instantaneously between insects and scraps of paper thrown into the air (Tirala, 1923). Indeed, the highly specific forms evolved by some flowers indicate a considerable ability for form discrimination in the insects which fertilize them; for instance, some orchids resemble the receptive females of certain ichneumonids, and are visited only by the males which attempt to copulate with them (references in Baerends, 1950; *see also* Manning, 1956). Even insects which have no compound eyes may be capable of rudimentary form vision through simple stemmata by the use of head movements (Dethier, 1943).

In conclusion, two points from this brief discussion of form discrimination require emphasis. First, an animal's ability to discriminate form should not be assessed from the study of one type of behaviour only: training experiments using the foraging behaviour of bees probably do not reveal their full abilities because of the overriding influence of flicker in this context. Second, many animals, even higher vertebrates, seem to be incapable of discriminating patterns which appear quite distinct to us. Species may differ markedly in their abilities, and further carefully controlled comparative experiments are urgently needed.

5.3. Constancy and Perceived Movement

The question of generalization between patterns is related to that of stimulus constancies. Man sees as unchanging the sensory properties of an object even when the retinal image changes considerably. A cardboard circle of given size and colour retains these apparent characteristics in spite of marked changes in angle of regard, distance, and wavelength of the reflected light. Comparable phenomena have been shown to occur in various animals (references in Vernon, 1952; Thorpe, 1963a). It is likely that this ability to perceive constancies depends on the use of higher order stimulus variables (*see* p. 66) and the relations between the different parts of the sensory field, a view which is supported by recent findings on the functioning of the retina (pp. 80–5). Take, for instance, size constancy: why do objects not look smaller when observed from a greater distance in proportion as their retinal image becomes smaller? One issue here is that the stimulus for perceived size is not given merely by the dimensions of the projection on the retina, but by a comparison between that and the size of the elements of texture in the surrounding space. The latter gives an indication of distance (*see* p. 66), and thus the distance of the object is taken into account in the assessment of size (Gibson, 1959). Higher order variables are probably important also for animals, for many visual illusions whose effectiveness depends on the surrounding parts of the field are effective for a wide variety of vertebrates besides man (references in Thorpe, 1963a).

Constancies involving movement of the sense organ itself present an especially interesting case. If we turn our heads, the image of the world shifts over our retina, but the world appears to stay still. Yet a similar movement of the retinal image produced by movement of the external world gives us the appropriate impression that the external world is moving; our eyes may show nystagmus movements which can be interpreted as an attempt to fixate the

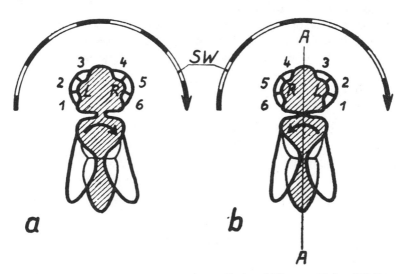

Fig. 5.7. The fly *Eristalis* in a rotating cylinder. (*After von Holst, 1954.*)

L, R indicate Left and Right eyes. *a*, head in normal position; *b*, head rotated through 180°.

moving world. How do we discriminate between movement of an image over our retina produced by change in the external world, and a similar movement produced by turning our heads? A similar problem arises when we consider the orientation of animals to their environment. If a fly (*Eristalis*) is placed on the axis of a vertical cylinder painted with vertical stripes, and the cylinder is rotated, the animal will turn in the same direction; it behaves as though attempting to keep in constant relationship to the world it sees. Yet the same movement of the image of the stripes across the eye occurs in ordinary locomotion, and does not induce these forced optomotor turning movements. What is the difference between the movement of the image over the retina caused by movement of the outside world, and that caused by movement of the organism itself?

It is helpful here to bear in mind a distinction, made by von Holst *et al.* (1950; von Holst, 1954), between exafferent stimuli, produced by movement in the external world, and reafferent stimulation, produced by the subject's own movement. If an animal moves its eyes or head, the stimulation produced by the movement of the image on the retina constitutes reafference, because it is the result of its own movement. If an object moves in front of the animal the stimulation is exafferent, because it is not a consequence of its own movement. Now in some way the insect distinguishes movement of the stripes relative to its body, when this is a consequence of its own movement, from the relative movement which results when the cylinder rotates. This is not due to a mere blocking of the optomotor reflex during self-initiated movements, for if the head is rotated through 180° about the axis of the neck, so that the positions of the eyes are interchanged, both types of response are upset. If the cylinder is rotated, the fly now moves in the opposite direction, as might be expected from the reversed order of the retinal elements (Fig. 5.7). If the insect itself starts to

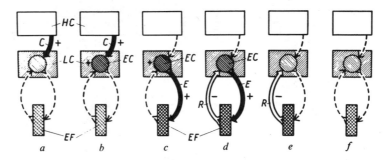

Fig. 5.8. Illustration of the reafference principle. For explanation, see text. (*After von Holst, 1954.*)

move while the cylinder is stationary, it spins rapidly in small circles until exhausted: if the optomotor reflex were blocked during self-initiated movement, one would expect it to move unhindered. Apparently, the reversal of the stimuli received by the fly as a consequence of its movement causes that movement to be increased. Other experiments (von Holst, 1950a) show that if the stimuli received as a result of movement are unchanged in direction but increased in strength, the extent of the movement is decreased.

On the basis of such results von Holst and Mittelstaedt suggested that such orientational movements are the result of a comparison between the actual afferent stimulation and that which should have occurred (i.e. the Sollwert) according to the momentary motivational situation. In the present instance (Fig. 5.8), they suggest that self-initiated movements are the result of a "command" from a higher centre which activates a lower one (*a* and *b*, Fig. 5.8): this may then send motor impulses or "efference" to the muscles at *c*. The state thus induced in the lower centre is called the "efference copy." In

Fig. 5.8 these efferent processes are shown in black, the reafference produced by the movement thus induced in white (Fig. 5.8 *d*). The efference copy and the reafference are compared in the lower centre. If they exactly compensate each other the movement ceases (Fig. 5.8 *e, f*). If the reafference is too great or too small, the· movement is increased or decreased appropriately. Rotating the head of the fly causes the reafference to be reversed: when the command induces turning to the left, the reafference is that normally appropriate to turning to the right, with the result that the self-initiated movement to the left is accelerated. In the normal fly rotation of the cylinder produces an unbalanced exafference, and the fly turns to compensate: when the eyes are reversed, the fly turns in the opposite direction (*see also* Dzimirski, 1959).

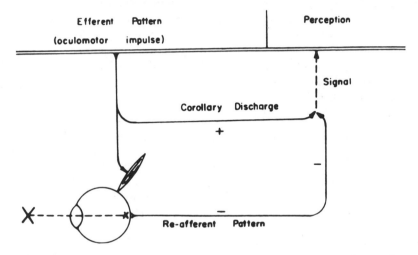

Fig. 5.9. Relation between eye movements and perception. (*After Teuber, 1961.*)

The reafference model thus enables us to understand both the behaviour of the normal fly and that of the fly with its head reversed. It involves a comparison between the sensory input actually received and a Sollwert, comparable to that which we have already encountered in the control of skilled movements. In the present case the basic assumption is that the Sollwert of the sensory input is determined by the efference copy (better called the "corollary discharge"; Teuber, 1961) which accompanies the initial command. A comparable model has been elaborated independently by MacKay (1962).

A similar explanation can be applied to the case of perceived movement. Helmholtz (1867) suggested that non-visual knowledge of the movement of the eyes depends on judgment of the "effort of will" required to move them. Evidence supporting this view was obtained by Brindley and Merton (1960): when the conjunctival sacs were anaesthetized and visual clues excluded, human subjects were unable to assess the amount or direction of their eye-movements unless those eye-movements had been produced by the unhindered action of their own eye muscles. Now any particular efferent discharge to the eye muscles will normally result in a particular movement of the image of an external object over the retina. Discrepancy between the displacement of an image as expected on the basis of the efferent discharge (the Sollwert) and that actually received will be interpreted as movement in the external world. Von Holst's model for this is shown in Fig. 5.9 (*see* von Holst *et al.* 1950; MacKay, 1962; Held, 1961; Teuber, 1961): its value can be seen by considering three ways in which the image can move across the retina:

(*a*) Its movement could be the result of a voluntary movement of the body, head or eyeball, the external world remaining stationary. In such a case the observer registers his own movement, and the external world is perceived as stable. In terms of the model, we can say that the efference copy or corollary discharge is just matched by reafference from the retina, or that the Sollwert involves just that movement of the image across the retina which actually occurs.

(*b*) If the eyeball remains still, a similar movement of the image of the external world across the retina caused by an actual movement of the external world is perceived as such. In this case there is no corollary discharge, the Sollwert is one of no movement of the retinal image, and the perception is produced by the unmatched afferent impulses.

(*c*) A third possibility is to move the eyeball mechanically by exerting slight pressure with the finger to the side of the eyelid. Here again, the afference is unmatched by a corollary discharge, and the external world appears to move.

An even more convincing demonstration can be obtained if the eye is mechanically fixed. If the subject then intends to move his eyeball, he perceives the environment to move even though there has, in fact, been no movement of the image over the retina. The perceived movement can then be understood as a consequence of the corollary discharge unmatched by reafference. In all cases the direction of the perceived movement is that predicted by the hypothesis (*see also* Gregory, 1958). The complexity of such comparator mechanisms is shown by experiments with human subjects which indicate an interplay between sensory and postural factors in perception; for instance tilting the body influences the relative sensitivity of the two palms (McFarland *et al.*, 1962).

In general, then, the consequences of the movement of a pattern of stimulation across a receptor surface are not immediately predictable: they depend on an interaction with other aspects of the internal state. It is also evident that the perception of movement of the environment and the control of the body's orientation with respect to that environment are in effect the same problem.

Orientation of the body with respect to the environment has been studied in some detail in animals, and will be discussed in Chapter 7. A consideration of the role of experience in mechanisms of spatial perception and orientation, which involves some further elaboration of this reafference model, is postponed until Chapter 21.

5.4. Physiological Correlates of Sensory-Perceptual Filtering

Although the limits of physical change to which an organism is sensitive are determined by the characteristics of its sensory cells, we have seen that, within the sensitive range, some patterns of stimulation are more effective than others. How far can this selectivity within the sensory field be understood in physiological terms? Although our knowledge of the neurophysiological correlates of perceptual phenomena is still scanty, it is growing rapidly (Horn, 1962).

In any sensory modality, stimuli of a high intensity are more likely to be responded to than those of lower ones. This finding is related to two types of physiological observation: first, that increase in stimulus intensity results in the excitation of a higher proportion of the fibres leaving the sense organ; and second, that there is some systematic relation between the stimulus intensity and the frequency of nerve impulses (Adrian *et al.*, 1926; Matthews, 1931; Hartline *et al.*, 1932; Fuortes, 1958). This latter relationship, though usually logarithmic, may be complicated in a number of ways. In the first place, the rate at which the sensory endings adapt to a stimulus varies greatly (Adrian, 1928). Second, in some receptors there is a considerable resting frequency of discharge: this may increase or decrease according to the direction of stimulation, as in the lateral line organs of fishes and the vestibular organ of various vertebrates (Hoagland, 1933a, b; Sand, 1937; Löwenstein *et al.*, 1940; Gernandt, 1949). Furthermore, some sensory units respond to a decrease rather than an increase in physical energy. In the optic nerve of the frog, for instance, some fibres respond only at the cessation of stimulation, and some respond both to an increase and to a decrease of illumination (Hartline, 1938; Barlow, 1953; *see* p. 83). In the auditory pathway of the cat, some (second order) neurones show a spontaneous discharge which is increased by tones of some frequencies and decreased by others (Galambos *et al.*, 1944). For these reasons, and because in most sense organs the inputs from many sensory endings converge on to one nerve fibre, and the impulses in any one sensory fibre pass to a number of post-synaptic cells (e.g. Weddell *et al.*, 1955), an increase in impulse frequency along one fibre cannot be unequivocally interpreted as the result of increased stimulation of a localized receptor; such information can be extracted only from data coming from an area of the receptive surface, and with a knowledge of the response characteristics of the fibres in question. However, in spite of these complexities, the greater the total change in stimulation the greater is the change in impulse frequency likely to be, and it will thus be the more easily detected against the background of "spontaneous" impulse activity.

As discussed on pp. 64–5, within any one sensory modality qualities of sensation do not correspond directly to simple physical scales, and the neural mechanisms by which they are assessed are still far from clear. For instance it has been suggested that discrimination of the various somaesthetic qualities (touch, deep pressure, cold, warmth, pain) may depend on spatial and temporal patterns of discharge (e.g. Weddell, 1955); and the sensory code on which taste discriminations are based is reflected in the relations between the frequencies of discharge in a number of simultaneously active taste fibres (Pfaffmann, 1964).

Objects tend to be more conspicuous when they are moving than when they are stationary. In the first instance, this is a consequence of sensory adaptation: the discharge from most receptors declines with time under conditions of constant stimulation (Adrian et al., 1926; Hartline, 1938). Indeed, our own visual perception depends upon the saccadic movements of the eyes, which occur about every quarter of a second even when we fixate an object as steadily as possible: in the absence of relative movement between object and retina some or all of the image disappears permanently (Campbell, F. W. et al., 1961; Barlow, 1963). Although retinal ganglion cells which show little or no adaptation have been found in the cat (Kuffler et al., 1957), it is probable that the information they provide is not used in form discrimination. If a complex figure is stabilized on the retina by the use of a contact lens its parts tend to disappear and reappear intermittently, their visibility fluctuating independently (Pritchard et al., 1960). The frequency with which the image disappears can be reduced by simultaneous stimulation through other sensory modalities or through the other eye (Cohen, 1961), suggesting an influence of central factors. However, it is not clear what part slipping of the contact lenses on the cornea played in these findings (Barlow, 1963).

The greater conspicuousness of moving objects is also helped by another mechanism which has the even more interesting effect of emphasizing edges and increasing contrast between stimulus and background. Hartline (1949) illuminated a single ommatidium of the lateral eye of the King Crab (*Limulus*), recording the resultant impulse train from the corresponding fibre of the optic nerve. A few seconds later a nearby ommatidium was illuminated, and the discharge from the first was found to decrease. When the order in which the ommatidia were illuminated was reversed, the inhibitory effect was found to be reciprocal. Mutual inhibitory relations of this type were found between many pairs of nearby ommatidia in *Limulus*: the effect depended on the integrity of a plexus of nerve fibres lying in the region behind the ommatidia. This is known as "lateral inhibition" (Hartline and Ratliff, 1956; Hartline et al., 1956).

Comparable effects have since been found in vertebrates. In the frog, some of the ganglion cells in the retina give a short discharge of impulses if the illumination either increases or decreases, but none under conditions of constant illumination (ON–OFF cells). If the whole retinal field by which such a cell is influenced is illuminated, the resultant discharge is smaller than with illumination of the centre alone—stimulation of the peripheral part of the field inhibits the discharge from the ganglion cell evoked by a stimulus delivered to the centre of its receptive field (Barlow, 1953).   Comparable results have been obtained in cats (Kuffler, 1953; Wiesel, 1960), where the effect varies with dark adaptation (Barlow *et al.*, 1957), and in other parts of the nervous system (Mountcastle, 1957).

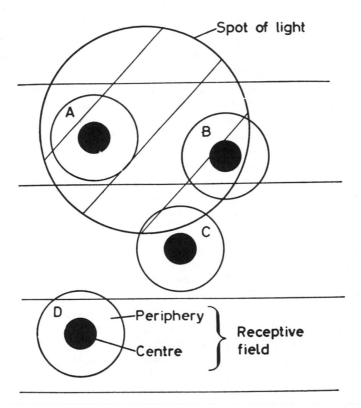

Fig. 5.10. Diagrammatic representation of the sensitive fields of four retinal cells, three of which are influenced by a spot of light. (*After Horn, 1962.*)

Such "lateral inhibition" between peripheral and central areas of the receptive field of a ganglion cell helps to accentuate boundaries between differently illuminated parts of the field. This can be understood as follows. Consider four cells whose receptive fields lie near a boundary at which a change in illumination occurs (Fig. 5.10). The receptive fields of cells *A* and *B* will be more strongly stimulated than those of C and D. If there were no lateral inhibition, and response strength depended merely on the area of the receptive field stimulated, the discharge of the 4 cells would be in the order $A > B > C > D$ and the edges would be blurred. By lateral inhibition, however, a cell whose receptive area is wholly within the area of greater illumination (A in Fig. 5.10) will have its discharge reduced by comparison with a cell B whose peripheral and inhibitory field is partially outside. On the other hand, the stronger illumination of the peripheral and inhibitory region of cell C, whose centre lies in the area of weaker illumination, will reduce its discharge by comparison with a cell D lying wholly within the more weakly illuminated area. The discharge from the 4 cells will thus be $A < B \gg C < D$, and the change in illumination at the boundary will be accentuated (Horn, 1962).

Such lateral inhibition will, of course, be an additional factor increasing the conspicuousness of moving objects as compared to stationary ones. More than that, however, it has been shown that the receptive fields of some units in the visual cortex of the cat are not circular but cigar-shaped, a central area being flanked by antagonistic zones. The fields may be oriented vertically, horizontally or obliquely, and in some cases the flanking zones are asymmetrical. Such units would give information not only about movement as such, but about its direction with respect to the axes of the field (Hubel *et al.*, 1959, 1961, 1962). Studies of a variety of points on the sensory pathways of different species disclose a marked divergence in such functional properties of the cells, a divergence whose significance is not yet understood (Arden, 1963, *see also* Barlow *et al.*, 1963).

We have already seen that, in frog and cat at least, the retinal ganglion cells are specialized in such a manner that they respond to different parameters of stimulation. Much of this work was based on stimulation of the retina by point sources of light and recording from single fibres in the optic nerve. Like Gibson (e.g. 1959), Lettvin *et al.* (1959) suggest that this method of stimulation can tell us little about how the eye functions normally. They used, instead, a matt grey hemisphere, 14 inches in diameter, and concentric to the eye, on the inside of which objects could be moved about by means of magnets placed on the outside. In many of their experiments the objects used were a black disc 1 degree in diameter and a rectangle 30 by 12 degrees. These investigators identified five types of ganglion cell in the frog's eye:

1. *Sustained contrast detectors.* These give a sustained discharge if the edge of an object either lighter or darker than its background moves into the field and stops there. There is no response to a change in the general illumination.

2. *Net convexity detectors.* These respond to a small object passed through the field, or to the convex edge of a dark body moved into or across the field. The response is greater, the greater the convexity of the edge until the object becomes less than half the width of the field. It is also greater if the edge is moved

jerkily than if it is moved smoothly. If a dotted pattern, with the dots no farther apart than half the width of the visual field, is moved across, there is practically no response; but if any dot moves differentially, the cell responds as if that spot were moving alone. There is no response to changes in the general illumination, and that to a convex edge depends on the sharpness of the edge but not on how much darker the object is than its background.

3. *Moving-edge detectors.* These respond to a moving edge, whether dark on light or light on dark. The response increases with velocity, but is little dependent on general illumination. These are the same as the ON–OFF fibres mentioned above (p. 79).

4. *Net dimming detectors.* These respond to a reduction in illumination. The effect of a moving object depends on its size and relative darkness, but darkening of the periphery of the field has less effect than darkening of the centre.

5. *Absolute darkness detectors.* This a small category of fibres with large receptive fields which discharge more rapidly the darker it is.

The receptive fields of these detectors increase from about 2 deg. to about 15 deg. in the order given above, and the first two types are about thirty times as frequent as the third and fourth.

The first four types each project in an orderly way on to the optic tectum, though each into a different layer. Responses of contrast detectors can be detected in the superficial layers, the convexity, moving-edge and dimming detectors at successively deeper layers. The responses of the absolute darkness detectors are found at the same level as the moving-edge detectors. The tectum thus contains four sheets of endings, each containing a map of the retina in terms of one type of detector. Through these sheets project dendritic branches of the deeper-lying tectal cells, each of which is thus influenced by the several properties of one particular area of the retinal field. The image is thus seen in terms of the distribution of combinations of the qualities registered by the detectors (*see also* Grüsser-Cornehls *et al.*, 1963).

Three points about this description of the functioning of the frog's visual system demand emphasis. First, the hitherto convenient division into sensory and perceptual phenomena, with its implications that the latter are due to something which the higher levels "do" to the messages received from the sense organs, ceases to be useful (*see* Teuber, 1960, 1961). It is clear that the message sent to the brain is not simply the coding of a series of spots of light of varying intensity: the ganglion cells collectively transmit a message which is already highly organized and interpreted. Further organization may occur at each successive level; for instance, in the cat a sequence of changes takes place in the visual pathways (Kuffler 1953; Hubel *et al.*, 1959, 1961, 1962).

Second, however large the gap still to be bridged, the fact that the frog's retina can code relatively complex qualities in this way confirms the view that such qualities may form the basis of perceptual phenomena (*see* pp. 65–6, 74).

Finally, it must be emphasized that the functioning of the frog's retina may well differ in many respects from that of other vertebrates. It seems, for instance, that it differs considerably in the amount of spontaneous activity (Granit, 1947). Lettvin and his colleagues themselves point out that the mechanism they describe for the frog is peculiarly suited to its prey-catching and predator-escaping existence. Nevertheless, the principle that the input from the eye to the brain carries information concerning qualitatively different parameters of the stimulation appears to be of widespread applicability. In the optic nerve of the crab *Podophthalmus vigil* information is carried by a variety of types of fibre. Among other characteristics these differ according to:

(a) The area of the visual field to which the fibre responds: this ranges from the whole to quite small portions of the field.
(b) The type of stimulation eliciting the maximal response, ranging from fast-moving large objects to changes in the intensity of stationary illumination.
(c) The amount of contrast necessary for maximal response.

In this species there are also numerous fibres running to the eye and responding to visual stimulation of the other eye and/or tactual stimulation of various parts of the body. Visual information is thus integrated with that from other sources in the eye, as well as elsewhere in the brain (Wiersma *et al.*, 1961).

Although it is well established that the retinal ganglion cells of vertebrate species, other than the frog, have similarly varied properties, it is not clear how much further precise comparisons can be taken. Hübel *et al.* (1959, 1961, 1962) point out that the cat has probably less specificity in retinal function than the frog, but more specificity at higher levels: they have demonstrated basically similar mechanisms of analysis at a cortical level (*see* Barlow *et al.*, 1963, for a further review). In birds, the presence of the pecten, a conical foliated structure which casts a shadow on part of the retina, probably acts to accentuate movement (Pumphrey, 1948).

This work on the functioning of sensory pathways may well herald a new advance in our understanding of perceptual phenomena, but knowledge is still exceedingly restricted. The use of stabilized retinal images is providing another means of attacking the problem of perception in human subjects, with the reservations made above about slipping of the contact lens (p. 80). As we have seen, if the image of a figure is stabilized on the retina it appears and disappears at intervals. If the figure is a circle or square, it does not disappear as a whole, but part by part, so that at any moment only one or two sides may be visible. This suggests that the perception of the parts is all-or-none, but the perception of the whole is not a unitary event (Hebb, 1963). Furthermore, meaningful figures disappear less rapidly than do less meaningful ones (Pritchard *et al.*, 1960). The visibility of a line stabilized on one retina is said to be enhanced by an unstabilized image on the other more when the latter is of a similar line than when it is not, suggesting a field effect in the lateral geniculate nucleus or visual cortex (Cohen, 1961). It seems at least possible that there is a relationship between those stimuli which give the most persistent stabilized images and those which are subjectively most conspicuous.

Here again, however, we must beware of generalizing between vertebrate groups. The importance of eye-movements varies between phyla—in birds, eye movements are usually slight and all distant objects are focused sharply simultaneously (Pumphrey, 1948). In mammals, on the other hand, sharp vision occurs only at the fovea, and scanning movements, together with a short-term retention, give sharp vision over a wide area. Although form vision probably precedes such eye-movements in phylogeny, where they are developed to give sharp localized vision, the information from them is likely to be used in the recognition of form (Gregory, in Thorpe 1963a). The use of eye-movements to mediate form vision is demonstrated at a different phyletic level by Dethier's (1943) work on the form vision of lepidopterous larvae, which have only a small group of simple "stemmata" on either side of the head.

The physiological mechanisms underlying form perception in most invertebrates are obscure, but some interesting leads have come in the case of *Octopus*. As we saw above, Sutherland has suggested that, in this species, an assessment of the vertical and horizontal projections of the figure plays an essential role in discrimination. It is thus interesting to find that the retinal elements are arranged in vertical and horizontal rows, and that the dendritic connections in the optic lobes are primarily in horizontal and vertical directions (Young, 1960, 1961). Furthermore, form recognition depends on maintenance of the correct head orientation, and may be upset if the statocysts are removed (Packard, A., quoted by Wells, 1962b).

5.5. Summary

1. Even among the energy changes to which an animal's receptor organs are responsive, some spatial or temporal patterns of stimulation are more effective in influencing its behaviour than are others. The effectiveness of some of these is not linked to particular types of behaviour, and depends on properties of the sensory/perceptual mechanisms.
2. In studies of human perception, the relation between the physical magnitude and the subjectively-assessed magnitude of a stimulus varies with the nature of the stimulus. In addition, the subjective sensory qualities (hue, brightness, etc.) do not correspond to particular physical dimensions, but to combinations of physical characteristics. In ordinary circumstances most stimuli do not act on single receptor cells, but on sense organs: gradients, ratios and changes in pattern of stimulation are essential components of the situation. For all these reasons physical measurements of stimuli can give a misleading impression of their potential effectiveness for influencing behaviour.
3. Species differ markedly in their abilities to discriminate between simple geometrical forms, and in the stimulus characters by which they do so.
4. Organisms must discriminate movement of a retinal image produced by their own

movement from that produced by a change in the external world. The "re-afference" model of the manner in which this is accomplished involves comparison between the stimulus changes which a movement (or lack of movement) should produce and that which actually occurs. Comparable mechanisms must occur in other types of perception.

5. Physiological evidence concerning the mechanisms of some perceptual phenomena is discussed.

6

Selective Response to Stimulation— Selection Specific to a Response or Motivational State

In Chapter 5 we discussed some examples of the influence of the sensory/ perceptual apparatus on the effectiveness of a stimulus in controlling behaviour. Some stimulus characters, however, are effective only when they contribute

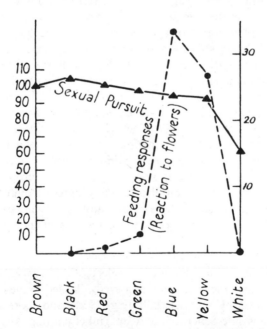

Fig. 6.1. Effectiveness of different colours in eliciting sexual pursuit and feeding responses from Grayling Butterflies. (*After Tinbergen, 1951.*)

to the elicitation of particular types of behaviour: in other contexts they are of little significance. Thus we have already seen that a model with a red belly is especially effective in eliciting attack from a male Three-spined Stickleback, while one with a swollen belly is especially effective in eliciting courtship.

The effectiveness of these characters must depend on mechanisms which are more selective than the general sensory/perceptual ones, and have some degree of response specificity. As another example, Fig. 6.1 shows the effectiveness of models of different colour in eliciting feeding responses and sexual pursuit from males of the Grayling Butterfly (*Eumenis semele*). The former responses are markedly influenced by the colour of the model, the latter are not: the effectiveness of particular colours is thus response-specific (Tinbergen *et al.*, 1943; *see also* Crane, 1955).

A note on a terminological point is necessary here. The action of a stimulus whose effectiveness is response-specific usually depends on the animal's being in a particular motivational state. When in that state, it is especially likely to respond to the stimulus in question. When the effectiveness of a stimulus is response-specific, the responsiveness of the organism is thus stimulus-specific.

Even where two different responses of the same species have not been studied, the nature of the stimuli found to be effective often makes it virtually certain that something more than the general sensory-perceptual mechanisms must be involved. Thus Marler (1961) argues that the results of Drees's (1952) careful study of the stimuli eliciting male courtship in a jumping spider are difficult to account for except in terms of a response-specific mechanism for stimulus selection. "The strongest responses were given to visual patterns with a certain size and orientation, divided into cephalothorax and abdomen, with legs having a particular size and orientation with respect to the body and with the species pattern of black and white shapes on the abdomen. Outside the breeding season the response disappeared and all models evoked either prey-catching or avoidance, according to size" (Marler, *loc. cit.*).

In practice a quite superficial acquaintance with the behaviour of a species reveals the presence of response-specific stimulus selection mechanisms. Thus, members of nearly every species not only respond appropriately to many objects in their environment, but also to many signals from conspecific individuals. Since the responses to these objects and signals are appropriate, each must have stimulus characters specific to the response it elicits (*see* Chapter 4).

6.1. The Concept of the "Innate Releasing Mechanism"

If stimulus characters are responded to selectively, the organism must have some means by which the selection is achieved. This led to the postulation of a mechanism, termed by von Uexküll (e.g. 1934) and Lorenz (1935) "das angeborene auslösende Schema", and by Tinbergen (e.g. 1951) the "innate releasing mechanism" (IRM). This concept, used to symbolize the specific relations between a particular stimulus character and a particular response, has been of great value. It can be criticized, however, on two main grounds.

In the first place, the term IRM is often used with the implication that the mechanism is specific to a particular response, when the evidence for its existence is based solely on the study of that response. As we have seen, when the stimulus characters relevant to a given response have been identified by comparison of the effectiveness of situations possessing and lacking those characters, they could owe their efficacy to sensory/perceptual mechanisms not specific to the response in question. Two alternatives are thus open. One is to use the concept of "innate releasing mechanism" to cover all mechanisms of stimulus selection: in this case the IRMs for different responses overlap, and each IRM is certainly not a unitary mechanism. Alternatively, as Tinbergen (1955) advocated, the concept can be confined to cases in which particular stimulus characters have been shown to be effective for one response and not for others.

Marler (1961) recognized three types of stimulus selection: that which is due to the characteristics of the sensory equipment; that which is due to the perceptual mechanism's greater responsiveness to some patterns of stimulation than others; and finally the filtering which seems to demand the postulation of a selective process specific to one particular response. In the light of recent work, however, the distinction between the first two cannot be upheld. We have already seen that a good deal of "perceptual" filtering may go on in the sense organ itself (pp. 82–5), so that a division between "peripheral" filtering in the sense organs and "central stimulus filtering" by the mechanisms of normal "perception" is often misleading. Furthermore, cases are known where a sense organ has become specialized in the service of one particular response, so that it responds only to the stimuli appropriate to that response (e.g. p. 55): here, as Marler points out, response specific filtering is sensory in origin. Thus while the view, that the filtering of incoming information occurs at a number of stages between sense organ and response mechanism, represents an important advance over the earlier view of a unitary releasing mechanism, the classification of those stages given by Marler is an oversimplification.

A second criticism of the "innate releasing mechanism" concept is that comparable selectivity from the total stimulation which impinges on the organism may depend on, or be influenced by, learning: the label "innate" is thus misleading. In addition, as we shall see, stimuli not only elicit responses, but also control behaviour in other ways; for instance by orienting the animal or bringing a sequence of behaviour to an end. Selectivity in responsiveness is not confined to stimuli which "release". Thus, while selective responsiveness is a fact, it is not helpful to postulate a unitary "innate releasing mechanism", especially when it is implied that such mechanisms operate only for "innate" behaviour (see Chapter 19), and "releasing" stimuli.

6.2. The "Search Image" and "Reward Expectancy"

Many of the experiments discussed so far have been concerned with stimulus characters effective for all the individuals of a species. It is now necessary to consider some cases where the stimulus characters may be effective only for one animal in a particular motivational state. In such cases their effectiveness is a consequence of previous experience with similar stimuli.

It is not uncommon for us to miss an object which is in front of our noses when we are looking for an object with a similar function but different visual characteristics. Von Uexküll, for example, described how he failed to notice a glass carafe on the dining table when he was expecting to see a clay pitcher, and referred to his experience in terms of a "search image" of the pitcher which did not fuse with the carafe.

The concept of a changing "searching image" is equally necessary below the primate level. Von Uexküll records that a hungry toad given one earthworm will subsequently attack earthworm-like objects, but if given a spider it will snap at bits of moss or ants. In a study of the response of Jays and Chaffinches to the well-camouflaged stick caterpillars of geometrid moths, de Ruiter (1952) found that, once a bird found a caterpillar, it would go on pecking at similar-looking sticks for some time afterwards.

In a posthumous paper, the late L. Tinbergen (1960) placed the concept of a "searching image" on a more precise basis as a result of his studies of the hunting behaviour of titmice (*Parus* spp.). He argued that the proportion of a bird's diet made up by a given prey species might be expected to depend on the probability of the bird encountering that prey while foraging, and thus on the prey density. Field observations of predation by tits on the Hymenopteron *Acantholyda nemoralis* showed that at low (and high) densities the percentage taken fell below expectation. L. Tinbergen ascribed the small amount taken at low prey densities to the insufficient experience of the birds with the prey: with increasing density they learn to find it more efficiently, and the proportion taken approaches expectation. He thus suggested that the adoption of a "specific searching image" occurred only at a critical prey density, and that a certain frequency of encounters was necessary for its maintenance (*see also* Mook *et al.*, 1960).

Gibb (1962) studied the predation of tits on insect larvae which spend the winter concealed beneath the cuticle of ripening pine cones. The birds locate their prey by tapping the cone, and then excavate the larvae. Gibb found that predation was very light at low prey densitities, increasing abruptly as the density increased: this suggested the operation of something like a "specific search image". In addition, the percentage of larvae taken in areas where the density was very high was below that which might be expected from the extent of predation where the density was lower. Gibb interprets this as indicating that the birds learnt what prey density to expect in a given general area, and slackened their search when the expected number of larvae had been taken from the cones, as indicated by the traces of previous attacks. More direct evidence to confirm this possibility would be of great interest.

In these field observations on the operation of a specific searching image, the implication is that the organism is responsive to a particular pattern of physical stimulation. As we have seen, in our own species at least, there is evidence that selection can be exercised in favour of members of a class of stimuli which share little in the way of physical characteristics. Had von Uexküll been looking for "something to hold water" he might have found the carafe more easily.

The concept of "reward expectancy" has been used by Tolman and others in a basically similar context. If a monkey is allowed to see some food placed under one of two containers, to which it is subsequently allowed access, it shows some ability to choose the correct one. If a banana is hidden under one of the containers while the monkey is looking, and the experimenter then substitutes for the banana a less preferred food, such as a lettuce leaf, the monkey may reject it and behave as though searching for the banana (Tinkel-paugh, 1928). Similar results have been obtained for rats and chimpanzees (Cowles *et al.*, 1937).

The concept of a "search image" could, of course, be open to some of the objections already raised to the "innate releasing mechanism". Indeed it comes close to the original concept of an "(angeborene auslosende) Schema" from which that of innate releasing mechanism arose (Schleidt, 1962). But "search image" carries no implication of limitation to stimuli which operate in a particular way, and need not imply a unitary mechanism.

6.3. Selective Attention and the Suggested Centrifugal Control of Afferent Pathways

"Selective attention" usually refers to a limitation of responsiveness by the organism such that some stimulus features control its behaviour over a con-siderable period, and do so to the exclusion of the other physical stimuli impinging on it at the time. Like the "innate releasing mechanism" and the "search image", therefore, "selective attention" is used with reference to specificity in responsiveness controlled by the internal state: although we ordinarily use "search image" only for stimuli not yet present, there is wide overlap between the concepts.

Peripheral adjustment of the sense organs so that they are especially effective for one part or category of the stimulus field plays a large part in selective attention. For instance, when we attend to a sound, we adjust the position of our heads, and the tensor tympani muscle at the same time sets the tension on the ear drum. The peripheral adjustments in visual attention are more compli-cated, but include (Horn, 1965):

(a) Convergence of the eyes in such a manner that the image falls not only on the most sensitive part of the eye, but also on corresponding parts of the two retinae. In the cat, it has been shown that this results in the activity generated in the two eyes summating at a number of neurones in the striate cortex (Hübel *et al.*, 1962).

(b) The lens of the eye is focused to bring a sharp image on to the retina.

(c) The amount of light falling on the retina is adjusted by controlling the diameter of the pupil.

(*d*) Eye movements occur, bringing different parts of the retina into play and thus maintaining activity in the optic pathways.

The precise nature of such peripheral adjustments varies with the species and the sense organs, but it is clear that sense organs are not mere passive transducers of the stimulation which falls on them, but are subject to variations in responsiveness. Most vertebrate sense organs receive a sympathetic supply, and in one case at least, the touch receptors in the frog, stimulation of the sympathetic system influences the sensitivity of the sense organs (Loewenstein, 1956).

As we have seen, however, selective attention to stimuli with some degree of response-specificity cannot be due solely to general sensory/perceptual mechanisms—processes related to the current motivational state must be controlling the selectivity. There is also considerable evidence that the processes involved in human selective attention are not solely peripheral. This comes in part from experiments in which human subjects are required to select from two or more sets of stimuli arriving simultaneously (Broadbent, 1958). For instance:

(*a*) If a subject is asked questions simultaneously in two different voices, and receives visual instructions beforehand about which voice he must listen to, he can subsequently answer questions much better than if the instructions come after he has heard the voices. Since the material which is discarded depends on experience, this can hardly be a peripheral masking mechanism (Broadbent, 1952).
(*b*) The probability of two messages being received simultaneously depends on the amount of information (in a technical sense) which they contain, rather than on their physical characteristics; there is thus more interference between the messages, the larger the number of possibilities from which they are chosen. Two messages which contain little information are more likely to be dealt with than two messages which contain much information (Poulton, 1956; other references in Broadbent, 1958).
(*c*) If two speech passages are recorded on the same tape by the same voice, a listener can use his experience of the probabilities with which words or phrases normally follow each other in speech to separate them: this is clearly not sensory (Cherry, 1953).
(*d*) Words of significance to the subject, such as his own name, are more readily selected from a noisy background than are words without such significance (Howarth *et al.*, 1961).

In selective listening experiments, the selection is not absolute. Cherry, *loc. cit.*, asked subjects to repeat continuously words which were fed into one ear, and ignore words arriving at the other ear. If the voice in the second ear changed during the experiment (e.g. from a man's voice to a woman's and back again), some knowledge of this was retained (*see also* Broadbent *et al.*, 1963a, b). This again implies that the selective process must be central.

We must, therefore, consider the mechanism of these more central selective processes. It has been suggested by a number of workers (e.g. Horn, 1952; Adrian, 1954) that they may depend on centrifugal influences controlling activity in the sensory pathways. Although centrifugal fibres undoubtedly exist in at least some sensory pathways (e.g. Granit, 1955b; Galambos, 1956), the evidence which earlier appeared to favour their having a role in selective attention has since been challenged. In view of the widespread interest which the problem has aroused, it is worthwhile to consider briefly the evidence and the principal areas of contention.

On the one hand, a number of lines of evidence show that centrifugal fibres can control the sensory input. Thus, we have already seen that mammalian muscle-spindles contain an intrafusal muscle fibre which has its own motor control through the small ventral root γ-efferents. The discharge of the spindle is thus determined both by the state of the skeletal muscle and by the rate of discharge of the γ-efferents (p. 37 and Fig. 3.10). One consequence of this is that, for any given muscle length, the spindle afferent can show a range of discharge rates depending on the activity of the γ-efferents. The activity of the γ-efferents is, in turn, regulated centrally, for Granit and Kaada (1952) showed that γ-efferent activity is facilitated by stimulation of the reticular system.

The input from peripheral exteroceptors, like that from muscle spindles, can be modified centrally. For instance, Hagbarth *et al.* (1954) showed that central stimulation changes the volleys of impulses in the spinal cord induced by dorsal root stimulation (*see also* Hagbarth *et al.*, 1959), and Galambos (1956) that centrifugal impulses travelling in the olivo-cochlear bundles can suppress activity in the auditory nerve of cats (*see* e.g. Desmedt *et al.*, 1961; Desmedt, 1962). Similarly, Jouvet *et al.* (1956) found that stimulation at some points in the reticular formation would weaken potentials induced in the cochlear nucleus even in animals whose muscles were curarized (*see also* Desmedt *et al.*, 1958). Such studies show a centrifugal control of sensory input, but, of course, they do not necessarily prove that this control operates in selective attention in the intact organism (Livingston, 1959).

In the auditory system, the electrical response evoked by a sound in a number of brain structures, including the cochlear nucleus, has been thought to change when the animal's attention shifts from the auditory to the visual modality. Thus changes in electrical potential in the cochlear nucleus of an unanaesthetized cat, produced by click sounds, were observed to be reduced when the cat was shown a mouse (Hernández-Peón *et al.*, 1956; *see also* e.g. Hernández-Peón *et al.*, 1957, Galambos, 1959). Similarly, it was reported that photically evoked responses at the visual cortex, lateral geniculate body and optic tract were reduced in amplitude when the animal's attention was attracted by non-visual stimuli. Such experiments were interpreted to mean that, when an animal pays attention to stimuli arriving by one modality, non-relevant sensory input in other modalities is reduced near the periphery.

In the case of the auditory pathway, it was supposed that this was due to inhibitory impulses, two principle sources for which were suggested. Hernández-Peón and his collaborators (1957) believed the brain-stem reticular system (*see* Chapter 9) to be responsible, a view consistent with evidence from the somesthetic system. Desmedt (e.g. 1960, 1962; Desmedt *et al.*, 1961), on the other hand, gave evidence for an extra-reticular descending system of fibre connections which have an inhibitory influence on nerve cells in the cochlear nucleus.

Other workers, however, have not always been able to confirm such results. For instance, Jouvet and Lapras (1959), working with human subjects, claimed that the potentials evoked by flashes of light in the optic radiation were augmented during periods in which the subject was attending to the flashes. But using quantitative techniques to assess the size of the evoked potential, van Hof *et al.* (1962) found an increase in only one out of fifteen subjects.

Even where changes in the size of an evoked potential have been demonstrated, it has been suggested that interpretation of their significance is premature (*see* Horn, 1965). Many of them can be accounted for by changes in orientation of the sense organ or other peripheral changes. Galambos (1960), for instance, has shown that reliable changes in auditory nerve activity are never found in cats attentive to visual, auditory and other stimuli after their auditory muscles have been cut. In the visual system Naquet *et al.* (1960) showed that changes in the diameter of the pupil have a profound effect on the evoked potential recorded from the optic tract and lateral geniculate body, so that changes in photically evoked potentials may be due to pupillary changes accompanying fear or convergence. The amplitude of the evoked potential at the visual cortex is less dependent on the diameter of the pupil, but is influenced by whether or not the animal is visually scanning its environment. When it is, the potentials evoked by flashes of light are reduced in size compared with those evoked when the animal is sitting still and not scanning. Thus, if a tone evokes visual searching behaviour, the evoked potential to a flash is reduced. If the tone fails to elicit this behaviour, the evoked potential is not reduced below the control level (Horn, 1960). In addition, there is no simple relationship between the magnitude of the evoked potential and the effective sensory inflow. The former cannot be used unequivocally as an index of the central consequences of a peripheral stimulus (*see* p. 79).

All these factors must be taken into account in interpreting the work of Hernández-Peón and his collaborators. It thus remains uncertain whether the changes in the evoked potentials which sometimes occur in sensory pathways have to do with selective attention.

Outside the sensory pathways (e.g. elsewhere on the cortex) the size of the evoked potential does seem to be related to whether or not the subject attends to the stimulus eliciting the response (Chapman *et al.*, 1964). The significance of this change in terms of neural function is, however, still obscure, since the origin of the potential is not known.

Studies of single cells in the afferent pathways, however, have shown that a small proportion are weakly affected by activity in a heteromodal pathway. For instance, Horn (1963) took recordings from single cells in the cat's visual cortex when the animal was given visual stimuli (flashes) and somesthetic stimuli (weak electric shocks to the skin). Many of the cells studied responded to both stimuli. In some cases the two types of stimuli had a similar effect, augmenting or reducing the rate of discharge, while in others their effects were opposite. When the stimuli were presented together, the response of the cell was always different from that given to one stimulus alone. Horn cites a number of studies demonstrating a similar effect (*see* e.g. Akimoto *et al.*, 1961), and gives evidence that the reticular system is involved. If any stimulus, as well as producing a specific response in the sensory pathway appropriate to it, exerts also (via the reticular system) a diffuse influence on the cortex, this would amount to an increase in noise and tend to obscure the pattern of discharge in all pathways. However the effect, while present, is not strong. Although it could account for the observation that the presence of one stimulus influences the probability of another being detected, it seems insufficient to account for the exclusion of information which occurs during selective attention.

Thus all the phenomena of selective attention cannot be understood in terms of adjustment of sense organs and noise in the sensory pathways. Not only is there no physiological evidence that the processes primarily responsible for selective attention operate in the sensory pathways, but the behavioural evidence indicates that selection can be guided by quite subtle criteria. When information is to be discarded by human subjects, it is not discarded at random: the filter can be set to exclude not only signals defined in terms of physical parameters—intensity, frequency, direction—but also in terms of other characteristics (e.g. letters *v.* numbers). The physiological processes involved are as yet quite unknown.

The magnitude of the problem is apparent if one considers the number of stimulus situations to which an animal or a human can pay attention or respond differentially: it is apparent that the nervous system discriminates a vast number of possible stimulus configurations. The same point arises even more forcibly when one considers the number of situations an animal, and even more so a man, *could* discriminate: it is difficult to imagine that there can be a mechanism for every object that one can recognize (Uttley, 1954), let alone for every one that one *could* (Barlow, 1961).

As a partial solution of this problem, Barlow (1961) has pointed out that most sensory messages contain a great deal of redundancy, and could be compressed before recognition is attempted. The compression would involve reversible coding in addition to the irreversible filtering we have been discussing so far. If the redundancy in the message was reduced in stages, the complexity of the process would be considerably reduced.

The compression of sensory messages by removal of redundancy involves just those factors by which we recognize it, and thus constitutes a step towards recognition. Thus, if small dots are placed on a screen, different random distributions of dots will be difficult to recognize, but an orderly pattern easy. We see here a possible line of attack on the problem of why some patterns are more conspicuous than others (p. 62).

As examples of redundancy reducing mechanisms at the sensory-perceptual level, Barlow refers to sensory adaptation (*see* p. 79), lateral inhibition (pp. 80-2) and movement detecting cells (pp. 82-4). He thus regards the detection of changes in stimulation, of edges and of movement which these mechanisms facilitate as being almost incidental consequences of mechanisms whose primary function is the removal of redundancy. In the case of lateral inhibition there is suggestive evidence that the existence of the mechanism is related to the existence in the input of the very sort of redundancy which it removes. Thus, lateral inhibition does not occur in the dark adapted retina, but does under conditions of uniform background illumination: it therefore seems to be a consequence of the correlated activity of many receptor cells (Barlow *et al.*, 1957). Comparable mechanisms could exist at higher levels in the nervous system, developing to deal with the specific form of redundancy in the animal's environment, and thus making possible new discriminations. Thus, Barlow suggests that constant features in the stimulus situation cause particular types of redundancy in the sensory messages, and the nervous system then actively modifies its code in order to eliminate them. The rate at which the code is adjusted must, of course, vary at different levels, for perceptual illusions may last seconds, while the effects of wearing inverting spectacles last for days. The relationship between Barlow's view of the nervous system actively adjusting its activity to remove redundancy from the input, the von Holst/Teuber/Held models of the comparator unit (pp. 74-9 and Chapter 21), and Sokolov's picture of the habituation of the orienting reflex (pp. 97-102), will be apparent.

6.4. The "Orientation Response" and Response to Novelty

When an animal is subject to a new or unusual form of stimulation, it is likely to show an "orientation response" (or "orientation reflex") in which its sensitivity to stimulation, and especially to the stimulus in question, is enhanced and its readiness for action increased. The orientation response thus includes many of the changes just discussed in the context of selective attention. Originally studied by Pavlov (1955), and recently in detail by Sokolov (1960), it involves first somatic changes (eye movements, body movements, etc.) which result in the sense organs being brought to bear on the source of the stimulus. These are accompanied by vegetative changes (in respiration, heart rate, vascularity, galvanic skin responses, etc.) which are correlates of an increased general readiness to respond. There are also changes in the electroencephalogram, which may have a similar function. Thus Lindsley has produced evidence that the rhythm of electrical changes in the cortex is associated with a cycle of responsiveness to stimulation. In the orientation response slow cortical waves tend to be replaced by irregular activity. In this the different cortical units are presumably no longer synchronized, so that some are always excitable and thus ready to respond to incoming signals (Lindsley, 1961).

In order to understand the further elaboration of the orientation response with continued stimulation, we must consider what happens if a novel stimulus, originally eliciting an orientation response, is repeated at intervals. If the stimulus is without consequence, or has no correlates to which the animals respond, there is first a reduction in those physiological components of the response which are associated with generalized sensory alerting, so that it becomes limited to components related to the sensory modality of the original stimulus. The "generalized orienting response" thus changes to a "localized orienting response". This localized response then either wanes, or becomes replaced by an "adaptive response" which tends to reduce specifically those features of the stimulating situation which elicited the initial response. As a familiar example of the latter, an increase in illumination results in pupillary contraction and thus a diminution in the light entering the eye.

If, on the other hand, the stimulus has consequences or significant correlates, the elaboration of the response depends on their nature. If it becomes a conditioned signal for some other response, then the generalized response becomes changed to a localized one much as before, though the latter shows less subsequent diminution. If the stimulus is of high intensity or painful, the orientation response changes into a defensive response. This may consist in withdrawal or running away, or in a variety of responses which tend to protect the animal from stimulation—immobility, blinking, and so on.

The distinction Sokolov uses between the orientation response (or reflex), the defensive response and the adaptive response, all of which may be elicited by previously novel stimuli, is a useful one, though of course the categories intergrade. One of the most significant characteristics of the orientation response, and one which distinguishes it from the other two, is the manner in which it wanes with the repetition of the stimulus, provided the latter is without significant correlates. This waning is not merely a consequence of a reduction in sensitivity. Thus, if elicited repeatedly with a light stimulus a little above threshold, the response ceases after a while. If the intensity of the stimulus is then reduced a little, the response reappears. This finding suggests that the waning is specific to the particular stimulus which elicited the response. Another example illustrating this is shown in Fig. 6.2. When a light stimulus subtending 1 degree and focused on a point 40 degrees to the nasal side of the centre of the retina was presented at 40-second intervals, the EEG response faded. If the focus of stimulation was changed by 10 degrees, the response reappeared immediately: the waning was thus specific to the point on the retina stimulated.

The stimulus specificity of the waning of the cortical response has been demonstrated by Sharpless *et al.* (1956). Studying the cortical arousal (*see* Chapter 9) produced in sleeping cats by sounds, they distinguished two patterns of arousal—a long-lasting one subject to habituation, and a shorter one less susceptible. The latter probably depends on the thalamic reticular system. The former is probably mediated by the ascending reticular system, and plays a preparatory or protective role: the waning which occurs with repeated elicitation of the response is highly specific to the stimulus (*see also* Rowland, 1957).

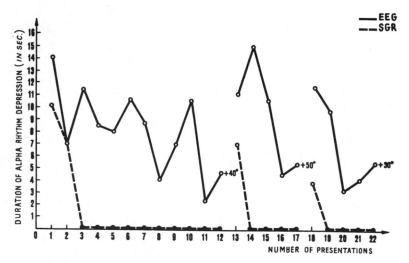

Fig. 6.2. Habituation of α-rhythm and skin galvanic response to stimulation by a light spot focused on a point on the horizontal meridian of the projection perimeter on the nasal part of the retina. (*After Sokolov, 1960.*)

After the 2nd presentation, the generalized reaction is completely inhibited. The localized orienting reaction (α-depression) is diminished only. A change of position from 40° to 50° (from the central fixation point) evokes generalized reaction (skin galvanic response and increased duration of α-rhythm depression). Repetition of same stimulation evokes decrease in local orienting reflex and complete disappearance of generalized orienting reaction. Change to 30° produces, again, a generalized response and increase of the α-rhythm depression. Habituation is specific to the point of retina stimulated.

The evidence also shows that the waning of the orientation reflex is an active process. After the response has disappeared, it can often be elicited by presenting the stimulus when the subject is drowsy, suggesting that the waning is due to an inhibitory process which does not function under these conditions.

On the basis of such findings, Sokolov has suggested that the orientation reflex appears whenever the sensory input does not coincide with a "neuronal model" previously established in the brain. The force of this suggestion is

illustrated by an experiment in which the orientation reflex to a standard
sound of a certain duration is allowed to diminish as a consequence of repeated
stimulation. If a similar sound of shorter duration is then given, the orientation
response appears at the end of the sound, that is, when the sound becomes
different from the standard, which had lasted longer. If, on the other hand, a
longer sound is given, the response appears at the point at which the stimulus
ought to have stopped. Sokolov thus suggests that the "neuronal model" is set
up as a consequence of repeated stimulation, and if at a later time a stimulus

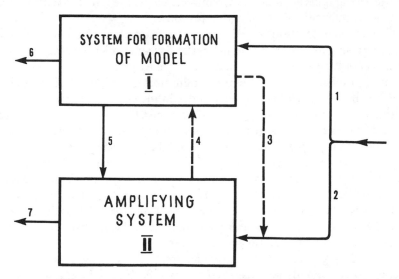

Fig. 6.3. Schema for the orienting reflex. (*After Sokolov, 1960.*)

   I. Modelling system. II. Amplifying system. 1 = specific pathway from sense organs
to modelling system; 2 = collateral to amplifying device; 3 = negative feedback from
modelling system to synaptic connection between collaterals from specific pathway and
amplifying system; 4 = ascending activating influences from the amplifier upon modelling system; 5 = pathway from modelling system to amplifying system (this is the pathway through which the impulses signifying concordance are transmitted from the
modelling system to the amplifying system); 6 = to the specific responses caused by
coincidence between the external stimulation and the neuronal model; and 7 = to the
vegetative and somatic components arising from the stimulation of the amplifying
system.

is received which does not coincide in all parameters with the model, an orientation response occurs, and the organism's power for obtaining information
about the unusual properties of the stimulus is thereby increased.

   Such an hypothesis is also in keeping with other data on response decre-
ments to alerting stimuli. For instance Bartoshuk (1962a, b), studying heart
rate acceleration in human neonates, found that after the response to an 8-second
tone, which changed from low to high frequency, had waned, it could be elicited
again by a tone whose frequency changed in the opposite direction. Similarly
Engen *et al.* (1965) found that after the breathing response of human neonates

to a mixture of odours had waned, it could still be elicited by one of the components.

Sokolov's schema is shown in Fig. 6.3. He supposes that the input reaches both the modelling system (via 1) and the amplifying system (via 2). The latter route can be blocked by the modelling system (3). The amplifying system can increase the discriminatory power of the modelling system (4). If there is coincidence between the input and the model, various specific responses, such as a conditioned reflex, may be elicited (6). If there is no coincidence, impulses pass to the amplifying system (5), and thence to the various vegetative and somatic components of the orienting response.

A block diagram of this type is, of course, based on behavioural data, and need carry no implications about the particular anatomical structures involved in producing the effects. In fact, electrical correlates of the waning of the orientation reflex, in the shape of a diminution in the potential evoked by a stimulus, have been claimed to occur both in the afferent pathways and more centrally. Hernández-Peón et al. (1957) claimed that the potential evoked in the cat's cochlear nucleus by an auditory stimulus gradually decreased as the stimulus was repeated. The attenuation of the electrical response, however, usually occurred only after several thousand stimuli had been administered, whereas the behavioural response waned rapidly. Similar results were obtained by Galambos et al. (1956). Later workers, however, have not confirmed this finding. Using very rigorous techniques for the analysis of their data, Worden et al. (1963) found no consistent trend in the size of the evoked potentials when stimulation was continued for several hours.

Hernández-Peón et al. (1956) also claimed that the potential evoked in the lateral geniculate body and visual cortex by a flash of light gradually waned. In this case the finding was confirmed by subsequent workers, but it seems likely that it is to be explained by a gradual narrowing of the pupil (Fernández-Guardiola et al., 1961). It thus seems that the evidence for a gradual waning of the evoked potentials in the direct afferent pathways is not substantial or is still disputed (Horn, 1965).

As we have seen, however, there is clear evidence for changes in the electrical activity of the cerebral cortex, as recorded on an electroencephalogram, which parallel the behavioural habituation. When a subject is at rest, with his eyes closed, electroencephalography reveals a high amplitude rhythm of about 10 c./sec. This is replaced by a low amplitude high-frequency activity when the subject attends to or tries to perceive a visual stimulus. Novel stimuli are especially effective in blocking the rhythm, but this effect wanes with repetition. Gastaut et al. (1957) and Sokolov (1960) have shown that a novel stimulus initially elicits high-frequency activity from points widely distributed over the cortex, but as the stimulation is repeated, the activity becomes limited to the area of the sensory modality concerned, and then disappears completely. In this case the course of the waning of the electrical response parallels that of the behavioural response. A further parallel lies in the fact that the waning of the electroencephalographic response is specific to the particular stimulus used. When Sharpless *et al.* (1956) used tones to awaken lightly sleeping cats, they studied the change in the electroencephalogram from the slow waves occurring during sleep to the low voltage fast activity when the cat awoke. As soon as the sleep pattern had returned, the stimulus was repeated. Gradually the change in electrical activity ceased to occur, and the stimulus had no effect on the EEG pattern or on behavioural arousal. If, after a stimulus of a certain tone had ceased to be effective, another tone was given, it would be effective in arousing the animal. Of particular interest was the finding that, although the EEG changes disappeared with repetition of the stimulus, there was no decrease in the amplitude of the evoked potentials at the cortex, but rather a slight increase.

Working with single cells, Horn *et al.* (1964) have found a small region of the mid-brain of rabbits where the change in activity produced by a stimulus attenuates rapidly with repetition of the stimulus. The cells in this tecto-tegmental region were tested with a variety of stimuli, some cells being sensitive to input through only one modality, some to several. Sixty-three out of seventy-two cells tested showed an attentuation of response as the stimulus was repeated. As with the electroencephalographic response discussed above, the speed of the waning was comparable to that of a behavioural response, and the waning was specific to the particular stimulus used: when the response of a cell to one stimulus had waned, it would still respond to another novel stimulus. In other species it has been claimed that damage to this tectotegmental region impairs the ability to attend to stimuli, and stimulation improves tachistoscope performance (Horn, 1965). A similar case of waning in a single cell has been recorded in the mollusc *Aplysia* (Hughes *et al.*, 1963; Hughes, personal communication).

The conclusion to be drawn from the evidence at present available, therefore, is that behavioural habituation is accompanied by at most minor changes in the direct afferent pathways (with the exception of the sensory cortex), but is related to changes in unit activity in the brain-stem and to changes in the EEG pattern. Apparently it is with the study of habituation in single cells that future research on the mechanisms underlying the tendency for novel stimuli to capture the attention should be concerned (Horn, 1965). Whether or not such techniques will also provide data relevant to the changes in selective attention to subtle stimulus characters, as discussed on pp. 87–93, remains to be seen.

It will already be apparent that the orientation response intergrades with some kinds of exploration in which the animal moves about its environment, either alert to all changes within it, or investigating one object after another, or a combination of these two. The factors of the stimulus situation most conducive to behaviour of these sorts have been reviewed by Berlyne (1960):

they include its novelty (the time since it was last encountered, or its degree of resemblance to situations encountered previously), complexity, its intensity and contrast, the poverty of the preceding environment, its effective value, and so on. Such behaviour is discussed in more detail later (Chapters 15 and 26).

6.5. Stimulus Selection—Conclusion

As discussed earlier, selection of the stimuli impinging on an organism must occur continuously. In many cases, and especially in simple organisms and the simpler responses of higher organisms, the model of particular stimulus-response connections which are activated whenever the right stimulus happens to come along works well enough. If we are considering the knee jerk or the scratch reflex, the question of stimulus selection raises no problem.

When it comes to the question of responsiveness to particular stimulus characters, we are familiar with man-made devices like locks and telephone dials, which respond selectively to particular stimulus configurations, and some indications of the physiological processes which actually occur in the nervous system are beginning to appear (pp. 79–85, 91–102).

However, it cannot be too strongly emphasized that, for behaviour of any degree of complexity, the conception of the organism as passively filtering the stimuli impinging on it becomes inadequate, and mechanical analogies of this type can give a false impression of simplicity.

In the first place, the physical variables are encoded in the sense organs as nerve impulses. The coding may involve the abstraction of higher order quantities, such as rate of change of illumination (pp. 80–5), or rate of change of texture (pp. 65–6). At this or a later stage the coding also involves the elimination of redundancy, and this itself may contribute to specificity of responsiveness (pp. 95–6).

Second, the effectiveness of the encoded message in inducing a response may depend on comparison with a pre-existing message. The necessity for postulating a process of comparison arises from studies of perceptual constancy (Chapter 5), from the response specificity of selection and the phenomena of the specific search image (pp. 89–91), and from studies of habituation (pp. 97–102).

We have seen how, in skilled movements, the response may depend on a comparison between the actual degree of muscular contraction and the Sollwert, and here we see a comparable phenomenon on the sensory side. In the following chapters we shall see that comparator processes are basic at nearly all stages of the mechanisms underlying complex behaviour.

6.6 Summary

1. The effectiveness of some stimulus characters is specific to one response or group of responses.
2. The concept of "innate releasing mechanism", which has been used in the past to account for cases of selective responsiveness, can be misleading.

3. Many examples of searching behaviour can be described by postulating a "search image": the animal's further behaviour depends on coincidence between the stimuli it encounters and the search image it has already acquired.

4. There is considerable evidence that the sensory input into the central nervous system is controlled by centrifugal fibres, but the suggestion that these fibres operate in selective attention is controversial. The mechanisms involved in selective responsiveness to particular stimulus characters are thus still not clear.

5. When a novel stimulus is presented to an animal it shows an "orientation response": its responsiveness to the stimulus is enhanced and its readiness for action increased. The further elaboration of this response if the stimulus is repeated depends upon its consequences. If the stimulus is without significant correlates, the response wanes. The properties of this waning can be accounted for on the supposition that the animal forms a "neuronal model" of familiar sources of stimulation: non-coincidence between the stimulation received and a neuronal model leads to an orientation response.

6. Behavioural habituation, as seen in the waning of the orientation response, is accompanied by, at most, minor changes in the direct afferent pathways, but is accompanied by changes in the EEG pattern and by changes in the responsiveness of certain cells in the brain stem.

7

Orientation

Some activities of animals are performed without orientation to the environment. At the reflex level, the knee jerk or the ejaculatory reflex, once elicited by the appropriate stimulation, has no special spatial relationship to objects in the environment. Similarly with some examples of more complex behaviour— a particular environmental situation may play a part in the elicitation of a Great Tit's song, but song is then delivered with no specific orientation.

For the most part, however, animals regulate their activities in spatial relationship with the environment—locomotion is guided towards the proper goals, prey-catching movements are directed towards the prey, courtship towards the female. In this chapter we shall consider how this is achieved.

7.1. The Orienting Stimuli

The first stage in analysing an orientation mechanism is the identification of the stimuli in relation to which the animal is oriented. Often, as in most prey-catching and courtship responses, these are the same as those which elicit the response. As we have seen in Chapter 3, however, in other cases they are not: the flight of a Chaffinch to cover is guided by stimuli quite different from the alarm call which elicited the flight in the first place. Another example is provided by the gaping response of nestling thrushes. When the eyes are fully open this is both released and guided by visual stimuli, but the particular visual characteristics differ for the two functions. For an object to release the response three characteristics are important; it must be within certain limits of size, be above the horizontal plane of the nestling, and show movement. The response is oriented towards a protrusion of the object's outline, which has a diameter of about one third of that of the body: it must also be above the body and closer than it is to the nestlings (*see* Fig. 4.6). This response illustrates another point— the control of the orientation changes with age. When the nestlings first hatch they are blind, and their gaping is directed vertically: it is released by mechanical or auditory stimuli, but oriented by gravity. Not only are the stimuli which release and direct the response different at the two stages, but the changeover to visual control takes place at different times: there is a period during which the response is released by visual stimuli but still oriented by gravity (Tinbergen *et al.*, 1939).

Often, as with a moth flying to a candle flame or a male songbird courting a female, the general nature of the stimuli governing orientation is clear, though for a precise physical description experiments with models (as described in Chapter 4) may be necessary. Difficulties can arise when the response is to physical factors outside the range of our own sensitivities. Marine crustaceans (e.g. *Palaemon* sp.) are able to steer a straight course for considerable distances when they are unable to see the sea bed or any other landmarks. Since the course is usually roughly at right angles to the sun, it seems likely that the sun is being used as a compass. Experiments with the species *Mysidium gracilis* have raised the possibility that the sun is not being used directly, but through the polarization pattern. In the laboratory, *Mysidium* tends to orient at right angles to the the plane of polarization (Bainbridge *et al.*, 1957) (*see* Fig. 4.7). Polarized light is known to be used for orientation by a number of other arthropods (e.g. Jander *et al.*, 1960): for instance bees, which normally orient by the sun, can make directional flights when the sun is obscured provided a small portion of blue sky remains, as the light coming from it is polarized in a characteristic fashion.

Another example is the fish *Gymnarchus niloticus*. In avoiding obstacles as it swims backwards, and in identifying its prey from a distance, it shows powers of orientation beyond those which could be mediated by its lateral line system or its poorly developed eyes. In fact, these fish produce a weak but regular electric pulse: by means of receptors sensitive to changes in an electric field they can detect objects whose conductivity differs from that of water (Lissmann, 1958; Lissmann *et al.*, 1958) (*see* p. 57 and Fig. 4.8).

7.2. Classification of Orienting Movements

The ways in which animals become oriented with respect to environmental stimuli are so diverse that it is not possible to classify them in any wholly satisfactory way. However, certain categories have proved useful over the years, especially for the orientation responses of invertebrates. These have been set out in detail by Kühn (1919) and Fraenkel and Gunn (1940), whose system incorporates many of the ideas of earlier writers. The following discussion is based largely on their work and that of Kennedy (1945), though it diverges in some details.

Kinesis

The first distinction, between kinesis and taxis, depends on whether the animal's body is oriented with respect to the source of stimulation. In kinesis, which we shall consider first, it is not. The stimulus produces merely a change either in speed of movement or in rate of turning, and this alters the position of the animal in relation to the source of that stimulus.

Woodlice (*Porcellio scaber*) tend to aggregate in moist places. This is due to an influence of the relative humidity on the locomotory activity of the animals:

as the humidity increases, the proportion of animals which are motionless increases. The animals therefore become aggregated in the damper regions. A similar aggregating effect occurs when the change in conditions produces merely a retardation of movement, in the same way that cars, travelling on through journeys, become concentrated in towns where their average speed is low. Such an influence on linear velocity is known as "orthokinesis".

The term "klinokinesis" is used to refer to cases in which the rate of turning is affected by external stimulation. The planarian *Dendrocoelum* tends to aggregate in the darker parts of its habitat: although locomotion continues, the

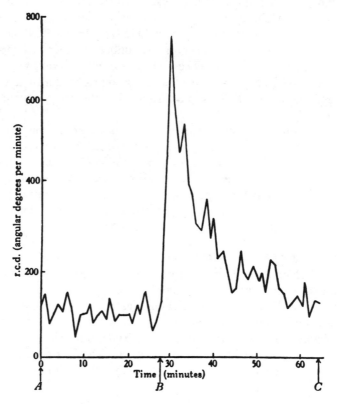

Fig. 7.1. Relation between light intensity and rate of change of direction (r.c.d.) of *Dendrocoelum*. *A–B*, in darkness. At *B*, the light was switched on, the r.c.d. increased, but slowly returned to the basal value. (*After Ullyott, 1936.*)

animals tend not to leave dark regions once they reach them (Ullyott, 1936). This is a consequence of two factors. First, the animals change direction frequently as they swim along, and the rate of change in direction is increased by an increase in the light intensity (Fig. 7.1). Second, this response to an increase in light intensity is subject to fairly rapid adaptation: a given light intensity therefore induces a higher probability of turning in an animal, not yet adapted to that intensity, moving up the gradient, than in an animal moving down the gradient, which has already started to become adapted to even higher intensities. Paths towards the darker region thus tend to be longer than paths away from it, and the animals aggregate there (Ullyott, 1936).

Another example is given by Wigglesworth (1941). The human body louse finds its host, in part, by klinokinetic responses to temperature, humidity and smell. When adapted to an unfavourable environment the louse goes approximately straight (Fig. 7.2). If conditions become more favourable, it continues on this way. But if, having experienced these more favourable conditions, it enters a less favourable zone, it starts to turn. Thus, by keeping straight when the stimulus remains constant or becomes more favourable, but turning when

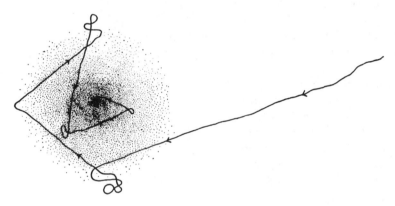

Fig. 7.2. Hypothetical track of a louse approaching the centre of some favourable diffuse stimulus. (*After Wigglesworth, 1941.*)

it becomes less so, it gradually reaches the most favourable conditions. This case differs from the previous one in that the rate of turning decreases with *increase* in intensity of stimulation, whereas in *Dendrocoelum* the rate of turning decreases with *decrease* in light intensity. In both cases the responses bring the animal into favourable conditions.

Ullyott, *loc. cit.* and Fraenkel *et al.*, *loc. cit.* regard adaptation as essential for klinokinetic displacement along a stimulus gradient. Without it, they suppose the animals will turn more at one end of the gradient than at the other, but there will be no resultant movement up or down. Their argument here is not convincing, and is valid only under certain conditions. Consider an animal which shows no adaptation, so that the rate of turning is a function of stimulus intensity. Suppose that it turns more as the stimulus intensity increases. The probability of turning of an animal which moves up the gradient will be increasing, while that of an animal which moves down will be decreasing. On average, paths down the gradient or with a component down the gradient, will tend to be longer than paths starting from the same point but with a component up the gradient. The animal will thus tend to shift down the gradient, even though it shows no adaptation.

There are conditions, however, under which this shifting will not occur; namely if the probability of turning is so high that the animal turns so soon that the difference in probability of turning produced by moving up or down is negligible. This is more likely to happen if:

(a) The intensity of stimulation changes only slowly with distance.
(b) A given change in stimulation produces only a small change in rate of turning.
(c) The movement over the ground is slow.
(d) The frequency of turning is high.

In such cases there will be less tendency to shift down the gradient, and the animal will be likely to remain pursuing a convoluted path in one particular region. Indeed, there may even be a tendency to shift up the gradient, for the following reason. Since the probability of extensive progression in any given direction will be smaller the greater the rate of turning, the animals will tend to stay longer in regions of high stimulus intensity. In a population of animals, individuals which wander into such a region will tend to stay there, and the population may tend to shift up the gradient.

Thus in the absence of adaptation there could be a klinokinetic shift up or down the gradient, depending on the relations between the parameters enumerated above.

The occurrence of adaptation complicates the issue still further. If adaptation is immediate, then the stimulus intensity will be effectively constant everywhere and the rate of turning will not alter along the gradient. No klinokinetic shifting can then occur. However, the tendency to shift down the gradient which, as indicated above, can occur with no adaptation, will be enhanced by some degree of adaptation, as Ullyott suggested (see pp. 106-7). Furthermore, the trapping effect that occurs when the rate of turning is high relative to the rate of movement is reduced by adaptation: as adaptation occurs, the probability of turning decreases and the animal makes the longer paths necessary for it to escape. Davenport et al. (1960) were thus correct in supposing that slow adaptation could assist a klinokinetic aggregation near the region where the rate of turning was greatest, though they omitted to specify the other relationships necessary for this to occur.

Jennings's (1906) description of the manner in which Paramecia become aggregated in a drop of acid water is well known: the animals reach the drop by chance when swimming in random directions, but tend to turn when they reach the boundary on the way out. This "phobotaxis" clearly bears at least a superficial relation to klinokinesis, the change in stimulation as less favourable conditions are approached producing a sudden rather than a gradual increase in probability of turning.

Taxes and Transverse Orientations

In kineses there is no orientation of the body with respect to the source of stimulation: the change in spatial relationship to that source is achieved through quantitative variations in the activity of the animal. In taxes, by contrast, the animal's body takes up a particular direction: the taxis may be combined with locomotion so that the animal moves towards, away from, or at a fixed angle to the source. The term taxis is sometimes (but *see* p. 115) restricted to cases in which the stimuli are simple and, in the case of visual stimuli, form vision is not involved.

Klinotaxis

In klinotaxis the orientation of the body does not necessarily require a receptor itself capable of discriminating the direction of the source of stimulation. Provided the receptor is not equally accessible to stimulation from all directions, the animal can compare the intensities of stimulation on the two sides of its body by turning the receptor or receptors first one way and then the other. The comparison is, of course, successive, and enables the organism to turn until the two sides are stimulated equally. An example is the response of maggots of various common flies (*Musca, Calliphora, Lucilia*) to light during the period preceding pupation. The photosensitive structures are at the anterior end of the body, and are shaded from light coming directly from behind. As the animal crawls, it swings its head first to one side and then to the other. A comparison between the intensities of stimulation falling on the two sides of the body determines the extent of the lateral movements and also their relation to the contractions which bring up the rest of the animal, and thus sets the animal's course (Fig. 7.3).

By observing the behaviour of maggots kept under conditions of dim diffuse light, Gunn (cited by Tinbergen, 1951) showed that the turning depends on successive comparisons between the stimulation on the two sides of the body. As the maggot turned its head to the left side, a second light, hanging centrally above the animal, was switched on momentarily. This was repeated every time the head moved to the left, but not when it moved to the right. As a result, the animal circled towards the right. If the second light was switched on momentarily only when the head was to the right, the circling was to the left. It thus seems that orientation in a horizontal beam is not due to a direct response to the direction of the beam, but to successive responses whose strength varies with intensity of the incident light.

In practice, klinotaxes are relatively rare as responses to light, for most animals have eyes capable of discriminating the direction of light directly. They are, however, commonly used as a means of orienting to chemical stimuli; for instance by the flat-worm *Planaria* in orienting to bait (Köhler, cited by

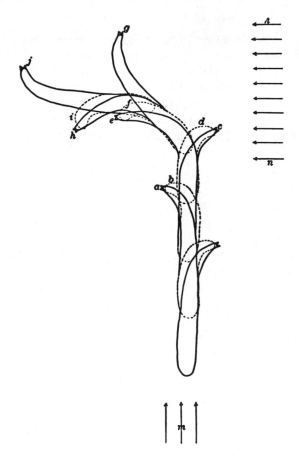

Fig. 7.3. Klinotaxis in the maggot. (*After Mast, 1911.*)
At *d* the light *m* was switched off and *n* switched on.

Fraenkel *et al.*, *loc. cit.*). If a small piece of bait is placed in a dish containing a planarian, the animal soon starts to move about. It then crawls along a convoluted path, tending gradually to approach the bait. This may be a form of klinokinetic reaction. When it gets nearer to the bait it crawls straight towards it, swinging the fore-part of its body from side to side: this is apparently a phase of klinotaxis. This more efficient method of orientation may not be possible when the animal is farther from the bait because there the gradient of stimulation is not great enough.

Tropotaxis

In klinotaxis the animal makes, in effect, successive comparisons of the stimulation impinging on its receptors as they are turned from side to side. Tropotaxis differs in that the comparison is simultaneous: it thus depends on bilaterally symmetrical receptors arranged in such a way that they are stimulated unequally when the animal is not oriented towards or away from the source of stimulation. This simultaneous comparison makes possible orientation to or from a localized source without the lateral swings or wavy movements necessary in klinotaxes: turning occurs if at any instant the intensity of stimulation on the two sides is not the same.

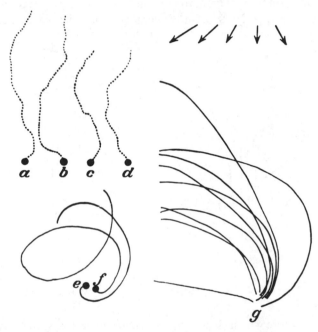

Fig. 7.4. Tracks of photopositive *Armadillium* blinded on the right side. (*After Henke, 1930.*)

   a–d in darkness; *e, f*, with the light overhead; *g*, in a beam whose direction is indicated by the arrows.

In theory, this type of orientation can be recognized in two ways. First, unilateral elimination of the receptors in a diffuse field of stimulation will cause the animal to turn continuously towards one side: however much it turns the intensity of stimulation on the two sides cannot be equalized, and so the circus movements continue. Second, if the animal is influenced by two sources of stimulation whose fields cross, it will pursue a course towards or away from a point between the two sources: it seems to move in such a manner that the tendencies to turn to right and to left are just in balance.

An example is given by the crustacean *Armadillium*, which often behaves in a phototropotactic manner. If blinded unilaterally it makes circus movements (Fig. 7.4), and intact animals usually (though not invariably) go between two lights (Fig. 7.5). Cases of pure tropotaxis, however, are not easy to find, for it is often combined with telotactic responses: these are considered below.

The "dorsal light reaction", by which many aquatic animals keep the dorsal (or ventral) side uppermost, was distinguished from tropotaxis by Fraenkel and Gunn because the animal moves, if at all, in a plane at right angles to the source of stimulation, rather than towards or away from it. Tinbergen (1951), however, has pointed out that this distinction is based on a failure to separate the orientation component from the locomotion which may accompany it. As discussed earlier (pp. 20-2), a movement may be oriented by stimuli quite

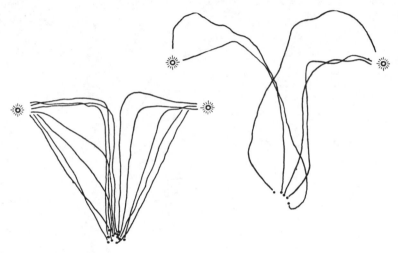

Fig. 7.5. Tracks of photopositive *Armadillium* with two equal lights. (*After Müller, 1925.*)

different from those which elicit it, and the two can be analysed independently. In some cases the orientation is independent of any form of locomotion, but this need not imply that it differs from otherwise similar cases which are accompanied by locomotion.

The dorsal light reaction does, in fact, show the characteristics of tropotaxis. The fish-louse *Argulus* sp. normally swims with the dorsal surface to the light. If the light comes from below, it swims dorsal surface down. If the source of light is moved, it either rolls or turns a front somersault to maintain its orientation. If one eye is destroyed it makes continuous rolling and spiralling movements, showing that the dorsal light reaction normally depends on a balance of stimulation through the two eyes (Herter, 1927).

In the fish *Crenilabris* the orientation is controlled by both a dorsal light reaction and by the labyrinth. If the labyrinths are removed, the fish orients with its dorsal surface towards the light (Fig. 7.6). If the labyrinths are present, however, the position is a compromise controlled partly by the labyrinths and partly by the dorsal light reaction: the nature of the compromise depends on the intensity and direction of the light (Fig. 7.7). If one eye is removed, the fish at first rolls towards the intact side. Comparable phenomena in amphibians have been studied by Jahn (1960).

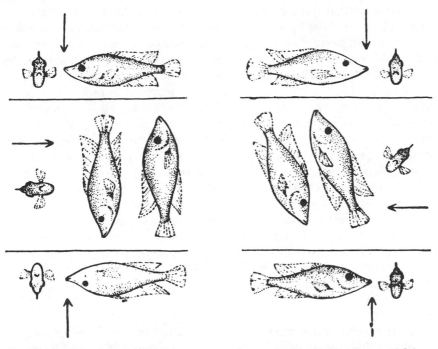

Fig. 7.6. Dorsal light reaction in labyrinthectomized *Crenilabris* in beams coming from different directions. (*After von Holst, 1935d.*)

Fig. 7.7.   As Fig. 7.6, normal fishes.

There seems, then, to be no justification for Fraenkel and Gunn's distinction between tropotaxis and the dorsal light reaction. As Dr J. S. Kennedy has pointed out to me, however, a convention to restrict the term "taxis" to cases involving locomotion is current in the literature: we do not, for instance, usually describe standing upright as "geotaxis". The means by which animals achieve particular patterns of spatial distribution with respect to their environment is of great ecological significance, and it is here that the study of "taxes" has been most actively pursued. Since the argument is solely terminological, there seems no point in pursuing it further.

Until recently, it was thought that most tropotactic responses of insects could be understood in terms of variations in the "sensitivity" of the ommatidia. Consider, for example, the orientation of *Eristalis* when exposed to two lights of different intensities. The fly at first orients towards a point between the two lights, and nearer the stronger light than the weaker. On the view that the orientation is due to a balance between the turning effects produced by the light shining on the two eyes, the stronger light shining on, say, the left eye is balanced by the weaker light shining on the right eye. Since the course is nearer to the strong light than the weak, the ommatidia stimulated by the latter are more posterior than those stimulated by the former. Thus the turning tendency produced by the strong light falling on the more anterior ommatidia is balanced by that produced by the weaker light on the more posterior ones. The posterior ommatidia must, therefore, be more sensitive than the anterior ones. By varying the conditions it is possible to map out the sensitivity of the ommatidia: Dolley *et al.* (1929) found that the sensitivity increased 55 times over a sector of only 23 degrees of the eye. "Sensitivity" is, of course, an *ad hoc* hypothesis invoked to explain the experimental facts, and is not to be thought of as a property of the ommatidium itself, but of the whole turning reaction mediated by it. It has, however, proved useful in accounting for a considerable wealth of detail derived from experiments in which orientation to two sources of stimulation, or orientation of unilaterally blinded animals, was studied. But even in laboratory experiments detailed observations have shown it to be inadequate. Studying the insect *Notonecta*, Lüdtke (Fraenkel *et al., loc. cit.*) found that the variation and plastic adaptation of the orientation required the postulation of variables additional to those involved in a sensitivity map: this shows the explanatory system to be insecure (Fraenkel *et al.*, 1940). An alternative method of approach to these problems is discussed later in this chapter.

Telotaxis

Both klinotaxis and tropotaxis depend on balance: the animal orients itself by equalizing the intensity of stimulation on the two sides of the body. Telotactic orientation does not depend on simple balance: if there are two sources of stimulation operating through the same modality the animal orients towards one or the other, and not in an intermediate direction. This suggests that the influence of one of the stimuli must be inhibited. An example is shown in Fig. 7.8: the hermit crab orients either to one source or the other. Bees behave similarly: furthermore, if blinded unilaterally, they first show circus movements but then orient towards the light source. The circus movements can be explained as being due to light entering the very sensitive posterior ommatidia: these soon become adapted, and the animal then fixates the source with its anterior ommatidia and moves towards it. However, adaptation in the ommatidia cannot account for the inhibition of the response to objects in the visual field other than those to which the insect orients. This question has been considered by Wallace (1962) who believes that the inhibition is on the motor rather than the sensory side (contrast Chapter 6).

Kühn (1919) used the term telotaxis to describe such responses as the orientation of a dragonfly towards its prey. Fraenkel and Gunn prefer to restrict it to cases in which the stimulus does not involve form vision, on the grounds that it could otherwise be used to include responses which involve complex mechanisms such as, "motives, learning and so on which are generally thought to be absent in the elementary reactions which we are considering". The argument here depends on the status accorded to the classificatory system: if it is regarded as concerned with mechanisms, then Fraenkel and Gunn are certainly correct. But since this system is based for the most part on descriptive observations of the behaviour of the whole animal it is preferable not to make assumptions about similarities in physiological mechanism between examples of any of the classes of kinesis or taxis. Tinbergen (1951), like Kühn, includes responses to

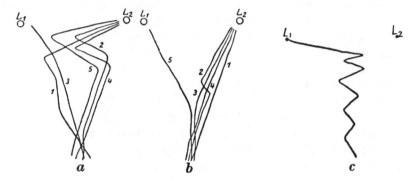

Fig. 7.8. Tracks of hermit crabs (*a* and *b*) (after von Buddenbrock, 1922), and an isopod *Aega* (*c*) in a two-light experiment (after Fraenkel, 1931). (*From Fraenkel et al., 1940.*)

configurational stimuli in this category; for instance the orientation of the gaping response of nestling thrushes towards the parent's head (p. 104).

Menotaxis

In the classic cases of telotaxis, the animal orients directly towards or away from the stimulus. Menotaxes, or light compass responses, involve orientation at a constant angle to the direction of a source of stimulation. The path of a homing ant is guided, in part, by the direction of the sun; if the apparent direction of the sun is slowly changed by the use of a mirror, the ant changes course accordingly (Schneirla, 1933).

Mnemotaxis

As we have seen, Fraenkel and Gunn restricted their classificatory system to cases which did not involve configurational stimuli. Even in invertebrates, however, some orientation responses depend on complex stimulus situations.

For instance, the hunting wasp *Philanthus triangulum* uses a number of land-marks simultaneously when returning to its nest (van Beusekom, 1948). Tinbergen *et al.* (1938) carried out an extensive series of experiments in which the wasp's use of landmarks round the nest entrance was studied. When the wasp had had opportunity to learn the initial lay-out, the landmarks were rearranged in various ways. The results indicated that the insect's return was guided by the relation of the nest entrance to the whole configuration of land-marks, and did not depend on stimulation of special parts of the retina by particular landmarks (*see also* van Iersel, 1965).

Kühn (1919) distinguished cases such as this as "mnemotaxis", in part because of the configurational nature of the stimuli involved and in part because these stimuli must be learnt. Of course, learning may also be involved in telotaxis and menotaxis, and Tinbergen (1951) emphasizes that these distinctions are of degree only. The apparent simplicity of telotaxis may be only illusory, as it also involves a configurational visual field even though one point in it is singled out. The relations between these categories will be mentioned again later in this chapter.

Utility of the Kinesis-Taxis Classification
Many additional examples given in Fraenkel and Gunn's book show how this classificatory system brings order into diverse examples of orientation. Here it is necessary to make two reservations. First, the categories have been worked out largely during the course of laboratory studies on relatively simple animals in simplified situations. In the field, with higher animals, and even in laboratory studies of simple animals in more complex situations, the categories become less useful: the responses are not readily classifiable into one or the other category, and different types of orientation seem to occur together or in close succession, so that the distinctions between the categories fade. This, of course, does not invalidate the system, but merely places limits on its usefulness. Second, it is necessary to exercise care before making assumptions about the extent to which the responses of any one category share similar mechanisms. Assignment of a particular case to one or other category depends on an assess-ment of the role of individual receptor organs, but not on an analysis of all that happens between stimulus and response: it thus tends to over-simplify. The distinctions made in the Fraenkel and Gunn classification are useful in so far as they refer to different types of spatial manoeuvre, but can be dangerous if taken to imply types of physiological mechanism.

7.3. Analysis of Orientation in Terms of Control Systems
In recent years a considerable advance in the understanding of orientation mechanisms has been made not only from attempts to extend the analysis to a neuronal level, but also by applying the methods used for the study of control systems in engineering. We have already seen some preliminary examples of

this approach in Chapter 5. To achieve orientation, the animal must have a mechanism which receives information from the outside world, a means of changing its orientation, and a mechanism for relating the two. These can be linked in a variety of ways: it is possible to define the alternatives in terms of information flow diagrams, and then to decide between them experimentally. In a similar manner the functioning of each of the sub-systems can be analysed in terms of its sub-systems, and so on. The approach thus aims at specifying the functions of the physiological mechanisms underlying the orientation: a knowledge of the sorts of jobs these mechanisms do should aid in their identification (e.g. von Holst et al., 1950; von Holst, 1954; Hassenstein, 1959; Mittelstaedt, 1960, 1961, 1962, 1964).

Open Systems

If the movement produced by the effectors has no consequences which influence the further effect of the external stimulus, the receptor-effector system is said to be an open one. Any orientation mechanism in which the stimulus is over before the movement is completed must be of this type. Male fireflies (*Photinus*) orient fairly accurately to brief flashes of light. Since the fireflies may turn correctly even though they do not start until after the flash is over (Mast, 1912), the output of the system (the change in the orientation) cannot influence the input (the angle between the flash and the body's axis): the system is thus of the open type.

For a basically similar reason, the rapid strike of the forelegs by which mantids capture their prey must also be based on an open system. Information about the position of the prey is received by the compound eyes: the output of the system is the deviation of the strike from the axis of the body. In theory, information about the direction of the strike relative to the prey (i.e. the error) could be fed back into the system by the eyes while the strike is in progress, but, in practice, the delay before this could produce any effect would be greater than the time required to extend the forelegs. The extension of the forelegs thus cannot influence the input, and the system is an open one (Mittelstaedt, 1962).

In the cases considered so far, the initial deviation of the stimulus has affected the receptor, which, in turn, has activated the effector organs—this arrangement is in the form of a chain. Another type of open system is that in which the external change can both affect the receptor organs and produce a physical displacement. The effector, however, produces a compensatory movement which precisely counteracts the deviation which would have been produced by the input. An example of such a "mesh" arrangement is shown in Fig. 7.9. A man standing upright in a small boat sees a wave approaching from abeam; the wave provides both a stimulus, which is received through the eyes, and a force, which tips the boat. The man, however, can bend his leg in such a manner that the effect of the wave is precisely counteracted, and his body remains upright.

It will be apparent that the correct functioning of open systems depends on the precision of their calibration: the movement produced by the effectors must be just appropriate for the measured deviation. In the mantid case this calibration does not depend on previous learning, for young nymphs can capture the first *Drosophila* they encounter. On the other hand, when a man

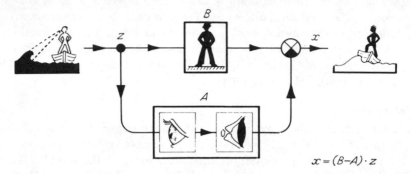

$$x = (B-A) \cdot z$$

Fig. 7.9. A mesh: the sailor sees the wave coming and takes appropriate action as it arrives. (*From Mittelstaedt, 1961.*)

throws a dart or uses the mechanism described above to remain upright in a small boat, the calibration depends on practice. The mesh system has the peculiar characteristic, not shared by other control mechanisms, that it can produce continuous absolute orientation—the effect of disturbing influences can be anticipated and counteracted as they occur. This, however, depends on previous precise calibration (*see also* Mittelstaedt, 1964).

Closed Systems—Feedback Control
In many cases the animal can assess its deviation continuously, and respond accordingly. The consequences of the initial activity of the effectors can thus be

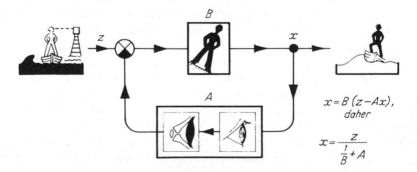

$$x = B\,(z - Ax),$$
$$daher$$

$$x = \frac{z}{\dfrac{1}{B} + A}$$

Fig. 7.10. A loop: the sailor perceives the change in his orientation by sighting a distant object and takes action after some tilting has occurred. (*From Mittelstaedt, 1961.*)

fed back into the system and influence its subsequent course. An example of this is shown in Fig. 7.10. In this case the man maintains his position by observing a stationary object not influenced by the wave. As the wave tilts the boat, he perceives the change in his position and takes the action appropriate for rectifying it.   Most examples of simple tropotactic orientation can easily be

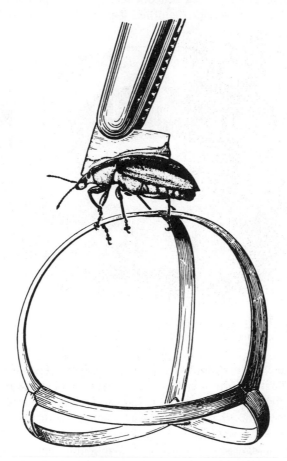

Fig. 7.11. The Y-maze-globe, used for studying the orientation of *Chlorophanus*. (*After Hassenstein, 1959.*)

pictured as involving negative feedback in this way—the animal turns until the deviation of the relevant body axis from the direction of stimulation is 0 degrees (or 180 degrees): just so long as any deviation remains, the turning continues.

As an example of this method of approach we may first consider in some detail a precise analysis of the mechanism controlling an optomotor response made by Hassenstein (1959: Hassenstein *et al.*, 1959) using the beetle *Chloro-phanus*. In this case the turning tendency of the beetle was measured by the sensitive Y-maze-globe method. The Y-maze-globe consists of six pieces of straw joined at four points to form Y junctions (Fig. 7.11). The beetle is suspended and carries the maze by its feet. As it walks, the beetle must remain stationary but the globe rotates beneath it. As each Y junction reaches the beetle, it must turn one way or the other. The ratio of left to right turns is a

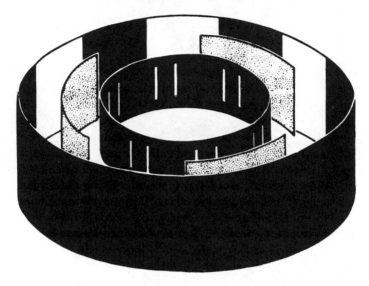

Fig. 7.12. Arena used for studying the orientation of *Chlorophanus.* See text. (*After Hassenstein and Reichardt, 1959.*)

sensitive measure of the optomotor turning tendency. Hassenstein used this device in combination with a special method for eliciting the response. The insect was surrounded by a stationary cylinder containing a pattern of vertical slits. Round this was another cylinder, also stationary, with a pattern of stripes on it. Between the two was a third rotating cylinder which contained vertical gaps. The rotation caused a pattern of changing illumination of the vertical slits whose sequence, width and intensity varied with the precise arrangement of the slits and stripes. This produced an optomotor response in the insect. A typical arrangement is shown in Fig. 7.12.

Hassenstein was able to show that the physiological unit in the eye comprises two ommatidia. The basic stimulus situation for an optomotor response consists of two successive stimuli in adjacent ommatidia: responses to more complex situations are built up from these basic units. Each ommatidium can cooperate only with its immediate neighbour or with the next but one, and there is no interaction between ommatidia separated by more than one unstimulated ommatidium. The optomotor response is strongest when successive stimuli follow each other at $\frac{1}{4}$-second intervals, though some response appears even when the interval is 10 seconds. If a train of more than two stimuli is used, all possible combinations are assessed by the animal, and the response is increased; thus with three stimuli the response depends on all three possible pairs.

By varying the succession of stimuli, Hassenstein showed that the turning tendency resulting from the movement of the stimuli depends on five parameters: the interval between the successive stimuli, the spatial interval between

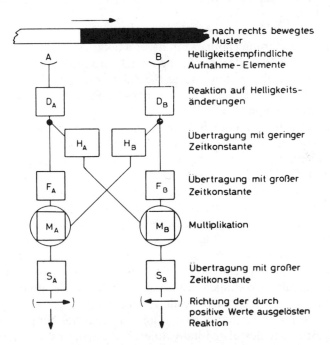

Fig. 7.13. Diagram to illustrate the control of the optomotor response in *Chlorophanus. See* text. (*From Hassenstein, et al., 1959.*)

them, the nature of the series, and the magnitude and sign of the single stimuli which are being related. The underlying mechanisms are represented in terms of a control diagram in Fig. 7.13, which indicates the simplest possible interrelations which will account for the results of the experiments.

Suppose the stimulus contour passes receptor elements A and B with a time interval Δt: in a more natural situation the length of this interval would depend on the relation between the movement of the external stimulus and that of the animal. Short signals are induced in the differentiation units A and B. These can pass to the multiplication units M_A and M_B via two pairs of filters, H_A, H_B and F_A, F_B which have respectively short and long resonance times. If the contour moves slowly, so that Δt is more than the duration of the response in the F units (say, more than 10 seconds), one of the inputs of the multiplication unit will be zero, and its output will therefore be zero. If, however, Δt is shorter than the time taken by the signals in the slow reacting elements to fade, M_A is affected at least momentarily by simultaneous signals from both sides. This, of course, occurs only because of the longer resonance duration of the F levels, the strength of the signal arriving from F_A being only that which corresponds to the after-effect there. When (and only when) M_A receives simultaneous signals from both sides, its output influences S_A and causes a movement in the direction A–B.

Since the H units have a short resonance time, M_B does not receive simultaneous messages through both its inputs, and thus has no output. Conversely, if the movement is from B to A, M_B and not M_A produces an output. It will be seen that the faster the contour moves (i.e. the shorter Δt), the less damped is the signal in F_A when the signal from B arrives, and thus the greater the output of the multiplication unit.

Although the block diagram is discussed here only in relation to the passage of a simple contour across the eyes, the scheme accounts quantitatively for the insect's response to groups of contours and other complex patterns (Hassenstein, 1959, 1961; Hassenstein et al., 1959).

This study of the optomotor response of *Chlorophanus* shows how analysis in terms of control systems can lead to a precise mathematical description of orientation behaviour. At a more descriptive level its advantages can be seen most clearly in cases where the Sollwert is variable. Thus explanations of tropotactic orientation in terms of balanced stimulation and variations in the "sensitivity" of the different parts of the sense organ worked reasonably well so long as animals were studied in stereotyped and simple situations. But, in practice, the sign of a tropotactic response can change; the tsetse fly *Glossina*, for instance, is positively phototactic at low temperatures but negatively so at high ones. Are we to postulate totally different mechanisms, with a reversal of the sensitivity gradient (*see* p. 114) for the two cases? The difficulties become even more marked in the case of menotaxis, for instead of having one (or two) preferred directions, the animal can orient at almost any angle to the direction of stimulation. The foraging ant can pursue many different paths, each in a different direction from the sun. Indeed, many arthropods can allow for the daily change in azimuth of the sun: they maintain a constant compass direction while the sun, with respect to which they are oriented, moves across the sky (e.g. von Frisch, 1950). In such cases one could suppose that a large number of mechanisms is available, one for each particular orientation. On this view each possible menotactic orientation to a visual stimulus would depend on the stimulus being located in a particular region of the eye. Each possible region of the eye would thus be the centre of its own system of reflexes which could serve to correct any deviation of the stimulus from that region, only one such system being in action at any particular time. But measurement of the deviation of the stimulus from so many different possible reference points would require an immensely complicated mechanism, and no satisfactory suggestion as to how it could be achieved has yet been made.

It would be more economical if the deviation of the source from an anatomically fixed coordinate, such as the median plane of the head, were measured. This could then be fed into a system in which it is compared with a target value (i.e. Sollwert) determined centrally. The control system would then be the type shown in Fig. 7.14. This system is basically similar to that discussed in Chapter 5 in the context of responses to relative movement (pp. 74-9). In both cases movement depends on a comparison between input from receptors and a Sollwert, the value of which can be varied independently.

That menotactic orientation does not depend on a totally independent mechanism, but is in some way superimposed on a tropotactic response, is suggested by Jander's (1957) observations on the ant *Formica rufa*. For

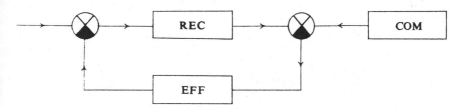

Fig. 7.14. General characters of a control system with variable "Sollwert". *COM* is a sub-system which feeds in signals corresponding to the required "Sollwert". The input to *EFF* thus depends on the difference between the output of *REC* and that of *COM*.

instance, menotactic orientation develops through a gradual change from a tropotactic response: the continuing influence of the latter accounts for the mistakes which the ant makes during the early stages of acquiring the menotaxis. Furthermore, once acquired, the menotaxis is in some degree independent from the original tropotaxis: if the sign of the tropotaxis is changed from positive to negative (for instance when the ant starts to return to the nest), the nature of the menotaxis is not altered.

Yet another line of evidence, showing that the tropotactic response has a continuous independent existence even while the ant is oriented menotactically, can be obtained by switching off the light source by which the animal was orienting, and turning on a second source at 180 degrees to it. If the ant was initially oriented towards or away from the first light, it is equally likely to turn clockwise or anticlockwise to the second (Fig. 7.15). If the ant had been menotactically oriented to a light in one of the front quadrants, then it usually turns towards the second light source in order to gain its new orientation (bottom left) but if the light was initially in one of the posterior quadrants, it turns away (bottom right). If the animal was originally oriented laterally to the light, it turns towards the light if on an outward expedition, and away if returning to the nest. Thus, in each case the direction of the turn made to regain the meno-tactic orientation seems to be influenced by the sign of the phototaxis (Jander, 1957).

Such experiments suggest that the acquired tendency to orient with respect to a stimulus to one side of the axis is superimposed on a pre-existing phototactic response, in such a manner that the angle between the stimulus source and the body axis is assessed and the turning tendency depends not, as previously, on

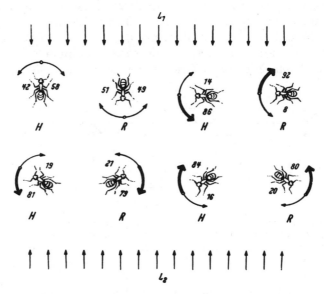

Fig. 7.15. Phototaxis and Menotaxis in the ant *Formica rufa.* (*From Jander, 1957.*)

The figures indicate the number of times the ants turned to left and to right when the direction of the light changed from L_1 to L_2. *H* indicates outward journey; *R*, homeward journey.

the difference between that angle and 0 degrees (or 180 degrees), but between it and the required angle between the body axis and the stimulus (the Sollwert). The precise manner in which such a system operates has been considered in more detail by Mittelstaedt (1962).

It is in just these cases of menotactic orientation variable with respect to the external stimulus that discussion in terms of control systems brings most clarification. For instance, where related species maintain markedly different postures, the differences may depend on the setting of the feedback loop. A few teleosts swim with their heads higher than their tails, the longitudinal axis being more or less permanently inclined to the horizontal. Examination of the utriculus and observation of the behaviour of fish in a centrifuge shows that the mechanism whereby this peculiar posture is maintained differs between species. In *Thayeria obliqua* the otoliths are oriented horizontally when the fish is in its normal oblique position. The inclined posture can thus be regarded as due to the peculiar orientation of the otolith organs. Centrifuging can have no effect on the input from the gravity receptors, and the fish does indeed maintain its posture when gravity is increased to 2·2 g. In *Poecilobrycon eques* the inclination to the horizontal changes with age. Its otoliths are oriented parallel to the longitudinal axis of the body: they are thus inclined to the horizontal. If this species is centrifuged, its posture becomes more horizontal. The change in the weight of the otolith causes a change in the strength of the signal

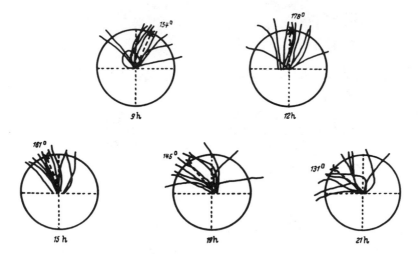

Fig. 7.16. Orientation of *Velia currens* on a vertical surface at different times of day. (*From Birukow and Oberdorfer, 1959.*)
The X indicates the mean direction.

from the sense organ, and thus a change in posture. In this species, therefore, the inclined posture is a consequence of a change in the setting of the gravity feedback system, similar to the modification of the ant's orientation which results in the light compass response (Braemer *et al.*, 1958).

Similarly, the control system model indicates that when the direction of menotactic orientation in one individual changes, we need postulate not a new orientation mechanism complete with sensitivity gradients as discussed on p. 114, but merely a change in the Sollwert. It has already been mentioned that many animals which orient by the sun can allow for the sun's azimuthal movement and thus keep a constant compass direction (e.g. Birukow, 1954; von Frisch, 1950; Jander, 1957). In other cases, transposition of orientation from one sensory modality to another is possible. For example, if ants (*Myrmica* sp.)

or beetles (*Geotrupes* sp.) are forced to change from orientation to a light on a horizontal plane to orientation with respect to gravity on a vertical plane, the orientation to the new stimulus is related to that which had been held to the earlier one. This suggests that there is a mechanism, which is common to both types of stimulus, for "setting" the orientation with respect to whichever stimulus is controlling it (Birukow, 1954, 1964; Vowles, 1954 a, b).

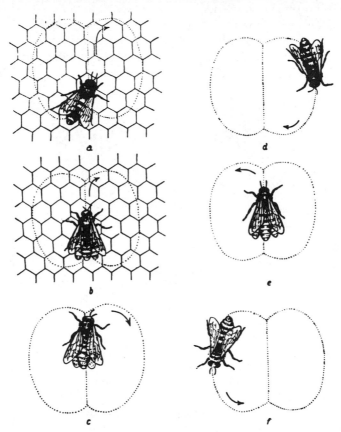

Fig. 7.17 (*a*). Communication of the distance and direction of a food source by the honey bee. The waggle dance. (*From von Frisch, 1954*).

The bug *Velia currens* orients due south by the sun. It allows for the sun's movements, and when orienting by an artificial light source in the laboratory the angle between the body-axis and the direction of the stimulus changes with the time of day. Thus the insect heads to the left of the light in the morning, towards it at midday, and to the right in the afternoon. When orienting with respect to gravity on a vertical surface, there is a similar diurnal change—the insect climbs up and to the right in the morning, up and to the left in the afternoon (Fig. 7.16). The similarity between the rhythmic changes in orientation to light and to gravity, which also parallel a diurnal change in activity, suggest that there is a basic rhythm responsible for all three, which is itself controlled by the natural day–night sequence (Birukow *et al.*, 1959). In such cases the postulation of a central control system involves great economy of hypothesis over the view that a separate mechanism is involved for each menotactic response (*see also* Birukow, 1954; Fischer, 1961). Similarly the dung-beetle *Geotrupes silvaticus* has daily rhythms both of activity and in its orientation to

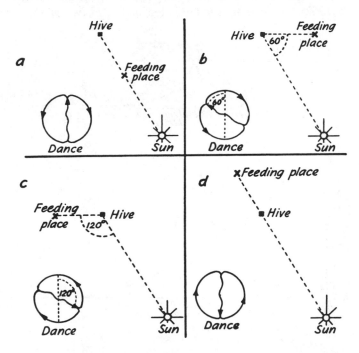

Fig. 7.17 (b). Communication of the distance and direction of a food source by the honey bee. Indication of sun's bearing on a vertical comb surface. (*From von Frisch, 1954.*)

The small diagrams on the left show the dance as it appears on the vertical comb.

the sun: the menotactic mechanism is presumably linked to the mechanism which controls the periodicity of activity (Geisler, 1961).

Such abilities as these enable hive bees to communicate messages about the location of a source of food. If a worker bee discovers a source of food within 150 yards of a hive, she performs a "round dance" on the comb when she returns: she goes round and round in rapid circles, turning first one way and then the other. Other workers try to follow her in her dance, and are then stimulated to set out on foraging flights in the vicinity of the hive. They are assisted in this by receiving some of the scent of the food source from the dancing bee.

If the food source is more than 150 yards from the hive, a returning successful forager performs a "waggle" dance: she moves in a narrow semicircle, turns along its diameter, then describes a semicircle in the opposite direction, and so on. As she runs along the diameter, she wags her abdomen from side to side (Fig. 7.17 (*a*)). The work of von Frisch (e.g. 1953) has shown that this waggle dance conveys information about both the direction and the distance of the food source. The distance is indicated by the tempo of the dance—the further off the source, the slower the dance—or possibly by the accompanying sound (Wenner, 1962). The direction is indicated in one of two ways. If the dance

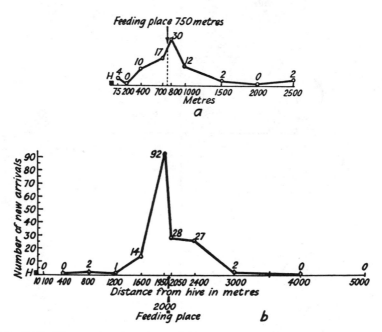

Fig. 7.18. The results of two experiments on communication in the honey bee, with the feeding places 750 and 2,000 metres from the hive. (*From von Frisch, 1954.*)

occurs on a horizontal surface, the direction of the straight part of the dance is the same as that of the food source. If, as is more usually the case, the dance takes place on a vertical surface, the angle between the straight part of the run and the vertical is the same as that between the horizontal direction of the sun and the feeding place (Fig. 7.17 (*b*)). The accuracy of the information conveyed by the dance can be shown by placing similar food sources at varying distances or directions from the hive: the number of bees visiting each source in two such experiments are shown in Fig. 7.18.

For the waggle dance to be successful, it is not essential that the sun should be visible—bees can orient to the plane of polarization of light coming from a blue patch of sky. Furthermore, forced to take an indirect route between hive and food source by an obstacle, the bearing shown by the dance is the direct "bee line" between the two. More recent work on this problem is reviewed by Thorpe (1963a) and Lindauer (1961).

Representation of the orientation mechanism as a control system producing approximation to a Sollwert also helps in the clarification of a number of other findings. Thus, as we have seen, when orientation is controlled by bilaterally symmetrical organs, removal of one of them may upset the equilibrium: if one labyrinth is removed from fishes or frogs, the animal tends to turn towards the operated side (Schoen, 1950; Kolb, 1955). Blinding in one eye produces a tendency to turn towards the intact side in a number of invertebrates—for instance *Acilius* and *Dytiscus* larvae (Schöne, 1951): this can lead to a rotation about the longitudinal axis. Similarly, unilaterally blinded fish swim with the intact side lower (Schoen, 1951; von Holst *et al.*, 1954). However, in many cases such an asymmetrical posture disappears with time—there seems to be a "central compensation" for the sensory asymmetry (Schoen, 1950; Kolb, 1955). Thus the frog *Rana temporaria* recovers normal posture in about 10 days after being blinded in one eye and in about 3 months after removal of one labyrinth (Jahn, 1960). This recovery depends on input through the intact organ: the recovery of unilaterally blinded animals is delayed if the animal is given less than half an hour's light per day. Similarly, the recovery of fish after removal of one labyrinth is accelerated if the gravitational field is increased. The continuing input through the remaining sense organ thus produces gradual adjustment in the central input—output relations (*see also* Butz-Kuenzer, 1957).

When orienting movements are controlled by more than one type of sensory input, their relative influences may be determined by non-specific input received through sense organs not concerned in the orientation (Birukow, 1951) or by various aspects of the internal state (von Holst, 1950a, b; Braemer, 1957). Thus, if the geotaxis and dorsal light reflex determining the position of a fish are made to compete, the latter tends to dominate when the fish is feeding, but the geotaxis when the fish is at rest.

The influence of feeding on the geotaxis in this case was studied by von Holst and Mittelstaedt (1950). If a passive fish is tilted, the statolith organ is affected and the fish shows motor movements which bring it back to its normal position. During normal feeding, however, spontaneous tilting often occurs, and it may be asked why the postural mechanism permits such movements and does not immediately tend to pull the fish back to a normal position. One possibility would be that the postural reflex is blocked during self-initiated movements. That this is not the case has been shown experimentally. If the animal is placed in a centrifuge, the force on the otolith is increased. If one then measures the self-initiated tilting movements, they are found to have decreased in magnitude. Thus the righting response is not switched off during "voluntary" movements, but regulates them continuously through the afferent feedback. This is, of course, comparable to the mechanisms discussed on pp. 76-9.

Another instance of motivation influencing orientation was studied by Schöne (1962) in water-beetle larvae (*Dytiscus* sp.). In this species the orientation of the head to a light source changes with the type of behaviour shown (e.g. swimming upward, swimming downward, etc.). The "reference positions" (Sollwert) when the light came from above were determined for a number of behaviour patterns by measuring the angle between the incident light and the dorso-ventral axis of the head. Then all but one or two stemmata were covered so that a particular angle of light incidence was forced on the larva. The efforts to regain the Sollwert led to a continuous turning tendency, which could be measured. It was found to vary as a sine-like function of the light angle imposed. The curves for the different reference positions all showed maxima and minima at 90 and 270 degrees, but differed in their heights above the abscissa: the changes in reference position are thus apparently brought about by a shift of the turning tendency along the ordinate.

More complex problems arise when the sense organs are themselves oriented at an angle to the body. A case in point is the prey-catching response of the mantis. Although, as we have seen, the overall response is of the open type (p. 117), the head is freely mobile with respect to the thorax and, thus, information concerning the deviation of the prey from the optic axis is insufficient to control the direction of the strike with respect to the axis of the thorax, which carries the striking legs. Mittelstaedt (1960, 1962) has pointed out that three types of mechanism are possible:

1. The head position could be measured proprioceptively and added to the optic information so that the forelegs strike in the appropriate direction (Fig. 7.19*A*). Although proprioceptors, in the form of hair plates between head and thorax, are present, this possibility is unlikely: if the head is turned through 10–20 deg. to one side and fixed to the prothorax, the animal misses its prey to the opposite side. It thus behaves as if it did not notice its head deviation.

2. A copy of the input of the system controlling head orientation could be added to the optic output (Fig. 7.19*B*).

3. The optic output could be fed back negatively into the system controlling head orientation so that the head turns towards the prey. The final steady state of this optic loop would then determine the direction of the strike (Fig. 7.19*C*).

Since the mantid does, in fact, fixate its prey before striking, the last hypothesis appears the more likely. However, this cannot be the whole story, for unilateral deafferentation of the neck proprioceptors results in an error in striking to the opposite side: the proprioceptors must thus play some role. Such animals also show a permanent head deviation, and it is presumably this which leads to

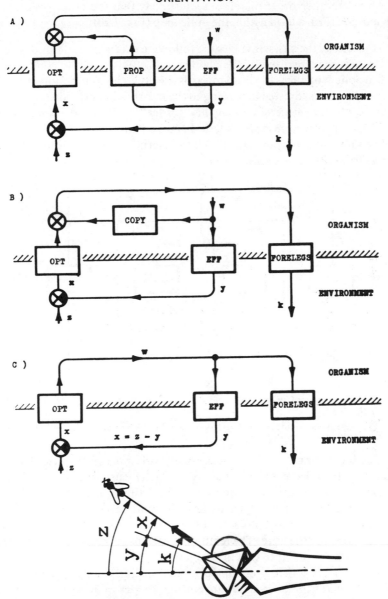

Fig. 7.19. Three basic solutions for the problem of prey localization. (*After Mittelstaedt, 1962.*)

OPT: sub-system which yields information about deviation *x* of the prey from the eye axis; PROP: sub-system which yields information about deviation *y* of head from body axis; EFF: sub-system which controls deviation *y* of head according to its input variable *w*, the "order"; COPY: sub-system which transmits a "copy" of the order *w* to the optic output; FORELEGS: sub-system which controls the deviation *k* of strike from the body axis; *z*: deviation of prey from body axis. *A* proprioceptive mesh, *B* copy-mesh, *C* loop with branch-off.

the contralateral error. It therefore seems likely that the proprioceptors and neck muscles form a loop within the optic loop (Fig. 7.20).

On this model the strike involves the following stages:
(a) The prey is recognized by the mantis.
(b) The optic loop turns the head towards the prey, the contraction of the neck muscles being adjusted according to the information provided by the optic loop. Movement ceases when this "order" is balanced by information from proprioceptors indicating the head's position.
(c) The same optic output is then used to determine the deviation of the fore-legs from the body's axis.

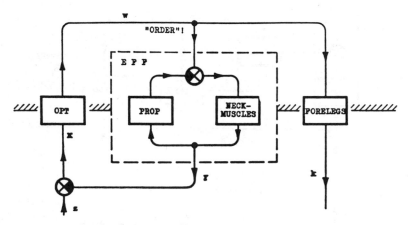

Fig. 7.20. Control pattern of prey localization in mantids. (*After Mittel-staedt, 1962.*)

The control pattern of EFF (*see* Fig. 7.19c) is a loop which turns the head into the posi-tion determined by the order w.

Basically similar mechanisms are probably widespread in insects: for instance Volkonsky (1939) has described the way in which locusts orient the side of their bodies towards a source of radiation. If an artificial source of radiation is provided, the locust first rotates its head in small jerks, thereby presumably stimulating neck proprioceptors: the orientation of the body is then changed to conform to that of the head. The relationships of head, neck and body effectors may thus well be similar to that in the mantid.

It is clear that the theory of control systems is likely to lead to an increased understanding of these oriented movements. By describing what the orienta-tion mechanism accomplishes, a control diagram indicates the complexity which it must have.

7.4. Bird Migration and Homing
Perhaps the most studied and puzzling cases of animal orientation are pro-vided by the long-distance flights undertaken by birds during migration, long-

range feeding expeditions, or homing. Bird orientation raises somewhat different issues from the work discussed earlier in this chapter, in part because the nature of the stimuli are not yet known, and in part because it involves more than merely maintaining a given direction. However, space permits only a brief survey here: recent reviews have been given by Matthews (1955), Kramer (1957, 1961), Adler (1963), Lindauer (1964) and others.

Any species in which the young birds migrate to winter quarters before the adults do must possess an ability to fly in a constant direction. This ability was

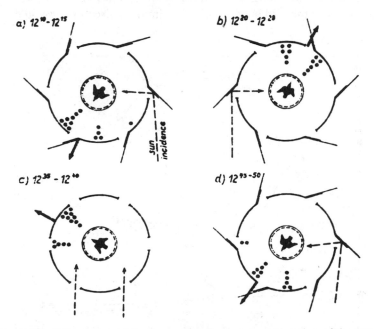

Fig. 7.21. Orientation of starlings when the apparent direction of the sun is changed by mirrors. (*After Kramer, 1952.*)

Records of an experiment consisting of four different parts. Broken lines show incidence of sunlight; dots average the bird's position in successive periods of 10 sec. each. (*a*) Mirror position "A". (*b*) Mirror position "B". (*c*) No mirrors. (*d*) Again position "A".

demonstrated, for instance, by Schüz (1949): White Storks (*Ciconia ciconia*) were taken from East Prussia to be reared and released after the local migration was complete in Western Germany. The recoveries indicated a strong tendency to fly SSE, which would be appropriate for the population from which they were drawn but not for the storks living in the area of the release.

The sensory clues which permit orientation of this type can be studied under aviary conditions. During the migration season aviary birds show intense activity ("Zugunruhe"), during which they tend to head in the same direction as they would if free to migrate. Under these conditions starlings remain oriented only so long as they can see the sky, and the sun is not obscured. If the apparent direction of the sun is changed by mirrors, the orientation of the birds changes accordingly (Fig. 7.21).

The direction of the sun, of course, changes with the time of day, but the migration direction does not. The bird must therefore be able to correct for the movement of the sun—it must have an internal "chronometer". This has been shown by experiment (Hoffmann, 1953). The chronometer depends on the light-dark cycle, and can be upset by providing an artificial cycle out of phase with the natural one. The exact method by which the sun is used, however, is still uncertain. If the bird merely uses the azimuthal direction, it would have to

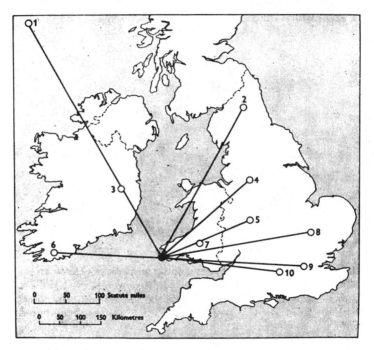

Fig. 7.22 (a). Points at which Manx Shearwaters from Skokholm Island were released. (*After Matthews, 1955.*)

make allowance for the varying rate at which this changes through the day. Alternatively it has been suggested, as part of a more detailed theory of navigation, that the bird extrapolates the sun's observed path to find the highest point: this is always due south in the northern hemisphere, and could serve as a fixed reference point (Matthews, e.g. 1955). The experimental data, however, indicate that starlings can orient using the azimuthal direction alone (Hoffmann, 1953). Of course, nocturnal migrants cannot obtain their direction by the sun, but they may use other celestial clues. Even this may not be the whole story, since it has been claimed that Robins in captivity can retain a preferred direction corresponding to the migratory direction with no optical reference points at all (Fromme, 1961): Perdeck (1963), however, was unable to repeat this result.

Birds are, however, capable of much more than flying a fixed course. Some of the evidence comes from the study of migrant birds displaced from their

Fig. 7.22 (b). Orientation of Manx Shearwaters at unknown points, in sunny conditions. (*After Matthews, 1955.*)

Results for thirteen experiments superimposed, from points 1, 2, 3, 5, 8 and 10 in Fig. 7.22 (*a*). The direction of home is indicated vertically on the diagram, and the length of each bar is proportional to the number of birds leaving in that direction.

normal starting point before release. We have already seen that young storks treated in this way migrate in the direction characteristic of the population from which they were drawn, and a similar result has been obtained with young starlings captured in Holland and released in Switzerland. However, adult starlings similarly displaced flew not in the direction they would have taken if undisturbed, but to the place where they had wintered previously: this involved a difference in direction of about 60 degrees (Perdeck, 1956). Thus birds can show real goal orientation, and this seems to depend on previous experience of the goal.

The same point is demonstrated by experiments on homing. It is now clear that homing pigeons can direct their flights towards the home loft when released in strange country. Although it has been suggested that some of these homing experiments can be explained in terms of random search, there are many cases in which this can be ruled out. In some, the speed of return was so rapid that random search could not have occurred, while in others the birds showed a significant orientation towards home within a very short period after release (Fig. 7.22 (a) and (b) from Matthews). Orientation towards home when released at an unknown point implies both that the bird is goal oriented, and that it can perform the equivalent of fixing its present position on a grid of two coordinates, calculating the course to steer to regain the coordinates characteristic of home, and steering it. This does not mean, of course, that the bird goes through the sequences of calculations necessary for a human navigator who uses, say, a wireless position line, a sextant observation on the sun, nautical almanac, chart, ruler, protractor, and so on. In fact our knowledge of how this is achieved is still so incomplete that we do not know what measurements the bird takes to fix its position on release. It is established that the bird does not respond to forces resulting from the earth's magnetic field, and it is unlikely that it responds to forces due to the earth's rotation. Observations of the sky seem to be important, since pigeons are disoriented when the sky is overcast, and they home less well if confined where they cannot see the horizon from the home loft than if the whole sky is visible (Kramer, 1959).

Matthews (e.g. 1955) suggested that diurnal birds could obtain the necessary information from observations of the sun's arc, provided they could "remember" the characteristics of the sun's arc at home. If, on the basis of observations over a limited period, the arc is extrapolated to the highest point, comparison of the altitude with that at the home will give a measure of the difference in latitude. The angle subtended by the arc joining the observed sun to the highest point would give a measure of longitude if compared with the angle occurring at the same time at home. Matthews's hypothesis has been criticized by Kramer (e.g. 1957) and Wallraff (1960), chiefly on the grounds that it is extremely improbable that the bird could make measurements of the accuracy which it demands, and that the initial orientation sometimes occurs before the sun can have moved any appreciable distance along its arc. Further, his hypothesis does not explain many of the results of homing experiments. For instance, for any one position of the loft, pigeons home with greater success when released from some directions than from others. Indeed, if orientation from many release points round one loft is assessed, the deviations from the homeward direction seem highly irregular. Homing ability also varies with the season of the year, the weather, and other environmental factors (Kramer, *loc. cit.*). Furthermore, as noted above, some authors have even claimed that orientation occurs in caged birds not permitted to see the sky (Fromme 1961).

Although doubt has been cast on whether celestial navigation occurs at all, Pennycuick (1960) has amended Matthews's scheme in such a way as to overcome some of its difficulties. He suggests that the bird measures the sun's altitude and rate of change of altitude. This, he claims, overcomes the major difficulties of the sun-arc hypothesis, since the accuracy of observation demanded is within the bird's capabilities. So far, however, crucial evidence is lacking. Also, Matthews (1961) has answered some of his critics, showing that some of the discrepancies between the results of different experiments may be due to a "nonsense" tendency to orient in a particular direction just after release.

The late Gustav Kramer (e.g. 1961), who either carried out or inspired many of the most crucial experiments on bird orientation, considered any hypothesis which entailed the use of the sun for pin-pointing extremely improbable. He supposed, instead, that the two steps of homing orientation are independent—the bird first determines its position relative to home by some unknown means, and then uses the sun as a compass to orient towards home. Evidence in partial support of this view has been provided by experiments in which the internal clock of pigeons was shifted by subjecting them to a dark–light rhythm advanced or retarded on the natural one. The change in orientation this produced was similar to that which would be predicted if the pigeons used the sun only as a compass for orienting their flight and determined their position by some other method (Schmidt-Koenig, 1961).

The problem is the more interesting because it has been shown that night migrants show similar navigational abilities when exposed only to the stars. Using the directional nature of migratory restlessness, Sauer (1957) showed that various species of warblers, tested during the autumn migration season, oriented in the same way as they would if on migration when they could see only the central part of the starry sky. The birds became disoriented when the stars were hidden by cloud, or when they were exposed only to diffuse light. In other series of experiments the birds were exposed not to the night sky but to the dome of a planetarium: when the planetarium display was similar to the local night sky, the birds took up the appropriate migration direction.

For some species of birds, migration direction is known to change along the migration route. The Lesser Whitethroat first flies south-east from Germany to the Balkans, and then turns southwards. Sauer claimed that he was able to reproduce this change in direction by changing the display in the planetarium: when a pattern similar to the local night sky was shown, the bird headed south-east, but when the display was appropriate to a more southerly latitude, it headed closer to the south. It thus seemed to be able to assess its latitude from the stars and adjust its course accordingly.

In other experiments with the same bird the display was changed to resemble a longitude shift. When the planetarium was adjusted to indicate a shift of 5 hours and ten minutes or 77°E, the bird was at first disturbed, and then oriented towards the proper starting point for migration in Germany. Longitude shifts in the opposite direction, however, did not produce correct orientation.

Later Sauer (1963) studied the migratory restlessness of ten hand-reared Golden Plovers (*Pluvialis dominica*) and found that they could navigate by day or night provided they could see the sun or stars. They could also compensate appropriately for geographical displacements.

The number of birds tested in Sauer's planetarium experiments was not great, and the interpretation of the results has been criticized (e.g. Wallraff, 1960), but the results do suggest that some night migrants can navigate using a a grid of two celestial coordinates. The precise nature of these coordinates remains to be analysed. It must be emphasized that navigation by the stars is intrinsically a simpler problem than navigation by a single celestial body such as the sun.

Although most studies of homing ability have used birds as subjects, comparable phenomena are found in other species. Studies of homing in mice, which include references to earlier mammalian work, are given by Lindenlaub (1955, 1960) and Bovet (1960, 1962). Compass orientation in lizards has been analysed by Fischer (1961), and homing in toads has been studied by Heusser (1958).

7.5. Summary

1. The first step in the analysis of an orientation response is the identification of the stimulus parameters with respect to which the orientation occurs.
2. The means by which animals adjust their position with respect to sources of stimulation can be divided into kineses and taxes. In the former the body is not oriented, the stimulus producing merely a change in speed of locomotion or frequency of turning. Taxes involve orientation of the body: various types have been distinguished by Kühn, and Fraenkel and Gunn.
3. The functioning of the mechanisms underlying oriented movements can profitably be described in terms of control system diagrams.
4. Bird homing and migration presents an especially complex series of problems since the orienting stimuli have not yet been identified, and they often involve navigation as opposed to mere orientation.

8

Changes in Responsiveness to a Constant Stimulus—The Drive Concept

A given stimulus does not always evoke the same response. If the external situation is constant, altered responsiveness of an animal must be ascribed to changes in its internal state. This and the following chapters are concerned with the nature of these changes.

In practice, changes in responsiveness are revealed in a number of ways. First, there are changes in the response given when a particular stimulus is presented on separate occasions. During the spring and early summer a caged male Chaffinch responds to a stuffed female mounted in the soliciting posture (Fig. 3.1, p. 18) with vigorous courtship behaviour, and often also with mounting and ejaculation. The same dummy elicits, at most, a weak response from a male in winter, or from a male who has just ejaculated. The internal states of the males in the last two cases must differ from that of a male in spring who has not recently been exposed to such a model. Second, there are changes in the frequency or intensity with which a response is given under constant external conditions: a Great Tit does not produce its song at regular intervals, but in a complicated pattern of bursts of singing which cannot be related to changes in the environment, and are, therefore, presumably a consequence of internal changes. Third, the strength of the stimulus necessary to elicit a response of standard intensity varies with time: the longer the period of food deprivation, the more unappetizing the food an animal will accept. Fourth, and related to the others, at different times an animal selects different categories of stimuli to respond to: sometimes those indicative of food, at others a nest site, or a mate, and so on. Finally, the strength of an aversive stimulus which an animal will withstand, or of an obstacle which it will surmount, varies with time: the longer a rat has been without food (within limits), the more highly charged the electric grid which it will cross in order to obtain food.

The nature of the internal changes on which such changes in responsiveness depend is usually considered as part of the problem of "motivation"; other aspects of this problem, such as the integration of separate responses into functional sequences and the directiveness of behaviour, will be considered later in Chapter 18. Here we shall be concerned only with such questions as "Why does the animal respond more strongly to this stimulus at some times than at others?"; "Why does it respond sometimes to this stimulus, sometimes to that?"; "What determines the beginning and end of each type of activity?"; "Why is the animal active at all?"

Conventionally, changes in behaviour ascribed to motivational factors are temporary and reversible, and thus distinguishable from the more permanent changes involved in learning. In practice both temporary and long-term effects may be a consequence of the same behavioural events: if a male Chaffinch mates successfully with a female dummy, his responsiveness is temporarily lowered, but there will also be a long-lasting increased responsiveness to such dummies. There is, in fact, no universal agreement as to what changes in behaviour should properly be described under the rubric of motivation, and no definition will be attempted here. In general, we shall include changes in response strength or responsiveness which are reversible but last longer than a second or two. It is convenient, however, to exclude changes which can readily be related to peripheral changes in the sense organs (accommodation, adaptation, etc.) and some changes in perception (Chapter 5) or effectors (e.g. muscular fatigue). In addition, discussion of near-permanent changes, whether they are the result of "maturation", "learning" or anything else, is postponed (*see* Section 3). Even with these exclusions, there is no implication that the remaining changes in behaviour, thus grouped as due to "motivational factors", are to be ascribed to a single type of mechanism. Our practice, rather, will be to start with a group of phenomena characterized empirically as involving changes in responsiveness to a constant stimulus (with the restrictions specified above), label them loosely "motivational", and then to attempt to analyse the processes responsible.

8.1. The Drive Concept

Changes in responsiveness to a constant external stimulus indicate the occurrence of temporary states internal to the animal which determine the responsiveness. Common speech uses such words as hunger, thirst or sexual urge to refer to these internal states. Provided certain precautions are taken, such "drive" concepts can be taken over as valuable analytical tools in many branches of experimental psychology, psychiatry and psychopathology, and they will be used in a number of contexts in this book. This does not mean, however, that they are universally valuable, and it is necessary to define the limits of their usefulness.

In the first place, drive concepts can be useful only if defined independently of the variations in behaviour they are supposed to explain. If they are postulated in numbers equal to those of the types of behaviour in question, they become *ad hoc* assumptions and lose any explanatory value. A child who is told that a train goes because of the "locomotive force" is left somewhat more puzzled than before, for the argument is circular (Lorenz, 1950). But if we observe that a rat, presented with water, drinks more if it has previously been deprived of water than if it has not, there are circumstances in which it is useful to postulate a "thirst drive". This "drive" will then be related, on the one hand to the period of water deprivation, and on the other to the amount of water the animal drinks when presented with water. In such cases the period of deprivation is often termed an "independent variable", being not affected by the behaviour observed; in this case, the amount of water drunk. The latter is termed a "dependent variable", and the postulated thirst drive an "intervening variable" (Tolman, 1932).

At this point, the use of a drive concept may not seem a very economical procedure, for it requires the establishment of two relationships (one between hours deprivation and "drive", and another between "drive" and amount of

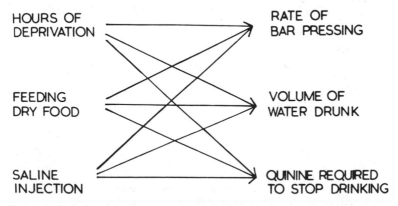

Fig. 8.1. Relationships between three independent and three dependent variables. (*After Miller, 1959.*)

water drunk) when we may be interested only in one (that between deprivation and amount drunk). Furthermore, in such a case there is no possibility of proving that one intervening variable cannot account completely for the data. Usually, however, we are interested in more than one independent variable and more than one dependent variable. To quote an example used by Miller (1959), an animal can be made "thirsty" by depriving it of water, by giving it dry food, or by injecting it with hypertonic saline. We can assess the consequences of these treatments by measuring the volume of water it drinks in a given time, by recording the rate at which it will perform a learnt response which is rewarded by water, or by assessing the concentration of quinine which it will tolerate in its drinking water. If we were to examine the relationship of each type of treatment to each method of measurement, there would be nine relationships to be established (Fig. 8.1). Alternatively, if we could suppose that each type of treatment influences an intervening variable "thirst", which in turn influences each of the response measures, it would be necessary to establish only six relationships (Fig. 8.2). The postulation of the intervening thirst variable has thus led to considerable economy (Miller, 1959).

However, such a procedure can be useful only to the extent that there is a good correlation between the various measures involved: that is, if one type of treatment is more effective than another as assessed by one type of measurement, it must also be so when assessed by another. Thus, where the fact that the various possible measures are correlated is of primary interest, an intervening "drive" variable is a valuable tool for research: where the extent to which the correlations are not perfect becomes important, then such a concept is misleading and can be a positive hindrance.

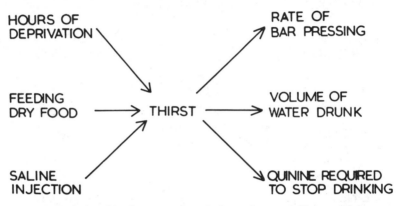

Fig. 8.2. Relationships between three independent variables, one intervening variable and three dependent variables. (*After Miller, 1959.*)

In practice, the extent to which the different measures are correlated varies with the measures chosen and the fineness of the analysis. Some data relating to the present instance are shown in Fig. 8.3 (Choy, cited by Miller, 1956). Rats were given 5 ml. of 2 molar saline by stomach tube, and the resultant "thirst" assessed in terms of the amount of water drunk in 15 minutes, the number of bar presses reinforced with water on a variable interval schedule given in 9 minutes, and the concentration of quinine in water that they would tolerate. As the figure shows, the three measures give rather different pictures: bar-pressing, unlike the other measures, showed little change 15 minutes after treatment; while only the amount of water drunk reached an asymptote after 3 hours. In view of this lack of agreement between measures, we must conclude that the postulation of a single intervening variable is too simple an hypothesis to account for all the changes in behaviour observed. As another example, Teitelbaum (1957) found that rats with certain hypothalamic lesions, although hyperphagic, showed less lever-pressing activity reinforced with food than non-operated animals.

However, this is not all. There are *in theory* an infinite number of ways in which even the amount of water drunk could be measured. We could assess the amount drunk in 1 second, 1 minute, 1 hour or any other period. According to which we choose we may get very different results. In fact, while a rat is actively engaged in drinking, the rate at which it drinks is very constant—6 to 7 tongue laps or 0·03 ml. of water per second. When thirsty rats are given water, they drink steadily at this rate for a few minutes, and then in short bursts over the ensuing

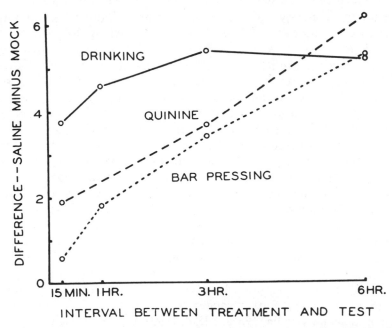

Fig. 8.3. Three methods of assessing the "thirst" of rats given 5 ml. of 2 molar saline by stomach tube. The ordinate indicates the amount by which the experimental test exceeded the control test, the nature of the units differing between the procedures used. (*After Miller, 1956.*)

period. For periods of deprivation of between 48 and 168 hours the initial period of continuous drinking is virtually constant (about 8 minutes), though subsequently the animals which have been deprived longer drink more frequently (Stellar *et al.*, 1952). Thus, if we were to assess the amount of water drunk in a period shorter than 8 minutes, we might conclude that periods of deprivation between 48 and 168 hours were all the same to the rat, though a longer period of drinking would reveal that they were not. Furthermore, our thirst variable would help us not at all in understanding the detailed course of drinking behaviour—for instance, the alternation of bouts of drinking with bouts of sniffing etc.—unless we postulate a series of additional intervening variables: at this stage use of a drive concept tempts us to over-simplify (*see also* Hilgard *et al.*, 1961).

In the case we have been considering, the concept of a "thirst drive" is useful in so far as it can be related to antecedent conditions and subsequent behaviour, and in so far as the alternative behavioural measures are correlated with each other. However, a relation with antecedent conditions is not an essential condition for a drive concept to be useful. Sometimes it is convenient to use one to relate the behaviour under study to measurements of other aspects of the animal's organic state, such as hormone concentration or skin resistance, or to other types of behaviour it shows. Hormone concentration, like water deprivation, might be regarded as antecedent to the drive, but skin resistance or behaviour shown in other situations may be dependent variables and may vary with the internal state in a similar manner to the behaviour in which we are interested. Even the hormone concentration might be assessed by means of another dependent variable, such as the size of a cock's comb. If we are concerned with the behaviour of the whole animal the direction of the causal relations is thus often immaterial: drive can be anchored by non-directional mathematical relationships to two sets of data, both of which refer to consequent events. This situation is especially liable to arise in the early stages of the study of a new species. If the animal shows a bizarre movement whose significance is unknown, the first clues may come from its temporal association with other movements. A temporal correlation between movements indicates that they are somehow causally linked, and one possible preliminary hypothesis is that they share causal factors ("or a drive")—an hypothesis which subsequent evidence may confirm, deny, or elaborate. The more sophisticated use of this approach is discussed in Chapter 16.

Even within the reservations discussed so far, however, the use of drive concepts carries with it further dangers which can be avoided only through constant vigilance (Hinde, 1956a, 1959d, 1960), and it is necessary to discuss them briefly.

For one thing, the word itself can make difficulties because it has been used by so many different authors in so many different ways. "Drives" may refer to stimuli or responses, physiological or psychological states, extraneural or intraneural states, mathematical intervening variables, or to combinations of these. They may be "biogenic", in which changes in behaviour are related directly to changes in the internal state of the animal, or psychogenic, in which they are not.* Such a diversity of meanings is of course quite justifiable provided the author keeps within the limits of his own concept, but it does impose a strain on the reader.

Even within one usage, however, there is a tendency to use "drive" as a

---

* Further discussion of these usages will be found in the Nebraska Symposia on Motivation (1953 et seq.); Hilgard (1948); Peters (1958); Estes *et al.* (1954), etc.

blanket variable—drive concepts are used to provide unitary explanations of a variety of characteristics of behaviour which may depend, in fact, on diverse mechanisms. For instance:

(a) The temporal persistence of the effects of stimuli and of activities. Stimuli may be ineffective when first presented, and influence behaviour only after repeated presentation. It thus appears that their effects are stored. Further, once evoked, a given pattern of behaviour may persist for some time after the stimulus is removed. Such observations are sometimes ascribed to "persistence of the drive".

(b) Temporal grouping of activities. The various patterns of behaviour in an animal's repertoire do not appear at random, but in functional groups. This could be due simply to its being a chain sequence, where each activity brings the animal into the stimulus situation which elicits the next (see p. 295). Another possibility is that the grouping is due to a sharing of internal causal factors which persist over time. In the latter case they may be spoken of as having a common "drive".

(c) Directiveness. The statement that behaviour is "directive" may imply either that it continues until a certain goal stimulus situation is achieved, or that variable means (i.e. more than one type of behaviour, characterized objectively) are used to a constant end. Some authors describe such behaviour as being associated with "motives" and not merely with drives (e.g. Peters, 1958): here the terms "drive" and "motivation" are used interchangeably.

A unitary concept of drive can be taken to imply that these diverse characteristics of behaviour depend on the same features of the underlying mechanism. There is no *a priori* reason why this should be so, and some reasons for thinking to the contrary will be given later.

In addition, there are theorists whose concern it is to assess the usefulness of the hypothesis that "drive reduction" is essential for learning to occur (e.g. Brown J. S., 1961; Miller, 1961a, b). This approach can lead to the postulation of drives to explain learning; for instance a "manipulation drive" when it is found that monkeys learn to manipulate mechanical puzzles (Harlow *et al.*, 1950). But at this point there is a danger of circular argument. "Drive" can, of course, be defined as that which is reduced when learning occurs, but if the drive concept is to be used to explain changes in responsiveness to a constant stimulus, then the question of whether or not learning is necessarily accompanied by drive reduction is an empirical one (see pp. 414-8).

Another difficulty that arises when drive concepts are used in the interpretation of the temporal patterning of behaviour concerns the units of behaviour to which they should be applied. For instance, the nest-building activities of canaries can be analysed into gathering material, carrying it to the nest, and sitting (building) in the nest. These activities are all limited to one season of the year, all show related short-term fluctuations, and are all inhibited by stimuli from the nest. We could thus usefully argue that all are governed by a nest-building drive. But the correlation between them is not absolute, and to account for the pattern of changeover from one activity to the next it is necessary to postulate that each is accompanied by a self-suppressing effect (Hinde, 1958a). This latter could perhaps be taken care of by postulating additional variables which modify the relationship between the nest-building drive and each of these activities. But each of them is itself complex, consisting of component activities which fluctuate more or less together. Are we then to postulate separate gathering, carrying and sitting drives? If so, where is the process to stop? At this point the concept of a nest-building drive ceases to be useful (cf. Wiesner *et al.*, 1933).

Another aspect of the drive problem that must be mentioned concerns again the temptation to over-simplify when drive concepts are involved. In many theoretical systems it is implied that the independent variables—hormone dosage, hours of food deprivation, external stimuli, or whatever—affect behaviour either in only one way, by influencing drive, or in two ways, by their consequences on drive and their role as stimuli in influencing the nature of the behaviour which the animal shows. In practice, such variables affect the organism in diverse ways, and their influence on behaviour is far from simple. Some examples of this will be discussed later (Chapter 10).

Finally, since drive concepts are used to explain activity, drives are often spoken of as though they activated behaviour in the same manner as physical energy can activate a physical system. Indeed in some theoretical systems, such as those of Freud (1915), McDougall (1923), Lorenz (1950) and Tinbergen (1951), some of the properties of physical energy have been imputed to drive concepts, so that drives are referred to as being "stored" or "expended", as "flowing away" or "sparking over". An element of this sort of confusion has also been present in the work of some learning theorists who invoke drive concepts to explain the elicitation of vigorous responses to weak stimuli, assuming that the force with which a rat pushes a bar is correlated with the strength of the drive. This confusion between drives as postulated to explain changes in responsiveness and drives as forms of physical energy has led to serious confusion (*see* discussion by Carthy, 1951; Kennedy, 1954; Hinde, 1956a, 1960).

More serious still, however, is the temptation to look for the activating or energizing drive inside the organism. However willing the drive theorist may be to rally physiological data to his aid, to look inside the nervous system for drives, defined in terms of behaviour, is a logical mistake; and discussion about where drives originate is based on a misconception. Although the drive theorist will not find any drives inside the organism, he will find physiological correlates. He may find, for instance, that changes in the frequency of copulation per day is correlated with androgen levels, and hope to find that minute-to-minute fluctuations in sexual behaviour are correlated with other physiological changes. But as the analysis proceeds he will inevitably find that he is not talking about drives any more: the drive, so useful at an earlier stage, has just ceased to be relevant.

Having thus emphasized the difficulties and dangers into which drive concepts can lead us, it may seem that their usefulness is limited. This, however, is true of all explanatory concepts, and in this case the limits are wide. We shall use drive concepts in some of the following chapters, and find that they have a valuable role in permitting the formulation of unifying principles which cover a variety of observations and experiments. Such principles, however, relate to a particular level of analysis, and it will be profitable for the moment to proceed to a finer level to consider the manner in which variables under the control of the investigator influence changes in responsiveness to a constant stimulus.

8.2. Summary

1. There are no clear criteria for distinguishing changes in behaviour which are to be ascribed to motivational factors from those which are not. There must be no implication that those which are so labelled are due to a single type of mechanism.
2. Drive concepts are most likely to be useful when they lead to an economy in the number of relationships between independent and dependent variables which must be specified. They can be valuable when a positive correlation between the possible dependent variables is of primary interest, but are misleading when the extent to which such correlations are not perfect becomes important.
3. Drive concepts can be useful for relating dependent variables, with no reference to antecedent conditions.
4. Drive concepts can be dangerous if used to explain diverse characteristics of behaviour which could result from quite different aspects of the underlying mechanisms; if they lead to over-simple implications about the manner in which independent variables affect behaviour; or if linked with energy models.
5. As physiological analysis proceeds, drive constructs cease to be relevant.

9

General and Specific Aspects of "Drive"

We are accustomed to think that each activity of an animal is governed by a number of factors (independent variables) which are more or less specific to that activity. For instance, in most vertebrates male sexual behaviour varies with the concentration of testicular hormones, the presence of certain external stimuli, and so on. Feeding behaviour varies with the period since the animal last ate, and with certain consequent internal changes, and again with the external stimuli present, but only varies to a relatively limited extent with sex hormone concentration. It is thus possible to identify for each type of behaviour a number of factors with which its occurrence is more or less closely correlated.

This cannot be the whole story, however, for a very hungry animal will not copulate—the period of food deprivation also has some effect on sexual behaviour. A variable normally considered relevant to one type of behaviour thus has an effect on the occurrence of another. In this case the effect is negative, and it can be described easily enough in terms of priorities and inhibiting effects: in the food-deprived animal food-searching behaviour is prepotent and sexual behaviour suppressed (*see* Chapter 17). It is also possible, however, that an activity can be influenced positively by a factor not normally considered relevant to it: thus certain carnivores (Beach, 1947), gulls (Armstrong, 1950) and monkeys (personal observation) are especially likely to show sexual behaviour after a mild disturbance; and painful stimulation, such as that arising from an electric shock to the foot, elicits fighting in a number of mammalian species (Ulrich *et al.*, 1964). Indeed there are factors which influence all the types of behaviour in an animal's repertoire: to cite an extreme example, cockroaches become torpid if the environmental temperature falls below a certain limit. The variables which influence behaviour may thus have either specific effects on a limited group of behaviour patterns or more general effects on more or less the whole repertoire of the organism, or both.

The same problem appears in the ways in which drive concepts have been used. One way we have already discussed by reference to the example of thirst —"drive" is used as an intervening variable or postulated internal state which is linked, on the one hand, to particular preceding circumstances or treatments and, on the other, to a limited number of types of behaviour. On this view it is necessary, in order to account for all the behaviour of an organism, to specify a number of drives: one related to, say, drinking behaviour, another to feeding, another to fear, another to sex, and so on. The relative strengths of the various drives are thought of as playing a primary (though not, of course, exclusive) role in determining both what the organism does and the intensity with which it does it.

Many writers, on the other hand, use a concept of "general drive" which is related only to the intensity* of the behaviour shown. On this view the sort of behaviour which appears depends on the stimulation impinging on the animal, and on its previous experience in the situation. Thus, while only part of the sensory stimulation has an influence in determining what sort of behaviour the animal shows, all "motivational variables"† and stimuli operating are supposed to contribute to the general drive and influence its intensity. In Hull's (1943, 1952) formulation, which was the most comprehensive theory of this kind, the intensity with which any behaviour is shown depends on a multiplicative relationship between the "habit strength" appropriate to it and the general drive, the latter depending, in turn, on all stimuli and motivational variables impinging on the organism at the time (*see also* Spence, 1956).

Brown (1961), one of the more vigorous recent proponents of the general drive view, takes his stand in the first place on a theoretical issue. He rejects drive concepts which function in determining both the nature and intensity of activity primarily because the former function is "traditionally reserved for cognitions or associative tendencies", and argues that, "If both drive and habit are to be included in our theories, then the two should affect behaviour in different ways; otherwise only one construct seems to be required". He then argues that if "drive" is to function only as an activator, it cannot be directed towards any one specific goal or selectively activate one type of associative tendency, since this would involve also a directive function: drive must, therefore, be general.

As an example of the opposite view, Tinbergen (1952) appeals to common

---

* The term intensity is intentionally used loosely in this book. Usually it refers to the amplitude or frequency of a movement, but it is also applied to patterns of behaviour which do not involve movement; for instance incubation can be said to be more or less intense, one criterion being the strength of the extraneous stimulus required to interrupt it. In general, it can be said that nearly all statements about intensity can refer to a probability measure of the response in question. They thus usually carry some implication about the causal factors for the behaviour in question, and their relation to those for other patterns which are acting at the time, as assessed from observed behaviour. For this reason one type of behaviour is sometimes said to be more intense than another when there is evidence that the two share causal factors but the absolute level required by the former is greater.

† The term "motivational variables" is used for independent variables believed to be associated with relatively long-lasting changes in the internal state (*see* p. 193) such as hours of food deprivation, sex hormone concentration, stimuli previously associated with shock, etc.

sense. He points out that each activity has particular factors associated with it, and doubts that "excitement" could ever be "really general".

At first sight the problem should be simple enough to settle empirically. Does change in a motivational variable influence the intensity of one type of behaviour, or all? Unfortunately, the issue is not so clear cut as the use of drive concepts would imply. An animal can do only a limited number of things at a time, and so a supposedly non-specific effect could only be proven by observations of specific activities each in a situation appropriate to it. In any case it is impracticable to observe all possible activities to prove non-specificity. Although this may seem an academic point, it is rare that proponents of a general drive theory have observed even two different activities in the same experiment (*see below*). In any case changes in motivational factors do not produce a simple effect, either specific or general, but have multiple and ramifying consequences in the systems controlling behaviour. A distinction between specific and non-specific effects of a stimulus change is therefore often difficult to draw; and the question is more profitably phrased in terms of how specific or how general the effects of each factor may be. It is, however, worth while to consider some examples of the various types of evidence used to support the view that motivational factors may have a non-specific effect.

9.1. Interrelations between Hunger, Thirst, Fear and Sex

Some anecdotal observations on the influence of mild disturbance on sexual behaviour have already been mentioned. Similar phenomena are well known to naturalists, and have been quoted especially in the literature on displacement activities: this will be discussed further in Chapter 17. Here we are concerned with laboratory studies which appear to show the action of one external factor, "need state" or "drive", on behaviour normally dependent on another. In each case in which an effect has been demonstrated, we must ask whether the evidence supports the view that the effect of the independent variable is in fact likely to be general, or limited to only a few activities.

1. *Hunger on Thirst or Vice Versa*. Miller (1948a) trained rats to run down an alley for water, and then tested them when they were not thirsty. They ran faster and drank more if they were hungry when tested than if they were not (*see also* Webb, 1949). As Miller points out, however, hunger and thirst are closely related: both are influenced by peripheral stimuli from mouth, throat and stomach, and some of these may be common to both states. The influence of the one on the other could thus be a consequence either of peripheral changes (Verplanck *et al.*, 1953; *see also* Warden, 1931), or of specific central interactions (e.g. McFarland, 1963).

The relationships between hunger and thirst have also been studied in another sort of experiment aimed at evaluating the concept of a general drive. If a given set of conditions influence a general drive state, then differences between animals under these conditions will be due, in part, to individual differences in the relationships between deprivation conditions and drive. If the concept of a general drive state is to be useful, these individual differences should be valid for all types of deprivation. In fact, when rats are tested under various conditions of food and water deprivation, the individual differences have little generality across deprivation conditions (Anderson, 1938; Bolles, 1959).

2. *Fear or Anxiety on Hunger and Thirst.* Although mild disturbance or shock usually disrupts the current behaviour, a number of studies have shown that electric shock will increase the response of rats to food or water, provided it is administered in a situation different from that in which they are tested (Miller, 1959; Siegel *et al.*, 1949; Amsel *et al.*, 1950; Siegel *et al.*, 1951; Muenzinger *et al.*, 1952). In some of these studies the dependent variable was the amount of food or water ingested, in others the speed of running in a situation in which the animal had previously been reinforced. The direction of the effect, however, does depend closely on the conditions: if the shock is administered in the test situation it may lead to a reduction in the amount ingested (Amsel, 1950).

A careful study by Tugendhat (1960a, b) of the influence of electric shock on the feeding behaviour of Three-spined Sticklebacks is of special interest here. This author did not confine her attention to one measure of behaviour, and recorded the behaviour of the fish in both the "home area" and the "food area" of the tank. These were partially separated by a partition, and the fish were shocked only in the latter. After electric shock the behaviour while feeding was that normally characteristic of more severe deprivation—the number of completed feeding responses per time spent feeding was increased. But shock also decreased the amount of time spent feeding. Over the whole test, therefore, shock might produce either an increase or a decrease in the total number of prey animals eaten, the latter being more likely with high shock intensity.

Although these experiments are certainly compatible with a general drive hypothesis, other explanations are possible. For instance, fear-producing stimuli are likely to produce peripheral effects, mediated by the autonomic system. Some of these, like dryness of the throat in land animals, could affect ingestion. The hypothesis that pain or fear affects feeding and drinking through these peripheral changes, though perhaps not likely, cannot be ruled out.

In other cases, reinforcement may have played a role. For instance, Sterritt (1962), whose study is in some respects comparable to that of Tugendhat, studied how electric shock influenced the feeding of pigeons. The shock was administered for 5 seconds in each minute, and was not under the bird's control. The birds ate more when the shock was on than was eaten by unshocked controls during a comparable period. However, when the shock was off the experimental birds ate less than the controls, and consumed less *in toto*. The increased eating during the period of shock was interpreted as "superstitious" learning (Skinner, 1948): eating was reinforced because it was followed by shock reduction (*see also* Fowler, 1963).

3. *Hunger or Thirst on Avoidance Responses.* Rats run faster to escape from pain or fear when moderately hungry or thirsty than when satiated. Even the amplitude of the unconditioned startle responses given to a loud noise is greater in rats motivated by both hunger and conditioned fear, than if motivated by either separately. Furthermore, rats which are hungry show greater startle responses than recently satiated animals (Fig. 9.1, Meryman, quoted by Brown, 1961).

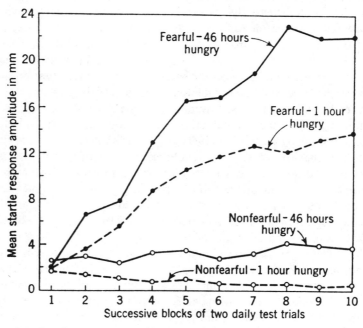

Fig. 9.1. Startle-response amplitude as a function of fear, no fear, intense hunger, weak hunger, and their combinations. Startle responses to a pistol shot were tested in four groups, two of the groups being rendered fearful by being given an electric shock in the test situation once a day. (*After Brown, 1961.*)

Such results are more difficult to interpret in terms of specific peripheral effects than are the experiments showing an effect of fear or anxiety-inducing stimuli on feeding or drinking, though it remains possible that peripheral conditions (e.g. in the throat) common to hunger or thirst and anxiety could act as conditioned stimuli for the latter.

4. *Fear or Anxiety on Sexual Behaviour.* In addition to anecdotal observations, a number of experimental studies have demonstrated a positive effect of fear or anxiety-producing stimuli on sexual behaviour. Beach *et al.* (1955) found that the administration of electro-convulsive shock to male rats decreased the rapidity with which sexual arousal occurred; for instance there

were longer delays before mating started, and a slower recovery from ejaculation. At the same time, however, there was an increase in reactivity to the stimuli derived from coitus—a greater rate of intromission, a decrease in the number of intromissions before each ejaculation, and a higher number of ejaculations per test. After considering various possible explanations, they considered an effect of the shock treatment on the functioning of the autonomic system, with consequent repercussions on sexual behaviour, as the most likely. In a later paper Beach and Fowler (1959b) found that anxiety engendered by previous experience of being shocked in the situation reduces the amount or duration of sexual stimulation necessary to produce ejaculation in male rats. A similar effect is produced if mild (but not strong) shock is given each time the male mounts the female.

Larsson (1963), also studying copulatory behaviour in rats, found that two 1-minute periods of handling by the experimenter during a copulatory sequence resulted in an increase in sexual activity and a reduction in the number of intromissions before the first ejaculation in older males, but not in younger ones. He suggests that the absence of an effect in the younger animals was due to their sexual behaviour being near the maximum already. Larsson also refers to earlier studies showing that the sexual activities of old males is greater in the active part of the light/dark cycle, and also while copulating in a group (*see also* Larsson, 1956).

It may also be noted that Jarmon *et al.* (1961) did not find that food deprivation led to an elevation of sexual behaviour in guinea-pigs with the scoring system that they used.

5. *Sexual Factors on Feeding and Drinking Behaviour.* Rats trained to run a maze when hungry or thirsty subsequently run faster when tested during oestrous than at other times (Felsinger, quoted by Miller, 1959). Such a finding must be considered with reference to many other studies showing variations in running wheel activity and other types of behaviour with the oestrous cycle. These indicate that the oestrous cycle is accompanied by profound physiological and behavioural changes which go beyond the alterations in sexual receptivity. Although a correlation between running speed to food and sexual receptivity could be interpreted as due to an influence of sex hormones on a "general drive", it would still be necessary to specify the generality of the effect.

In Hull's conception, all need states and stimuli were thought of as contributing towards a general drive, which then influenced all behaviour. In principle, no one of the studies just quoted can give conclusive support for this hypothesis, because the effects on at most two types of behaviour were assessed in each case. Nevertheless, the evidence that need states or stimuli relevant to one type of behaviour can augment another is considerable. Whether such effects are best considered in terms of a concept of general drive is another matter. Some alternative possibilities—peripheral mediators, major changes in endocrine balance, reinforcement and so on—have been mentioned already. The possible role of the reticular system will be considered later.

Miller (e.g. 1959) has explored yet another possible theoretical explanation. Whereas Hull supposed that the various motivational variables had completely generalized effects, Miller suggested that drives have some of the same properties as strong stimuli, drive generalization occurring as a special case of stimulus generalization. Thus finding that rats, trained in a runway when hungry but tested when satiated, would run faster if given an electric shock just beforehand, Miller suggested that the habit learnt when hunger "stimuli" were present generalized to pain. Since the internal states are so different in the two cases, Miller suggested that the generalization might be based on similar states of muscular tension occurring in the two conditions. As Miller himself points out, no definitive experiments which could decide between his hypothesis and Hull's have yet been done.

It would seem, then, that studies of the interrelations between different activities provide a certain amount of evidence which could be interpreted in terms of a general drive hypothesis, but the case is far from proven: alternative explanations of the experimental data are possible.

9.2. Aspects of the General Sensory Input—"Level of Activation"

A second type of evidence concerning general effects of independent variables comes from studies in which responsiveness to a variety of stimuli, or performance in a skilled task, has been shown to vary with the general level of sensory input falling on the receptors. Such effects have been suspected for a long time in insects, where the ocelli (simple eyes) often seem not to mediate specific responses, but to accentuate responses to light stimuli received through the compound eyes. Their precise function, however, is far from clear (Dethier, 1963).

Similar effects occur in vertebrates, one of the earlier detailed studies being due to Birukow (1951). If a frog is placed on a table which is tipped rhythmically once every 5 seconds, the animal makes compensatory movements which tend to maintain its orientation in space. These compensatory movements continue for long periods with no decrement. The response is mediated primarily through the semicircular canals: in an optically homogenous field, or in darkness, the responses are weaker, but still show no decrement. However, if the optic nerve is severed, the response does slowly wane. Apparently the input from the retina, even under conditions of darkness, enables the responsiveness to increase again to its previous level between successive tilts of the platform, whereas in the absence of this input it cannot. A similar effect is produced by deafferentation of other parts of the body; for instance, severance of dorsal roots 8–10. Proprioceptors and other enteroceptors work in the same way as the eyes in maintaining the "tone" of the neuromotor apparatus.

This study of Birukow's deals with the influence of diverse sensory input in maintaining a response. A greater bulk of work has been concerned with the effects of stimulating one sensory modality on the sensitivity of another. The effects are, however, complex and may involve either an increase or a decrease in sensitivity, many examples being given in London's (1954) review of Russian work: thus no generalization claiming that stimulation through one modality either increases or decreases the sensitivity of others can have general validity. Furthermore, it has been shown that sensitivity thresholds vary not only with stimulation through other sensory modalities, but also with various other aspects of the state of the body. Thus, skin sensitivity varies with the menstrual cycle in women (Herren, 1933), and can be increased by exogenous hormones in canaries (Hinde and Steel, 1964; *see also* p. 169).

Neurophysiological evidence for these effects has also been obtained: stimulation of one sensory system may lead to a change in the electrical response evoked by stimulation normally considered appropriate to another part of the central nervous system (*see* p. 95). For instance, Gerard *et al.* (1936), working with cats, found that the potentials evoked in the brain-stem by the tick of a watch were larger when the eyes were simultaneously exposed to light than when the animal was in darkness. By recording from single cells Horn (1963) has shown that the activity of the cells in the visual cortex of the cat can be affected by stimulation of the skin as well as by retinal illumination. In this case some of the cortical cells responded in the same direction to the two types of stimulation, while others responded in opposite directions: the effect is thus neither simple nor general.

The level of the total stimulation to which an organism is exposed may influence not only its sensitivity to external stimulation, but also a number of other physiological variables—muscular tension, skin resistance, the pattern of electrical activity in the brain, the heart rate, and so on. These measures show some correlation with activity of almost any sort, and with some degree of consistency change in one direction with increased stimulation of the organism, and in the opposite with decreased stimulation. In human subjects they are related not only to stimulation in the ordinary sense of the term, but also to changes in motivating conditions, to activity or readiness for activity, problem solving, and so on (Duffy, 1962).

Such findings have led to the suggestion that the non-specific effects of external stimulation, motivational factors, or self-engendered activity, are such as to produce a state which can be scaled along a continuum from drowsiness to extremes of alertness and responsiveness. Concepts such as "vigilance" (Head, 1920), "the specific vigilance reaction", "psychological arousal" and "activation" (e.g. Duffy, 1951, 1962; Malmo, 1959; Bindra, 1959; Lindsley, 1960), as well as general drive, have been coined to describe the changes involved.

The relations between these concepts have recently been discussed by Duffy (1962). On her view, the various physiological measures mentioned above can be used as indices of the "level of activation" of the organism, which is produced either by stimuli or other extra-neural effects, or by mental activity. This "level of activation" is supposed to be related to the rate at which energy is released by metabolic activity in the tissues, the inadequacy of measures of total metabolism as indicators of the level of activation being ascribed to the influence of the local energy reserves within the body. "Activation", as assessed by the various physiological indices mentioned, has in fact been shown to be related to reaction time, speed of movement, intensity or extent of response, and various other measures of performance: a well-known example is the way in which the extent of the knee jerk is increased when the fist is clenched.

The concept of a "level of activation" or "arousal" has a strong subjective appeal, but, as with so many other concepts used in the study of behaviour, the limits of its usefulness must be defined. It could be valuable over a wide range of situations only if the various indices by which the "level of activation" is assessed were highly correlated. This is not in fact the case. Lacey (1966) has cited much evidence that complete dissociation between "arousal" or "activation" as measured by physiological and by behavioural signs can be produced in a number of ways, including pharmacological techniques and localized lesions in the central nervous system. For instance, atropinized dogs show a pattern of electrical activity in the cortex characteristic of sleep, but complete behavioural arousal (Wikler, 1952). Again, Feldman et al. (1962) showed that cats with bilateral lesions of the posterior hypothalamus cannot be behaviourally aroused, although desynchronization of the cortex—an index of physiological arousal—can readily be produced. The converse dissociation was produced in some degree by bilateral lesions in the midbrain reticular formation. These and other studies show that the various indices of arousal—autonomic, electrocortical and behavioural—are separable experimentally. Furthermore, evidence for such dissociation is also available for normal human subjects not subjected to drugs or other experimental insult. In fact, as Duffy herself points out, even the correlations between somatic indices of activation are not always high, in part because the response to any particular stimulus situation is nearly always patterned to meet the demands of that situation. Thus Lacey et al. (1963) showed that patterns of heart-rate and skin conductance responses depend on the nature of the situations to which human subjects are exposed: they offer evidence that heart rate increases with tasks requiring rejection of environmental information (e.g. mental arithmetic) and decreases with tasks requiring its intake (e.g. exposure to flashes, with requirement merely to report on their colour or pattern), while skin conductance increases with both. Lacey (1966) cites a number of other studies also leading to this view (see, for example, Ax, 1953; Malmo, Shagass et al., 1951; Malmo, 1959), and offers an explanation of the lack of correlation between cardiac and conductance measures, supported by physiological evidence, in terms of a feedback mechanism from the cardiovascular system on cortical activity.

It is thus clear that "activation" processes are multi-dimensional, the correlations between the indices emphasized by Duffy being in part a consequence of the limited number of situations studied. Thus attempts to measure activation or arousal along a linear scale overlook qualitative diversity: the concept is useful only so long as the dependent variables are correlated, and thus only within very limited groups of situations.

A second difficulty with the concept of a "level of activation" comes from experiments in which the total sensory input is varied beyond the normal experimental limits. Most of this work has been concerned with reduction in the input, and has used human subjects. Characteristically they are confined in soundproof and an-echoic chambers, wearing gloves to reduce tactile stimulation and restrict movement (sensory isolation); or they are kept under conditions (e.g. wearing translucent goggles) in which the stimulation falling on their receptors is deficient in patterning, but relatively little changed in amount (perceptual isolation). Periods ranging from a few hours to several days under such conditions produce deficiencies in a wide variety of intellectual, perceptual, orientational and physiological tests: these deficiencies are often accompanied by hallucinations and dream-like states in which coherent thinking is difficult. The subjects sometimes respond to the decrease in stimulation by an increase in "activation", as indicated by the physiological indices discussed above (Bexton *et al.*, 1954; Solomon *et al.* (eds.) 1961): there can thus be no simple relationship between sensory input and "level of activation".

Such studies demonstrate that normal behaviour disintegrates when the general sensory input falls either in amount or patterning below a certain level. It would, however, be premature to interpret the dysfunction as a consequence merely of the quantitative level of sensory input. It is not even clear that fewer impulses pass up the sensory nerves during sensory isolation, for while some cells in the cat's retina fire more frequently in the light than in the dark, for others the opposite is the case, and in some no change can be detected (*see* p. 79). Furthermore, as discussed in Chapters 5 and 21, there are reasons for thinking that regular relationships between different types of sensory input may be necessary for integrated behaviour: it may be the absence of these relations, rather than the low quantitative level, that is responsible for most of the behavioural abnormalities accompanying sensory or perceptual isolation.

The concept of "level of activation", therefore, has limits to its usefulness. It also carries with it a danger which derives from the readiness with which it, and similar concepts, is held to be congruent with the concept of "general drive" (e.g. by Brown, 1961). Any such argument is likely to involve a missing link. The evidence on which Duffy's concept of "level of activation" was based was concerned primarily with showing that there is a number of consequences common to many and diverse motivational variables. This is not the same as saying that they reflect a general state causal to all possible activities.

While there may be general (e.g. metabolic) factors which influence the intensity with which all, or most, activities are shown, such as those revealed by the study of diurnal or circadian rhythms (*see* p. 226), this is not the same as saying that *all* independent variables which influence the intensity of any activity influence that of all activities.

Work on such topics has, however, thrown into relief the important possibility that there are optimum limits of sensory input for responsiveness, efficiency or performance. On this view the relation between quality of performance and "activation" has the form of an inverted U (Duffy, 1962; Schlosberg, 1954; Leuba, 1955; Hebb, 1955). So far we have been concerned with evidence for the rising arm of the inverted U, with increase in the dependent variables or improvement in performance as the input increases. What is the evidence for a decrease in performance as the input increases still further?

Some of it comes from common experience. Many human activities depend on a tendency to seek moderately high levels of stimulation—much of the entertainment industry depends on this fact (Hebb, 1949). The level of stimulation sought, however, is either only moderately high or else soon relieved. Very intense stimulation is experienced as unpleasant, and performance under such conditions deteriorates; for instance in combat (Marshall, 1947) or disaster (Tyhurst, 1951). There is also experimental evidence that sensory overload, resulting from intense multisensory input, may lead to deterioration in performance and grossly abnormal motivational states (Lindsley, in Solomon *et al.*, 1961).

Data supporting an inverted U-shaped relationship between motivational factors and performance are also available from studies of animals. Various measures of performance, such as pressing the bar in a Skinner box for food reinforcement, are related in a curvilinear manner to the period of deprivation. In rats, the rate increases up to about 24 hours of food deprivation, but then falls off. Bélanger *et al.* (1962) argue against the usual view that the falling off is due to inanition, and suggest that it is due to a decrease in efficiency when "arousal" passes a certain level.

The effect of intense motivational factors varies with the difficulty of the task. Broadhurst (1959) tested rats on a brightness discrimination which had to be made under water. The rats were first kept submerged for periods of 0 to 8 seconds, before being released to swim through a T-maze. If they turned correctly they could come to the surface to breathe. For easy discriminations, performance was little affected by the period of submergence before release, but for a difficult discrimination it was better with a period of 2 seconds than 0, 4 or 8 seconds.

Another type of evidence sometimes considered relevant here comes from studies in which animals are allowed to control the intensity of stimulation they receive. Many of these have used rats as subjects, the animals being able to turn light on or off by moving a lever. While a number of these investigations have shown that rats will learn to press a lever if it is followed by an increase in the illumination (e.g. Girdner, 1953; Marx et al., 1955; Kling et al., 1956; Hurwitz, 1956; Hurwitz et al., 1958; Kish, 1955), others have shown the opposite effect, the animals learning to press a lever to decrease the illumination (Keller, 1941; Flynn et al., 1952; Roberts, C. L., et al., 1958; Barry et al., 1963): in some of these studies the rats were found to work both to turn the light on and to turn it off.

It is difficult to compare the intensities of illumination used in these different experiments, but one possible hypothesis is that there is a preferred level: with low light intensity its onset is more likely to be reinforcing than its removal, while with high light intensities the reverse is the case. Lockard (1963a) gave rats two levers, one of which would turn on a diffuse overhead light, while the other turned it off. The intensity of the light varied between groups. The bright light intensities tended to be more aversive to animals previously kept in the dark than to animals kept in the light. The optimum is thus influenced by the previous experience (see also Roberts, C. L., et al., 1958; D'Amato et al., 1962; Kish et al., 1962; Lockard, 1963b): it also varies with age (Levin et al., 1959). Comparable data indicating a preferred level of input are available for other types of stimulation and other species (Girdner, 1953; Barnes et al., 1961; Harrington et al., 1962; Baron et al., 1962; Fox, 1962).

However, such experiments are not always easy to interpret and are open to more than one type of explanation (Lockard, 1963b). While they are compatible with theorizing which postulates an optimal level of the sensory input, other explanations are possible: for instance, the reinforcing value of light onset and offset could be related to its property of stimulus novelty (Berlyne, 1960). Barry et al. (1963) found that bar-pressing by rats was reinforcing regardless of whether it turned the light on or off, and Premack et al. (1957) showed that the rate at which rats would press a bar with light reinforcement increased with the length of a preceding period in total darkness. Such findings are consistent with a novelty hypothesis (see also Roberts, C. L., et al., 1958). The persistence of the behaviour over days, however, rather counts against this view.

The finding that rats prefer a certain intermediate level of illumination will not be unexpected to the naturalist, but falls far short of showing that there is an optimum level of general input. If the latter were the case, the preferred level of illumination would be expected to decrease with increase in other types of stimulation or motivation. The data at present available do not support this view: Clayton (1958) found that water-deprived rats pressed a bar producing light more than did controls; and both Forgays et al. (1958) and Davis (1958) obtained the same result when comparing hungry with satiated animals. (Hurwitz et al. (1958) obtained negative results). Again, the hypothesis of an optimum general level of input would predict that an increase in motivation would lead to an increase in the rate at which an animal would work to remove stimulation, but this also is not confirmed by the experimental evidence:

Dachowski (1964) found that the response of rats trained to turn off a bright light extinguished equally rapidly whether or not they were water-deprived if the light was on during extinction.

That specific stimulation is usually attractive when mild, but aversive when strong, has been shown in a number of other contexts. For example, Beebe-Center et al. (1948) found that rats prefer saccharin to plain water when the concentration is slightly above threshold, but water is preferred to higher concentrations (see also Weiner et al., 1951). Similarly, Warren (1963) found that fluid-deprived mice tended to prefer low concentrations of the alkaloid sucrose octa-acetate (which tastes bitter to man) to water, but avoided higher concentrations. Although studies of this type are sometimes quoted by authors other than the original investigator in discussions of evidence for the occurrence of an optimal level of general activation, they are not, in fact, relevant to them: the relationship of stimulus intensity only to the response relevant to that stimulus was assessed (see also Haber, 1958).

Another type of evidence which seems to indicate that there is an optimum level of input comes from studies in which animals are able to administer intracranial electrical stimulation to themselves by performing a suitable operant task. Olds (e.g. Olds et al., 1954; Olds, 1961) has shown that rats will press a lever to give themselves electrical stimulation through electrodes permanently implanted in certain areas of the brain ("reward areas"). Elsewhere ("punishment areas") electrical stimulation may be aversive. In some reward areas, however, a prolongation of the stimulus at the same intensity seems to be aversive (Roberts, 1958; Bower et al., 1958). Reynolds (1958) found that the rate of bar-pressing shown by a rat was related in an inverted U-shaped fashion to voltage magnitude: with increase in the intensity of stimulation the rate of bar-pressing increased to a maximum and then decreased. Such experiments must not be interpreted too lightly, for large differences in input voltage or train length may involve qualitative changes in the physiological nature of the stimulus. Over a considerable range of train length for a constant current stimulus, Prescott (1964) found that rats adjusted their response rates so that they received a more-or-less constant amount of electricity. Further, pulse trains longer than those self-selected may still not be aversive (Keesey, 1964).

As with bar-pressing for light, the rate of responding for intracranial stimulation may be increased by food deprivation (Brady et al., 1957). It is also positively correlated with the variations in activity which accompany the day/night rhythm and the oestrous cycle. This does not favour the hypothesis that the rat adjusts its bar-pressing to receive a constant optimal amount of general input. An alternative possibility is that the effect of motivational factors is to alter the optimum level of input, that is, to change the level of input (specific or general) for which the animal works (Prescott, loc. cit.). A similar hypothesis could be applied to light reinforced bar-pressing.

This view receives some support from a different type of experiment. One way in which an animal can control the input into its central nervous system is to alter its general activity. It is well known that the opportunity to run in a running wheel is reinforcing for rats, the animals tending to run so that a given amount of activity occurs in each 24 hours (Kagan *et al.*, 1954). The amount of activity varies with the motivational state: for instance it changes with the oestrous cycle (Richter, reviewed Munn, 1950). Kavanau (1963), working with Deermice (*Peromyscus crinitus*), has shown that the activity level varies according to the motivational state at the time. These animals will learn to press levers to operate an activity wheel, whether the lever unlocks a previously locked wheel, or starts or stops one driven by a motor. The patterns characteristic of spontaneous free-wheel activity tend to be repeated when the operation of the wheel requires an instrumental act, whether that act operates a motor-driven wheel or unlocks a free-running one. However, the Deermice do not accept motor-driven running which is initiated by the experimenter. If they have been trained to operate the motor with on and off levers, they will stop the motor if it is started by an outside agent and vice versa. Thus they resist any change in activity imposed on them from outside.

In summary, there is clear evidence that behaviour becomes inefficient outside certain limits of sensory input. The mechanisms involved, however, are far from clear. The dysfunction which accompanies a low level of input is certainly not necessarily due to inadequate "activation", for the indices of activation may be high. Indeed, in many cases the operative factor may be not the low total level of input, but the absence of ordered relations between movement and consequent feedback (Chapter 21). Likewise the effects of excessive stimulation may be due to interfering responses, distraction of attention (p. 91) and so on. Also, although normal functioning requires the level of sensory input to be within certain limits, there is little hard evidence to suggest that, within those limits, an increase in any type of input will necessarily increase the intensity of behaviour: the extent to which any particular pattern of behaviour is shown depends primarily on factors specific to that pattern. Finally, while animals have a "preferred level" for many kinds of exteroceptive and proprioceptive input, additional motivational factors such as hunger, which should increase the level of activation or "general drive", may in fact increase the amount of stimulation sought. On the hypothesis that the animal seeks an optimum level of general input, they would be expected to produce a compensatory decrease. In practice, the preferred level of input (specific or "general") usually varies directly with the motivational state.

9.3. The Reticular System

In recent years interest in the role of general sensory input in determining responsiveness and the efficiency of performance has been brought to a focus through studies of the ascending reticular activating system and the diffuse thalamocortical projection system in mammals. These include diffuse columns of nerve cells extending through the lower brain as far as the thalamus, and consisting of a network of cells with short fibres: their functions include the maintenance of cortical and behavioural (*see* pp. 155-7) "arousal" by relaying general sensory input to the cortex (e.g. Moruzzi *et al.*, 1949; Jasper *et al.*, 1958; Worden *et al.*, 1961; Lindsley, 1956, 1961).

As the principal sensory pathways travel up through the brain-stem they give off collaterals to these systems, which, in turn, have a diffuse projection

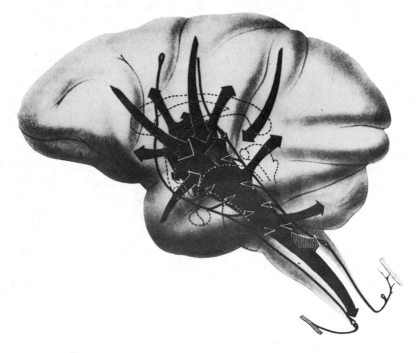

Fig. 9.2. Diagrammatic representation of the relationships of the reticular formation. (*After Worden and Livingston, 1961.*)

The thin-line arrows indicate collaterals from sensory and motor pathways to reticular formation. The thick arrows entering the formation indicate corticofugal influences. The arrows leaving the reticular formation indicate its ascending influences to cortex and cerebellum, and its descending influences to motor mechanisms and (hatched arrow) central sensory relays.

on to the cortex (Fig. 9.2.) Several sources of evidence indicate that activity in any sensory system, as well as causing activity in its specific cortical projection area, also has a diffuse effect on the cortex. Thus electrical stimulation of the reticular formation of an animal in light sleep or light anaesthesia can produce arousal as indicated both by a change in the EEG record from the synchronized slow waves characteristic of such states to low amplitude fast waves, and by the behavioural response: comparable arousal can be produced by sensory stimulation. (As might be expected, the response of the cortex to electrical stimulation of the reticular system differs in some ways from that which occurs with stimulation of specific sensory nuclei; for instance there is a difference in the manner in which the cortical potentials change with depth into the cortex (Jasper, 1961).) Lesions in or barbiturate anaesthesia of the ascending reticular system lead to a lack of behavioural responsiveness to external stimulation: the primary sensory pathways can conduct to the cortex but perception or discrimination does not result. Stimulation of any peripheral nerve gives evoked potentials throughout the reticular formation. Most of its units are activated by a variety of inputs, though there is also evidence for a degree of specificity (*see* below).

Thus behavioural arousal, cortical EEG arousal and reticular activity usually go together, and much of the evidence indicates that the cortical arousal, mediated by activity in the reticular formation, is a necessary accompaniment to a stimulus for a behavioural response to occur. Further evidence indicates that reticular activity can increase the efficiency of responsiveness. For instance, when Lindsley (e.g. 1961) presented pairs of light flashes separated by a 50 millisecond interval to a cat, the cortex gave only a single evoked response to each pair. When the reticular system was electrically stimulated, however, the cortex showed a separate response to each flash for about 10 seconds after the cessation of reticular stimulation.

However, as we have seen, dissociation between the indices of behavioural and physiological arousal sometimes occurs. Furthermore, the relationship between the level of input into the reticular system and cortical functioning is not a simple one. Strong electrical stimulation of the reticular system produces not only arousal but also apparent discomfort, fear responses and fleeing. While moderate activity in the reticular formation aids cortical functioning, a very high level of activity in the brain-stem decreases sensitivity (e.g. Lindsley, 1956). Thus, Fuster (1958) found that, while tachistoscopic perception in monkeys was enhanced by mild stimulation in the mesencephalic region, the contrary effect could be produced if the strength of the stimulus was increased. Stimulation of the reticular system itself may have both facilitatory and inhibitory effects on the responses of cortical cells (e.g. Akimoto *et al.*, 1961).

The reticular system receives its input not only from the main sensory pathways, but also from the cortex, the limbic system, the basal ganglia and the cerebellum. Thus electrical stimulation of the monkey cortex can elicit evoked responses from the reticular system—responsiveness is mostly diffuse, but there is some evidence for specificity. Through its effect on the reticular system, localized cortical stimulation can activate the entire cortex.

The reticular system can also be influenced by the endocrine state of the animal. Sawyer (quoted by Dell, 1958) assessed the effects of injections of oestrogen and progesterone on the threshold for electrical stimulation of the reticular formation in the rabbit, using cortical arousal as the criterion. He found that this threshold diminished to about 10 per cent of its initial value at the time when oestrous behaviour appeared. It thus seems that certain hormones, acting via the brain-stem reticular system, may affect the responsiveness of the cortex.

The output of the system passes not only to the cerebral cortex, but also to the cerebellar mantle, brain-stem and spinal cord. It has facilitatory and inhibitory effects on the spino-motor outflow: the more rostral portions augment spinal reflexes and voluntary movements, while the more caudal parts have an inhibitory effect. For instance, a cat's reaction time in removing its foot from a metal plate when given an electric shock is shortened by increasing the sensory input or by direct stimulation of the reticular system (Isaac, 1960).

Although it was thought formerly that the system was quite non-specific, evidence of differentiation within it is now accumulating. For instance, particular cells in the reticular formation may be responsive to one sort of stimulation but not to other sensory modalities. Furthermore, the anterior part, lying in the thalamus, is structurally more complex than the rest, and the nuclei within it are connected to specific parts of the cortex (e.g. Jasper, 1949). The relationships between cortical and subcortical structures are clearly intricate, and the cortical "arousal" effect is probably only a crude description of one of the functions of this system (cf. pp. 93-6). Livingston *et al.* (1954) describe its role as that of a "transactional link" for all parts of the nervous system.

Although the realization of the importance of the reticular system has led to a greatly increased understanding of brain functioning, as yet it provides no easy answer for questions of motivation. The apparently non-specific action of the reticular system has frequently been quoted in support of a concept of general drive (e.g. Hebb, 1955), but the evidence at present available does not warrant it. There is clear evidence that the reticular system influences sensory/ perceptual mechanisms and reaction times, and that reticular activity must be between certain limits if functionally integrated behaviour is to occur. But there is as yet no satisfactory evidence that increase in reticular activity within those limits results in an increase in the intensity or frequency with which a particular pattern of behaviour is shown. It can be argued at most that any non-specific aspects of reticular functioning would be compatible with a general drive theory of behaviour, not that they require one. Another suggestion, that the reticular system acts as a homeostat regulating input–output relations (Lindsley, 1960), is also not yet substantiated: the role of the reticular system in controlling input is still not clear (*see* Chapter 6).

9.4. Conclusion on General v. Specific Effects of Sensory Input and Motivational Factors

In summary, there is clear evidence that the proper integration of behaviour requires that the level of ordered sensory input be between certain limits. On the other hand, there is no clear evidence that the intensity of behaviour is determined equally by all the motivational factors and stimulation acting at the moment, as a general drive hypothesis demands. In the present state of the evidence, the reasonable assumption is that, within limits, the intensity of any one type of behaviour depends only on motivational factors more or less specific to it, and that others are of relatively minor importance. Just how general or how specific the effects of any particular stimulus or motivational state may be is a matter for empirical investigation.

9.5. Summary

1. Most factors that influence an animal's behaviour have a limited sphere of influence; they affect some types of behaviour and not others. There is, however, also evidence for more general effects. While some theorists use drive concepts specific to particular types of behaviour, others postulate a "general drive", which is supposed to energize all the patterns of behaviour in an animal's repertoire.
2. Studies of the interrelations between hunger, thirst, fear and sex provide some evidence which could be interpreted in terms of a "general drive", but alternative explanations are also possible.
3. The various sensory inputs to which an organism is exposed interact with each other.
4. Changes in various physiological indices (e.g. skin resistance, heart rate) are correlated with activity of many sorts, and have been used as indices of the "level of activation" of the animal. The utility of this concept is limited: the correlations between the different indices are often not high.
5. The concept of "level of activation" is not necessarily congruent with that of "general drive".
6. A number of lines of evidence indicate that responsiveness, efficiency or performance deteriorates if the sensory input falls outside certain limits. Animals show behaviour which results in the stimulation remaining within these limits.
7. Motivational factors may influence the level of stimulation for which an animal will work.
8. The brain-stem reticular system has a general effect on behaviour, and the functioning of other parts of the brain require reticular activity to be within certain limits. Evidence drawn from studies of this system, however, does not demand a "general drive" theory of behaviour.

10
Motivation: The Specific Effects of Hormones and of Stimuli

In this chapter we shall side-step the drive issue (*see* Chapters 8 and 9) by considering some of the independent variables traditionally studied in experiments on motivation. For the moment, discussion will be limited to the more commonly studied activities—feeding, drinking, and various aspects of reproductive behaviour: the extent to which it is possible to extract principles of motivation common to these and other activities will be considered later (Chapter 15). Furthermore, discussion will be limited to two categories of independent variables which might be described as "motivational factors"—hormones and stimuli.

10.1. Hormones

Most of the work on the influence of hormones on behaviour has been concerned with reproductive behaviour, and it is here that the problems are most clearly defined. Evidence for a hormonal influence on the reproductive activities of vertebrates is of three main types (Beach, 1948; Young, ed., 1961a):

1. Correlations between the occurrence of reproductive activities and the enlargement or secretory activity of the endocrine glands. In many seasonally breeding animals the gonads are enlarged, and certain gonadal cells show secretory activity, during just that period in which the reproductive activities are most common. For instance, Bullough (1942) showed that the appearance of various aspects of reproductive behaviour in the Starling (*Sturnus vulgaris*) is related to the growth of the gonads in the early part of the year. This species normally breeds in the spring. There are two races which breed in Great Britain. One is sedentary: the gonads of these individuals develop precociously during the autumn, and this is associated with a revival of sexual activity. In the other race, which leaves the country in the autumn to winter farther south, there is no autumn recrudescence of the gonads and no autumn sexual behaviour.
2. The frequency or intensity of sexual behaviour is reduced after gonadectomy. The rapidity of this decrease, however, varies considerably between species (*see* p. 383).

3. Injection or implantation of certain hormone preparations increases the frequency of reproductive responses. For instance, Noble *et al.* (1942) showed that injections of testosterone propionate into male chicks led to the appearance of the sexual behaviour patterns of the adult cock— crowing, copulating, and so on—while female chicks treated with oestrogen squatted for treading males. Similar results have been obtained with mammals: pre-puberally castrated male rats fail to show sexual behaviour, but administration of androgens restores sexual activity. Similarly, the sexual receptivity of spayed female rats is restored by treatment with combinations of oestrogen and progesterone (Beach, e.g. 1948). Many similar results are given in reviews by Beach (1948), Eisner (1960), Lehrman (1961), Young (1961a), Guhl (1961) and others.

In general, male sexual behaviour of higher vertebrates is induced by androgens, while female sexual behaviour is induced by oestrogens and gestagens, alone or in combination. However, perhaps because these are all steroids of similar chemical combination, it is not always easy to define clear-cut differences between their actions. Thus under certain circumstances oestrogen may activate male behaviour in males as well as female behaviour in females (Beach, 1948). Generalizations applicable to all vertebrates are hard to make, for in some species sexual and aggressive behaviour, as well as parental behaviour, are influenced directly by pituitary hormones (e.g. Aronson, 1965). Indeed, it is not even possible to generalize about which patterns of behaviour are under hormonal control and which are not: many of the responses made by female mice to their young, for instance, are elicited equally easily from primiparous females, females pregnant for the first time, virgin adult females, adult males who have seen their mate taking care of a litter, and inexperienced adult males. It is thus improbable that differences in hormonal state play a significant role in controlling these responses (Beniest-Noirot, 1958; Noirot, 1964a; *see also* Leblond *et al.*, 1937). Mice appear to be peculiar in this respect, for in other species of rodents maternal behaviour is elicited more readily from recently parturient females than from virgins or males (*see also* Rowell, T. E., 1961).

Hormones affect behaviour in diverse ways. Here we shall not consider the general effects of hormones on growth or metabolic functions. Nor shall we discuss their effects on the morphological structures which are employed in behaviour, though the influence of sex hormones on the hypertrophy of the brachial musculature used by frogs in amplexus (Aronson *et al.*, 1945), or on the comb used by cockerels in display, certainly exemplify important ways in which sex hormones affect behaviour. Rather we shall confine our attention to the four possible mechanisms by which hormones might influence behaviour listed by Lashley (1938a):

(i) The hormone stimulates the growth of new nervous connections.

(ii) The hormone acts by inducing specific changes in various organs, and these mediate sensory impulses which influence the central nervous system.

(iii) The hormone increases the excitability of specific sensorimotor mechanisms in the central nervous system.

(iv) The hormone increases the general excitability of the organism.

With regard to the first of these possibilities, sex hormones do exert a profound influence on the development of the nervous system at any early stage, especially during ante-natal or pre-hatching life (Young *et al.*, 1964; Young, 1965). There is, however, little indication that a hormonally influenced growth of new nervous connections is the factor determining the change in behaviour which occurs at the onset of sexual maturity. Thus male hamsters show some elements of the mating pattern even when castrated and adrenalectomized before puberty, showing at least that the sensorimotor mechanisms involved can develop independently of the increased androgen production at this time (Warren *et al.*, 1957). Similarly, the castration of immature male pigeons does not completely prevent the development of copulatory behaviour (Carpenter, *cited* Beach, 1951b; *see also* Schwartz *et al.*, 1954).

Evidence for Lashley's fourth suggestion, that hormones affect the general excitability of the organism, has already been considered (pp. 163-4). We may now consider points (ii) and (iii) above.

First, some instances in which hormones influence behaviour by causing changes in a peripheral organ. In the copulation of rats, ejaculation depends on stimulation received through the penis during a series of intromissions. Beach *et al.* (1950) have shown that one of the effects of androgens is to increase the density of cornified papillae between the epithelial folds of the glans penis, and that there is a close correlation between the appearance of the papillae and sexual behaviour. Thus one of the ways in which androgen influences the sexual behaviour of rats is by altering the sensitivity of the penis. Other changes in the penis, for instance in the penile musculature, which may result from an alteration of the androgen level, are reviewed by Rosenblatt *et al.* (1958a, b).

Another example which has been cited in this context is the effect of oestrogen injections on the dominance relations of chimpanzees. Although oestrogens lower the dominance status of male castrates, they raise that of female castrates. It appears that the latter effect is due to the oestrogen injections producing engorgement of the sex skin: Birch *et al.* (1950), utilizing the fact that the female's swelling can be temporarily suppressed with progesterone, found that the dominance status of the female varies with the degree of swelling when the oestrogen level is kept constant and high. The effect of oestrogens on the males may be centrally mediated.

The influence of the pituitary hormone prolactin on the parental feeding of doves is due, at least in part, to a peripheral effect. Doves, unlike other birds, feed their young on a "milk" formed by a sloughing of the epithelium of the crop. Prolactin causes the enlargement of the crop, which normally takes place before the young hatch. Lehrman (1955) has shown that sensory stimulation from the enlarged crop plays an essential role in the induction of parental feeding. If this afferent stimulation is cut off by the application of a local anaesthetic to the crop region, the proportion of adults which will feed squabs is reduced, whereas local anaesthesia elsewhere does not prevent parental feeding. Prolactin is thus instrumental in inducing parental feeding by its effect on the crop. (These results have been criticized recently by Klinghammer *et al.* (1964), who found that some feeding by adult ring doves could occur in the absence of prolactin-induced crop engorgement. The difference between the two experiments may lie in the fact that Klinghammer and Hess's birds were brought into contact with young during the course of incubation, while in Lehrman's experiments the squabs were placed in the nest of a non-incubating bird. This suggests that the peripheral effect of prolactin is on the tendency of the adult to orient towards the young from a distance.)

Another probable example of hormones influencing behaviour through their peripheral effects comes from studies of the nest-building behaviour of domestic canaries. In this species the stimulation the female receives from the cup of the nest, which she herself has built, has an important influence on many subsequent aspects of reproductive behaviour: it affects, for instance, the amount of nest-building behaviour shown, the selection of nest-material, the date of egg-laying, and so on. The effectiveness of stimuli from the nest-cup is enhanced by the development of a brood-patch—the female loses the feathers from her breast, which becomes vascular and also more sensitive to tactile stimulation (Fig. 10.1). These changes in the brood-patch are under hormonal control. The hormones thus influence behaviour in part through their effect on the brood-patch (Hinde *et al.*, 1963; Hinde and Steel 1962, 1964; Steel *et al.*, 1963, 1964; Hinde, 1965).

A slightly different case is that in which a hormone produces a change in behaviour not by affecting a particular organ, but by influencing general bodily functions. Nest-building by rats, for instance, is increased by thyroidectomy, gonadectomy, adrenalectomy and hypophysectomy (Richter, 1937). Since nest-building is known to be closely influenced by temperature, it seems possible that this is partly due to the decrease in body temperature which follows removal of these structures (Kinder, 1927).

These, however, are by no means the only or even the usual ways in which hormones affect behaviour. As Lashley suggested, they may influence the central nervous system directly: thus Kent *et al.* (1949) produced oestrous behaviour in oestrogen-primed hamsters by introducing progesterone into the brain ventricles in dosages that were insufficient when administered subcutaneously.

In mammals this central effect of sex hormones is exerted primarily on the hypothalamus. Thus hormone administration is effective in facilitating mating behaviour from cats in response to sacral and vaginal stimulation if the brain is sectioned above the hypothalamus, but not if the section is below (Bromley *et al.*, 1940; Dempsey *et al.*, 1939). Comparable studies have been made of the toad *Xenopus laevis*. This species uses three clasping patterns in sexual behaviour: a "tonic clasp", which in normal mating may be maintained for several hours on end; "backward kicking", given in response to movements of the female and

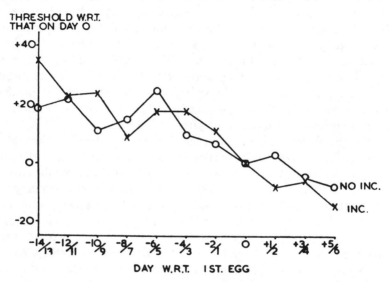

Fig. 10.1. Changes in the threshold of tactile sensitivity of the canary brood-patch around the time of egg-laying. (*After Hinde, Bell and Steel, 1963.*)

Ordinate—tactile threshold. Abscissa—date with respect to laying of first egg. Data for birds which subsequently did and did not incubate their eggs are plotted separately, but do not differ significantly.

serving to keep the male in place; and "forward kicking", given if the male is stimulated by another object (such as the experimenter's fingers) and serving to push that object away. These patterns are elicited by tactile stimuli to the pads and throat skin, by stretch stimuli to the fore limbs, and so on. They can still be elicited if the brain is transected in the anterior medulla, but not if it is transected either more posteriorly, or in the mid-brain. Evidently transections in the posterior medulla eliminate the coordinating mechanisms, while transections anterior to the medulla set free mechanisms which are inhibitory. Intact *Xenopus* are normally sexually inactive in the laboratory, but they can be made responsive by an injection of chorionic gonadotrophin (Russell, 1954). Variations in hormone level, however, have little effect on the behaviour of the transected males. Thus, the hormones presumably act on the regulatory mechanisms in the anterior part of the brain, and not on the control mechanisms in spinal cord and medulla (Hutchison *et al.*, 1963).

This direct action of hormones on the central nervous system has been demonstrated elegantly by Harris *et al.* (1958), working on the induction of sexual receptivity in the female cat by oestrogens. In this case it had already been shown that stimuli from the genital area were not necessary for the manifestation of female sexual behaviour, for total deafferentation of the pelvic erogenous zones failed to inhibit oestrous behaviour. Harris and his collaborators were able to localize the site of action of the hormones more precisely by implanting very small quantities of solid stilboestrol dibutyrate into the brain. When such implants were made in the posterior hypothalamus of spayed cats there was full development of sexual behaviour even though the genital tract remained anoestrous. Furthermore, similar implants made subcutaneously or at other sites in the central nervous system did not induce sexual behaviour. It could be concluded, therefore, that the hormones influence behaviour by affecting hypothalamic structures.

Comparable data are available for rats. Implantation of oestradiol in the medial-basal preoptic and anterior hypothalamic regions of spayed rats produced behavioural sexual receptivity, though implants placed elsewhere in the hypothalamus, or subcutaneously, were ineffective (Lisk, 1962a; *see also* Lisk, 1962b). Furthermore, after implantation of oestradiol in the arcuate nucleus the diameter of the nucleoli of the neurones in that area decrease, a change which is accompanied by gonadal atrophy, suggesting a functional hypophysectomy (Lisk and Newlon, 1963).

Evidence suggesting that hormones may affect central nervous structures directly has been obtained in a quite different manner by Olds (e.g. 1961). Electrodes were implanted into rats' brains and connected in such a way that the rat could stimulate its own brain by stepping on a pedal. When the electrodes were in certain positions the animals would stimulate themselves regularly for long periods of time (*see* p. 197). Olds claims that this positive area is itself differentiated into sub-areas, in some of which performance is improved by, for instance, hunger, and in others by higher androgen levels. In the latter cases the effectiveness of a standard electrical stimulus to particular areas of the central nervous system is enhanced by the hormone treatment. As discussed on p. 197, however, the evidence published so far is not wholly convincing.

Any particular type of behaviour may be influenced by hormones in a number of different ways. Indeed most hormones act in more than one way, and may have both central and peripheral influences. Even the central effects may be multiple. Thus Michael (1961) suggested that the mechanism underlying receptivity in cats is separate from, and requires a higher hormone level than, that underlying the sexual reflexes. More detailed data illustrating a similar point for rats will be considered in Chapter 15. Furthermore, the effect of hormones is not necessarily that of augmenting responsiveness; for instance, oestrogens inhibit aggressiveness in female Golden Hamsters (Kislak *et al.*, 1955). To take a quite different type of case, after copulation female grasshoppers cease to be receptive to males. This depends on the filling of the receptaculum seminis with sperm, and the effect is probably not neurally mediated, but depends on a chemical factor (Haskell, 1960).

It must also be stressed that a hormonal influence on one type of behaviour may have consequences ramifying through much of the rest of the animal's repertoire. Michael *et al.* (1963) found a relation between the stage of the menstrual cycle and both mounting and grooming behaviour in Rhesus Macaques. The amount the female grooms the male reaches a minimum, and the amount the male grooms the female a maximum, in mid-cycle. This does not necessarily indicate a direct influence of hormones on the mechanisms for grooming, for the fluctuations in grooming may depend on changes in social status (*see* Rowell, 1963).

The finding that a response is influenced by hormones does not mean that its occurrence is solely a function of hormone concentration. For one thing, in many species behaviour which is later hormonally influenced occurs during a short period of early development when there are no apparent endocrine changes. Infantile sexuality is not peculiar to man—many birds show incomplete courtship and nest-building behaviour when a few weeks old, long before their gonads attain breeding condition (e.g. Curio, 1960). As yet, of course, the presence of some hormonal basis for such precocious behaviour cannot be ruled out.

Again, experience often has an important influence on hormonally mediated behaviour. For example, progesterone is much less effective in inducing incubation behaviour, and prolactin in inducing parental feeding behaviour, from inexperienced ring doves as compared with experienced ones (Lehrman, 1955, 1962; Lehrman *et al.*, 1960). Further examples are given in Chapter 23.

Furthermore, the occurrence of hormone-influenced behaviour is also a function of many other aspects of the physiology of the animal. Grunt *et al.* (1953) have shown that the level of sexual activity attained by individual male guinea-pigs before castration was correlated with that shown after the operation when the animals were receiving standard androgen treatment: thus the level of responsiveness to a given hormone level is a characteristic of the individual. Beach and Fowler (1959a) obtained a similar result for rats, and Whalen *et al.* (1961) concluded that individual differences in copulatory behaviour were due to differences in ability to make use of circulating androgens rather than the androgen level itself. Similarly, Goy *et al.* (1956–7) have demonstrated strain differences in the responses of female guinea-pigs to sex hormones.

Even when it seems certain that the hormone is producing its effect on a particular locus in the brain, it must be remembered that other parts of the central nervous system may influence the strength of the response. Removal of parts of the forebrain from male rats leads to a reduction in sexual responsiveness correlated with the amount of tissue removed. In experiments by Beach (1940, 1944), ablation of 60 per cent or more of the neocortex led to a complete cessation of sexual behaviour, while ablation of less than 20 per cent had no effect. However, the effects of cortical ablation can be offset by the administration of androgens—the more cortex that has been removed, the more androgen is needed to restore sexual behaviour to a standard level. A similar result was obtained with pigeons (Beach, 1951b). More recent studies show that the deficit is not solely a function of the amount of tissue removed, for frontal lesions produce more severe effects than do more posterior ones in cats (Zitrin *et al.*, 1956) and rats (Larsson, 1964). Using spreading cortical depression induced by application of potassium chloride, Larsson (1962) also found that functional decortication prevented the copulatory activity of male rats. Unlike the results obtained by Beach for female rats, Larsson found a differential effect on some components of the female's copulatory behaviour.

In the foregoing discussion we have considered only the routes by which the internal hormonal state influences responsiveness to stimuli, and not the influence of environmental stimuli on the hormonal state. It is, of course, well known that the gonadal condition of cyclically breeding animals may be influenced by external factors, and the particular example of domesticated canaries is discussed in Chapter 15. Another type of case which has been studied in some detail recently is the influence of "stress inducing" social and other environmental stimuli on the functioning of the pituitary-adrenal cortex system. Discussion of this lies outside the scope of this book, but some aspects are mentioned in Chapter 23. (*See* e.g. Harris, 1955; Clarke, 1953; Chitty, 1957; Barnett, 1958, 1963).

10.2. Stimuli

During the spring, male Three-spined Sticklebacks leave the sea and migrate up river to their breeding grounds. This migration is due to a hormonal change involving primarily the pituitary and thyroid glands (Baggerman, 1958). During this period, they do not behave aggressively if they encounter other males, and they do not show nest-building behaviour. When they reach a suitable site for breeding, their behaviour changes. They start to patrol a limited area, to attack other males, and to dig a pit in the sand. Evidently these new forms of behaviour depend on stimuli from a suitable territory as well as on an appropriate hormonal state.

Observations of this kind have been used (e.g. Lorenz, 1950; Tinbergen, 1951) as a basis for distinguishing between stimuli which elicit particular responses when the animal encounters them ("releasing" stimuli), and those which act continuously to determine its specific state of responsiveness ("motivating" stimuli). Stimuli from an intruding male would come into the former category, stimuli from the territory into the latter. There is, however, little evidence that releasing and motivating effects depend on different types of mechanism, and the distinction seems to depend on the nature of the stimuli rather than on the way they act: motivating stimuli are continuously present, while releasing stimuli appear more suddenly (Hinde, 1954d). Of course, where external stimuli act by influencing the endocrine state there is a clear case for distinguishing this mode of action from stimuli which elicit a response directly.

Thus we shall discuss here the role of stimuli which influence responsiveness to other stimuli, without implication about the mechanism by which this is achieved. They may produce their effect by continuous direct action, or by inducing durable central nervous or hormonal states. Furthermore, they may result in either an increase or a decrease in responsiveness.

Augmenting Effects

One example of an augmenting effect has already been mentioned (pp. 168-9)— stimuli from the enlarged crop increase the readiness of experienced adult doves to feed squabs: the application of a local anaesthetic to the crop region reduces responsiveness (Lehrman, 1955). Stimuli from the engorged breasts play a comparable role in lactating women.

The precise extent to which internal sensory stimuli contribute to the responsiveness of mammals in feeding, drinking and sexual contexts is still controversial. Although it seems clear that stomach contractions play an important role in subjective feelings of hunger in man, they are not essential for the occurrence of feeding behaviour in adult mammals. Tsang (1938) removed the contractile main bulk of the stomach from 7 rats, and then tested for activity and maze performance. For the first 5 days the maze performance of the operated animals was little different from that of controls, but in the next 2 days they appeared to be very poorly motivated, and their activity was reduced. Bash (1939a, b) approached the problem by severing the vagus nerve and destroying the sympathetic nerve trunks. Many of the rats, although making a good surgical recovery, at first refused food and, in some cases, starved to death. Those which recovered maintained good health and increased in weight, but showed abnormalities in the diurnal rhythm of feeding. He thus suggested that gastric contractions play an important role in feeding behaviour, but are not essential: other contributory factors can take their place. Morgan et al. (1940a, b) found that resection of the vagus nerve failed to eliminate the augmentation of hunger by insulin, but rather enhanced the effect. They interpreted this as indicating that the nutritive conditions of the organism are more important in the control of hunger than are stomach contractions. From these studies it is clear that, while stimuli from the stomach play a role in normal eating behaviour, they are not essential for it to occur. Similarly, peripheral stimuli from the mouth/throat region do not play an essential role in the initiation of drinking behaviour, central osmoreceptors being largely responsible for indicating water deficit (e.g. Verney, 1947).

Similar data are available for sexual behaviour. Normal copulatory responses are shown by female rats after removal or denervation of the uterus and vagina (Ball, 1934), and by female cats after denervation of the genitalia (Bard, 1935). Male rats deprived of testes, prostrate gland and seminal vesicles copulate normally after androgen treatment (Beach, 1947; Beach *et al.*, 1963).

Such experiments indicate that input from some of the organs normally concerned with a response is not essential for that response; but they do not show that such input has no role. Other experiments demonstrate that some as yet undiagnosed characteristics of the states of hunger and thirst can act as cues

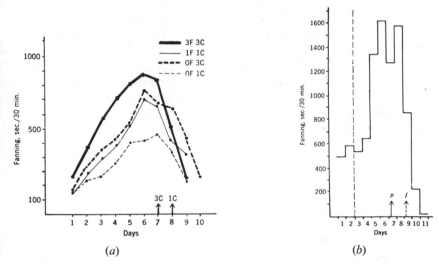

(a)   (b)

Fig. 10.2. (a) Changes in the amount of parental fanning shown by male Three-spined Sticklebacks on successive days after the eggs were laid. The figures indicate the number of clutches present in the nest, *C*, and fertilized, *F*. The arrows indicate the average hatching days of the young. (*After van Iersel, 1953.*)

(b) Frequency of fanning of a male Three-spined Stickleback which had its original clutch replaced by a fresh one on the second day of the parental cycle. Hatching day of original clutch and foster clutch shown by arrows labelled *p* and *f* respectively. (*After van Iersel, 1953.*)

for a differential response, but do not tell us whether the cues are central or peripheral. For instance, Hull (1933) showed that rats could learn to take one of two possible paths when hungry, and the other when thirsty, though the process of acquisition was slow and performance not perfect (*see also* Bolles, 1958; Wickens *et al.*, 1949). Similarly, Amsel (1949) showed that some rats could learn to escape a painful stimulus by running one way when hungry and the other way when thirsty (*see also* Levine, 1953; Jenkins *et al.*, 1949).

These cases have been concerned primarily with stimuli operating on the surface of or inside the body, but stimuli with more distant origins also may have motivating effects. The influence of stimuli from the territory on the Stickleback's aggressive behaviour in spring has already been mentioned briefly (p. 173). Another case serves to emphasize an additional point, namely that, just as a given hormone may influence a particular pattern of behaviour by affecting more than one part of the internal mechanism, so also may stimuli have multiple effects. The parental fanning of the male Three-spined Stickleback, which serves to aerate the eggs in the nest, normally increases from day to day until the eggs are 6 days old: it then falls fairly steeply (Fig. 10.2 (a)). Since the initial increase is steeper the more eggs that are present in the nest, and since fanning increases in water poor in oxygen and rich in carbon dioxide, it is probable that the initial increase in fanning activity is due to the increasing metabolism of the eggs. However, such a direct effect is not the only way in which the eggs influence fanning activity. If the eggs are replaced, when a few days old, by a clutch of fresh eggs, the curve of fanning has two peaks, one just before the day on which the original clutch would have hatched, and the other the day before the new clutch hatches. Thus stimuli from the original clutch must produce an effect which continues for some days after their removal (Fig. 10.2 (b)). Stimuli from the eggs therefore not only have an immediate influence on fanning activity, they also produce a long-term effect: the latter is presumably mediated by a change in some internal factor. Since van Iersel also showed that the later the time at which the young eggs are substituted for old ones, the smaller is the influence of the new clutch, this internal factor presumably becomes progressively stronger with time relative to the effect of the new eggs (van Iersel, 1953).

In most of the cases cited so far, the motivating effect is on one response only, or on a small group of responses. Territorial stimuli, however, influence a number of different activities in the male Stickleback, and we shall see later that the sharing of common motivational factors by a number of different patterns plays an important part in the integration of behaviour (Chapter 18).

Consummatory Stimuli

Not only must the various activities of an animal appear at appropriate times, but they must also cease when they are no longer appropriate. Often this is achieved by a self-regulating system—a pattern of behaviour may be terminated by stimuli which the animal encounters as a result of that behaviour. Such stimuli are often referred to as "consummatory stimuli."* An example is again

* Sevenster-Bol (1962) suggests that the descriptive term "consummatory act", which is usually applied to fixed action patterns that come at the end of a chain of behaviour (e.g. Thorpe, 1963a), should not be confused with causal factors that bring about "drive reduction". She therefore regards the term "consummatory stimuli" as inappropriate, and prefers "cut-off input" instead. It would seem, however, that the term "consummatory stimuli" is already well established in the literature.

provided by the stimuli from the territory of the Stickleback, for these stimuli are not only "motivating" for aggressive and nest-building behaviour, but also "consummatory" for migration. A suitable habitat brings migration to an end even though the hormonal state which gave rise to it is still (presumably) present. Similarly, the presence of a female decreases the probability of appearance of many of the activities of male song birds which function in pair formation, including song. The presence of another member of the species brings to an end the appetitive behaviour of a bird separated from its flock (Hinde, 1952) or a fish from its school (Keenleyside, 1955). Stimuli from the mother, or from siblings, similarly inhibit the "distress" calls of young domestic chickens (Collias, 1952; Kaufman et al., 1961), Rhesus monkeys (Harlow et al., 1959), and Chimpanzees (Mason et al., 1962). Other examples are discussed by Prechtl (1952), Moynihan (1955), Baerends (1959b), Igel et al. (1960), Wiepkema (1961), and Beer (1961).

One of the best analysed cases of a reduction in responsiveness brought about by a specific external stimulus is given by Sevenster-Bol (1962) for the courtship of the Three-spined Stickleback. The male of this species, having built a nest, courts egg-laden females who enter the territory with a "zig-zag dance" (see pp. 295-6). The courtship culminates with the female swimming through the nest and depositing her eggs there: the male follows, fertilizes the clutch, and then usually attacks the female. In an experimental situation, the frequency of zig-zagging by the male to a standard stimulus is reduced immediately after fertilization and his aggressiveness is increased. Evidently some aspect of the culmination of courtship in fertilization produces a reversal of the relative probabilities of the zig-zag dance and aggressive behaviour. In order to isolate the factors responsible, Sevenster-Bol varied (i) whether or not courtship occurred, (ii) whether or not fertilization occurred and (iii) whether or not the clutch was retained. The reversal of the zig-zag dance/aggression relationship was found to be primarily a consequence of the presence of a fresh clutch of eggs in the nest, and to a lesser extent of stimuli from the spawning female, but not of the occurrence of fertilization (Fig. 10.3). Thus the act of fertilization and the discharge of sperm play no significant part in the subsequent decreased tendency to show the zig-zag dance to females. In addition, it was found that the recovery of the zig-zag dance/aggression relationship occurred about twice as fast in the absence of a clutch as in its presence: the preceding occurrence of courtship and fertilization did not affect this recovery. Stimuli from the clutch thus have a suppressing effect on courtship behaviour.

In this case, recovery occurred in an hour or so: a second type of reduction in sexual responsiveness in the Three-spined Stickleback, studied by van Iersel (1953), occurs after several fertilizations, and has a recovery period of several days. This indicates that the processes underlying the decrease in sexual responsiveness are not unitary, and differ in their recovery periods (see Chapters 13 and 15).

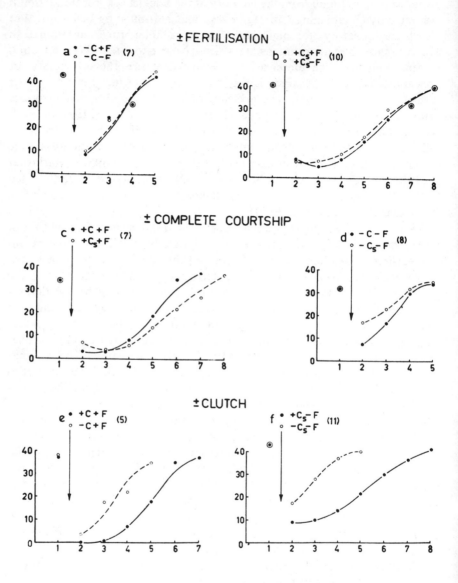

Fig. 10.3. The number of zig-zags shown by male Sticklebacks in "sex tests" in successive trials given at 10-minute intervals. (*After Sevenster-Bol, 1962.*)

C—a clutch is laid in the nest by a female. *F*—the male fertilizes a clutch in the nest. C_s—the male is given a clutch of eggs obtained by stripping a female, no female being introduced into his tank. The dots indicate tests with the supposedly greater amount of "sex-reducing factors", and the open circles those with the supposedly smaller amount. Figures in brackets indicate number of cases.

Consummatory stimuli share many properties with those which augment responsiveness. Just as positively motivating stimuli may act continuously to augment specific responsiveness, so may consummatory stimuli act continuously to decrease the probability of certain responses. Just as one set of positively motivating stimuli may affect several types of response (e.g. the Stickleback's territory), so also may consummatory stimuli (e.g. the influence of stimuli from the Stickleback's eggs on courtship behaviour). Just as any one response may be influenced by several motivating stimuli (e.g. the Stickleback's aggression is influenced by stimuli from the territory, by temperature, light etc.) so any one response may be reduced by several consummatory stimuli (e.g. the distress calls of the chick by contact, warmth, visual stimuli from the mother etc.).

In both cases there is a procedural difficulty in the way of establishing that the effect is a direct one. A stimulus may be consummatory for one activity but elicit another. Its inhibitory effect on the former could thus occur only because it increases the probability of the latter, or vice versa. Usually, however, these possibilities can be differentiated by assessing the predictability of the sequence of the two patterns. If the stimulus switches off the first activity, but the second does not regularly follow, its effect on the first is more likely to be direct. For instance, the threatening behaviour of one Herring Gull to another may be brought to an end by the second bird fleeing, in which case the threatening bird is very likely to follow, or by the second bird attacking, in which case the threatening bird flees. In these cases the new situation acts by eliciting a second activity (chasing or fleeing), and it is this which interrupts the threatening. But if, when threatened, the second bird adopts an appeasement or submissive posture (*see* Chapter 16), the threatening bird may cease to be aggressive and change to any one of a number of activities—feeding, preening, and so on. Here, the new situation seems to have a directly inhibitory effect on the threatening behaviour, and what follows depends on other factors in the situation (Tinbergen, personal communication).

A related point is discussed in detail by Wiepkema (1961). Sevenster-Bol *loc. cit.* considered that the frequency of zig-zag dances shown by a male Stickleback was a measure of its sexual tendency. She therefore concluded that the decrease in the frequency of zig-zags produced by stimuli from a new-laid clutch indicated a reduction in the sexual tendency as such. Wiepkema points out that, in practice, stimuli from the eggs result in an increase in some other sexual activities; for instance, creeping through the nest and ejecting sperm. Sevenster-Bol's interpretation of the mechanism underlying sexual behaviour was thus over-simple because sexual behaviour was assessed in terms of only one character. Wiepkema further suggests that the shift in behaviour following perception of the eggs is a consequence of a change in the relative attacking and fleeing tendencies of the male (*see* Chapter 16), i.e. his "A/F ratio". On this view the influence of the egg-stimuli on the frequency of the zig-zag dances is not direct, but a consequence of an increase in aggressiveness. Wiepkema presents comparable data for the Bitterling (*Rhodeus amarus*), where egg-laying increases both the sexual and the aggressive tendencies of the male: since the aggressive tendency affects the sexual movements differentially (*see* p. 267 and Fig. 16.13), the consequences depend on relations between the two tendencies.

As we have seen, the role of internal stimuli in augmenting eating and drinking behaviour in mammals is not clear, but they do act as consummatory stimuli. An animal usually stops feeding long before the concentration of nutrients in the blood-stream has reached peak level, and before tissue needs are satisfied peripherally. The cessation of feeding is, in fact, brought about by stimuli received during eating, or soon afterwards. The manner in which this occurs has been studied in mammals by severing the oesophagus and bringing the two cut ends to the surface. If such an animal eats, the food drops out of its throat and can have no direct effect on the stomach ("sham feeding"). Alternatively, food can be introduced into the stomach directly. It is thus possible to separate the effects of stimulation in the mouth/throat region from the effects of changes in stomach contents. Using this technique, Lorber *et al.* (1950) found that sham feeding produced an almost immediate cessation of gastric motor activity in dogs, and Berkun *et al.* (1952) that milk administered by mouth reduces the hunger of rats (as measured either by a consummatory or an instrumental response) more than milk introduced directly into the stomach (*see also* Kohn, 1951). Oral factors are thus likely to play a role in bringing feeding to an end.

This oral effect is probably mediated by the taste receptors: saccharin, which is sweet tasting but non-nutritive, is effective in reducing the hunger of rats when administered by mouth, but not when injected directly into the stomach (Miller, 1957). Proprioceptive stimuli consequent upon chewing and swallowing may also be important.

The particular oral stimuli produced by the food also play a part in the control of specific hungers (Young, 1949). If more than one type of food is available an animal usually does not satiate itself on only one of the possibilities, but distributes its choices among the various food items. In both birds (Vince *et al.*, 1963) and Rhesus monkeys (Weiskrantz *et al.*, 1963) the extent of this distribution is a function of experience: in the latter case the primary effect of experience is to decrease the rate at which the animal becomes satiated with a new kind of food.

Although oral and pharyngeal factors may play a role in controlling eating, they are not essential—at any rate in rats. Epstein *et al.* (1962) fitted rats with chronic gastric tubes which by-passed the receptors in mouth, nose and pharynx (Fig. 10.4). The rats were able to feed themselves by pressing a bar: this resulted in the delivery of a small volume of liquid diet into the stomach. In this way they could regulate their own food intake by direct intragastric ingestion (Fig. 10.5). The animals regulated their food intake and body weight with precision for periods of 17 to 44 days, responding appropriately to dilution of the liquid food or to changes in the volume of the individual stomach loads. That stimulation of the oesophageal receptors had in fact been successfully eliminated was checked by the finding that the adulteration of the food with quinine did not affect the intake. Thus post-ingestion factors must be sufficient to control intake.

There is, in fact, considerable evidence that feed-back from the stomach plays a role. Janowitz *et al.* (1949) found that the amount of sham feeding which occurred before satiation greatly exceeded the food deficit, indicating that although oral factors alone can produce cessation of feeding, they are less

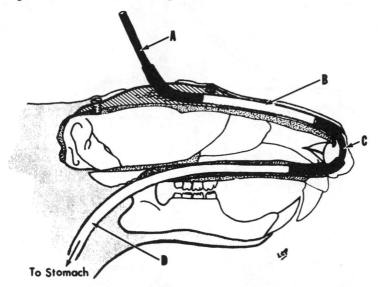

To Stomach

Fig. 10.4. Nasopharyngeal gastric tube used for delivering liquids to rat's stomach without stimulation of the oropharyngeal receptors. (*After Epstein and Teitelbaum, 1962.*)

effective than oral and gastric factors together. Similarly, Berkun *et al.* (1952) found that milk injected directly into the stomach is more effective than saline (*see also* Smith *et al.*, 1955, 1957; Kohn, 1951; Stellar *et al.*, 1954). The precise nature of the gastric effects is not clear; both chemical effects and mechanical stretching may be involved (Miller, 1957). Although bulk in the stomach depresses eating behaviour (Smith *et al.*, 1957), this may not be the sole effect because intake of bulk is varied to compensate for nutritive value of food (Adolph, 1947). Miller (1957) has evidence that the action of a balloon, inflated in the stomach, in reducing feeding behaviour is related to the induction of nausea rather than to satiation.

The interaction between oral and post-ingestion factors is complex. In rats with both oesophageal fistulae and gastric cannulae, Mook (1963) showed that the influence of a particular oral stimulus varied with the nature of the substance reaching the stomach. For instance, intake increases with increasing concentration of glucose tasted if water enters the stomach, but decreases if hypertonic saline enters the stomach. The manner in which the immediate stimuli from the food, the amount ingested and the previous nutritive state of the animal interact have also been studied by Collier *et al.* (1961).

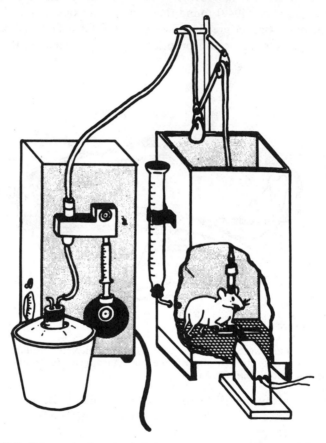

Fig. 10.5. Schematic drawing of the apparatus used for studying intra-gastric self-feeding by rats. (*After Epstein and Teitelbaum, 1962.*)

The role of changes in blood composition which occur subsequent to the food's arrival in the stomach is controversial. Kohn (1951) regarded it as "exceedingly improbable" that changes in the general level of nutrition played any significant role in the short-term effects of eating. Blood from hungry and satiated animals, injected into others, has no differential effect on their rate of eating (Siegel *et al.*, 1954), and Smith *et al.* (1957) could find no evidence that blood sugar plays any direct role in the control of hunger. On the other hand,

Bash (1939b) quotes evidence that denervated stomach muscle transplanted to another part of the body contracted when the intact stomach did, which suggests that the stomach contractions that occur in hunger are controlled via the blood. Another possibility is that the hypothalamus itself is influenced directly by the blood stream: there are probably central receptors sensitive to changes in glucose concentration (Review by Cross, 1964) and osmotic pressure (Verney, 1947). Recent evidence indicates that the gluco-receptors may be located in the liver (Russek, 1963). McCleary (1953) believed that his finding, that both the nature and amount of substances with which the stomach was pre-loaded influence the rate of ingestion immediately afterwards, suggested a role of blood composition in controlling eating. Coppock *et al.* (1954) investigated this further by delivering food directly into the blood-stream. If a rat is given a direct intravenous injection of glucose whenever its head is in a certain position, it keeps its head there for longer than if it is just given saline. The results of a similar experiment with dogs and rabbits, however, produced no such clear-cut effect: the rabbits did spend more time in places where they had been injected, but this could have been a consequence of secondary reinforcement (Chambers, 1956). The evidence is thus not consistent, but lends some support to the view that blood nutrients may play a part in controlling eating, at least in some species.

It has also been suggested that feeding is inhibited by the extra heat produced in assimilating food and preparing it for oxidation by the tissues. After feeding there is a rise in temperature in the centre of the body, and an even greater rise in skin temperature, which is correlated with the decrease in appetite. Furthermore, the effectiveness of various foodstuffs in producing satiety is related to the heat produced in preparing them for oxidation. It may be that the influence of changes in glucose concentration on feeding behaviour is related to the correlated changes in heat production (Adolph, 1947; Brobeck, 1955; Hamilton, 1963).

A comparable complexity exists in the control of drinking behaviour. Oral factors have some inhibitory effect, for sham drinking (i.e., drinking when the oseophagus has been severed and the two ends brought to the surface of the neck) does, after a time, lead to a cessation of drinking behaviour: in dogs this does not occur until the animal has drunk much more than its water deficit, and the satiation is very temporary. In rats, the importance of oral factors in controlling drinking behaviour has been shown in a different way. Thirsty rats will lick at an air jet, and this "air drinking" results in an abnormal loss in weight through evaporation of saliva: it nevertheless produces a reduction in water consumption in a test given immediately afterwards. The air blast cools the mouth, just as drinking water does, and the response is presumably due to a failure to discriminate between the immediate sensory consequences of drinking water and those of drinking air. Air drinking acts as a reward for thirsty rats, but not for satiated ones (Hendry *et al.*, 1961).

Stomach distension, whether produced by a balloon or by liquid, and changes in blood composition also play a role in controlling drinking, though their relative importance varies between different mammalian species (Bellows, 1939; Towbin, 1949; O'Kelly, 1954; Montgomery, A.V. *et al.*, 1955; Moyer *et al.*, 1962). Clark *et al.* (1961) have shown that a thirsty monkey will learn to press a bar to get isotonic saline injected into his blood-stream, but will not press it when satiated with water. Although specialized osmoreceptors may be involved (Verney, 1947), there is also evidence that the osmotic pressure of the body fluids, the chloride concentration in the blood, and the volume of the cells in the body may all influence drinking behaviour (Adolph *et al.*, 1954). Drinking is affected by injection of minute amounts of saline into the brain itself, indicating that there is a direct effect on the central nervous system (*see* p. 197).

In these cases, then, it is clear that the cessation of eating or drinking is controlled by a number of different consequences of the behaviour. The manner in which these interact with the positive factors to determine whether or not the animal eats is demonstrated by brain stimulation experiments. Miller (1960) found that although thoroughly satiated rats can be induced to eat more by brain stimulation, as ingestion proceeds progressively stronger electrical stimulation is necessary to elicit eating.

That the various inhibitory effects are not merely additive, but differ in kind, is indicated by differences in their time relations. Towbin (1949) found that the satiation of thirst which follows sham drinking (i.e. when no water enters the stomach) is only temporary, and the animal soon starts drinking again. The study by Stellar *et al.* (1952), mentioned previously on p. 143, illustrates the same point. When thirsty rats are given water, they drink steadily at a constant rate for a few minutes, and then drink in short bursts over the ensuing period. For periods of deprivation of between 48 and 168 hours, the initial period of continuous drinking is virtually constant (about 8 minutes), though subsequently those animals which have been deprived longer drink more frequently. It thus seems that the initial period of rapid drinking is brought to an end by immediate consequences of drinking, and does not depend on the satisfaction of tissue needs. If the water deficit is not satisfied, these immediate consequences produce only temporary satiation.

This discussion of the control of eating and drinking has been confined to mammals, but comparable data are beginning to be available for other groups. In the Three-spined Stickleback, for instance, at least two factors govern the rate of feeding—one gastric and the other systemic (de Ruiter *et al.*, 1963). In the blowfly, also, feeding is regulated by feed-back stimuli which arise as a consequence of imbibing food, though the mechanism is, of course, quite different. In this species the feeding response occurs in the presence of an adequate sensory input from mouth and leg receptors which are sensitive to sugars and are stimulated by the food substance. Initially, it continues so long as this sensory input is maintained: if the receptors become adapted, feeding ceases temporarily until recovery has occurred. However, prolonged cessation of feeding cannot be ascribed to sensory adaptation: the threshold of stimulation necessary to elicit the response rises during feeding and remains high after feeding has ceased for many hours, long after the sensory adaptation has disappeared. This threshold elevation, which varies with the type of food eaten, is regulated from the fore-gut. Dethier *et al.* (1958) believed this control to be mediated by the recurrent nerve which passes to the brain. They found that if the recurrent nerve is sectioned there is no elevation of the response to sugar, and the fly feeds almost continuously. Evans *et al.* (1960), however, were unable to repeat this result, and point out that a hormonal link in the control of threshold is still possible.

An even simpler mechanism operates in the blood-sucking bug (*Rhodnius*). This animal imbibes blood by means of an abdominal pump. The pump ceases to operate when the abdominal pressure reaches a critical level, at which point the emptying stroke of the pump is not initiated. Thus the size of the meal depends in part on the ease with which the outside of the animal can be stretched (Bennet-Clark, 1963).

In these pages, the role of consummatory stimuli in bringing behaviour to an end has been discussed. In conclusion it must be said that in some of the cases cited the stimuli play a dual role, having both incremental and decremental effects on the response in question. For instance, ingestion of saccharin solution by mouth, but not by stomach, reduces a rat's subsequent consumption of sucrose solution (Miller, 1957). The taste of saccharin thus has consummatory properties. Nevertheless, rats drink more saccharin solution than water, so that the taste of saccharin augments drinking behaviour. Similarly, rats will work harder to obtain a moderately strong glucose solution than a weaker one (McCleary, 1953; Guttman, 1954). Conflicting effects of experience are discussed further in Chapter 13.

10.3 Summary

1. Evidence for a hormonal influence on reproductive activities is of three main types—correlations between endocrine activity and the behaviour, the effects of removal of endocrine organs, and the effects of hormone treatment. Generalizations applicable to all vertebrates are hard to make.
2. Hormones may affect behaviour by enhancing the development of morphological structures used in the behaviour; by influencing the (early) development of the nervous system; by inducing changes in peripheral organs which mediate sensory impulses affecting the central nervous system; by affecting specific mechanisms in the central nervous system; and by exerting a non-specific influence.
3. Any one hormone may produce effects of several kinds, and may even influence one response in a number of different ways.
4. The occurrence of a hormone-influenced response is likely to depend also on many other factors internal and external to the animal.

5. The distinction between the releasing and motivating effects of stimuli, which has been made sometimes in the past, does not necessarily imply different types of mechanism or points of action.

6. Various internal sensory stimuli play a role, but not an essential one, in the motivation of eating, drinking and sexual behaviour in mammals. External stimuli may also have positive motivational effects.

7. When an activity is terminated because the animal encounters a particular stimulus situation as a result of that activity, that situation is referred to as a "consummatory stimulus".

8. Eating and drinking in mammals are controlled, in part, by consummatory stimuli arising from the several consequences (oral, pharyngeal, gastro-intestinal, metabolic, etc.) of ingestion. Their effects decay at different rates.

11

The Mode of Action of Motivational Factors upon Responsiveness

In Chapter 10 we discussed two categories of motivational factors—hormones and stimuli—and considered some evidence as to where and how they produced their effects. We may now continue this topic by considering more precisely some of the behavioural consequences of such factors.

Under natural conditions, and with the exception of certain hibernating species (Mrosovsky, 1964), most hungry animals show appetitive behaviour which involves visiting places where food is likely to be found. They are also especially likely to respond to stimuli indicative of food. The question thus arises, is the response a consequence of increased activity bringing the animal to places where suitable stimuli are encountered, or is the activity the result of increased responsiveness to stimulation? And, if an increase in responsiveness occurs, is it general, or limited to specific types of stimulation?

The traditional view, that deprivation results directly in more locomotor activity, was challenged by Campbell et al. (1953). They suggested that the deprivation produced an increase in responsiveness to stimulation rather than activity *per se*. In their experiment, food-deprived rats showed only a little more activity than a control group if kept under very constant conditions, but considerably more activity if kept in a more variable environment. It thus seemed that the deprivation increased activity by lowering the threshold of responsiveness to environmental change. Hall (1956) failed to get adequate confirmation of this, but Campbell (1960) obtained a similar result for water-deprived rats, and DeVito et al. (1959) for food-deprived monkeys. However, even if environmental conditions are carefully controlled, deprivation brings some increase in activity. Teghtsoonian et al. (1960) found that food-deprived rats kept in a sound-isolated, stimulus-controlled environment showed an increase in activity up to 10 per cent above the pre-deprivation level, though this was much less than the 400 per cent shown by rats kept under ordinary laboratory conditions. It thus seems that food deprivation causes some increase in activity even under constant conditions, though the increase is much greater in a variable environment.

The same problem has been studied by Evans *et al.* (1960) in a quite different species, the blowfly. Food deprivation is associated both with changes in the threshold concentration of sugar solution which will elicit feeding, and with locomotion. After feeding with mannose or fucose, locomotor activity increases steadily with time, whereas the threshold increases to a peak some hours after feeding, and then declines. In this species, therefore, activity and threshold lowering are not well correlated, and are presumably controlled by independent mechanisms. Since activity is reduced by injection of water into the haemocoel, dilution of blood may be the critical factor in its control. The mechanisms governing taste thresholds were mentioned on pp. 184-5.

In rats, activity changes also occur in association with the oestrous cycle. The activity changes are, however, much more marked when the animals have access to a running wheel than if they are kept in stabilimeter cages (Eayrs, 1954). The same is true also of the activity changes resulting from food deprivation (Weasner *et al.*, 1960). In the former case the rat runs inside a wheel which turns as a result of its own activity, while in the latter the floor merely tilts slightly as the rat moves: there is thus a considerable difference in the stimulation which the animal receives from its own movements. As discussed earlier, therefore, the motivational changes seem to be associated with changes in the reinforcing value of the stimulation produced by activity, rather than causing changes in activity directly. Kavanau's (1963) finding that wheel-running was positively reinforcing for Deermice if voluntarily initiated, but aversive if imposed by the experimenter, similarly suggests it has reinforcing consequences only up to a certain level of activity, which varies with the state of the animal.

In these studies the animals were kept in a relatively impoverished laboratory environment, and the types of activity they could show were limited. Under more natural conditions the appetitive behaviour of at any rate experienced animals is rather specific—a song-bird shows one type of appetitive behaviour when patrolling its territory, another when searching for food, and another when collecting nest-material. Even when the motor patterns are similar in the different cases, they are directed towards different situations and involve responsiveness to different stimuli.

Indeed, selective responsiveness to stimuli is often the most important feature by which different types of appetitive behaviour can be categorized. A Great Tit hops over the ground in much the same way whether feeding or looking for nest-material, but it responds to different stimulus objects (*see also* Chapter 6). Similarly, the adults of some species of Cichlid fish, while in the parental phase, may guard or lead *Daphnia*, normally their favourite food, as if they were their offspring (Baerends, 1957a): in this state they respond to the characteristics which *Daphnia* share with the young rather than to their food characteristics.

There is evidence that even the increase in activity induced by stimulation in hungry rats is limited to stimuli previously associated with food. Sheffield *et al.*

(1954) found that stimulus change was associated with an increase in activity only if feeding followed immediately, and not if there was a time lag of one or two hours. These results were confirmed and extended by Amsel *et al.* (1961). It appears that the response to stimulus change is selective, only those stimuli likely to signal relief of the deprivation being effective.

Granted that the stimuli to which the animal responds vary with its motivational state, the next question is the mechanism by which this occurs. One possibility is that the sensitivity of the sense organs themselves changes with the motivational state. Although the suggestion that selective attention is mediated by centrifugal control of activity in the sensory pathways is not well-substantiated (Chapter 6), the longer-term changes in hunger or sexual arousal could still depend on sensory factors. The evidence, however, is against such a view. In the blowfly, the time relations involved in the adaptation of the taste organs are quite different from those of hunger itself (Dethier *et al.*, 1958). In mammals, more direct evidence is available. Meyer (1952) found that 34 hours of starvation produced no changes in the salt, sweet or bitter thresholds of human subjects. Adrenalectomized, and therefore salt-deficient, rats have a low preference threshold for salt solutions, but Pfaffmann *et al.* (1950) found no difference in the gustatory nerve thresholds between normal and adrenalectomized rats (*see also* Carr, 1952). Similarly, sodium deficient rats select sodium chloride solutions in preference to water or solutions not containing sodium chloride, but there is no difference between deficient and non-deficient rats in the frequency of discharges produced in the chorda tympani by sodium chloride. Nachman *et al.* (1963) thus conclude that taste preferences are governed by a central mechanism which is affected directly by sodium levels. However, the possibility that there is a change in the patterning of the peripheral discharge even when the overall frequency is constant remains open.

A similar conclusion has been reached from studies of sexual behaviour. Intact male rats choose the arm of an olfactometer containing a receptive female in preference to that containing a female in anoestrous, while prepuberal or castrated males do not (Le Magnen, 1952). However, gonadectomy does not affect the ability of either males or females to distinguish between the odours of sexually active and inactive members of the opposite sex when running through the apparatus for water. Furthermore, the olfactory threshold for oestrous female urine is not affected by gonadal state (Carr *et al.*, 1962). It thus seems that the sex hormone affects the stimulus/response relation rather than the ability to discriminate the stimulus.

In many cases the effect of the motivational factors can thus be adequately described as a sensitization of particular stimulus/response relations. A food-deprived rat eats food when a satiated one ignores it; a male Chaffinch attempts copulation with a female dummy in winter only if treated with androgen. Often, as in this last case, the motivational factor influences not just one response, but a group of functionally related ones (*see* Chapter 18).

Crook's (1964b) observations on the nest-building of Weavers show that hormonal action may also influence the effectiveness with which movements are orientated. When building motivation is low, the stitching movements result in structures without the characteristic nest form, consisting of an unorganized webbing over the supporting twigs. Only in more active building are the building movements properly oriented. Thus with increasing nest-building vigour (presumably correlated with changing hormone levels), the building not only increases in amount but also, because the movements become

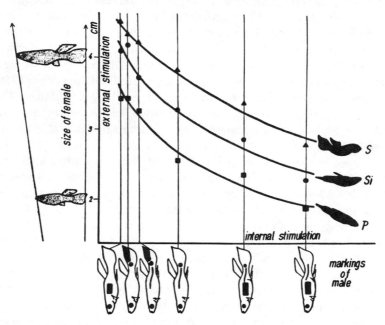

Fig. 11.1. The influence of the strength of the external stimulation (measured by the size of the female) and the internal state (measured by the colour pattern of the male) in determining the courtship behaviour of male Guppies. (*From Baerends et al., 1955.*)

Each curve represents the combination of external stimulus and internal state producing a particular type of behaviour, namely, posturing *P*, the sigmoid intention movement *Si*, and the fully developed sigmoid *S*.

properly adjusted to the structure, in qualitative effectiveness. Since the male may build simultaneously on several nests at different stages, this does not involve merely a change to a different type of movement: the building behaviour is adjusted to each of the nests in hand at the moment. Many comparable examples are given by Howard (1935).

Sensitization of stimulus response relations implies that there is an inverse relationship between the strength of the motivational factors and the strength of the stimulus required to elicit a response of given strength. An example is given by the work of Baerends *et al.* (1955) on the courtship of the male Guppy (*Lebistes reticulatus*). In this species the coloration of the male provides an index of his tendencies to attack, flee from and behave sexually towards the female. In Fig. 11.1 the colour patterns of the male are arranged along the abscissa in an order representing increasing tendency for the male to show sexual behaviour. The effectiveness of a female in eliciting courtship increases with her size: this is plotted on the ordinate. The curves represent the relations between internal and external factors required to produce particular patterns of behaviour: "posturing", "incomplete sigmoid" and "sigmoid". The same pattern may thus appear with a wide range of combinations of internal and external factors.

Even when stimulus characters cannot readily be measured along a simple physical scale, a similar principle applies. Thus we have already seen that the different stimulus characters effective for a given response (p. 53) can supplement each other—deficiency in one can be compensated by increase in another. It is as though the several stimulus characters fed into a common pool to produce a certain quantity of stimulation. The consequence is that, as the motivational factors increase, objects sharing fewer and fewer characters with the natural or optimal object are adequate to produce a response of given intensity: the range of effective stimuli thus increases. For instance, Prechtl (1953) showed that the range of stimuli which would elicit begging from the nestlings of passerine birds increased with hunger, and Beach (1942b) found that the lower the copulatory threshold of male rats, the greater the range of stimulus objects with which they would copulate. Similar effects occur in men, for ambiguous or non-existent stimuli are interpreted as related to food more by hungry subjects than by satiated ones (McClelland *et al.*, 1948; *see also* Vernon, 1952).

So far, three ways in which motivational factors affect behaviour have been mentioned—they may increase activity, influence selectivity in responsiveness to stimuli, and they may also be spoken of as sensitizing stimulus-response relations. We shall see later that these do not provide an adequate description of all the ways in which motivational factors affect behaviour. In the senses discussed on pp. 304-11, much behaviour is goal-directed; and goal stimuli have reinforcing properties. The motivational factors act by determining the goal (*see* Chapter 18).

11.1.   Summary

1. The increase in activity which often follows deprivation may be largely a consequence of an increased responsiveness to external stimulation rather than a direct effect of deprivation on activity.

2. The changes in activity which accompany the oestrous cycle in rats are related to a change in the reinforcing value of the activity-produced stimulation, rather than a direct effect of the oestrous cycle on activity.

3. An increase in the motivational factors for a given type of behaviour is accompanied by selectivity in responsiveness to stimuli.
4. This selectivity is usually not due to an influence of the motivational factors on sensory mechanisms.
5. Motivational factors can also be said to sensitize stimulus-response relations. There is an inverse relation between the strength of a stimulus and the strength of the motivational factors required for a response of a given intensity.
6. Motivational factors can also be described as determining the goals of behaviour.

12

The Hypothesis of a "Central Excitatory State"

When a male Chaffinch wakes from its roosting place in early spring, it may sing for a while, patrolling its territory intermittently between bouts of singing. During this period it is likely to attack or threaten any other males it sees. It may then fly down from the trees and feed on the ground for a while: often it feeds in close proximity to other males, whom it tolerates at a distance of a few feet. After a period of feeding it is likely to fly up into a bush to preen, and then return to singing. It shows, in fact, periodic changes from being concerned primarily with one group of activities to being concerned with another.

Such changes in behaviour presumably depend on changes in physiological state, each state having some degree of persistence in time. Nevertheless, they seem to be independent of changes in many of the continuously-acting extra-neural factors known to influence the behaviour in question: thus the Chaffinch sings only when in a certain hormonal condition and while on its territory, yet neither of these alters when it flies down to feed. This suggests that the activities are not influenced directly by these extra-neural factors, but depend on the state of central nervous mechanisms which mediate their effects.

Similarly, when a stimulus is presented to an animal, its response is not constant, but changes with time. Further, if such a stimulus is removed, a state of changed responsiveness to that stimulus, revealed if it is re-presented, persists for some time (e.g. in Chapter 13). If extra-neural factors are constant, such changes must be ascribed to the neural mechanisms mediating the response.

For such reasons various authors have postulated a "central excitatory state" or "central motive state". This is regarded as carrying the effects of the extra-neural factors, and of influences from other parts of the central nervous system, for some time, and as predisposing the organism to respond either more vigorously in general, or else in particular ways to particular stimuli (Sherrington, 1906; Lashley, 1938a; Beach, 1942b; Morgan, 1943, 1959, Stellar, 1954).

When it was first introduced by Sherrington, the concept of "central excitatory state" was used mainly to refer to changes in excitability which outlasted the stimulation of an afferent nerve by a few milliseconds. For instance contraction of the *tibialis anterior* of the dog can be elicited by stimulation of more than one cutaneous nerve. If just-threshold shocks are administered to different nerves the response is greatest when the stimuli are synchronous, and falls rapidly when the interval between them increases to about 20 milliseconds. Apparently, the first stimulus creates a central state which lasts for about this time. Although the experiments by Sherrington and his collaborators were concerned mostly with reflex responses within the spinal cord, the concept has been taken over to account for similar effects in more complex responses. In the latter cases the postulated central state has often been assigned to the hypothalamus (e.g. Stellar, 1954, 1960) since various types of evidence, drawn mostly from studies of mammals, converge to indicate that there are mechanisms there specific to particular types of behaviour. Thus:

1. Localized ablations in the hypothalamus produce specific effects on behaviour. For instance, in the rat, destruction of an area in the medial part of the hypothalamus, including the ventromedial nucleus, results in hyperphagia and obesity, while lesions in a more lateral area lead to aphagia, the animals starving to death in the midst of plenty. The two areas have thus been said to contain "satiation" and "feeding" centres respectively (Anand *et al.*, 1951; Miller, 1957; Teitelbaum, 1955). (Since lesions which influence eating often also influence drinking, and the interactions between eating and drinking are complex, (*see* pp. 150-1) it is not always clear which effects are primary (Morrison *et al.*, 1957a, b; *see also* p. 197).) Localized lesions can similarly affect other types of behaviour (e.g. Phoenix, 1961).

2. Electrical stimulation of particular regions of the hypothalamus may produce highly specific effects which are, in general, the reverse of those of ablation (Hess, 1954). For instance, stimulation of the lateral hypothalamus of rats induces feeding behaviour, while stimulation of the ventromedial region stops it (Anand *et al.*, 1951; Larsson, 1954). An example is given in Fig. 12.1 (Smith, 1961), which shows data from a rat with electrodes in both lateral and medial areas. The strength of stimulation was the same for both: it remained constant for the first half hour of each experiment, and was then increased slightly in the case of the lateral electrode and decreased for the medial electrode. The animal was starved for 18 hours before the beginning of each test. In spite of this, consumption was markedly depressed during the first half hour of stimulation through the medial electrode. With the lateral electrode, consumption was increased most markedly during the second half hour, as this was the period during which eating ceased in the control condition. The differences between the 6-hour points were not significant. Similar results have been obtained with goats (Wyrwicka and Dobrzecka, 1960), and stimulation of an area medial to the lateral hypothalamus in this species produces drinking (Andersson *et al.*, 1955).

Other types of behaviour which have been elicited by hypothalamic stimulation through implanted electrodes include attack, flight and rage, cooling, micturition and defaecation, sleep and motor activity. The mammalian studies have been recently reviewed by Akert (1961), and comparable results have been obtained with birds (Åkerman *et al.*, 1960). Hess (e.g. 1954), who did much of the pioneering work in this field with cats, found that with some electrode placements stimulation elicited the activities of looking for a sleeping place, lying down etc. (*see also* Nauta, 1946). The case for a "sleep centre" is, however, still controversial: the low-frequency direct-current pulses which Hess used could have blocked the influence of the reticular system in producing wakefulness.

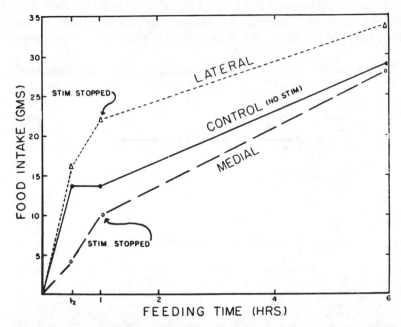

Fig. 12.1. Effects of stimulation of the lateral and medial hypothalamus on food intake. (*After Smith, 1961.*)

The intensity of stimulation was set at a value which did not produce somatic motor responses. It remained unchanged for the first half hour. For the second it was increased slightly for the lateral placement and decreased for the medial placement.

Although the behaviour produced by electrical stimulation sometimes consists merely of stereotyped movements, the effect seems to be a physiological one: the movements themselves are integrated, the different parts of the body adjusting their posture and tonus appropriately. The induced movements may interact with naturally occurring changes in behaviour, so that summation or mutual inhibition occurs, and the animal may even show behaviour whose goal appears to be the diminution or inhibition of the movement evoked (Delgado, 1962). Often, quite complex chains of behaviour are involved. Thus electrical stimulation in the thirst or feeding area will cause a goat to show a previously learnt instrumental response which has been rewarded by water (Andersson *et al.*, 1957; Wyrwicka, Dobrzecka and Tarnecki, 1960). Similarly, electrical stimulation of part of the hypothalamus of the cat produces first behavioural arousal, then a defensive position and certain vocalizations, leading subsequently to hissing, spitting and attack. This behaviour is accompanied by the autonomic changes which normally accompany such behaviour in the intact animal. The aggressive behaviour ceases as soon as the stimulation is discontinued, but a lowered threshold may persist (Hess, 1954; review by Akert, 1961).

That the effectiveness of intracranial electrical stimulation may vary with time, indicating the occurrence of internal changes in responsiveness, has already been mentioned (p. 160). Von Holst *et al.* (1963) describe such changes

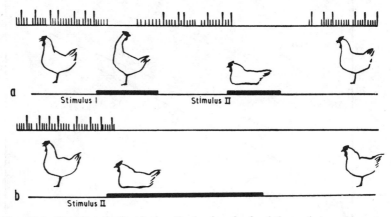

Fig. 12.2. Results of stimulating the brain of a fowl through two separate electrodes. (*After von Holst and von St. Paul, 1963.*)

Initially, the bird was cackling, as indicated by vertical marks on top line. The first stimulus produces "watchful staring", and a brief interruption of the scolding. The second stimulus produces "sitting down in sleepy mood" and a more prolonged interruption of scolding. Nevertheless, the scolding re-asserts itself. Only after a prolonged stimulus through the second electrode does the scolding disappear completely.

as involving a change of "mood". They point out that the tendency for an animal to show one type of behaviour has inertia, and is only slowly interrupted by stimuli for other responses. For instance, in Fig. 12.2 the previously present "cackling" mood is interrupted only briefly by an electrical stimulus which induces "watching-out", but more effectively by one which induces "sitting". However, a brief stimulus for sitting is insufficient to change the mood for long, and the cackling mood reappears. Only after a prolonged stimulus does its disappearance persist. Presumably, therefore, the stimulus induces a change in the organism which outlasts the stimulus. Usually, such effects are not of very great duration, but in some cases effects lasting even longer have been produced by stimulation known to have been in the hypothalamus: Delgado *et al.* (1953) found increases in food intake the day after stimulating the lateral hypothalamus of cats. Smith (1961) obtained a similar result with rats.

3. The administration of drugs, hormones or metabolites to localized areas may produce specific effects on behaviour. The "respiratory centre" in the hypothalamus is a well-known case; the influence of oestrogens on the hypothalamus of cats, discussed previously, is another (*see* p. 171). The injection of minute quantities of hypertonic saline into the hypothalamus of goats produces an appropriate increase in drinking behaviour (Andersson, 1953). Miller has extended this work using cats. Furthermore, cats work harder to obtain water after injections of hypertonic sodium chloride into the brain; this indicates that the injection produces the same general characteristics as thirst (Miller, 1959, 1961a, and pp. 198-202). Grossman (1960) found that adrenergic substances introduced into the feeding area induced eating, and cholinergic substances drinking. Specific effects of heating other loci have also been found (Ranson *et al.*, 1937; *see also* Cross, 1964).

Recent work has shown that intracranial (though not necessarily hypothalamic) infusion may produce not merely temporary changes in behaviour, but also long-lasting effects. Rats with ethanol chronically infused into the cerebral ventricles showed sudden and lasting oral preferences for moderately high ethanol concentrations: histological examination revealed no morphological alterations in the brain (Myers, 1964).

4. Another possible line of evidence for centres in the hypothalamus comes from experiments on the reinforcing effects of self-administered intracranial electrical stimulation. Olds (1958, 1962) has claimed that, within the areas of the brain from which reinforcing effects are produced (*see* p. 171), there are sub-areas in which the effects are enhanced by androgen or food deprivation (*see also* Brady, 1961). A relationship between self-stimulation and sexual behaviour is also suggested by Miller's (1961a, b) finding that electrode placements in or near the hypothalamus which produced ejaculation were more likely to prove rewarding in a self-stimulation experiment than those which did not (*see also* Olds, 1962). However, other evidence indicates that eating induced by externally controlled electrical hypothalamic stimulation and the behaviour involved in producing intracranial self-stimulation may depend on different mechanisms. For one thing, the electrical thresholds for the two effects differ. In addition, amphetamine, which decreases hunger by many behavioural tests, raises the electrical threshold for inducing eating and lowers that for self-stimulation (Miller 1960; Prescott, 1964).

Taken as a whole, the evidence indicates clearly the existence of mechanisms in the hypothalamus of great importance in the control of functional sequences of behaviour, such as those involved in eating, drinking and sexual behaviour. It is necessary, however, to make several reservations or qualifications.

One possible objection to experiments involving electrical stimulation of the brain is that the stimulus does not produce a specific response, but results in a general activation. This has been effectively answered by Coons *et al.* (cited Miller, 1960). Electrodes were implanted into the brains of rats in such a manner that stimulation induced eating only. If such animals were tested when satiated with food but mildly thirsty, they would leave the water spout to go to the place where they had previously learnt that food was hidden. If the effect of the stimulation was merely to activate an otherwise dominant but sub-threshold type of behaviour, the rats should have continued to drink instead of going to food.

Although central stimulation or central lesions can influence complex chains of behaviour as a whole, these experiments must not, of course, be taken to imply that the elements in such chains cannot be independently modified: a mass of direct behavioural evidence shows that they can. For instance, Kagan (1955) trained rats to run a maze to a receptive female in a goal box. If the males were allowed to mount but not to ejaculate when they reached the goal box, their maze performance improved but their tendency to show sexual responses decreased—appetitive and consummatory behaviour were influenced in different ways (*see also* Chapter 15). It is thus not surprising that lesions in one of the hypothalamic "centres" may not affect all aspects of a given type of behaviour equally. A hypothalamic lesion which causes a rat to overeat, and thus seems to increase feeding motivation, also causes a reduction in bar-pressing rewarded by food, a reduction in tolerance of quinine, and a reduction in speed of running to food: the lesion thus does not have similar effects on all aspects of the behaviour (Miller, 1957; *see also* Choy, quoted by Miller, 1960; Ehrlich, 1963).

Another question concerns the extent to which the results of central stimulation show all the properties of normally motivated behaviour. This has been carefully studied by Miller and his co-workers (reviewed 1961). In some cases they found that behaviour produced artificially in this way shared properties with that which occurs normally. Thus central elicitation of the cat's "alarm" reaction has all the functional properties of externally elicited pain and fear: (1) the stimulation can motivate, and its termination reinforce, trial-and-error learning; (2) it can be used to establish a conditioned response; (3) it can be used to condition an emotional disturbance to a distinctive environment and, after this, during trials without any further stimulation, the cats will learn to escape from that environment; (4) it can serve as a punishment to teach hungry cats to avoid food. Similarly, Roberts *et al.* (1964) found that the central readiness for attack produced in cats by hypothalamic stimulation had motivational and cue properties.

However, centrally evoked responses do not always have the properties of normally motivated behaviour. Rage responses, apparently similar to those produced by peripheral pain, differ from them in that they cannot easily be conditioned; and a cat in which the flight response was induced by central stimulation showed rapid escape learning but failed to show avoidance learning. Miller comments, "In investigating the motivating effects of central stimulation of the brain, it is unsafe to take anything for granted."

Similar difficulties arise with feeding and drinking behaviour. At some points stimulation elicits merely stereotyped gnawing movements (Miller, 1960). Reciprocally, when a lesion affects eating behaviour, it is not always certain that the deficiency is entirely a motivational one. Baillie *et al.* (1963) therefore investigated the possibility that rats rendered aphagic by lateral hypothalamic lesions might be suffering from lack of ability to eat. They found that animals conditioned to obtain food by lever pressing continued to press the lever after operation. Furthermore, rats conditioned to feed themselves through an intragastric injection by lever pressing continued to do so after operation even though showing aphagia and adipsia when offered food and water by mouth. They therefore conclude that the lateral hypothalamic lesions produce predominantly a motor failure—a true aphagia. There could also be an effect on the motivational control of eating (i.e. an anorexia), but this is temporary.

On the other hand, in many experiments the consequences of central stimulation seem very similar to those of normal hunger. Miller (1960) and his associates showed that central stimulation could cause a satiated rat to eat solid foods or drink liquid ones, elicit learned food-seeking habits, and cause a mildly thirsty animal to stop drinking water and go to find concealed food. Furthermore, the threshold of stimulation required was raised by the appetite-reducing drug dextroamphetamine (cf. p. 197); and cessation of stimulation acted as a reinforcement for the learning of a T-maze just as does the food which terminates hunger. However, the rewarding effect of cessation of stimulation can be obtained from points which do not elicit eating, and there are threshold differences between the effect of stimulation on eating and its rewarding effect; the reward effect and eating may thus be independent effects of the stimulation. These and other experiments by Krasne reported by Miller (1960) show clearly that the consequences of brain stimulation are far from simple (*see also* Tenen *et al.*, 1964).

Of special interest are experiments showing that the response elicited is characterized not by the motor movements of ingestion, but by the sensory feed-back obtained. When a rat with an electrode implanted in an area where eating is induced is stimulated, it will not drink water, but will drink sugar-water or milk, even though satiated. Apparently the stimulation engenders a tendency to respond in a way which brings a particular type of sensory feedback (Miller, 1960). Cats that attack objects as a result of hypothalamic stimulation are, similarly, not indiscriminate in the objects that they attack (Levison *et al.*, 1965).

Hyperphagia induced by hypothalamic lesions also may involve increased sensitivity to stimulation received by eating. Teitelbaum (1955) compared the role of stimulation from the food eaten in regulating the diet of normal rats, and rats made hyperphagic by hypothalamic lesions. Two types of hyper-phagic animal were studied: an obese group and a "dynamic" group prevented from becoming obese by restricted feeding. The normal animals, unlike the hyperphagics, regulated their diet appropriately according to the calorific qualities of the food, increasing their intake when the food was diluted with non-nutritive cellulose. The hyperphagics, by contrast, decreased their in-take. The obese hyperphagics, however, were more sensitive to the stimulus qualities of the food. Thus they decreased their intake when the food was adulterated with quinine at a concentration which did not affect the normals or the dynamic hyperphagics. Addition of dextrose caused an increased intake by the obese animals, had no effect on the dynamic hyperphagics, and resulted in a decreased intake by the normals, who were perhaps responding to the calorific value. The dynamic hyperphagics differed from the obese animals in that they over-ate heedlessly (*see also* Corbit *et al.*, 1964).

Whether this responsiveness of hyperphagic rats to stimuli from the food is specific to taste stimuli is a further question. Smith *et al.* (1961) found that preloading the stomach by tube had an even greater negative effect on the feeding behaviour of hyperphagics than on that of normal rats, and ascribe such results to an increased "emotional reactivity".

Another issue is whether the hyperphagia is *necessarily* correlated with increased sensitivity to stimulation from the food, or whether these are indepen-dent effects. Graff *et al.* (1962) confirmed that rats with ventromedial hypothal-amic lesions show a certain amount of "finickyness", but, by using rats with smaller lesions, they found that the neural mechanisms for hyperphagia and finickyness are separate, but overlap in area.

This evidence that the hypothalamic mechanisms influence responsiveness to the stimulation resulting from eating shows that the "central excitatory state" must not be thought of as a storing up of excitation ready to be released in specific activities. Rather, it would seem that the extra-neural motivating factors (Chapter 10) produce a condition in which both stimulus-response relations are facilitated and sensitivity to stimuli encountered as a result of the response is affected. To some extent, this is an inevitable consequence of our earlier discussion of consummatory stimuli: if behaviour is terminated by stimuli received as a consequence of that behaviour, the motivating factors which give rise to the behaviour must also increase susceptibility to those con-summatory stimuli. More than this is involved, however, for the behaviour is varied so that the consummatory stimuli are encountered—in other words, the goals are set (*see* Chapter 18).

While the neural mechanisms responsible are often referred to as centres, it is clear that they are not anatomically localized, but diffuse structures. The points from which any particular pattern of behaviour can be elicited by elec-trical stimulation are intermingled with points whose stimulation leads to different responses. Indeed, in view of the diverse functions which have been assigned to the hypothalamus, the multiple influences to which it is subject and effectors which it influences, an interpretation of hypothalamic function in terms even of functionally distinct centres is likely to be an over-simplification. Indeed it is necessary to stress in this context that some responses are common to many functional categories of behaviour. Cardiovascular changes, for instance, occur in the defence reaction (fight, flight and fright), adaptations to external heat or cold, sexual behaviour, and so on.

Further, the finding that the hypothalamus is important in a given type of behaviour must not be taken to imply that responsiveness depends solely on the state of a hypothalamic mechanism—clearly other parts of the central nervous system are also involved.* Hyperphagia in rats can be produced by forebrain lesions as well as lesions in the hypothalamus (Richter *et al.*, 1939). In sexual behaviour, Beach (1940, 1944) showed that removal of parts of the cerebral cortex resulted in a behavioural deficit which increased with the extent of the cortical damage. The change in behaviour, however, did not consist in the omission of particular parts of the sexual pattern, but in a general reduction of sexual motivation. This could be compensated for by administration of androgen—the greater the cortical damage, the more androgen was required to restore the sexual behaviour to the normal level. It seemed as though the cortex was exerting an excitatory influence on sexual behaviour synergic with that exerted by the androgens. Similar results were obtained after ablations of the telencephalon of pigeons (*see* Chapter 10).

To cite another example, the so-called rage response of cats can be abolished by hypothalamic lesions, evoked by stimulation in the hypothalamus, amygdala and midbrain, and can be shown by cats lacking a telencephalon. The normal response, however, depends on complex interrelations between telencephalon and diencephalon. For example, while removal of the neocortex may result in placidity, ablation of parts of the rhinencephalon results in an increase in ferocity. The rage response of hypothalamic cats not only lacks direction, but also has a very low threshold and practically no after-response: unlike normal rage, it ceases almost as soon as the eliciting stimulus is removed (Bard *et al.*, 1948). The contribution of the higher levels seems to be concerned with the release and regulation of the response, while the mechanism of expression depends primarily on the hypothalamus (*see* Akert, 1961). Even this, however, may represent an oversimplification, for acute lesions in the anterior part of the system have no effect on the threshold for electrical stimulation

---

* Even in lower vertebrates such areas are not merely command centres determining peripheral motor responses, but are also integrators of sensory input and proprioceptive feedback. Thus in *Xenopus*, clasping and feeding are coordinated by spino-medullary systems, occurring in response to the appropriate input in animals in which the CNS is transected just anterior to the Vth cranial nerves. However, the elicitation of clasping and feeding, and therefore the functioning of their respective control systems, depends on the integrity of the sensory as well as the motor innervation of the hindbrain (Hutchison, 1964).

applied more posteriorly, but coagulation in the midbrain and hypothalamus at first eliminates elicitation of threat behaviour by more anterior stimulation. Two weeks later, however, anterior stimulation can again elicit threat behaviour, but at a higher threshold (Brown *et al.*, 1963). Recent reviews are given by Brady (1960) and Stellar (1960), and the special importance of the limbic system has been stressed by Pribram (e.g. 1961) and Weiskrantz (1964).

In conclusion, the persistence of the effects of stimulation, and the fluctuations of behaviour which occur independently of changes in extraneural irritants, indicate the existence of central states of considerable endurance. On the whole, the physiological evidence supports this view, though it must not be thought that the central state is merely one of accumulated excitation or that response strength depends on the state of any one locus. There is considerable evidence that the central mechanisms can act by determining behavioural goals as well as by the sensitization of stimulus-response relations.

Summary

1. Under natural conditions animals show changes in behaviour which presumably depend on changes in physiological state, each state having some degree of persistence in time. Nevertheless, the changes seem to be independent of continuously acting extra-neural factors (e.g. hormones, external stimuli) known to affect the behaviour in question. This suggests that the activities are not influenced by these extra-neural factors directly, but depend on the state of neural mechanisms which mediate their effects.
2. Physiological evidence for such mechanisms is provided by studies involving lesions of the central nervous system, stimulation of the CNS by electrical and chemical stimuli, and perhaps by experiments involving self-administered intracranial stimulation.
3. In some cases the behaviour produced is stereotyped and abnormal, but in others it shows properties similar to those of normally motivated behaviour. Several lines of evidence indicate that the central mechanisms operate by influencing sensitivity to stimulation rather than by controlling particular movement patterns.
4. The central nervous mechanisms concerned are not anatomically localized.

13

Short-term Changes in Responsiveness Consequent upon Experience

When an animal eats, its tendency to continue eating is gradually reduced. We have seen in Chapter 10 that this can be ascribed at least in part to influences from the food ingested. But, even when there is no obvious new source of stimulation comparable to that provided by ingested food, the performance of a response is often associated with an increase or decrease in the probability that it will appear again: activity is accompanied by positive and negative feedback effects. Thus if the begging response of a young passerine bird is elicited by an appropriate stimulus a number of times in succession, the bird becomes unresponsive: the waning of responsiveness is a consequence of the presentation of the stimulus, and must be due either to a direct effect of perceiving the stimulus, or to proprioceptive or humoral effects of responding, or to some direct consequence of activity in the nervous mechanisms underlying the response.

In this chapter we shall consider the properties of the changes in responsiveness which occur in such circumstances, concentrating for the most part on short-term effects. More permanent effects are discussed in Section 3.

13.1. Waning in the Absence of Muscular Fatigue and Sensory Adaptation

A waning of responsiveness could, of course, be a consequence of metabolic fatigue: thus in *Drosophila* flying may wane independently of walking, but the waning is due to the depletion of carbohydrate reserves which are necessary for flying but not walking (Wigglesworth, 1949).

Muscular fatigue is, however, unlikely to be a major factor if, after waning, the same effectors can be used for a different response. When the skin of its back is stimulated, a frog will make a wiping movement over the spot with its leg. Franzisket (1953) studied the waning of this response by giving series of 100 stimulations, each series taking about 17 minutes. When such series were given for a number of days in succession, the proportion of stimuli which elicited responses increased from about 10 per cent to 60 to 90 per cent. If two series were then given one after the other in the same place, the number of responses to the second series was much reduced. However, such a reduction in the second series was not found if it involved elicitation of a different response, even though both responses used the same groups of muscles; for instance, wiping and pulling up the suspended hind limb when pinched. As another example, Eikmanns (1955) studied the waning of the orientation movement made by a toad to a fly dummy presented to one side of its body axis. This movement is normally a preliminary to catching the prey, but is nearly identical in form to the optomotor response made when the toad is placed in the centre of a striped cylinder which revolves about it. After a long series of presentations of the prey dummy the orientation response wanes, but the optomotor response can still be elicited at full strength. Further evidence against the view that muscular fatigue plays any significant role in such cases of waning comes from experiments showing that the decrement is specific to one stimulus or sensory modality: some examples are cited below (p. 205).

Similarly, adaptation of the sense cells can be ruled out if, after one type of response to a stimulus has waned, the same stimulus elicits a different response. If a reflexogenous zone round the mouth of a hungry human newborn is stimulated, the head is turned so that the mouth moves towards the point stimulated. The response wanes with successive stimuli, but its place may be taken by another response (turning away) mediated by the same sensory region of the skin, and presumably by the same sense organs (Prechtl, 1958). In other cases adaptation of the sense organ cannot be an important issue because the reduction in responsiveness applies also when the same response is elicited through a different receptor cell. The twitching response of the earthworm, which can be elicited by thermal, mechanical or galvanic stimulation, wanes with successive stimuli: the decrease in responsiveness to stimuli in a given modality affects also neighbouring segments, and thus cannot be due to changes in the sense organs themselves (Kuenzer, 1958; *see also* Franzisket, loc. cit.). Similarly, the waning of the scratch reflex of dogs (Sherrington, 1906) and the wiping response of toads (Kuczka, 1956) affects all points within several millimetres of the point stimulated.

Sensory adaptation is also ruled out in experiments in which a stimulus, the response to which has waned, again elicits a response when presented in a different context. For instance Engen and Lipsitt (1965), studying the breathing responses of human neonates to odour, found that when the response to a mixture of two odours had waned, it could be elicited again when only one of them was presented: clearly the initial waning cannot be regarded as sensory fatigue (*see also* Bartoshuk 1962a, b).

Another source of evidence that the waning can be independent of changes in both the sense organs and the effectors comes from studies in which the peripheral nerves or central nervous system are stimulated electrically. Von Holst et al. (1963) elicited a variety of complex patterns of behaviour by stimulation through electrodes permanently implanted in the brain of unanaesthetized chickens. If more than one electrode was implanted in the same animal, the same response could sometimes be elicited from different loci. Repeated stimulation in one locus led to a reduction in responsiveness which affected that locus only: stimulation through the other electrode was still fully effective. The waning process must have occurred between the electrode and the final common path.

To summarize, although muscular fatigue and sensory adaptation may be involved in many cases of waning in responsiveness, the evidence cited shows that changes occur also between the sensory cells and the effectors, and it is often these changes that play the major role.

13.2. Stimulus Specificity of Decremental Processes

Even where adaptation of the sensory cells is unlikely to be a factor, it is sometimes clear that if a response can be elicited by more than one stimulus situation, the waning is specific to the particular stimulus (or modality) used. We may consider some examples drawn from a variety of species ranging from annelids to vertebrates:

(a) The waning of the twitching response of the earthworm (*see* above) is at first specific to the sensory modality through which it is elicited. The specificity decreases if stimulation is prolonged (Kuenzer, 1958).

(b) *Drosophila* spp. show an orientation response both to a localized light source and to gravity. The response to either wanes after about 100 elicitations, but the response to the other is unaffected (Dürrwächter, 1957).

(c) The waning of the prey-catching response of the water-bug *Notonecta glauca* is specific at least to the side of the body on which the stimulus is presented. If a stimulus is presented three hundred times on the left side the proportion of responses elicited falls off markedly, but responsiveness to stimuli presented on the right side is unimpaired (Wolda, 1961).

(d) The equilibratory response of the frog *Rana esculenta* when the substrate is tilted is mediated by both eye and labyrinth. Responsiveness wanes when the animal is stimulated successively through one modality, but it still responds to the other (Butz-Kuenzer, 1957).

(e) If a small dummy is presented to a toad (*Bufo bufo*), the animal turns towards it. This movement is the first stage of catching prey. If the stimulus is presented successively so that it is in exactly the same position relative to the toad each time, the response wanes. The waning of the response is specific to the characteristics of the dummy (size, colour, etc.) and to the particular spot on the retina stimulated (Eikmanns, 1955).

(f) A toad makes wiping movements directed at any spot on its skin which is touched with the hand. The waning which occurs with repeated stimulation is specific to the particular area stimulated and, in some degree, to the frequency of stimulation. This case is especially interesting as there is evidence that the stimulus-specific waning can occur even if no response is given. Sudden stimulation with a bristle does not elicit wiping, but does lead to a reduction in responsiveness to subsequent stimulation of the same spot by hand (Kuczka, 1956).

(g) The gaping response of 5 to 7-day-old Chaffinches can be elicited both by shaking the nest and by imitating the call of the parents. If a sequence of one of these types of stimulus is given every two seconds until it ceases to be effective, 10–13 responses can be elicited. If, however, they are given in alternate short sequences, the young gape 40–46 times (Prechtl, 1953).

(h) The waning of the gobbling response of the turkey is specific to the particular sound stimulus used to elicit it, though the response to similar stimuli is also affected (Schleidt, 1954).

(i) The "mobbing" response given by Chaffinches to non-flying predators can be elicited by a wide range of stimulus objects, including owls, dogs, stoats, etc. It wanes gradually if the stimulus is presented continuously (Fig. 13.1). Some recovery occurs if the stimulus is removed, but if the response is elicited again even 24 hours later, the response on the second occasion is still reduced in strength in comparison with experimentally naive birds. This reduction in responsiveness is usually greater if the second stimulus object is the same as the first, but some decrement occurs even if it is not. The stimulus specificity of the decrement increases with the length of the initial presentation (Fig. 13.2; Hinde, 1961).

(j) If female mice are given ten closely successive presentations of a 1-day-old baby, the number of subjects showing licking and nest-building responses falls off on the successive presentations. If a 10-day-old baby is given immediately afterwards, the proportion of females showing these responses increases. Since a 10-day-old baby is a weaker stimulus than a 1-day-old baby for naive subjects, at least most of the waning during the first ten presentations must be more or less specific to the stimulus of a 1-day-old baby (Noirot, 1965).

(k) The waning of the directed head-turning response of the human baby is specific to the area stimulated. If the left-hand corner of the mouth is stimulated until the reactions disappear, a new response series of normal length can be elicited by stimulation of the other corner. In this case there is a suggestion that waning does depend on the elicitation of the response (cf. (f) above): at any rate a long series of stimulations given to a baby which is sleepy or engaged in some other activity does not result in a decrement in the response to stimuli given just afterwards when it is awake and not preoccupied (Prechtl, 1958).

(l) A change in responsiveness specific to a particular stimulus is probably also responsible for the phenomenon of "spontaneous alternation". If entries into the two arms of a T- or Y-maze are equally rewarded, rats will tend to alternate between them on successive runs. This could be explained either in terms of an alternation of responses (turning left and turning right), or in terms of an alternation of the stimuli to which the animal was responding. Montgomery (1952) and Glanzer (1953a, b; 1958) distinguished between these possibilities by using a cross-shaped maze. The animals were

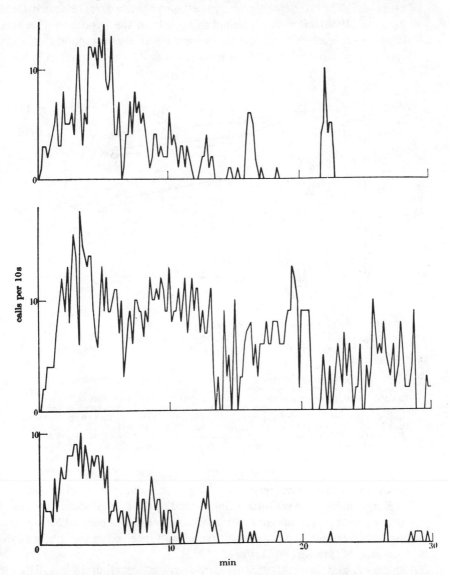

Fig. 13.1. Rate of calling by Chaffinches when mobbing a stuffed owl. Data for three individuals are shown. (*From Hinde, 1954a, by permission of the Royal Society.*)

Ordinate—number of calls per 10 seconds. Abscissa—minutes since stimulus presented.

started from the North (say) arm with the South arm blocked off, and
from the South arm with the North arm blocked off, on alternate trials.
At the choice point, therefore, the animal could enter the arm it entered last
time, or the opposite one, or it could turn the same way as last time, or the
other way. The rats tended to alternate the arm entered (*see* review by Dember *et al.*, 1958). Glanzer explained this result on the hypothesis that each
time the rat receives a stimulus it becomes less likely to respond to it, some
recovery occurring when the stimulus is absent. The distinction between

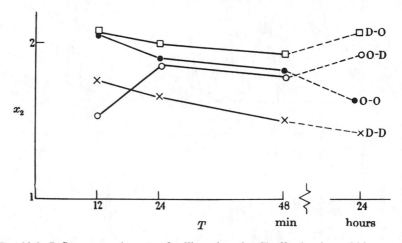

Fig. 13.2. Influence on the rate of calling given by Chaffinches in mobbing
a predator of 12 min to 24 hours exposure to a stimulus eliciting the same
response 24 hours previously. (*From Hinde, 1961, by permission of the Royal
Society.*)

Two stimuli were used, an owl, O, and a dog, D, and presented in the order indicated.
The ordinate indicates the strength of the response to the second stimulus ($x_2 = \log_{10}$
number of calls given in first six min of second presentation). The mean strength of the
response x_1 to the first stimulus presented was 2·28 for owl and 1·98 for dog. The abscissa
indicates the length of the initial presentation. The interval between the two presentations
was 24 hours. The response on the second presentation was less if the stimulus used was
the same as that used on the first occasion than if it was not (O–O v. D–O and D–D v.
O–D), the extent of this stimulus specificity increasing with the length of the initial
presentation.

stimulus alternation and response alternation is not quite so clear cut, however, for the way the rat turns is influenced by the stimuli which it received
after turning on the previous run as well as by those it received before turning: these can include proprioceptive stimuli received in the course of the
response of turning (Walker *et al.*, 1955).

(*m*) Sharpless and Jasper (1956) used the arousal reaction of the EEG in
sleeping cats as a dependent variable in assessing the waning of responsiveness to a tone. They found that the waning was specific to the quality,
modality and pattern of the stimulus.

(*n*) In their studies of the activity of single cells in the brain stem of rabbits cited on p. 101, Horn *et al.* (1964) found cells whose responsiveness waned with successive presentations of a stimulus, though they remained responsive to other stimuli.

Many other examples of a decrement specific to a particular stimulus are given, for example, by Sherrington (1906). Thus, in a number of cases which have been studied in detail in organisms ranging from earthworm to man, waning of responsiveness after exposure to a stimulus has some degree of specificity to the particular stimulus used. However, when an animal is satiated with food, it refuses all kinds of food; and when a mature male rat has ejaculated a large number of times, it refuses all females (but *see* p. 232). In such cases the waning appears to apply to the response as a whole, rather than to any particular stimulus. Response-specific waning has been claimed also in a number of other cases. In their studies of the feeding and mating behaviour of jumping spiders, Drees (1952) and Precht *et al.* (1958) found that waning of the fixation response (*i.e.* orientation towards the stimulus), as a result of repeated presentation of one stimulus in one place, was accompanied also by a decrease in responsiveness to other objects in other places (*see also* Kolb, 1955).

It is, however, difficult to make an absolute distinction between stimulus-specific waning and waning of the response as a whole. In some of the cases quoted above, the decremental effect generalized to other related stimuli as waning progressed: apparently response-specific waning may thus differ from stimulus-specific waning only in degree. In other cases in which the waning of responsiveness to one stimulus involves also decreased responsiveness to another, there is, in fact, a common element between the two stimulus situations. As we have seen, the mobbing response given by Chaffinches to owls was found to wane if a stimulus was presented continuously (Fig. 13.1): the decremental effect influenced also the responsiveness to other stimulus objects, such as dogs, stoats or snakes, which elicit the same response (Fig. 13.2). There was, however, a common element shared by the successive presentations, namely, the "circumstances of the experiment" (Hinde, 1954b, 1961).

13.3. Decremental Processes and Stimulus Inadequacy

Stimulus specificity of a decremental effect suggests that the waning could be related to some inadequacy in the stimulus which elicited the response—perhaps the waning is comparable to the extinction of a conditioned response which is elicited successively without reinforcement, and would not occur in a fully adequate situation. Certainly, in a number of cases the waning is more rapid with a weak stimulus than with a strong one. The twitching response of the earthworm, referred to above, wanes more rapidly to a weak stimulus, and longer series of strikes can be elicited from mantids by prey dummies which are moved jerkily than by dummies which move smoothly, and by dummies with wings and legs than by dummies without. Indeed, mantids cease to strike at some prey dummies behind glass in 2 or 3 minutes but will continue to strike at a live fly for several hours (Rilling *et al.*, 1959). Similarly, the courtship of the Hymenopteron *Mormoniella vitripennis* wanes more rapidly when the male is courting non-receptive females than when they are receptive (Barrass, 1961), and the mobbing response given by Chaffinches to predators wanes more slowly with a strong stimulus than with a weak one. However, in this last case at least, the more rapid waning with the weaker stimulus is an aspect of the weaker

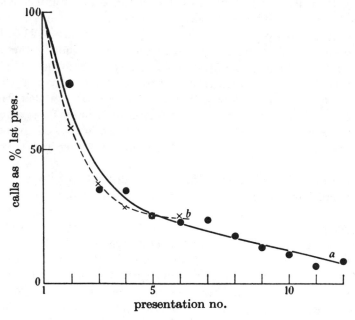

Fig. 13.3. Calling by Chaffinches while mobbing live Little Owl (continuous line) presented for 20 min a day, or stuffed Tawny Owl (broken line) presented for 3 min a day. The number of calls given by each bird were expressed as a percentage of the number given on the first day: the ordinate represents the mean. (*After Hinde, 1954b, by permission of the Royal Society.*)

response elicited: the regression lines relating the initial response strength to the rate of waning for different individuals are the same for both stimuli (Hinde, 1961).

In any case it is clear that waning occurs even with a natural stimulus object. This "mobbing" response wanes with time even if it is elicited by a live owl (Fig. 13.3 and Hinde, 1954a, b). Similarly, the responsiveness of a female mouse to her litter is reduced as a consequence of previous exposure to the young: virgin females exposed to babies only once a day give some maternal responses more readily than mothers living continuously with their own young

(Noirot, 1964a, b). As a further example, "spontaneous alternation" in a two-choice situation (*see* above) occurs even when both alternatives are reinforced.

The hypothesis that decreased responsiveness is due to deficiencies in the stimulus situation and would not occur with the natural stimulus object cannot be tested for activities like eating or mating: the natural object would elicit further responses (e.g. intromission) which would alter the situation. Waning in responsiveness to objects eliciting fear responses might well not occur if the object made an attack: this, however, is not evidence for a stimulus deficiency hypothesis, for it could be argued that the decremental effect still occurs but is masked by an incremental one which is induced (or augmented) by the attack. We shall return to this point shortly.

In view of such examples, it can be said that at least many cases of waning responsiveness cannot be ascribed to stimulus deficiency.

13.4. The Rate of Waning

The rate at which waning occurs varies between responses—while some are persistent, in others the decrement occurs rapidly. The retrieving response of mice, elicited by the high-frequency calls of the young, can be elicited 148 times in succession (Zippelius *et al.*, 1956; *see also* Noirot, 1965), while the directed head movements of the human neonate disappear after a few dozen (Prechtl, 1958). Precht *et al.* (1958) have shown that various responses of jumping spiders differ considerably in their persistence with successive stimulation as well as in their recovery rates. For any one response the rate at which waning occurs may depend on a variety of factors: thus with the photopositive response of *Drosophila* it varies with the rearing conditions (Dürrwächter, 1957), while with the directed head movements of human babies it varies with the exact point stimulated, the baby's posture, sleepiness, and so on (Prechtl, 1958).

13.5. The Rate of Recovery—The Multiplicity of Decremental Processes

An important characteristic of these decremental processes is the rate of recovery after waning. In some of the studies of waning responsiveness in invertebrates, recovery occurs rapidly and completely. After waning of the strike response of mantids to prey dummies, recovery occurs mostly in 5 minutes and is complete after half an hour (Rilling *et al.*, 1959). In his detailed study of the courtship of *Mormoniella vitripennis*, Barrass (1961) found that even when a male had courted 20 females in succession, recovery was almost complete in 1 hour and quite complete in 24. The movement used by toads in turning towards prey recovers from total waning to about 50 per cent of the initial level after 8 hours, and completely after a day (Eikmanns, 1955). Similarly, after a moderate degree of stimulation the twitching response of the earthworm recovers completely in 24 hours, though after strong stimulation for several successive days recovery is slow, reaching only 20 per cent after 10 days (Kuenzer, 1958).

In other cases, however, complete recovery takes a considerable time, if it occurs at all: usually the initial stages are fairly rapid, but the rate then slows down or ceases. To cite some examples, the prey-catching response of *Notonecta* recovers from a long series of stimulations rapidly during the first few minutes, but then more slowly, and is not complete after 24 hours (Wolda, 1961). Drees (1952) and Precht *et al.* (1958) found that several of the hunting and courtship responses of hunting spiders showed rapid recovery during the first few hours after waning, followed by a period of only slow recovery: the courtship dance, however, was exceptional in showing almost linear recovery with time. The wiping response of the toad recovers to 56 per cent of the initial level after 60 minutes but thereafter very slowly (Kuczka, 1956). The "chink" calls, given by a Chaffinch while mobbing a stuffed owl, cease almost completely after a 30-minute exposure. If the stimulus is then removed, recovery reaches about 55 per cent after 30 minutes but the remaining decrement is virtually permanent (Hinde, 1954b). The Siamese Fighting fish (*Betta splendens*) will display to its own mirror image. If permitted access to a mirror for a number of days the response, as measured by the frequency of "challenges", falls off. The effect of various recovery periods after a 10-day exposure to a mirror were assessed. Recovery after periods of 15 minutes to 24 hours was not statistically significant, but after periods of 2 days and 4 days it was (Clayton and Hinde, in prep.). When there is a phase of slow recovery like this, or a permanent decrement, the effects of periodic bouts of stimulation may be cumulative. An example is shown in Fig. 13.3: if an owl is shown to a Chaffinch daily, the response falls off progressively (*see also* Chapter 15).

A period of rapid recovery followed by a period of only slow recovery, or no recovery at all, suggests that at least two processes are involved in the initial waning. This, again, is reminiscent of the extinction of conditioned responses, where the response decrement has often been ascribed to two factors, one temporary and the other permanent (e.g. Hull, 1943). Even this, however, involves oversimplification, for decremental processes resulting from any one response may have recovery periods ranging from seconds to years. In the case of the Chaffinch's owl-mobbing response these processes can be classified into three groups according to whether the effect lasts for seconds (*see* p. 216), or for minutes, or is near-permanent (*see* above). At this point the distinction between "motivational" changes and "learning" may become obscure, for the temporary changes are usually studied under the former rubric, while the latter come within most definitions of learning. Thorpe (1963a) reserves the term "habituation" for relatively permanent decremental changes of this sort (*see* p. 405).

Evidence that more than one process may be involved in the waning of responsiveness comes also from the fact that different aspects of the response may wane, or recover from waning, at different rates. In studying the cardiac acceleration produced in human neonates by sounds, Bartoshuk (1962a, b) gave series of 40 trials at 60-second intervals. The pre-stimulus heart rates for trial 2 were higher than those for trial 1, indicating that at this point the effect of trial 1 lasted for at least 60 seconds. By the end of the series, however, the pre-stimulus heart rate had returned to the initial value, although there was still an immediate response to the stimulus. Thus the tonic response waned more rapidly than the phasic one (cf. Sharpless *et al.*, 1956). On a much longer time scale, the "tail flip" response of goldfish (Rodgers *et al.*, 1963) and the fleeing response of ducklings (Melzack, 1961) wane quite rapidly, but in both cases an orientation response towards the stimulus is very persistent (*see also* Evans *et al.*, 1960; and Moyer, 1963).

That more than one decremental process may be involved is also supported by physiological evidence. In the cockroach, the waning of the evasive response produced by air blasts on the anal cerci is largely due to the lability of the giant fibre/motor neurone synapse, but some slow waning also occurs in the receptor cells (Roeder, 1962b). In the withdrawal response of the earthworm clear evidence for a dual process is available. This response, elicited by tactile stimulation at one end and mediated by the giant fibres in the ventral nerve cord, wanes with repeated stimulation. By electrical recording from various points between sense organs and effectors, Roberts (1962) showed that failure of transmission occurred between the sensory neurones and the giant fibres, and between the giant fibres and the motor neurones. Rapid fatigue to repetitive stimulation was not shown in the muscle, in the neuromuscular junctions, or in the junctions in the motor neurone tracts. A similar result had previously been obtained for the worm *Nereis* by Horridge (1959a). If the waning of such very simple responses is due to changes at at least two points, how much more complex may be the changes underlying waning in responsiveness among vertebrates? It is thus not unexpected that experiments involving electrical stimulation of the mammalian brain should demonstrate waning processes with diverse time constants. In general, the response evoked by stimulation of the motor cortex wanes in a few seconds, while that evoked by stimulation of the motor pathways lasts for up to an hour. Other areas, such as parts of the hypothalamus, show no fatigue after 72 hours of continuous stimulation (Delgado, 1962).

The evidence cited in this section thus indicates clearly that an apparently simple behavioural decrement may be the result of diverse underlying processes.

13.6. Incremental Processes, and their Interaction with Decremental Ones

A further complication comes from the fact that the elicitation of a response may be accompanied by a tendency towards an increase in response strength instead of, or as well as, a tendency to a decrease. With the directed head movements of the human baby, intense reactions occur more quickly the higher the frequency of stimulation used: the early stimuli increase responsiveness to the later ones (Prechtl, 1953). By analysis of the behaviour sequences during the courtship of certain Glendulocaudine fishes, Nelson (1964) obtained evidence that the male's courtship was self-facilitatory. After the maternal behaviour of adult mice to one-day-old babies has waned as a consequence of successive presentations, they will respond more strongly to a 10-day-old-baby than will animals with no such immediately preceding experience (Noirot, 1964c; *see also* pp. 219 and 375). If spinal frogs are touched with a bristle one hundred times per day, the number of responses given increases from 4–14 to 60–90 over 5 to 7 days. The increase occurs only if the animal is allowed to respond. Similarly, if the croak reflex is elicited a large number of times by finger pressure on

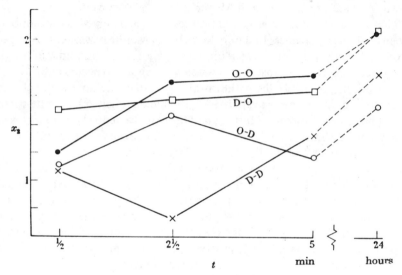

Fig. 13.4. Influence on the rate of calling given by Chaffinches in mobbing a predator of a 12-minute previous presentation. Conventions as in Fig. 13.2, but here the abscissa indicates the interval between the presentations. (*After Hinde, 1961, by permission of the Royal Society.*)

the back, it may start to occur spontaneously. Furthermore, stimulation with bristles may then elicit croaking instead of the more usual foot-wiping (Franzisket, 1963; *see also* Kuczka, 1956).

The positive or excitatory effect which accompanies a response may continue to mount after the response itself is over. In the male rat, ejaculation occurs only after a number of intromissions. If the interval between intromissions is forcibly increased, the number of intromissions required for ejaculation is decreased. The full effect of each intromission does not seem to be realized for 0·5 minute, and since intromissions normally follow each other at intervals shorter than this, the maximal effects of each are never attained under normal conditions (*see* p. 229).

As with the processes which lead to a decrease in responsiveness, the various incremental processes accompanying one type of response may have decay periods varying from seconds upwards. The calls accompanying the mobbing response of the Chaffinch will again serve as an example. In one series of experiments two stimulus objects were used, a stuffed owl and a toy dog, the former eliciting the stronger response. Each experiment consisted of two stimulus presentations in which the two objects were used in all possible combinations (Figs. 13.1, 13.2 and 13.4).

The consequences of an initial stimulus presentation on responsiveness on a second occasion when the interval between presentations was short ($\frac{1}{2}$ to 5 minutes) or long (24 hours) were considered separately. Although the number of calls given in the second presentation was usually less than the number given in the first, there was considerable evidence that the decremental processes concealed less powerful but none the less influential incremental ones. In the case of the long-term effects (24 hours rest interval between presentations) this evidence was of three types:

(a) Although the number of calls given in the second presentation was reduced, the latency of the first call was also reduced.

(b) With most stimulus combinations, the longer the initial presentation, the smaller was the response on the second. With the sequence owl–dog, however, the reverse was the case. Apparently in this case an incremental effect resulting from presentation of the stronger stimulus increased with the length of that presentation more rapidly than did the concurrent decremental effect (Fig. 13.2).

(c) Another experiment involved tests with two owl models. Although the models looked similar, one had eyes and the other did not: they therefore differed markedly in effectiveness. When the more effective model was shown first, the response to the weaker one, presented 24 hours later, was actually greater than that shown by naive birds.

For the short-term effects (i.e. interval $\frac{1}{2}$ to 5 minutes), the evidence for an incremental effect was as follows:

(a) In every stimulus presentation the rate of calling increased gradually, reaching a peak only after 2 or 3 minutes (Fig. 13.1).

(b) The response strength on a second presentation did not increase smoothly with the length of the rest interval, but shows marked and significant fluctuations (Fig. 13.4). These could be accounted for in terms of the interaction of incremental and decremental effects having different decay periods.

(c) Since the response strength shows an initial increase at the beginning of each presentation, it seems that the incremental effects build up more rapidly than the decremental ones. Any incremental effect is therefore more likely to be evident if the initial presentation is short, when the effects of decremental processes are minimized. If the first presentation lasted only 2 minutes and the interval between presentations was varied between 3 seconds and 24 hours, the response in the first minute of the second presentation was usually greater with rest intervals of 2½ or 5 minutes than with longer or shorter rest intervals. This, again, is consistent with the suggestion that there are interacting incremental and decremental processes. Presumably, the former are masked by the latter after very short rest intervals, revealed by the decay of the decremental effects after 2½ to 5 minutes, and subsequently decay themselves (Hinde, 1954b, 1961).

For this response there is thus strong evidence for incremental effects which are relatively permanent, and also for others which decay over a period of a few minutes. This is not all, however. The calls are given in phrases of 1–6 calls, the intervals between phrases being considerably longer than the intervals between the calls in a phrase. Describing it in one way, a single call is likely to be followed immediately by another, but a short series is likely to be followed by silence. This raises the possibility that each call is associated with very short-term incremental and decremental effects, which build up and decay at rates which, though different, are measurable in seconds.

A comparable case, involving very short-term incremental and decremental effects, concerns the singing of the Chaffinch. Each male has a repertoire of songs and, during an outburst of singing, gives a sequence of songs of one type followed by a sequence of another. The intervals between songs within a sequence (that is, between songs of a similar type) tend to be shorter than those between sequences. Since intervals of less than three seconds between songs are extremely rare, it would seem that each song is accompanied by an inhibitory effect on singing which is dissipated with time. That this inhibitory effect is a consequence of performance is suggested by the fact that the interval tends to be shorter after the occasional incomplete song. Now if this inhibitory effect were specific to the song type just uttered, alternation between song types would occur more frequently than on a random distribution of song types: in fact the opposite occurs. There is, thus, a tendency to repeat the song just uttered rather than to switch to another type: this we may describe as a facilitative effect. The singing pattern of the Chaffinch thus implies, as a minimum requirement for explanation, inhibitory and facilitative effects consequent upon performance (Hinde, 1958b; see also Isaac et al., 1963). In the domestic turkey the frequency distribution of intervals between "gobbling" is affected by deafening, indicating a role of auditory feed-back in the inhibitory effect (Schleidt, 1964).

That incremental and decremental effects occur simultaneously is not *necessarily* an indication of great complexity in the underlying mechanism. Hughes et al. (personal communication), working with the mollusc *Aplysia*, stimulated the right giant cell, whose axon makes direct synaptic contact with the left giant cell, and recorded from the latter. The recording showed a biphasic synaptic potential with an initial depolarizing phase and a longer lasting hyperpolarizing phase. With repetitive stimulation the post-synaptic potentials summated to produce a hyperpolarizing effect at low frequencies and a depolarizing effect at high frequencies of stimulation. Thus, depending on the frequency of stimulation, a single synapse displays the properties of both inhibition and excitation.

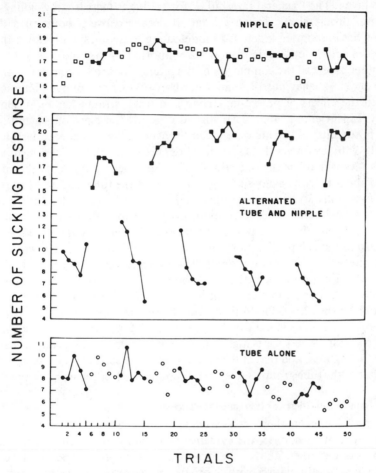

Fig. 13.5. Number of sucking responses given by human newborns in series of trials with a bottle nipple (top line), a tube (bottom line), and alternating runs of five trials with each (centre). *See* text. (*After Lipsitt and Kaye, 1965.*)

These studies demonstrate not only that incremental or facilitatory effects with widely varying time courses may accompany the performance of any one type of response, but also that the observed behaviour depends on a complex interaction between the various incremental and decremental effects. As another example, the mobbing behaviour of the Blackbird (*Turdus merula*) involves two types of call which are given in flight or when the bird has a strong tendency to fly. In a detailed study of the moment-to-moment fluctuations in calling, Andrew (1961a, b, c, d,) found it necessary to postulate at least two variables. The "action potential" is increased with the tendency to fly and is reduced by calling, but recovers rapidly. Its level determines which of the two calls is given. The "general threshold" for calling is increased by calling and thus rises progressively during a bout: it decays between bouts of calling. Andrew has elaborated a detailed model along these lines, and shown that a number of predictions made from it are supported by the data.

Another aspect of the complexity of the interactions that occur is illustrated by the sucking behaviour of human newborns, where a complex interaction between the effects of preceding strong and weak stimuli has been demonstrated (Lipsitt *et al.*, 1965). Two stimuli were used, a piece of $\frac{1}{4}$-inch tubing and a bottle nipple. Infants were given fifty successive trials, each lasting ten seconds with an interval of 30 seconds between trials. Two groups of infants received either the one stimulus or the other throughout: the nipple elicited about twice as many sucking responses as the tube. A third group was given five trials with one stimulus and five with the other, alternately. Whereas the infants given one stimulus throughout showed no consistent change in the number of responses given on each trial through the series, the third group tended to give more responses to the nipple and fewer to the tube as the series progressed, though the difference was not clearly significant (Fig. 13.5). Furthermore, within each block of five trials with the nipple the response rates started low and finished high, while with the tube it started high and finished low. That this cannot be due merely to a lasting effect of the previous stimulus is indicated by the finding that the response rate at the end of each nipple series was higher than that shown by the group given the nipple throughout, and that at the end of each tube series tended to be lower than that of the tube group: some sort of contrast effect seems to be involved.

13.7. Stimulus Specificity of Incremental Processes

While most decremental processes seem to be specific to the particular stimulus used to elicit the response, the evidence concerning incremental processes is meagre. As described above, the proportion of wiping responses given by spinal frogs to stimulation with a bristle increases on successive days. The response can be elicited by stimulating both medial and lateral areas of the back, but a long series of stimuli applied to one area does not involve increased responsiveness to stimulation of the other (Franzisket, 1963). In this case, therefore, there is some degree of specificity to the locus of the stimulus. In other studies, however, the contrary seems to be the case; for instance the exposure of an animal to a frightening stimulus often results in an increased responsiveness to a wide variety of stimuli eliciting similar types of behaviour ("pseudo-conditioning"; Hilgard *et al.*, 1961). Since, in this case, the behaviour concerned involves avoidance, fear or startle responses, the effect may be mediated by a changed pattern of activity in the autonomic system.

Another case, in which the incremental effect appears not to depend on any common stimulus characters between the initial "priming" experience and the test situation, concerns the maternal behaviour of mice. A much higher proportion of adult mice respond maternally to a live 1-day-old baby than to a drowned one, and there is strong evidence that this is due to the ultrasonic cries emitted by the former (Noirot, 1964b, c; 1965). Responsiveness to a drowned baby is, however, increased by previous exposure to a live one, even if there is an interval of several days in between. What is more, the effect occurs even when the adult has no opportunity to make tactile contact with the live baby. Experiments in which virgin females were exposed to young, confined inside tins with and without holes, thereby providing both auditory and olfactory or only auditory stimuli, indicated that the ultrasounds increase subsequent retrieving and nest-building, but the olfactory stimuli affect (or affect also) licking and the adoption of the lactation position (Noirot, 1964c, 1965, in prep.).

Turning to neurophysiological studies, there is again some evidence that incremental effects may not be specific to the particular stimulus used. We have seen that when stimulation by two electrodes in different loci of the brain-stem of chickens elicit the same response, the waning which follows stimulation of one of them is specific to the locus stimulated. If, however, both loci are stimulated simultaneously with a voltage which would have been sub-threshold when applied to only one, a response may occur. The summation must occur at or beyond the point where the effects from the two loci meet (von Holst *et al.*, 1963).

It must be emphasized that the few cases which provide evidence about the stimulus specificity of an incremental effect are extremely diverse, and certainly involve quite different mechanisms. Generalizations would thus be premature.

13.8. Interaction Between Responses

The performance of one response may affect the ease with which others can be elicited. On the one hand, the decrement in one response may involve also decrement in others. In jumping spiders waning of the "jump" is accompanied by a reduced readiness for "approach", and vice versa (Precht *et al.*, 1958). On the other hand, decrement in one response may be related to an increase in the probability of others, and even to the appearance of another response to the same stimulus. A number of examples are given by Prechtl (1958). When the directed head-turning movement of the human neonate has waned, the same stimulus may elicit turning away. When the gaping of young Chaffinches to a shaking of the nest has waned, crouching occurs. This is called by Prechtl "central reset". Sometimes both incremental and decremental effects occur. In a study of aphid behaviour Kennedy *et al.* (1964) have demonstrated that flying can have both incremental and decremental effects on settling responses: which predominates depends on a variety of factors including the period spent flying and the stimuli for settling (*see* p. 303).

In a number of cases there is evidence suggesting that waning involves a gradually increasing probability that the response in question will be interrupted by other types of behaviour. Thus the gradual waning of drinking which occurs after a previously deprived rat is given water involves an increase in the lengths and frequency of the pauses in drinking, during which the rat is occupied in other activities (Stellar *et al.*, 1952). Whalen (1963b) makes a similar point with the mating behaviour of the cat (*see also* Hurwitz, 1957, and Chapter 17).

13.9. Conclusion

In considering these examples of changes in responsiveness to a stimulus we have drawn evidence from diverse responses of animals at all phyletic levels. The accuracy of the generalizations made must therefore be tailored to the diversity of the data. However, it is clear that in any particular case our initial assumption should not be that there is a single process underlying the change in responsiveness: rather we must expect processes with varied characteristics, presumably occurring at different points in the underlying nervous mechanism. Furthermore, in the absence of evidence to the contrary, it would be safe to assume that exposure to a stimulus will be accompanied by processes (with varied time characteristics) leading to an increase in subsequent responsiveness and also to processes leading to a decrease. The actual response (or lack of it) observed on a subsequent occasion will be a result of these varied processes. Similar conclusions relating to the performance of a skilled task by human subjects have been formulated by Ammons (1947), though, with more complex tasks, repeated performance affects the integration of the individual responses as much as (or as well as) the actual occurrence of the responses themselves (Bartlett, 1953).

Further understanding will depend on an analysis aimed at separating the various processes involved and assessing their characteristics. The studies cited above suggest that it may be useful to classify them according to their decay periods, according to whether they produce incremental or decremental effects, according to the extent to which they are specific to the particular stimulus used to elicit the response, and according to whether they depend on actual performance of the response in question. In the case of complex responses, however, such a classification must involve a considerable degree of approximation, and is only a first step.

13.10. Summary

1. Response to a stimulus is associated with changes in responsiveness when the stimulus is presented again. In many cases these are not attributable to changes in the sense organs or effectors.

2. The decremental consequences of responding are usually more or less specific to the particular stimulus which elicited the response.
3. The decremental effects cannot be ascribed solely to inadequacy in the stimulus situation.
4. The rate at which waning occurs varies considerably between responses.
5. The rate of recovery also varies: often, a period of rapid recovery is followed by a period of slow recovery or of no further recovery. This suggests that in such cases more than one decremental process may be involved. Physiological evidence supports this view.
6. Incremental processes may accompany and interact with the decremental ones.
7. The incremental effects are often not stimulus specific.
8. A decremental effect on one type of behaviour may be accompanied by either incremental or decremental effects on others.

14

Spontaneity and Rhythmicity

In the preceding chapter we saw that successive or continuous presentation of a stimulus may result in a waning of responsiveness. Recovery from the decremental processes involved occurs "spontaneously" with the passage of time. This raises the more general question of the extent to which changes in behaviour can be spontaneous.

Semantic difficulties arise easily here. "Spontaneous" is used in the present context to refer to changes in the output of a system without a known corresponding change in input. Whenever spontaneity is discussed, therefore, it is necessary to specify the system under consideration. Behaviour of the whole animal may be called spontaneous though the change in central nervous activity controlling it depends on changes inside the body. Similarly, the output of the nervous system may be spontaneous when that of its components is not, and the spontaneous firing of a nerve cell depends on complex chains of events within it.

Furthermore, since recognition of spontaneity depends on an absence of correlation between input and output, the distinction between spontaneous and environmentally elicited is one of degree only. It depends, in fact, on the length and variability of the sequence of events within the system which preceded the activity, and which are uninfluenced by extra-systemic factors. If the chain of internal events is long enough the activity appears to be spontaneous.

At the behavioural level, spontaneity thus consists of changes in behaviour not closely related to changes in exteroceptive stimulation, and is a commonplace. We have already seen that, as motivational factors increase in strength, less external stimulation is required to elicit a given response (Chapter 11): in the extreme case, no stimulus is necessary, and the response appears spontaneously. A number of dramatic cases have been described by Lorenz (1935) as "vacuum activities". For instance a well-fed Starling, which had had no opportunity to catch flies for some time, suddenly went through all the movements of searching for a fly, catching it and killing it, although no fly was discernible to the observer. Similarly, canaries deprived of nest-material will perform the movements of weaving material into a non-existent nest (Hinde, 1958a). In such cases it is the performance of a fixed action pattern out of context which easily catches the observer's attention: similar changes in appetitive behaviour, as when the Starling searched for a fly, are more commonplace and go unremarked.

The lack of a sharp dividing line between the spontaneous and stimulus-elicited activities of the whole animal is also illustrated by Franzisket's (1963) studies of decerebrated and intact frogs. The croak reflex is normally elicited by blunt pressure on an area of the back. Stimuli were given at 5-second intervals 500 times a day for 3 weeks. After this training, spontaneous croaking occurred about twice a day, though it was never observed over a period of several weeks before the training. As a result of frequent stimulation, therefore, a reflex response became spontaneous. On a different time scale, von Holst *et al.* (1963) used electrical stimulation of the brain to induce "geckering" in hens. If the stimuli were repeated at short intervals, the threshold voltage required to elicit the response decreased. If they were sufficiently rapid, the threshold fell to zero, that is, the reaction became spontaneous.

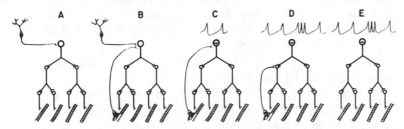

Fig. 14.1. Diagrams of hypothetical types of nervous mechanisms producing patterned movement. (*After Bullock, 1961.*)

The three levels of neurones represent branching chains in whose junctions integrative properties may alter the actual impulses and deliver them to the effectors. *A* and *B* are shown with receptors, *C*, *D* and *E* with spontaneous pacemakers. *B* and *C* have proprioceptive feedback acting on the trigger neurone, while in *D* it influences only the shaping of the pattern. *See* text.

The question of the spontaneity of the nervous system, that is, changes in output independent of changes in either exteroceptive or interoceptive stimulation, merges with that of the patterning of nervous discharges necessary for the coordination of complex movements, as discussed in Chapter 3. If a simple input produces a patterned discharge, the patterning of the output is at least in part determined centrally. If the input is tonic and the output rhythmical, then the rhythmical changes involve spontaneity as well as central patterning. Thus many of the cases discussed in Chapter 3 as evidence for central patterning are relevant here also. Of course, whenever the output of a system is rhythmic there must be some feedback (in a broad sense) effect whereby the consequences of the activity affect its own repetition, but in spontaneous rhythms this is inside or part of the system (*see* discussion by Grey Walter, 1959).

The relations between the systems controlling the patterning of particular movements and the rhythmicity in their appearance are summarized in Fig. 14.1 (Bullock, 1961). The timing of the rhythm may depend on either peripheral or central factors.

(a) The timing cues come from the periphery. In such cases the patterning of the response itself may be determined centrally, even though elicitation depends on external factors: for instance, an object approaching the eye results in a patterned discharge leading to an eye-blink (Fig. 14.1 A). If there is sensory feedback from exteroceptors or proprioceptors, discharge may be rhythmical (Fig. 14.1 B): in this case the initial input may just serve a triggering function.

(b) Timing cues from central pacemakers. This case differs from the previous one only in that a central pacemaker is present which, as it were, rings an alarm at intervals (Fig. 14.1 C to E). In practice, the distinction between the systems shown in Figs. 14.1 B and C may be hard to make: if feedback starts the next cycle before the central pacemaker, the existence of the latter is concealed. In most cases the external feedback modulates the spontaneous rhythm, which would be altered but not broken by its removal (see Chapter 3). Of course, the operation of the central pacemaker may itself depend on activity in feedback loops.

In some cases the feedback may act not on the pacemaker but on its followers: it will then modulate the form but not the frequency of the rhythmic output. Bullock quotes the disturbances in walking in a tabetic or blinded man as an example (Fig. 14.1 D). In any case the feedback is likely not to be simple, as implied in the diagram, but to involve a complex mixture of positive and negative, specific and diffuse, fast and slow adapting influences. Absence of any sort of feedback control external to the pacemaker appears to occur in some rhythms of short periodicity (Fig. 14.1 E). The electric organs of Gymnotid fish, which discharge at a constant rate uninfluenced by external feedback, is a case in point (Lissmann, 1958). Others, like the lobster's cardiac ganglion and the sound production mechanism of the cicada, have been mentioned already.

In fact, the occurrence of rhythmic processes in the central nervous system, after it has been experimentally isolated from peripheral influences, has now been demonstrated in a considerable number of cases; for instance in the ventral nerve cord of *Dytiscus* (Adrian, 1931), and in a slug ganglion (Hughes *et al.*, 1956). Horridge (1959b) has shown that the rhythm of swimming movements in medusae is of nervous origin, and P. L. Miller (1960) that the respiratory movements of the Desert Locust are controlled by a pacemaker in the metathoracic ganglion whose activity continues in the isolated nerve cord, though its activity may be modified by carbon dioxide (*see also* Ikeda *et al.*,

1964). Of course, such examples do not imply that spontaneous activity of individual neurones is necessarily rhythmical—it may be random (e.g. Werner *et al.*, 1963).

Although the occurrence of a rhythm of central nervous origin seems thus well established, experiments involving total isolation of parts of the nervous system must be interpreted with caution. C. H. F. Rowell (personal communication) recorded from the prothoracic-mesothoracic connective of a locust (*Schistocerca gregaria*) as the mesothoracic ganglion was progressively isolated from peripheral input. With increasing isolation there was a reduction in electrical activity until total isolation occurred. When the last connective was cut, however, there was intense activity in the neurones in the ganglion and an increased synchronization between them.

Of course, in any case the rhythmic output of a cell-group depends on certain tonic steady-state conditions. For instance, Kerkut *et al.* (1958) showed that the isolated abdominal ganglia of a crayfish (*Astacus fluviatilis*), the nerve cord of a cockroach (*Periplaneta americana*) and the pedal ganglion of a slug (*Agrolimax reticulatus*) all show a spontaneous discharge. The discharge, however, depends markedly on temperature: if the temperature is changed and the preparation given a few minutes to settle down, a new steady rate of discharge appears. For each preparation there is an optimum temperature at which the rate of discharge is maximal, though this optimum may vary with the temperature at which the animal has been kept. Sudden changes in temperature produce marked fluctuations in the rate of discharge.

More recently, techniques of recording from single units, and the use of microelectrodes which penetrate the cell body, have taken this study of the electrical activity of the nervous system down to the cellular level (e.g. Bullock, 1961; Roeder *et al.*, 1960). Many individual cells show spontaneous discharges, originating from certain regions of the cell (the pacemaker loci) which may influence part or all of the rest of the cell. Some cells have more than one such locus, with different temporal characteristics. Such changes in the state of a cell may affect its responsiveness to influences from outside, and may even affect other neurones electrotonically, as well as generating spike discharges (*see also* Chapter 6 and Bullock, 1958, 1959a, b; Bullock *et al.*, 1957).

Most of the cases of rhythmic output from the nervous system have involved a periodicity measurable in seconds or parts of seconds—quite a different order of magnitude from the changes in behaviour which we see in the whole animal, with a time course of minutes, hours or days. Nevertheless, rhythms of comparable time periods, which appear to be spontaneous, are well known. The polychaete worm *Arenicola marina* lives in a U-shaped burrow. A burst of feeding movements occurs every 6–7 minutes, and every 20–60 minutes there is a sequence of tailward creeping, forward irrigation, tailward irrigation and defaecation. Such a cyclic pattern could result from responses to regularly recurring peripheral events—empty gullet, full rectum, and so on—

but the evidence strongly suggests this is not the case. The outbursts apparently begin without external stimulus or biological need, and subside without satisfaction. It is highly probable that there are two biological "clocks", one for each of the principal rhythms mentioned above. The brain is unnecessary for the continuance of the rhythms, but the ventral nerve cord is essential, and the spontaneity depends in part on the wall of the oesophagus (Wells, 1950, 1955).

The diurnal or circadian rhythms of activity shown by nearly all organisms have recently been subjected to intensive study. While some authors (e.g. Brown, 1960) maintain that in such cases the rhythmicity is under the control of external time-signals, there is considerable evidence that in many cases it is controlled endogenously. At the very least there must be mechanisms for maintaining the rhythms over short periods of time, for they often persist in organisms kept under carefully controlled conditions or transported across many degrees of longitude. Harker (1958a) has suggested that the internal clock system in multicellular animals is not limited to one part of the body, for isolated tissues show circadian rhythms. It seems rather that there may be a basic metabolic circadian rhythm in all cells of plants and animals, and that the rhythms shown by the whole animal result from interactions between the various cell groups. In the cockroach, at least two distinct clock systems have been isolated, each capable of maintaining an accurate periodicity in the absence of the other. One of these is a neurosecretory system, while the other is thought to be associated with the nervous system. In addition, the cells of the midgut show a rhythm of sensitivity to a hormone: this appears to be independent of known endocrine systems and of the nervous system (Harker, 1958b; 1964).

Summary

1. "Spontaneity" implies change in the output of a system without a known corresponding change in input.
2. Examples of spontaneity at the behavioural level are commonplace. There is no sharp dividing line between spontaneous and stimulus-elicited activities.
3. Rhythmical output from a system may depend on external timing cues, often resulting from feedback consequences of its activity, or on an internal pacemaker. The activity of the latter may of course depend on its own internal feedback.
4. Rhythmic activity in the isolated nervous system has been demonstrated in a number of cases. Spontaneous rhythmic activity is also well known in single cells.
5. Spontaneous rhythms in the behaviour of the whole animal having periodicities measurable in minutes, hours or days have been studied in a number of cases.

15

Diversity in Motivational Mechanisms

In the preceding chapters we have seen that changes in motivation can be ascribed to changes in central nervous states (Chapter 12) which are themselves influenced by longer-acting extra-neural factors (Chapters 10 and 11), by eliciting stimuli (Chapters 4, 5 and 6), and by the consequences of the activity itself (Chapters 10 and 13). We have also seen that the motivational states may vary independently of extra-neural factors (Chapter 14), and that they can influence behaviour by determining the goals to which it leads as well as by increasing the probability of particular stimulus-response sequences (Chapters 11 and 12).

So far, however, the diversity of the behaviour considered has been limited, and we must ask whether general principles applicable to other types of behaviour can be found. In this chapter, therefore, we shall summarize and extend the preceding ones by considering the changes in responsiveness found in a few examples of functional categories of behaviour. In doing so, our concern is solely with relatively short-term changes in behaviour: problems of integration and development are considered later.

15.1. Eating, with Special Reference to Rodents
The studies discussed in Chapter 12 indicate that eating behaviour in rats is a consequence of interaction between central excitatory and inhibitory mechanisms: the parts of these mechanisms probably affect both the motor patterns of feeding and responsiveness to stimuli from the food (pp. 187-9). How the effects of deprivation are registered is not apparent, since the evidence on the role of interoceptive stimuli is not clear (p. 174). Possibly, blood composition affects receptors in the central nervous system (p. 182). Certainly, experiential factors play a role also, including those determining the temporal rhythms in the animal's behaviour (p. 379).

When the excitatory factors are predominant, the animal shows a type of appetitive behaviour which is likely to bring it into the presence of food. This is, in part, a direct consequence of deprivation, but results largely from an increased responsiveness to external stimuli (p. 187). While showing this appetitive behaviour it is especially sensitive to stimuli likely to be indicative of food (p.189). These elicit such activities as catching, preparing and eating, the details varying with the species and the circumstances.

When eating occurs, feedback effects from the mouth/throat region and the stomach, and from changes in blood composition and body temperature, swing the balance in favour of inhibition. These decremental processes take effect before the basic tissue needs are relieved, and decay with varied time courses (p. 184). Furthermore, they may affect the consummatory behaviour of eating independently of the appetitive behaviour which usually leads up to it: it is for this reason that hunting behaviour is often shown by satiated animals (Lorenz, 1935; Hinde, 1953b).

The central excitatory and inhibitory mechanisms are not simple, for the various dependent variables by which feeding behaviour can be assessed are only loosely correlated with each other (pp. 141-3). The diversity of the factors which control the relative attractiveness of different foods and the amount eaten can hardly be overemphasized. For instance, in rats, novelty of the food may lead either to an increase (Welker *et al.*, 1962) or a decrease (Barnett, 1963) in the amount eaten; in adult monkeys the latter effect predominates, but may be overcome by the sight of another animal taking the food (Weiskrantz *et al.*, 1963). Social factors have a more immediate importance in puppies (James 1953; James *et al.*, 1956) and birds (Katz, 1937; Lorenz, 1935; Tolman, 1964); and the amount of food eaten may also be influenced by the amount present (Ross *et al.*, 1962).

15.2. Male Rodent Sexual Behaviour

The male rat's sexual behaviour depends on the presence of circulating androgens (pp. 166-7). These produce their effects both centrally, by influencing the hypothalamus (p. 171), and peripherally, by affecting the genitalia (p. 168). The central effects of the hormone are augmented by influences mediated by the cortex, which, in turn, presumably depend on experience (pp. 172-3). Even when hormonal levels are high, the male is not sexually responsive all the time: periods of sexual responsiveness are succeeded by periods during which the animal is engaged in other matters. Presumably, these changes in responsiveness are determined in part centrally, in part by stimuli received as a result of sexual behaviour itself, and in part by the incidence of factors specific to other types of behaviour (pp. 152-3).

From time to time the male shows appropriate appetitive behaviour and is especially responsive to external stimuli of the type normally provided by a receptive female. These elicit mounting attempts. Mounting is followed by a brief intromission, after which the male dismounts. A series of such intromissions with brief pauses between is concluded by one in which ejaculation occurs. There is then a longer interval (the post-ejaculatory refractory period) before another series of intromissions starts.

The time relations of these copulatory sequences have provided important evidence concerning the consequences of feedback from intromission and ejaculation. If a male is allowed access to a female for an hour, the number of intromissions per ejaculation at first falls and, in some cases, later rises, while the post-ejaculatory refractory period rises throughout (Beach and Jordan, 1956; Larsson, 1956). The consequences of intromission and ejaculation are thus by no means simple. In order to explain such results, Beach and Jordan (1956) postulated the existence of two mechanisms: an arousal mechanism which mediates the increase of sexual excitement leading to copulation, and a copulatory-ejaculatory mechanism. The state of the arousal mechanism was held to be indicated by the latency after the female is introduced before the first intromission, and by the refractory periods between one ejaculation and the next intromission (Fig. 15.1 (a) and (b)). Since the refractory periods increase after each successive ejaculation, it was supposed that a series of ejaculations has a cumulatively inhibitory effect on the arousal mechanism. If the male is allowed to copulate to sexual exhaustion (criterion 30 minutes without mounting), the latency, as shown by a subsequent test, remains high for several days: it was thus suggested that the arousal mechanism does not regain its maximum responsiveness for about a week.

The state of the copulatory mechanism was held to be indicated by the number of intromissions necessary to produce ejaculation, and by the latency between the first mount of each series and ejaculation (Fig. 15.1 (c)). Since the number of intromissions per ejaculation falls in the successive ejaculations of a series, it seems that intromission or ejaculation has a sensitizing effect on the copulatory mechanism (see also Larsson, 1958).

The view that two separate mechanisms are involved is also supported by endocrinological evidence. Beach (1942b), Beach et al. (1949), and Whalen et al. (1961) found that, with increasing androgen dosage, the range of stimulus objects eliciting mounting from male rats increased and the latency before mounting decreased. The number of intromissions before ejaculation, however, showed no correlation with androgen level. They therefore concluded that sexual responsiveness, as measured by mount or intromission latency, is directly related to the level of circulating androgen. By contrast, the ejaculatory process, while requiring a certain minimum androgen level, is not affected by additional amounts of hormone.

The time relations of the excitatory state which follows intromission have been subjected to more detailed analysis. The number of intromissions required to produce ejaculation is reduced by enforcing a delay after each one, provided the delay exceeds the normal intercopulatory interval of 45–60 seconds and does not exceed 3–5 minutes. With intervals of more than 10 minutes ejaculation is prevented, though some males go on copulating for several hours, making up to 40 or 50 intromissions (Larsson, 1956). There would thus seem to be an excitatory process, consequent upon intromission, which increases for at least 3 minutes after intromission and then decays.

Beach and Whalen (1959b) traced the decay of this excitatory effect in more detail by permitting a male rat 1, 4 or 7 intromissions, and then enforcing a rest interval by removing the female for a period of from 7·5 to 120

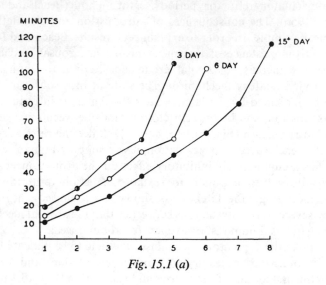

Fig. 15.1 (a)

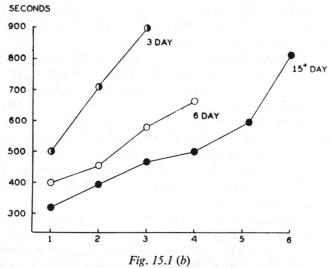

Fig. 15.1 (b)

Fig. 15.1. The course of sexual behaviour in the male rat. The animals were given either 3, 6 or 15 days recovery since complete sexual exhaustion (i.e. 30 minutes without mounting a receptive female). (*From Beach and Jordan, 1956.*)

Abscissa in each case indicates serial number of ejaculation.

(*a*) Time from beginning of test at which successive ejaculations occurred. (*b*) Duration of refractory periods following successive ejaculations.

minutes. The excitatory effect from the initial series of intromissions which still remained when the female was returned was assessed by comparing the number of intromissions then required for ejaculation with those required in control tests. The results showed that the excitatory effects of successive intromissions were cumulative, and continued to rise for some minutes after the last intromission. After 30 minutes the number of additional intromissions required had returned to about the number which would have been necessary if the series had not been interrupted: some excitatory effect remained even after 120 minutes (*see also* Bermant, 1964).

This further analysis showed that the effects of a series of intromissions and ejaculations are more complicated than the original scheme suggested. The effect of one series on the ejaculation latency (and the intercopulatory interval)

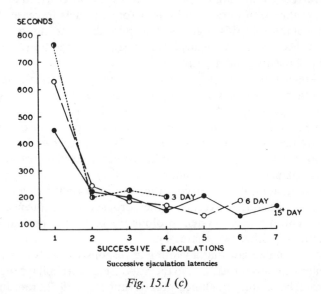

Fig. 15.1 (c)

(c) Successive ejaculation latencies (i.e. time from first mount to occurrence of ejaculation).

of a second persists for much longer than does its effect on the number of intromissions required to reach ejaculation. These two measures can thus not be regarded as indices of the state of a unitary mechanism (Beach and Whalen, 1959a, b). In addition, the view that ejaculations have an inhibitory effect on the arousal mechanism is open to question. If intromissions are prevented after the first ejaculation for an enforced rest interval, the mount and intromission latencies in the second series are shorter than those in the first: this suggests a stimulatory rather than a depressive effect on the arousal mechanism. Beach *et al.* (1959a) thus suggest that an initial series of intromissions ending in ejaculation has several more-or-less independent effects.

(a) A sensitization of the copulatory mechanism, resulting in a reduction in the number of intromissions required for a second ejaculation.

(b) A sensitization of the arousal mechanism, tending to produce shortened mount and intromission latencies and thus a reduced ejaculation latency.

(c) Non-sexual fatigue, which temporarily masks (b) but is cumulative over successive ejaculations and thus leads to progressively longer post-ejaculatory intervals. (It is not clear why this fatigue effect is specified as non-sexual: in view of the data given on pp. 203-21, it seems possible that ejaculation has both positive and negative effects on arousal, which decay with different time constants.)

Whether or not even this will fully account for the data remains to be seen. At least one further complication is introduced by the observation of Peirce *et al.* (1961a) that the mean duration of copulatory contacts increases through a series of intromissions: this suggests that, in addition to the sensitization effect, the reflex becomes more sluggish. Here again is a suggestion of simultaneously produced positive and negative effects.

Soulairac (reviewed Larsson, 1956) suggested from pharmacological evidence an even more complex mechanism, namely that the primary regulation of ejaculation, copulatory behaviour and intromission, and the refractory period, are due to different groups of factors. This is based on the observations that: (a) the frequency of ejaculations, but not the number of intromissions per copulation or the refractory period, is influenced by certain disturbances in the endocrine balance; (b) certain neuro-excitatory drugs influence the frequency of intromission, but not ejaculation, and have only a slight influence on the refractory period; (c) certain other drugs which influence enzyme activity in the central nervous system prolong the refractory periods without directly affecting the other two characters.

In an earlier section we saw that a waning of responsiveness is often specific to the particular stimulus rather than to the response, and a similar process may operate in sexual behaviour. In guinea-pigs (Grunt *et al.*, 1952), rats and many other mammals (Wilson, J. R. *et al.*, 1963) substitution of a new female when a male has become sexually satiated in a series of matings produces a renewal of sexual behaviour. The substitution of a new female is more effective than the removal and replacement of the one with which the male has just been copulating. Fisher (1962) showed that the number of intromissions required per ejaculation rose with the new female, as though the male were beginning to copulate again. This author found that, after sexual exhaustion, flashing lights and intermittent tones coupled with reintroduction of the same female also led to reactivation of the male's sexual behaviour, but the effect was small compared with that of a new female. Changing females had less effect on the capacity scores of old males than of young ones—perhaps they had become sophisticated about novelty.

Fowler *et al.* (1961) suggested that the effect of changing the female was due to attempts by the first female to repulse the male. Other studies have shown that, after a mounting, the female rat stays away from the male for a short period. The duration of this period varies with the nature of the previous mounting: after mounts without intromission, mounts with intromission, and mounts with ejaculation the median intervals are 13, 60, and 170 seconds (Peirce *et al.*, 1961a, b; *see also* Bermant, 1961; Kuehn *et al.*, 1963). In the cat, the behaviour of the female is certainly of importance. Substitution of a fresh female after the male has reached a criterion of sexual exhaustion leads to renewed intromissions. However, if the new female has just been mated with another male, the male under test achieves fewer intromissions before criterion than in the normal series. When a sexually fresh male is allowed access to a sexually exhausted female, little mating results (Whalen, 1963b).

Data for the course of sexual exhaustion are available for a few other sub-human vertebrates. The inadequacy of a unitary concept of sexual arousal has been stressed by Rosenblatt *et al.* (1958a, b), and Whalen (1963a, b) as a result of their studies of cats. Hamsters (Beach and Rabedeau, 1959), and mice (McGill, 1962b) are qualitatively similar to rats. A few data for Chaffinches are given by Hinde (1959c), and studies on domestic cocks are reviewed by Guhl (1962). Other references are cited by Schein *et al.* (1965); *see also* Hildreth, 1962 for *Drosophila*.

Mammalian male sexual behaviour has been discussed in some detail because the studies of Beach and his collaborators exemplify so well the manner in which humoral factors, external stimuli and feedback factors interact. The hormone has multiple effects, central and peripheral, which determine the general level of sexual activity over long time periods, while the external stimuli and feedback effects determine moment-to-moment responsiveness. It will be apparent that, for analysis of these interactions, the concept of a central excitatory state needs considerable elaboration: as mentioned previously, it was not for this level of complexity that the concept was coined by Sherrington.

15.3. Nest-Building of Female Canaries

The sequence of nest-building behaviour considered here consists of gathering nest-material, carrying it to a nest-site, and sitting in the nest-cup building the material into the structure. The latter involves a small number of stereotyped building movements. Like rat sexual behaviour, this is influenced by hormone levels—as the hormone levels increase, the sequence of behaviour is repeated more often, and is more likely to be completed (Warren *et al.*, 1959).

The course of building behaviour is much influenced by stimuli received as a result of building. The female becomes more sensitive to these stimuli as a consequence of hormonal changes, probably mediated peripherally (pp. 169 and 301). Thus, as in the rat, sex hormones have both central and peripheral effects. The stimuli received in the course of building produce the following effects:

(a) Each of the activities of gathering, carrying and building is accompanied by a self-inhibitory effect. The evidence for this rests on an analysis of the relations between the bout lengths of the different activities. As building activity as a whole becomes more vigorous, the median bout length of each activity first increases and then decreases in length. The decrease implies that each activity is interrupted by that which follows it. The changeover

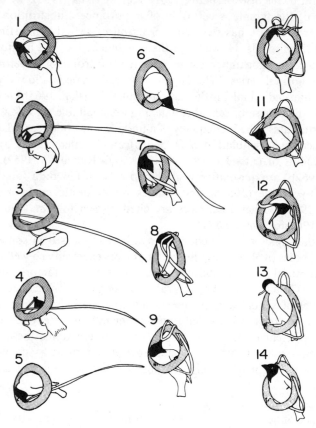

Fig. 15.2. A typical sequence of movements by a male Village Weaver-bird as he weaves a single strip, torn from a leaf-blade of elephant grass, into his ring. (*From Collias and Collias, 1962.*)

from each activity to the next does not depend merely on the stimuli for the next phase becoming available, and can be most economically understood in terms of a self-suppressing effect accompanying performance, the changeover occurring when the relative prepotence of the two activities changes (Hinde, 1958a).

(b) Stimuli from the nest which the female has built influence the frequency of certain nest-building movements.

(*c*) Stimuli from the nest-cup cause the female to select new sorts of nest-material. Under laboratory conditions, if grass and feathers are provided, grass is used for the main cup and feathers for the lining. The changeover depends on stimuli received from the grass cup (Hinde, 1958a; Hinde and Steel, 1962).

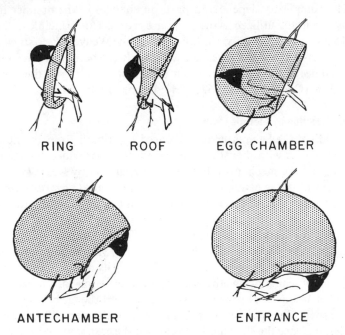

RING   ROOF   EGG CHAMBER

ANTECHAMBER   ENTRANCE

Fig. 15.3. Normal stages in nest-building by a male Village Weaver-bird. (*From Collias and Collias, 1962.*)

The diagrams show successively the building of the ring, and roof, the completion of the egg-chamber, and the building of the antechamber and entrance. Notice how the male perches in the same place while building throughout.

(*d*) Stimuli from the nest-cup produce a decrease in building behaviour: this normally occurs around the time of egg-laying (Hinde, 1958a).

(*e*) Stimuli from the nest-cup accelerate reproductive development and, thus, a new hormonal situation not conducive to building (Hinde *et al.*, 1959; Warren *et al.*, 1961a).

Since the feedback effects from some sorts of nest structure differ from those produced by others, there must be an optimum nest-structure which is maximally effective for each of these functions. In the normal course of events the inhibitory effects on building produced by the finished nest contribute to the cessation of nest-building, which is also due to the hormonal changes occurring at the time.

We see that, as in rat sexual behaviour, the hormonal state affects multiple central mechanisms as well as producing peripheral effects, and that there are multiple feedback effects from the behaviour, producing both positive and negative, short- and long-term effects. These are discussed further on pp. 301-2.

The nest of the canary is a relatively simple one, but even those of species which build complex structures depend on relatively few stereotyped movements. The complexity depends, in part, on changes in the manner in which these movements are utilized as the structure grows. This principle is illustrated in Figs. 15.2 and 15.3, which show how the Village Weaver (*Ploceus cucullatus*) builds its retort-shaped structure. At each stage in the building of the outer shell the bird perches in the same place, but orients its weaving to the edge of the existing fabric (Collias *et al.*, 1962; 1964; Crook, 1960c, 1964b).

15.4. Shell Selection by Hermit Crabs

In nest-building, the behaviour is influenced by stimuli from the nest whose effectiveness varies with their difference from those provided by a completed nest. A comparable mechanism has been studied also by Reese (1963) in his investigations of the selection of shells by hermit crabs (*Pagarus samuelis* and *Calcinus paevimanus*). The behaviour of hermit crabs towards the shells in which they live is independent of previous experience of shells. It involves a sequence of responses, each elicited by different properties of the shell, mediated to some extent visually but principally via the mechanoreceptors. In normal circumstances the properties of the shells release successive motor patterns each of which brings the crab into the situation for the release of the next. The behaviour thus proceeds as a chain until the crab has entered and righted the shell. The chain is not a rigid one, and the elements can be elicited independently. Once the shell has been entered the crab may go on showing the appetitive behaviour which normally serves the function of finding new shells. The amount of appetitive behaviour shown (as assessed by the amount of motor activity and responsiveness to shells) depends on the characteristics of the shell it has entered. The total stimulus value of the shell is determined primarily by two properties—weight and internal configuration—but others may also contribute. Only if the stimulus value is adequate does the appetitive behaviour and responsiveness to other shells decline. Thus, like nest-building, the behaviour continues until inhibited by the adequate consummatory situation.

15.5. Aggression in Passerine Birds

Passerine birds (e.g. Chaffinch, Yellowhammer (*Emberiza citrinella*), Great Tit) fight in a number of contexts, of which we will consider two: the fighting which occurs in winter flocks, usually near food, and that which occurs in defence of a territory. In the former situation, individuals a few inches or feet away may be attacked; while in the latter any conspecific male seen within a certain area, perhaps an acre or two in extent, elicits aggression. The motor patterns used in the two contexts are similar, except that certain threat postures may occur in territorial fighting but not in winter fighting. In either case fighting is elicited by a fairly specific set of stimuli from a conspecific individual. In the Chaffinch the red breast is important, in the Great Tit the broad black ventral stripe.

In most species, fighting over territories occurs only in the spring, when the gonads are active and sex hormones are being released. However, territorial fighting does not depend solely on hormone level. In cold weather, or early in the season, the bird may fluctuate from territorial to flocking behaviour over a period of a few minutes: at one moment the male may be feeding quietly on his territory in the company of a dozen other individuals, tolerating them at a distance of a foot or two, while the next he will fly up to a song post and attack any bird within a hundred yards. Correlated hormonal changes are unlikely, so we must presume that there are temporary central states which are independent of the more enduring hormonal states. These can be elicited by central stimulation in domestic cocks (von Holst *et al.*, 1963).

Field observations on a number of species show that fighting in the flock is more common when the weather is cold and food is scarce, unless conditions are very severe (e.g. Hinde, 1952; Stokes, 1962b). This, however, does not necessarily mean that the factors which cause an increase in feeding behaviour (e.g. a period of deprivation) also influence the threshold for fighting, as was implied previously (Hinde, 1952). In a study of captive Chaffinches, Marler (1956c) assessed the "50 per cent distance", that is, the distance between two individuals at which there was an even chance of their tolerating each other. This distance was 7 cm. for females and about 25 cm. for males. The incidence of aggression was then observed when the males were feeding simultaneously from perches fixed 20 cm. apart and subjected to periods of starvation varying from 45 to 180 minutes. The period of food deprivation did not affect the amount of fighting shown. Andrew (1957b) obtained a similar result in studies of captive Yellowhammers, and suggested that the increase in the number of aggressive encounters which occurred during deprivation was due to the increase in activity and, thus, in the frequency of encounters at local sources of food. (In other circumstances hunger might have the opposite effect— Keenleyside (1955) reported less schooling with hunger in certain fishes.)

In fighting over breeding territories in these species, it is not mere proximity but the presence of another bird within a particular area which elicits aggression. The territory owner patrols his territory, flying from tree to tree and being particularly responsive to stimuli indicative of intruders. He ignores a nearby rival outside the territory, but flies off to attack a more distant one who is within its boundaries. Only in the early stages of territory establishment is the aggressiveness not tied to a particular locality.

On the basis of their observations, Marler (e.g. 1957a) and Andrew, *loc. cit.*, emphasized the role of the external stimulus situation in eliciting aggression, regarding the internal state as of minor importance. However, even if the state of hunger makes no difference to the threshold for aggression, the fact remains that while behaving gregariously, other birds are attacked only if they come within a few inches, while an individual behaving territorially attacks other birds whenever they are seen within a certain area. The internal states which lead to flocking behaviour, on the one hand, and territorial behaviour, on the other, must have some influence. This may lie in giving significance to an external object with reference to which the fighting occurs. In the flocking situation, mere proximity is a cause of aggression, but in the territorial situation it is not the spatial relationships between the combatants which are important, but rather those between the rival and some external object—song post, nest site, etc. On this view the internal state can be regarded as determining a situation which the fighting serves to achieve—"no birds within a foot of me" or "no birds near my trees". It influences sensitivity to stimuli rather than the intensity of the behaviour (Hinde, 1956b).

Fighting, however, is not merely a consequence of responding to a stimulus situation that happens to arise when the animal is in the appropriate state. When in fighting mood a territorial bird shows appetitive behaviour for fighting in the sense that it patrols its territory, visiting places where it is likely to see intruders, and also has a lowered threshold for responding aggressively to other males. Indeed, Thompson (1963) has shown that domestic cocks and Fighting fish (*Betta splendens*) will learn an instrumental response which results in the appearance of the stimuli usually provided by the rival male. The reinforcing properties of the stimuli are greater, the greater their effectiveness in eliciting fighting responses. Similarly, Beach (personal communication) has shown that male C-57 mice will learn an instrumental response if this gets them into a situation where they can attack another mouse.

When birds attack a dummy, their aggressive behaviour waxes and wanes over a period of a few minutes. There are thus decremental (and probably incremental) consequences of responding. Since the response to a dummy wanes after a while, these decremental effects are presumably cumulative. With a real rival, however, aggressive encounters may go on for a long time: presumably incremental effects override the decremental ones. Under these circumstances, aggression may be brought to an end when the rival adopts a submissive posture (*see* p. 179), or when he disappears. In the latter case the termination of aggressive behaviour depends not on the achievement of a new consummatory situation, as with feeding, sexual or nest-building behaviour, but on the removal of the eliciting situation. In this respect it resembles fleeing (*see* below).

Although the fighting may have short-term consequences on the tendency to fight, there is little evidence that longer-term deprivation of an opportunity to fight causes an increase in the readiness with which fighting can be elicited (though *see* Kruijt, 1964). In this respect fighting differs from, say, feeding behaviour.

Other aspects of aggressive behaviour are considered later—the incidence and role of ambivalent threat postures on pp. 249-69, the role of frustration on p. 289, and the nature of its reinforcement on pp. 417-18.

15.6. Play

Play is a general term for activities which seem to the observer to make no immediate contribution to survival. The kitten playing with a piece of wool, or the dog chasing a ball, are common domestic examples which find parallels in the majority of mammals and birds and, perhaps, in lower species. For instance, young Kestrels spend much time swooping on sticks and other inanimate objects, and going through the motions of hunting non-existent prey (L. Tinbergen, cited in Thorpe 1963a). Although especially common in young animals, comparable activities are seen in adults; for instance, well-fed dogs and birds may go through the motions of hunting food even though they do not eat it if they find any (e.g. Lorenz, 1935; Hinde, 1953b; Wüstehube, 1960).

Play apparently occurs in the absence of the long-lasting motivational factors normally necessary for the activities in question; the animal shows hunting patterns when not hungry, or sexual behaviour though not sexually aroused. It is also terminated without the consummatory situation being reached—the mounting attempts of young Rhesus monkeys may not lead to either intromission or ejaculation. Presumably they wane through other consequences of performance (*see* Chapter 13).

Nevertheless, play is not merely the performance of activities in the absence of the motivational factors normally appropriate to them: Lorenz (1935) has pointed out that when young mammals are play-fighting, social inhibitions are maintained. Play may have an adaptive significance in providing an opportunity for learning about the environment, but its motivational basis is undoubtedly complex (*see* e.g. Inhelder, 1955; Holzapfel, 1956a, b; Tembrock, 1958; Thorpe, 1963a). Some types of play are more appropriately considered as exploration (*see* below).

15.7. Exploration

In all higher animals a sudden change in stimulation will usually elicit a movement of turning towards the source, a response described already in Chapter 6 as the "orientation response". They will also approach and examine strange objects with whatever sensory equipment is available to them. In a strange environment, they may move around and examine all of their surroundings—in other words, explore. Even within one species the types of behaviour which come within the broad category of exploration or investigation are diverse, and it is difficult to give a more precise definition than that they are such as to familiarize the animal with the source of stimulation.

Since the extent to which exploratory behaviour is evoked varies with the animal's previous experience of the situation, it would seem to be a function of the discrepancy between the perceived situation and the familiar world, or, using Sokolov's terminology, between the induced neural activity and the "neuronal model" which has been built up by experience. As might be expected, such characteristics of a stimulus situation as complexity and intensity, in addition to novelty, may increase its effectiveness in eliciting exploratory behaviour (Berlyne, 1960).

The stimulus situations which elicit such behaviour are clearly allied to those which produce fear responses (*see* below), the difference being primarily one of magnitude. A small change in the environment elicits investigation, a major one fear. Chaffinches and Great Tits keep their distance from owls, real or stuffed, but approach and investigate models with only a few owl-like characteristics (Hinde, 1952, 1954a; Marler, 1956b). With intermediate degrees of strangeness the animal vacillates, alternately approaching and avoiding the strange object (*see* Hebb, 1946; Melzack, 1952; Hebb *et al.*, 1954; Montgomery, 1955).

The probability that a given discrepancy will elicit exploration rather than fear responses depends on various aspects of the internal state. For instance, when a young monkey, reared on a cloth-covered artificial mother, is put into a room containing strange objects, it may freeze and cover its eyes, or run about screaming. If the artificial mother is present, however, the infant clings to it and its fear is allayed. In these circumstances it then soon starts to make exploratory forays about the room (Harlow *et al.*, 1959). Apparently the presence of the mother influences the internal state in a way which sways the relative prepotence of avoidance behaviour and exploration. The response of passerine birds to owls, mentioned above, provides another example. At a few weeks of age Chaffinches and Great Tits have a high threshold for fear responses. At this age a stuffed owl evokes approach and investigatory behaviour, with few signs of fear. A few weeks later the birds keep several yards away from such a dummy, the tendencies to approach and avoid being more or less in balance at that distance (Hinde, *loc. cit.*). The internal state apparently changes with age, though the manner in which this change depends upon experience is not known. Strain and species differences are also important here: wild rats are less likely to examine and more likely to avoid strange objects placed in their cage than are tame rats, a difference correlated with the larger adrenal glands of the wild forms (Barnett, 1958; 1963).

Even if it starts to examine a novel object, an animal may vacillate between investigation and other activities such as feeding and grooming. The precise effect of hunger on exploratory behaviour varies with the degree of hunger and the conditions of testing. Hunger usually decreases exploratory behaviour (Chapman *et al.*, 1957), but hungry rats are more likely to leave a familiar environment and explore an adjacent strange one than are satiated animals (Fehrer, 1956; *see also* Zimbardo *et al.*, 1958; and pp. 187-9). It may be suggested, however, that in the latter case the animals would show enhanced responsiveness to stimuli likely to be indicative of food, rather than to novel objects: the behaviour is therefore better described as appetitive to feeding rather than exploratory.

Thus, although at first sight the incidence of exploratory behaviour seems to depend primarily on stimulus factors, the internal state of the animal is important in several ways. First, the external situation's effectiveness depends on its relation to the familiar as established by experience. Second, the internal state influences whether a given degree of discrepancy elicits fear or exploration, and the intensity of either of them. Third, other types of motivation may conflict with exploratory behaviour. The importance of this internal state is consistent with the finding that an exploratory or investigatory mood can be elicited by brain stimulation, and may persist for some time after the stimulus ceases (von Holst et al., 1963).

Whether or not the tendency to show exploratory behaviour increases with preceding sensory deprivation is not clear. Charlesworth et al. (1957) kept rats in environments impoverished to varying degrees before giving them opportunity to explore a novel chamber, but found no large differences in the latency with which they entered the chamber or the time they spent there. Hill (1958), on the other hand, found that rats showed a period of increased motor output after confinement, and Butler (1957b) found that deprivation increased the tendency for Rhesus Macaques to show visual exploration. Clearly, even when an effect of preceding deprivation on exploratory behaviour is found, a number of alternative explanations may be possible, and it must not be assumed that the tendency to explore increases with time for the same reasons as does, say, the tendency to eat.

Exploratory behaviour may be extremely persistent. A wild rat encountering a new object in familiar territory will spend minutes and even hours investigating it before resuming its normal maintenance activities (Barnett, 1963). Of greater interest is the accumulating evidence that rats will learn to overcome obstacles on pathways to novel situations, and show, in a familiar situation, persistent appetitive behaviour which will lead to an opportunity to explore. Thus rats will cross an electrified grill in order to reach a maze containing a variety of objects (Nissen, 1930), and behaviour which leads to an opportunity to explore is likely to be repeated. Rats will run repeatedly down an alley which has an unfamiliar goal box at the end (Mote et al., 1942), and run faster when the stimuli in the goal box are changed repeatedly than if they are not, provided that the rats are satiated (Chapman et al., 1957; see also Schneider et al., 1965). Similarly, rats will learn to take that turn of a Y-maze which leads to a large open box containing rectangular blocks or a Dashiell maze (Montgomery, 1954; Montgomery K. C. et al., 1955). Krechevsky (1937) ran rats in a maze where they had the choice of two paths, both of which led to food. The sequence of turns in one of these paths was varied from trial to trial, while the other remained unchanged. The animals took the former more often than the latter. In such experiments the complexity of the stimulus objects cannot easily be separated from their novelty (Berlyne *et al.*, 1957), but the data suggests that it is primarily novelty *per se* which augments exploration (Schneider *et al.*, 1965). Monkeys confined in a dimly lit box, with a window giving a view of the outside world, will spend a high proportion of their time looking through it, and will also learn to perform a simple task which opens the window (Butler, 1953; Butler *et al.*, 1954). Not surprisingly, in view of the above discussion, monkeys work better if the result is an opportunity to see figures in motion (Butler *et al.*, 1963), but will not learn the task if it results in fear-provoking stimuli—the sight of a large dog or fear calls from a monkey colony (Butler, 1957a).

Such experiments have been thought to imply that exploratory behaviour is peculiar in that the animal seeks to increase the stimulation impinging on it. We have already seen that, although some types of behaviour (e.g. aggression) are usually brought to an end merely by the elimination of the eliciting factors, others (e.g. feeding, sexual behaviour, nest-building) involve seeking for consummatory stimuli, and it is these new stimuli which bring it to an end. If we wish to link exploratory behaviour to these we can point to the fact that it involves the elimination of the discrepancy between an internal representation of the familiar situation and the central consequences of perceiving the novel one, just as nest-building involves elimination of the discrepancy between the stimuli from the incomplete nest and those from a completed one. However, a basic difference lies in the fact that elimination of the discrepancy is a consequence not of a change in the stimuli impinging on the animal, but a change in the neuronal model so that it conforms to them. The novel stimuli are assimilated so that they cease to be novel. We shall return to this question in Chapter 26.

15.8. Fear Responses

The label fear responses is applied here to a diverse group of behaviour patterns, including, in the first instance, those leading to avoidance of the stimulus (e.g. locomotion away from it and self-protective responses), but also freezing, crouching and so on.* We have already seen that the causal basis of fear responses is closely related to that of the orientation response (Chapter 6) and exploration (*see* above), and we shall later discuss its role in a number of ambivalent behaviour patterns, such as the displays used in threat and courtship (Chapters 16 and 17).

For most species some stimuli have a special effectiveness in eliciting avoidance behaviour, and may be effective the first time they are encountered: for

---

* Recently Hogan (1965), in a detailed study of fear in chicks, has advanced cogent arguments for distinguishing "fear", associated with inhibition of activity, from "withdrawal". Similar arguments would no doubt apply to other species, though the necessity for the distinction will depend on the level of the analysis.

instance stimuli characteristic of predators prevalent in the area, or the alarm calls of conspecific individuals. Other stimuli acquire their effectiveness through conditioning, perhaps after association with situations whose effectiveness does not depend on experience. In addition, avoidance behaviour may be elicited by strange objects or novel situations, especially if they are very strange or involve high intensity stimulation (Hebb, 1946; Thorpe, 1963a).

Within any one species, which of the various responses indicated above is elicited depends on the nature of the external stimulus and on various aspects of the internal state, including experiential factors, hormonal state, and so on. In addition, when extraneural factors are apparently constant, the animal may pass through phases when it is more or less likely to flee. This implies the existence of central nervous states with some degree of persistence which influence responsiveness, a finding consistent with the fact that the behaviour can readily be elicited by central electrical stimulation at a wide variety of loci (p. 163).

However, the intensity of fear behaviour does not depend solely on the state of one part of the central nervous system: the avoidance behaviour induced by shock is reduced by removal of the sympathetic nervous system and by drugs which reduce sympathetic activity (Wynne et al., 1955).

Once avoidance behaviour has been elicited, it may persist until the stimuli are no longer present: in this respect it resembles aggressive behaviour. If persistent avoidance fails to achieve this result, however, habituation occurs; the previously fear-inducing object loses these properties, and the behaviour wanes, to be followed by exploration. Several studies show that, when fear responses are elicited by the sudden appearance of a new stimulus object, the fleeing response wanes much more rapidly with successive presentations than does the orientation response which it also evokes (see p. 213). Melzack (1961), on the basis of experiments in which Mallard ducklings were shown models of flying predators, describes this by saying that there is a progressive organiza- tion of behaviour in which the "emotional disruption" involved in fleeing is replaced by non-emotional orienting responses.

We may take up a general point here. Orientation and fear responses can be produced by a discrepancy between the stimuli impinging on the organism and a "neuronal model". However, fear is not always associated with discrepancy. Some strange stimulus situations are more effective than others in eliciting fear responses from all members of a species: they are apparently effective because they correspond to a "model" whose formation does not depend on previous experience. Thus fear can be elicited by either discrepancy or concordance. A similar point is illustrated by Andrew's (1964a) study of chick calls. This author interprets the causal basis of the calls in terms of "stimulus contrast". Stimuli are said to have "contrast" if the animal pays marked attention to them. There seems to be a considerable danger of circularity in such a defini- tion, but the interesting point here is that "contrast", according to Andrew, may occur either because the stimulus differs markedly from the familiar (i.e. lack of correspondence with a neuronal model) or because it serves as a conditioned stimulus signalling, for instance, the presence of food (i.e. correspondence with a neuronal model). Andrew shows that the same response (the twitter) can be evoked in either of these ways, that is, by either correspondence or lack of correspondence. Another response (the peep) is produced by even more intense stimulus contrast.

15.9. Conclusion

This brief survey serves to demonstrate that no easy generalizations about "motivation" are yet possible. Statements about the effects of deprivation on motivation, the extent to which behaviour is spontaneous, or the role of the performance of a stereotyped "consummatory act" in bringing behaviour sequences to an end, cannot be equally valid for the different types of behaviour shown by one animal, let alone for those of different species. The control of each type of behaviour is a separate problem: only when an adequate sample of behaviour types has been analysed can generalizations be attempted and the level of analysis at which they are useful assessed. The immediate aim for students of behaviour must therefore be, not to fabricate a general theory of "drive", but to provide precise analyses of a wider range of individual cases.

15.10. Summary

Work on the factors controlling a number of types of behaviour shows that the relative importance of extra-neural factors, of spontaneity, of feedback effects consequent upon performance, and so on, varies greatly from case to case. It is thus not profitable to search for general theories of drive applicable to all types of behaviour in all organisms.

16

Conflict—Courtship and Threat

In Chapter 12 we saw how a Chaffinch may successively sing and patrol its territory, then come down to feed on the ground, then fly up to a bush to preen, and then perhaps sing again. It engages first in one set of activities and then in another. Comparable observations could be made on any other species, and show that the different activities in an animal's repertoire do not appear at random, but in an orderly manner. In implying that the Chaffinch was always engaged in only one thing at a time, however, the description involved considerable over-simplification. Let us consider another case.

When a flock of Great Tits is feeding in winter, the individuals are usually spaced out over the ground. If one bird comes too close to another, threatening and fighting occur. The gregarious tendency which holds the flock together is thus balanced in part by aggressiveness engendered by proximity (pp. 236–8). As each bird feeds, it remains on the alert for approaching danger and for rivals, and frequently interrupts its feeding to look around: the efficiency of its feeding is thus limited by its watchfulness. From time to time the flock moves in a rather straggling fashion from one feeding site to another: the later birds to leave hastily finish the seed they were eating and fly rapidly to catch up with the flock: here feeding behaviour conflicts with the gregarious tendency. In such a flock, therefore, the birds do tend to engage first in one type of behaviour and then in another, but they are, in fact, rarely single-minded: for much of the time a tendency to show one type of behaviour is in conflict with tendencies to show others.

Before proceeding it is necessary to be a little more precise about the terms "tendency" and "conflict". In everyday speech, to say an animal has a tendency to behave in a particular way means that we have evidence that it is likely to do so. If it is likely to behave in a particular way, causal factors for the behaviour in question must be (potentially) present. Sometimes, therefore, "tendency" implies that such causal factors are present. Causal factors for a particular type of behaviour may, however, be present even when the behaviour is unlikely to appear: a hungry animal in the presence of food may not partake if "fear" is simultaneously elicited. In such cases we can say that the animal has a tendency to show the response (e.g. to feed), but the factors are too weak, or inhibited (Hinde, 1955/6). The use of the term tendency is suitable in the present context because it obviates the need for specifying the nature of the causal factors involved, though subsequently we may wish to analyse them in terms of hormone level or strength of stimulus, or relate them to concepts like drive or habit strength.*

If tendencies for two incompatible types of behaviour are simultaneously present, we may speak of them as being in conflict. In the case of the Great Tits in the flock, stimuli from another individual produce both a tendency to approach and a tendency to withdraw. The distance apart of individuals in the flock depends largely on a balance between these two tendencies: at the point of balance both are presumably present, but are in conflict and mutually inhibit each other. When the flock moves, the later individuals are influenced both by factors which normally elicit feeding behaviour, and by factors which induce following. These are incompatible and the resulting conflict modifies the feeding behaviour. It will be apparent that an animal which appears to be engaged in only one activity may yet be in conflict, the tendency to do something else having been totally suppressed by the causal factors for the on-going behaviour.

Just because most activities are self-terminating, either by bringing the animal into a consummatory situation (Chapter 10), or by removing the eliciting factors (e.g. Chapter 15), or in some other way (e.g. Chapter 13), most conflicts are soon resolved. But how quickly this occurs depends in part on the nature of the conflict itself. This can be seen most readily in conflicts which involve simultaneous tendencies to move in different directions.

When the two tendencies in conflict involve approaching two different objects some distance apart, we can label the situation an "approach/approach" conflict, without, of course, implying that the incompatibility is merely a physical one. In such a case the animal may reach a point in between where the tendencies to approach each object are in balance. Its position will then be unstable, for the tendency to approach either goal increases with its proximity. Any slight departure from the point of balance towards one goal will result in an increased tendency to approach that goal and a decreased tendency to approach the other. The conflict is thus easily resolved. On the other hand, an animal placed between two objects both of which it strives to avoid ("avoidance/avoidance conflict") is in a relatively stable situation. Since the tendency to avoid either object is likely to increase with its proximity, movement towards either is likely to lead to a return to the point of balance. Continued movement is possible only along a line at right angles to that joining the two objects.

A more interesting case occurs when the animal has simultaneous tendencies to approach and avoid a given object or situation. Suppose we train a rat to run up an alley for food, and then give it an electric shock at the goal box. When

---

* Berlyne (1960) speaks of the response as being "aroused" in this context, but confusion with "arousal" as used in a non-specific sense (*see* pp. 155–6) seems likely.

subsequently placed in the alley it may run a little way up, hesitate, turn back, and oscillate about a point some distance from the goal, or hesitate there grooming its fur or cleaning its paws. Its tendency to approach the food is balanced by a tendency to avoid further shock ("approach/avoidance conflict"). This situation has been the subject of a rigid analysis by Miller (1959). He points out that, for a position of stable balance to occur, the tendency to avoid the end of the runway must decrease with distance from it more rapidly than the tendency to approach. This is illustrated in Fig. 16.1. The gradients

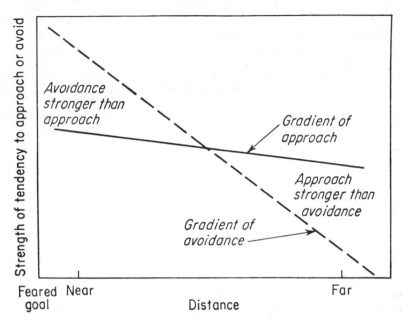

Fig. 16.1. Simple graphic representation of an approach/avoidance conflict. The tendency to approach is stronger far from the feared goal, while the tendency to avoid is stronger near the goal. *See* text. (From Neal E. Miller, "Experimental Studies of Conflict," in *Personality and the Behavior Disorders*, ed. J. McV. Hunt. The Ronald Press Company, 1944.)

are represented as straight lines for simplicity, but any lines with a continuous negative slope steeper for avoidance than for approach at every distance would do equally well. It is apparent that if it was the approach line which had the steeper slope, no stable balance point could be reached: the animal would either go right away or right up to the goal.

Miller verified this model by systematically enumerating certain postulates, drawing deductions from them, and verifying these experimentally—an example of precise systematic theory building. The crucial issue of the steeper slope of the avoidance line was deduced by Miller from the postulate that fear is a learned drive. On this view, stimulation from the end of the alley affects avoidance in two ways: by arousing fear motivation, and eliciting the specific responses of avoidance. Thus, increasing distance from the end of the alley weakens the avoidance response in two distinct ways. Hunger, on the other hand, is thought of as depending on internal physiological factors: increasing distance from the stimulus therefore does not affect the "drive", and affects approach only in that the eliciting stimuli become weaker. The gradient of avoidance is therefore steeper than that of approach.

The view that avoidance is affected by a change in the stimulus in two ways leads to a further deduction which can be tested. If rats are taught to run down an alley to avoid shock and then tested without shock (*a*) in the original alley and (*b*) in a different one, they should respond much less in the second situation because the change in the stimulus situation will weaken both the fear motivation and the learned response of running. On the other hand, if a similarly trained group is tested in both situations with the shock on, the drive will not be thus affected. The avoidance behaviour of these animals should therefore decline less in the second situation than did that of the first group. This was verified experimentally.

As yet there seems to have been no application of this method to cases in which both approach and avoidance depend similarly on the external stimulus, as would seem to be the case in the attack/flee or curiosity/flee conflicts discussed later in this chapter. Miller's system has, however, been extended for use in studies of the effects of drugs, and also to cover some types of neurotic behaviour (Dollard *et al.*, 1950).

Until such time as a conflict is resolved the animal's behaviour is more or less influenced by both sets of causal factors. Before discussing the types of behaviour that may result, we must consider how to recognize a conflict situation. How can we tell that an animal has tendencies to behave in more than one way at a time? In most of the cases discussed so far, the existence of a conflict situation is recognized by the experimenter because he is familiar with the animal's previous history, and knows that two sets of factors (for instance deprivation of food and stimuli previously associated with running to food, on the one hand, and stimuli previously associated with shock, etc., on the other) are present, either of which alone would lead to a completed sequence of behaviour. If a new observer were brought into the situation at this point, would he be able to tell what the rat was up to? By observing the rat's behaviour, would he be able to deduce that it was in a conflict situation, and the nature of the two types of behaviour which were incompatible? Comparable situations frequently present themselves in nature, and before the behaviour can be analysed it is necessary for the observer to detect the presence of conflicting tendencies.

As examples, we shall consider the analysis of threat and courtship behaviour in birds and fishes. Such behaviour often seems difficult to understand because of the variety and complexity of the movements which follow each other in rapid and apparently meaningless succession: this is because the goals to which many of the actions are directed are not reached, and are therefore not apparent to the observer. It becomes comprehensible only when the occurrence of conflict is recognized. A description of two actual cases will pave the way for a more critical assessment of the sort of evidence that can be used.

16.1. Threat and Courtship in Birds and Fishes

During the spring, Great Tits settle in pairs on territories which are defended primarily by the male. Along the boundary between territories is a narrow no-man's land where prolonged skirmishes take place. Actual combat is rare, but each bird attacks and flees in turn, and in between shows a bewildering sequence of postures and movements. Among these is a "head-up" posture in which the bird stretches its head upwards, craning its neck from side to side and holding its body almost vertical (Fig. 16.2 (*a*)). This posture may be followed

(*a*)   (*b*)

Fig. 16.2. (*a*) Head-up threat posture used by Great Tits in disputes over territories. (*b*) Head-forward threat posture used by Blue Tits in disputes over territories and in fighting over food. (*From drawings by Yvette Spencer-Booth.*)

by a flight away from the rival, it may just subside, or it may lead to a rather hesitant flight towards the rival.

A clue to the basis of the behaviour which occurs during these skirmishes is given by the observation that they are practically limited to the boundary region. If one male meets another on his own territory, he immediately attacks and the intruder flees. If, however, this territory-owner is surprised as an intruder on his neighbour's territory, the roles are reversed—the bird which is now the territory-owner attacks and the one which is now the intruder flees. The boundary area is thus one in which each bird's tendencies to attack and to flee are more or less in balance: sometimes one may predominate and sometimes the other. Since the head-up posture is followed sometimes by approach and sometimes by a flight away, it appears to be associated with a rather finely balanced conflict between the two tendencies. Similar arguments indicate that many of the other varied postures and movements used in the skirmish are also to be interpreted as based on conflicting tendencies to attack and to flee. Once the skirmish is seen to be associated with two incompatible tendencies, it becomes more comprehensible (Hinde, 1952).

Chaffinch courtship will serve as a second example. Early in the breeding season, male Chaffinches begin to threaten other birds in the flock. Females ready to form a pair do not fly off, but adopt a fluffed posture: the male then gradually desists from his aggressiveness and begins to show courtship behaviour. Whereas at first he used a threat posture with his body horizontal and pointed directly towards the female (Fig. 16.3), now his body is oriented laterally towards her (Fig. 16.4). This is related to a change in dominance: the male was at first dominant to the female, but now he gradually becomes subordinate to her, and she drives him away from food. In the later stages of his courtship, which may not be reached until some weeks after the initial pair formation, the male approaches the female only with hesitation, and uses small pattering steps and a zig-zag walk, holding his body upright and somewhat withdrawn from the female (Fig. 16.5). Many of his attempts at copulation are thwarted by his fear of the female.

It seems, therefore, that the female may elicit attack and fleeing behaviour from the male as well as sexual behaviour: what he does depends both on the stimuli she presents, and on his own internal state. Early in the season his behaviour to the female is primarily aggressive. As the tendency to behave sexually increases, the balance between his tendencies to attack and flee from the female changes in favour of the latter, and he behaves as if afraid of her. This is not due simply to a hormonal change or a general lowering of aggressiveness, for his readiness to attack other males is increasing at this time. Later still, when he begins to make copulation attempts, the main conflict is between tendencies to approach the female for copulation and to flee from her. Finally the former predominates and he mounts the female, but as soon as copulation is over he flees and gives the same call as that which is given in the presence of a flying predator (Hinde, 1953a; Marler, 1956b).

Correlated with these changes, the postures used by the male alter as the season progresses. At first, his head-forward threat posture, oriented directly towards the female, differs little from that used in winter fighting. In the early stages of courtship this is modified in such a way that the male's body is lateral to the female: this can be regarded as a compromise between approaching and fleeing. Later still he approaches the female for copulation with his body in

Fig. 16.3

Fig. 16.3. Head-forward threat posture of Chaffinch used in fighting over food. The body is oriented towards the rival. (*From a drawing by Yvette Spencer-Booth.*)

Fig. 16.4. Courtship posture used by male Chaffinch. The body is lateral to the female. (*From a drawing by Yvette Spencer-Booth.*)

Fig. 16.5. The posture used by a male Chaffinch approaching a female immediately before copulation. The body is fairly upright, and the approach hesitant. (*From a drawing by Yvette Spencer-Booth.*)

Fig. 16.5

a vertical position comparable to that adopted by a bird about to flee from a rival in front of it.

Similar principles apply to the female when the male attempts copulation. The female does not always show sexual behaviour: she may fly off or attack. This is shown in the case of the Greenfinch in Fig. 16.6: out of 102 "hovering

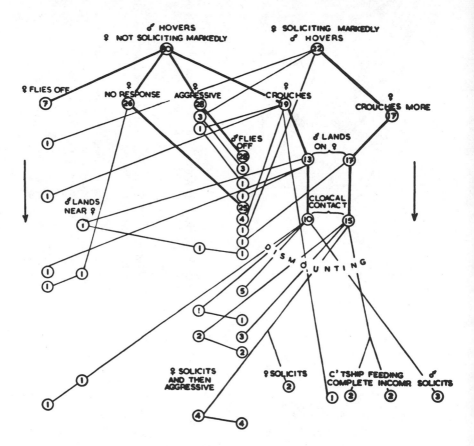

Fig. 16.6. Sequences of behaviour involved in copulation attempts by male Greenfinches. (*From Hinde, 1954c.*)

The figures indicate the number of times each situation was observed. The sequences start with the male hovering over the female, who may (right) or may not (left) have been soliciting previously. Read from top downwards.

approaches", only 25 led to successful copulation. Indeed, in 7 cases the female even reverted to aggressive behaviour after she had allowed the male to land on her back. Evidently proximity of the sex partner may elicit aggressive or fleeing as well as sexual behaviour from the female, just as with the male.

These examples of threat and courtship must not be taken to imply that the course of social encounters is simpler than is actually the case. Many additional factors are involved, such as the particular traits of the individuals concerned. Baeumer (1959), discussing fighting in domestic fowl, distinguishes three different types of fighting—between adult cocks, between hens, and between cockerels and hens holding positions of higher rank: the relative status of the individuals has an effect on the encounter which is superimposed on, or influences, the fluctuations in tendencies to attack and to flee. But the evidence that the diversity of behaviour shown in threat and courtship can be understood in terms of ambivalence between a relatively small number of behavioural tendencies is considerable.

In the cases discussed so far three groups of factors have been postulated: one of which if acting alone would lead to attack, one to fleeing, and one to sexual behaviour. The other types of behaviour which occur depend on particular strengths or relative strengths of the tendencies to behave in these three ways. Thus, each threat posture is associated with a particular range of strengths and relative strengths of tendencies to attack and to flee. Similarly, in a wide range of species pair formation is initiated by aggressive behaviour directed by a member of one sex (usually the male) to other individuals. Changes in the subsequent courtship behaviour can be understood in terms of changes in tendencies to attack, flee from, and behave sexually towards the sex partner.

Although tendencies to attack, flee and behave sexually are by no means the only ones involved, similar arguments have been applied not only to threat and courtship in a wide variety of species, but also to behaviour shown in many other contexts—nest-relief ceremonies, submissive behaviour, distraction and mobbing displays to predators, and so on. In each case recognition that the behaviour involves conflict, and identification of the incompatible patterns, leads to greater understanding (Tinbergen, 1952, 1959).

16.2. Nature of the Evidence used in Analysing Courtship and Threat Display

Much of the evidence used to support this view is based on field observation, and it sometimes involves a modicum of circular argument. It is therefore worthwhile to examine its nature in a little more detail. It can be classified as follows:

1. *The Situation*

Often, some evidence can be drawn from the situation in which the behaviour occurs. We have already seen one example of this in the case of territorial fighting—threat postures are used primarily on the boundaries, where there is reason to think that tendencies both to attack and to flee from the rival are in balance. Similarly, if a given display occurs only between potential mates and never between rivals, there is good reason for thinking that a sexual tendency is involved.

2. The Behaviour which Accompanies the Display

While displaying, an animal may edge towards or away from the object of its display. Oscillations or hesitation betray the presence of conflict, and the direction of movement indicates which tendency predominates at the moment.

In some species the external coloration can be used in a similar way, for changes in the motivational state are mirrored by changes in external coloration produced either by vaso-constriction/dilation or by chromatophores. Examples have been described from many phyla (e.g. Cephalopoda, Wells, 1962b: fishes, Lissmann, 1932; Baerends et al., 1955; Forselius, 1957; Keenleyside et al., 1962: lizards, Klausewitz, 1953: birds, Armstrong, 1947: mammals, Goodhart 1960). If a change in coloration is associated with (for example) a change in the probabilities of attacking and fleeing, and also with a change in the frequencies with which various display movements are used, an additional source of evidence as to the nature of the latter is available. A complex case has been analysed in detail by Baerends et al. (1955).

3. The Behaviour shown Before or After the Display

If a particular display is sometimes followed by an attack, and sometimes by fleeing, it is presumably associated with conflicting tendencies to attack and to flee. The underlying assumption here is that the tendency changes more slowly than the overt behaviour, so that the two patterns are likely to share common causal factors (internal or external to the animal) if they are closely associated in time (cf. Chapter 18). On this view, the relative strengths of the conflicting tendencies (that is, here, the relative probabilities that each will find overt expression) can be assessed by counting the relative frequencies of, e.g. attacks and fleeing movements which follow the display.

This method was first used by Moynihan (1955) to substantiate his view that the various threat postures of the Black-headed Gull were associated with different absolute and relative strengths of the tendencies to attack and flee from the rival, and has proved to be a powerful tool. However, some general difficulties in interpreting "sequential associations" must be pointed out. First, many of the changes in behaviour shown by a displaying animal are consequences of changes in the stimulus situation presented by its rival or mate. This difficulty can be circumvented by recording sequences of behaviour given to motionless dummies, or by selecting for analysis only those sequences in which the behaviour of the second animal did not change.

Another difficulty with this method is that many displays are seldom followed by pure expressions of one or other of the tendencies with which, according to other sources of evidence, they are associated. In one series of observations it was found that the pivoting display (Fig. 16.7) of the Goldfinch was associated with agonistic behaviour in 68 per cent of 152 cases observed, and with sexual behaviour (courtship feeding or copulation) in only 8 per cent.

Nevertheless, other evidence indicates that a sexual element is important in the display. Pivoting is associated with a call seldom heard in agonistic contexts, is much more common between mates than between flock birds, increases in frequency as the breeding season progresses, and is associated with a drooping of the wings which also occurs in other types of behaviour in which the sexual tendency is more conspicuous.

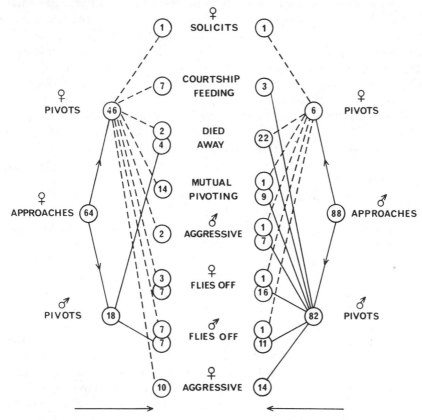

Fig. 16.7. Sequences of behaviour associated with the "pivoting" display of Goldfinches. (*After Hinde, 1955/1956.*)

The figures indicate the number of times each sequence was observed. Read from sides to centre.

Yet another difficulty is that movements may be associated together in time not because they share causal factors in any ordinary sense of the word, but because they share a low priority among the organism's activities and can occur only in the absence of response tendencies of greater priority. This may be one reason why different "toilet" or "comfort" movements tend to be associated together. Such movements rarely interrupt other types of active behaviour, but are themselves often interrupted (Andrew, 1956a).

4. *The Nature of the Display Itself*

In many analyses of display, the postures are regarded as the basic units. Each posture, however, can be analysed into components—raising of the wings, opening of the beak, spreading the tail, and so on. Further understanding of displays has been obtained by using these as the units, each posture being regarded as a combination of components.

In some displays there may be changes in the intensity of particular components and in the number of components present, but the components occur only in certain combinations: *A*, *AB*, *ABC*, *ABCD*, and so on. An example is the "soliciting" posture used by the female Chaffinch before copulation: successive stages in the posture are shown in Fig. 3.1, p. 18. This type of combination of components suggests that all depend on the same tendency but require different threshold levels.

At the other extreme the components could, in theory, occur in all possible combinations. For that to be the case, there would have to be as many independently variable groups of causal factors as there are components, and there would be no recognizable "postures", i.e. commonly occurring groupings of components.

In practice, most displays lie somewhere between the two. In a study of the agonistic behaviour of the Blue Tit (*Parus caeruleus*) Stokes (1962a) assessed the correlations between nine different components. Of the 36 possible two-component combinations, a strong correlation ($p < 0.01$) between the components was found in thirty-one. The correlation was in some cases positive; for instance a bird with fanned tail usually raised its wings as well. In others the correlation was negative—an erect crest never occurred with wings raised, tail fanned, beak open or beak down. Stokes made a more detailed analysis of five of the components—position of crest, body, nape, wings and orientation to the second bird. Out of the forty-seven possible combinations of the measures of these five elements, only twenty were actually observed, and eight of them accounted for 576 out of the 629 observations in which all these components were recorded. Such results justify the use of crude postures in the preliminary analysis of displays, but indicate that further refinement can be achieved by studying the components independently.

The relation between particular components and subsequent behaviour is not usually a precise one. Stokes (1962a) studied the relations between the presence of individual components in the agonistic displays of Blue Tits at a winter feeding station and whether they subsequently attacked, fled, or remained where they were. When a bird raised its crest or fluffed its body feathers it subsequently fled on 90 per cent of occasions, and never attacked. But for all other components the probability of subsequent attack, escape or staying was 52 per cent or less.

This relatively small correlation between particular components and subsequent behaviour was due in part to interaction between the components. For instance, in an otherwise non-aggressive situation raising of the nape feathers was correlated with an increased likelihood of attack, but when a bird was already in an aggressive posture, the raising of the nape was associated with a reduced incidence of attack. However, as we have seen, these components tend to occur in particular combinations, and these combinations show more reliable relationships with subsequent behaviour. One combination led to escape on 94 per cent of the occasions, another to staying on 79 per cent, and another to attack on 48 per cent.

Fig. 16.8. (a) Aggressive and (b) Anxiety forms of the upright threat posture of the Herring Gull. (*After Tinbergen, 1959.*)

There are also other types of evidence which suggest that particular components are associated with one or other tendency:

(a) Some components are in fact elements of one of the main types of behaviour occurring in the conflict situation. In the "upright" threat posture of the

Herring Gull the carpal joints are raised, the neck is stretched up and forwards, and the bill pointed downwards: these are components of attacking by wing-beating and pecking from above (Fig. 16.8). On the other hand, a lateral rather than head-on orientation to the rival, sleeking of the feathers, an upward pointing of the head and an upwards instead of obliquely forward position of the neck are components of escape. The posture is, in fact, a combination of these components of attack and fleeing, and the preponderance of one or of the other can be understood in terms of the relative strengths of the associated tendencies (Tinbergen, 1959).

(b) The postures in which the components occur. If a component occurs in postures which, on other sources of evidence, are known to be threat postures depending on conflicting tendencies to attack and flee, but never occurs in courtship postures, it presumably does not depend on the sexual tendency.

(c) The circumstances in which it occurs most often or most markedly. If a posture varies from one extreme, that is very often followed by fleeing, to another, that is very often followed by copulation, and if certain components are absent in the pre-fleeing form but present in the pre-copulation form, they can be said to be associated with the sexual tendency. Similarly, a component of a threat posture which is more marked when the bird is inside its own territory than when it is outside it, is likely to be associated with attack.

(d) The components with which it is associated. Vertical stretching of the neck in gulls provides an example here. This may be an intention movement of striking a rival, or an intention movement of mounting a mate. The other components with which the neck-stretching is combined provide evidence as to its significance in any particular case (Tinbergen, 1959; see also Stokes cited on p. 256).

(e) Comparative evidence. Sometimes a comparison of closely related species provides an additional source of evidence. For instance, the facts that the Skuas do not raise the carpals in the aggressive upright threat posture and do not use wing-beating in fights, give additional weight to the view that wing-raising is an aggressive movement in gulls, which do both (Tinbergen, 1959).

Using one or more of these methods, the relations between display components and behaviour tendencies have now been assessed in a number of birds and fishes. Although the quantitative relationships may vary with the season (Stokes, 1962a) the evidence that many components are associated with a particular behavioural tendency is strong. Furthermore, the relationships are similar in closely related species (Andrew, 1961e; Stokes, 1962b).

5. Factor Analysis

The methods discussed so far provide a basis for the understanding of many types of behaviour whose motivation is at first sight obscure. More recently further refinement of method (3) has been achieved by applying the techniques of factor analysis. The method consists of: (*a*) obtaining detailed recordings of sequences of identifiable elements of behaviour; (*b*) assessing the frequency with which each of these elements follows (or precedes) each other element, and hence determining the correlation coefficients between them; (*c*) determining whether these correlations could be deduced from correlations between the elements and a smaller number of hypothetical variables. If they can, then these new variables can be regarded as factors associated with two or more of the behavioural elements, and can be said to explain the original correlations.

Wiepkema (1961) has analysed the behaviour of the Bitterling in this way. The male fish defends a territory round a freshwater mussel, to which he will admit only ripe females. Such females are led to the mussel, and lay their eggs within its gills. The male then ejects sperm while skimming over the siphon of the mussel.

Wiepkema recorded the occurrence of twelve identifiable movements when a territorial male was presented with another male, an unripe female, or a ripe female. The correlation coefficients between these movements were calculated as indicated above, and then subjected to factor analysis. It was found that three factors accounted for about 90 per cent of the total common variance, further factors having no practical significance. The results could therefore be expressed in terms of a three-dimensional model (Fig. 16.9) in which the dependent variables were represented as vectors. In this model the correlation coefficient between any two activities is represented by the cosine of the angle between them: obtuse angles thus indicate negative correlations. The three common factors are shown at right angles to each other, their position being chosen so that each corresponds as closely as possible to a group of vectors. The length of each vector indicates the extent to which it can be explained in terms of the common factors introduced, and its projection on to each factor indicates the extent to which that factor is represented in it (i.e. its factor loading).

It will be seen that the vectors of four activities (head-butting, chasing, turning beats and jerking) were closely grouped around the positive side of factor 1. These movements have an obvious aggressive function, and thus factor 1 can be called the aggressive factor. Vectors for four non-reproductive activities, which include fleeing, are closely grouped around factor 2; while those for skimming and three other movements used in courtship lie close to factor 3. Factors 2 and 3 can thus be described as non-reproductive and sexual factors respectively.

Some activities (e.g. head-butting, chasing, fleeing, skimming) are almost pure measures of one or other of the factors, since their loadings on the others are almost zero. Others, while having high positive loadings on one factor, also have positive loadings on another: they thus depend on two or more factors. For instance, turning beats and jerking have positive loadings for both factors 1 and 2, and can thus be regarded as expressing both aggressive and non-reproductive tendencies. The latter is in fact probably multiple, the various non-reproductive activities being grouped together on the diagram because they occurred largely in the absence of aggressive or sexual behaviour. This, incidentally, exemplifies the way in which the results of a factor analysis require

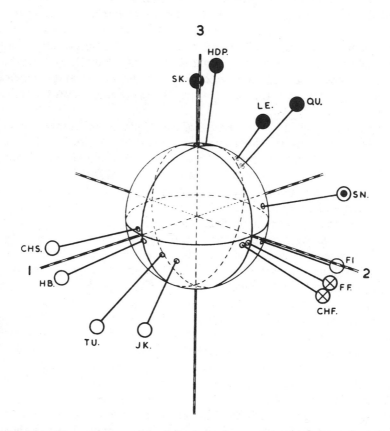

Fig. 16.9. The vector model of the behaviour of the male Bitterling as obtained from a factor analysis of the correlation coefficients between successive activities. (*After Wiepkema, 1961.*)

    The patterns of behaviour are abbreviated as follows: CHF = chafing, CHS = chasing, FF = finflickering, FL = fleeing, HB = head butting, HDP = head-down posture, JK = jerking, LE = leading, QU = quivering, SK = skimming, SN = snapping, TU = turning beat. The positive side of the aggressive factor is indicated by 1, the positive side of the sexual factor by 3, the positive side of the non-reproductive factor by 2. The vectors of the 12 variables are determined by the projections (i.e. factor loadings) of these variables on the three main axes.

information from other sources for their full interpretation (*see also* Overall, 1964).

Such an analysis enables the activities whose vectors have positive loadings for two factors to be arranged in a series of increasing loading by one factor and decreasing loading by the other. For instance, the agonistic movements can be arranged in a sequence of fleeing-jerking-turning beat-head butting-chasing which corresponds to an increase in the ratio of the aggressive factor to the non-reproductive (fleeing) factor (*see* Fig. 16.13).

Used in this way, the factorial method is a valuable adjunct to the methods used previously for assessing multiple motivation. Another example is provided in the study by Baerends *et al.* (1962) of the snap display of the Heron (*Ardea cinerea*). It remains true, of course, that the method is liable to the various difficulties discussed under (3) above. Furthermore, by itself it gives no information about the nature of the factors.

In the examples mentioned, the correlations between activities were assessed from a study of sequences of behaviour. Another possibility is to assess the strengths, intensities or durations of different activities in a large number of individuals. The analysis is then based on the correlations between these measures. For example, Bell (1960) examined thirty-seven measures of behaviour of human neonates: from the factor analysis five orthogonal factors emerged and were labelled Arousal, Depth of Sleep, Sensitivity-Strength, Oral integration and Foetal Position. In this case the factors referred to characteristics of the individual rather than of its motivational state.

6. *Independent Manipulation of Attacking and Fleeing*

Finally, it is sometimes possible to manipulate the strengths of the tendencies to attack and flee independently. Thus, Blurton-Jones (1958–9) identified the stimulus characters which would cause a pair of tame Canada Geese (*Branta canadensis*) to attack him and to flee from him. When he combined these characters, the geese threatened him.

We see, then, that the complicated activities shown by fishes and birds during threat and courtship can be understood on the view that tendencies for two or more incompatible types of behaviour are present.* In nearly every case the conclusion has been reached by the use of several independent types of evidence, none in itself conclusive but each pointing in a similar direction.

Although the cases discussed so far have involved principally conflicting

* The following is a representative selection of studies. *Fish:* Baerends *et al.* (1955); Barlow (1962a, b, 1963); Forselius (1957); Keenleyside *et al.* (1962); Morris (1954b; 1958a); Oehlert (1958); Wickler (1958). *Birds:* Andrew (1957a, 1961e); Baggerman *et al.* (1956); Brockway (1963); Crook (1960a, b, 1963); Delius (1963); Hinde (1952, 1953a, 1954c, 1955–6); Immelman (1962); Kruijt (1964); Kunkel (1959, 1962); Lind (1961, 1962); McKinney (1961); Marler (1956b); Morris (1954a, 1957b, 1958b, c); Moynihan (1955, 1956, 1958a, b); Moynihan *et al.* (1954); Rüppell (1962); Stamm (1962); Stokes (1962a, b); Tinbergen (1952, 1953, 1959); Wood-Gush (1956).

Fig. 16.10. Threat and fear expressions in cats. In each section fear increases from above downwards, and aggressiveness from left to right. (*From Leyhausen, 1956.*)

tendencies to attack, flee and behave sexually, these are by no means the only possibilities. Even in courtship, tendencies to nest-build, sing, behave sexually, beg, look around, and probably others are often involved (e.g. Andrew, 1957a; 1961e; Stamm, 1962; Kunkel, 1962; Crook 1963). Other displays such as the distraction and mobbing displays given to predators (Simmons, 1955; Arm-

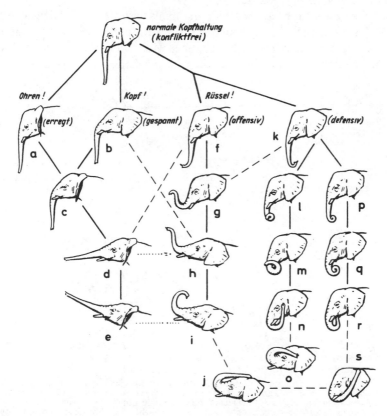

Fig. 16.11. Positions of head, trunk and ears shown by elephants in aggression, fear and threat. (*After Kühme, 1963.*)

Aggressiveness increases *a→d*. A forwardly directed trunk, *f*, is associated with activity or rage, a backwardly directed one, *k*, inhibition or fear. Position *i*, used in threatening by the bull, indicates some slight inhibition of aggressiveness as compared with *d* or *e*. Similarly, courage preponderates more in *n*, fear more in *p*, *q* or *r*; and the upward bending in *j* and *o* indicates more courage than *s*. Raising of the ears or head in association with these positions indicates increased aggressiveness.

strong, 1950, 1954; Hinde, 1954a) and nest-relief ceremonies, have also been shown to depend on ambivalence. Such conclusions, however, are not to be overinterpreted as implying that all displays, let alone all signals used in intra-specific communication, depend on conflict. When a bird sings, or feeds its mate, conflict is of minor significance.

16.3. Threat and Courtship in Other Vertebrates

The extent to which such principles are applicable also among the amphibia is not so clear (e.g. Gauss, 1961), but the courtship of one species has been interpreted in terms of an "interaction of drives" by Rabb *et al.* (1963). In some reptiles, also, courtship clearly involves aggressive components (e.g. Eibl-Eibesfeldt, 1955b; Kästle, 1964).

Sufficient work has been done with mammals to show that ambivalence plays a large part in many of their displays. For instance, Fig. 16.10 shows how the threat posture of the domestic cat changes with tendencies to attack and flee from the rival; the precise nature of the posture changes with the absolute and

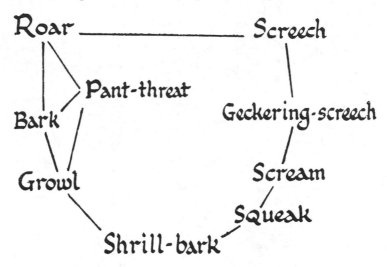

Fig. 16.12. Relationships of certain noises made in agonistic situations by Rhesus Monkeys. The lines indicate named noises between which intermediates have been recorded. (*After Rowell, 1962.*)

The noises are made in the following situations: *Roar:* made by a very confident animal, when threatening another of inferior rank. *Pant-threat:* made by a less confident animal wanting the support of the rest of the group in its attack. *Bark:* given by a threatening animal insufficiently aggressive to move towards the other. *Growl:* given by a mildly alarmed animal. *Shrill-bark:* the alarm call of the species, probably given to predators in the wild. *Screech:* Typically has an abrupt pitch change up and then down. Made when threatening a higher ranking animal, and when excited and slightly alarmed generally. *Geckering screech:* made by an animal being threatened by another. *Scream:* made by a losing monkey in a fight while being bitten. *Squeaks:* made by a defeated and exhausted monkey at the end of a fight.

relative strengths of the two tendencies (Leyhausen, 1956). Figure 16.11 shows the results of a similar study of the positions of the elephant's trunk (Kühme 1961, 1963). Tembrock (1962a, b) regards the threat displays of foxes as due to a superposition of attacking and defensive tendencies under the influence of social inhibition, and Walther (1958, 1960) found dominance changes to play an important role in the premating behaviour of Okapi. All the rodent species studied by Eibl-Eibesfeldt (1953), Grant *et al.* (1963) and Grant (1963) showed ambivalence between fleeing, aggression, and mating tendencies in social encounters (*see also* Peirce *et al.*, 1961a, b). Other mammalian display movements which have been interpreted in terms of ambivalence include those of the moose (Geist, 1963) and various primates (Hinde *et al.*, 1962; Rowell *et al.*, 1962; Rowell 1962; van Hooff, 1962). The case of the vocalizations used by Rhesus monkeys in agonistic situations is illustrated in Fig. 16.12.

This is not to say, of course, that all movements used in display and social communication depend on conflict. Andrew (1962) points out that many behaviour patterns which serve as signals, such as the scent marking of many mammals, and grooming, are not usefully described in terms of conflicting but incompatible tendencies.

Furthermore, Andrew (1963b) suggests that some movements given in conflict situations convey information as to the nature of that conflict, not because their components are associated directly with one or other of the conflicting tendencies, but by a more indirect means. For instance, lemurs raise their tails while threatening, and this could be said to indicate low fear and high aggression. However, when all the situations in which tail-raising occurs are considered, it is seen to be associated with a "high degree of facilitation of postural reflexes": since subordinate animals tend to show loss of tone in such reflexes, it appears in threat only in animals likely to attack.

Andrew (1963b, c) also argues that many primate facial expressions are in fact derived (in evolution) from protective responses which serve to protect the major sense organs and other sensitive areas against possible noxious effects from the source of stimulation: he believes their causation not to have changed in evolution. Such protective responses are, of course, related to fleeing. Andrew also suggests that many of the calls given by primates are associated with alerting (orientation, *see* p. 96) responses which serve to bring the major sense organs to bear on an object. While it may be that such responses play a more important role in the communicatory gestures of primates than in those of lower species, it remains true that many other primate expressive movements, both gestures and vocalizations, are associated with particular ranges of tendencies to attack, flee, and behave sexually.

The view that threat behaviour has a dual motivation has been criticized by Brown *et al.* (1963) on the basis of experiments which involved elicitation of agonistic behaviour by direct electrical stimulation of the central nervous system of cats. Finding that threat could be elicited by stimulation of only one area of the brain at a time, they argued that it therefore cannot have a dual motivation. In fact, this could be interpreted on the view that either "motivational" mechanisms for both attack and fleeing, or coordination mechanisms for threatening, come within the area affected by the electrical stimulus. Most of the rest of Brown and Hunsperger's data are consistent with an interpretation in terms of dual motivation. They found that threat-attack, threat and escape were elicited from related areas; that the response became less aggressive, and included more fleeing components, the more posterior the point stimulated; and that the extent of the aggressiveness of the threat elicited from any one locus was influenced by the strength of the electrical stimulus and by the external object presented. All these could be accounted for in terms of partially overlapping areas for attack and escape, with other factors influencing the precise balance produced by stimulation in any one locus.

In any case rather different results for chickens were obtained by von Holst *et al.* (1963). They found that, with a particular electrode placement in the brain-stem of a domestic cock, stimulation produced motor unrest. If a stuffed polecat was presented with the electrical stimulus it was vigorously attacked. If the electrical stimulation was continued beyond the attack, the cock immediately changed to fleeing. Thus stimulation in one locus, together with the external stimulus, produced both attack and fleeing.

Brown *et al.* also used another argument. The view that threat has a dual motivation is associated with an assumption of mutually inhibitory relations between attack and fleeing. They found that stimulation in the escape area augmented or hastened the threat-attacks obtained by simultaneous stimulation in the brain area appropriate to them. They write: "Present results, therefore, indicate that *mutual* inhibition between threat-attack and escape zones does not occur". Such negative results must be interpreted with much caution. For one thing, Brown *et al.* did not obtain "pure attack" from any of the loci they stimulated, though apparently it has been obtained by other workers (e.g. Wasman *et al.*, 1962; MacDonnell *et al.*, 1964). For another, considerable variations occur in the results of experiments involving simultaneous stimulation. Egger *et al.* (1963) found that amygdaloid stimulation at current strengths apparently ineffective when administered alone might either facilitate or suppress hypothalamically induced attack behaviour, depending on the locus stimulated.

Brown and Hunsperger's views have also been criticized on logical grounds by C. H. F. Rowell (1964; *see also* Brown, 1964). It is, of course, desirable that physiological data should be used in formulating hypotheses about behaviour (*see* Chapter 1), but caution is necessary before an interpretation valid at the behavioural level is revised in terms of physiological data whose own interpretation involves considerable basic assumptions.

16.4. The Nature of the Conflicts in Display

So far, we have assumed some degree of incompatibility between tendencies as assessed by groups of responses; for instance between all attacking patterns and all fleeing patterns and all sexual patterns. This assumption is based ultimately on the view that a series of situations could be found in which all types of behaviour associated with one tendency become less common or less evident, while those associated with another become more so; for instance attacking elements diminish and fleeing ones increase as a male crosses his territorial boundary into foreign ground. However, we have also seen that elements of behaviour patterns associated with different tendencies can occur together; for instance in display postures. The question thus arises, should the incompatibility be regarded as occurring between the overall tendencies, or between more basic elements of behaviour? The issues here echo some of those discussed in Chapter 8 in the consideration of unitary drive concepts.

Andrew (1956a), criticizing the older view that conflict situations involve incompatibility between tendencies to give groups of responses, argues that it is, "more accurate and more useful in predicting behaviour to say that tendencies to give two groups of responses are present, and that some of the responses of each group are incompatible with each other". He bases this view on evidence showing that the incompatibility between two responses does not depend on the drives they express. Thus, a passerine bird flicks its tail while hopping through twigs, when it has simultaneous tendencies to move by flight and by sidling along, and also when perched near a food dish at which a feared superior is feeding. In the latter case it has tendencies to approach (to feed) and to fly away (a fear response). The common factor in the two situations is that each involves a conflict between two locomotory movements, one at least of which involves flying. Similarly, the calls given by a Blackbird (*Turdus merula*) during the approach/avoidance conflict involved in mobbing an owl depend on a tendency to fly in the presence of a frightening object, but not on whether it flies towards or away from it (Andrew, 1961a–d).

Wiepkema (1961) also criticizes the view that incompatibility exists between the major drives or tendencies. He points out that, in many of the studies on which this view was based, the drives were assessed in terms of only one variable; for instance the frequency of zig-zags was held to indicate the sex drive of a male Stickleback. The results of his own detailed analysis of the reproductive behaviour of the Bitterling is shown in Fig. 16.13. Some external and internal factors were found to be common to groups of responses designated as sex, attack and fleeing. The corresponding internal mechanisms are labelled S, A, and F. The radiating lines indicate the relationships assessed from a study using factor analysis (p. 259) and other techniques. The letters down the right side refer to the various behaviour patterns observed. Some of the relationships were positive, some neutral and others negative; for instance an increase in the aggressive factors increases the frequency of chasing (CHS); decreases that of quivering and leading (QU, LE), both movements which occur in early courtship; and does not affect the purely sexual movements of skimming (SK). Thus the relationships cannot be explained by postulating inhibitory effects between major tendencies each of which is associated with a limited number of behaviour patterns.

Evidence such as this shows that descriptions of conflict behaviour in the form of inhibitory relationships between major tendencies may sometimes be

suitable only for the initial stages of analysis. More detailed study of incompatibility between the constituent patterns of behaviour is often necessary. This

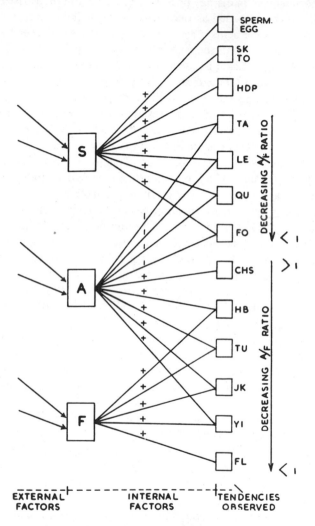

Fig. 16.13. Wiepkema's diagram of the reproductive behaviour of the Bitterling. (*After Wiepkema, 1961.*)

S, A, F symbolize the internal mechanisms that underlie the temporal association and
frequency of the different movements shown on the right. (The abbreviations for patterns
of behaviour are given in the key to Fig. 16.9, to which should be added the following:
TO=touching, TA=tail bending, FO=following, YI=yielding.) The arrows pointing
to S, A and F symbolize the external factors which stimulate these mechanisms. The
agonistic movements are arranged from above downwards in decreasing order of the
A/F ratio (*see* p. 261) as revealed by factor analysis. In accord with the experimental
evidence, increase in aggressive tendency is associated with an inhibitory effect on some
but not all sexual activities.

question will be discussed again in the next chapter: for the moment it must be emphasized that incompatibility even between responses does not necessarily imply physical incompatibility between the actions of the effectors. Even when we describe a conflict with terms such as "approach/avoidance", they are descriptive labels only: the essential inhibition may be a physiological one. When we find incompatibility between responses, the physiological mechanism need not be on the response side: it could involve, for instance, the mechanisms of selective attention (Chapters 5 and 6).

Further, as we have seen, incompatibility is a relative matter. When the two tendencies are of low or medium strength, the activities associated with each which occur during a given time interval may be independent of the strength of the other, but if one tendency is strong it may exert positive inhibitory effects on the activities associated with the other (Wiepkema, 1961; *see also* pp. 270–3). The relationships found thus depend in part on the precise conditions of study.

16.5. Summary

1. To say an animal has a tendency to behave in a particular way implies evidence that causal factors for the behaviour in question are present. In nature, more than one tendency is usually present at a time: such a situation is described as a conflict situation.
2. Most conflicts are soon resolved.
3. Some conflicts can be characterized in terms of incompatible directions of movement. The point of balance in an approach/approach conflict is unstable, but those in avoidance/avoidance or approach/avoidance conflicts may be stable.
4. The threat and courtship postures of fishes and birds can be understood in terms of conflicting tendencies to behave in incompatible ways. Characteristically, threat involves tendencies to attack and to flee, while courtship involves tendencies to attack, to flee from and to behave sexually towards the mate. In many species, however, other tendencies also play a part.
5. Evidence that threat and courtship postures occur when there are conflicting tendencies comes from study of the situations in which they occur, the behaviour which accompanies the display, the behaviour which occurs before or after the display, and from the components of the display. The technique of factor analysis can be used to assess evidence drawn from the study of the behaviour preceding or following the display.
6. Similar principles apply to mammals.
7. This approach to the study of display movements is essentially a behavioural one. Caution is necessary in postulating relationships with neurophysiological data.
8. To understand the behaviour shown in conflict situations it is necessary to consider both the extent of incompatibility between tendencies to show groups of activities and also that between particular activities or between the components of particular activities.

17

Behaviour in Conflict Situations

When animals are used for behavioural experiments in the laboratory, motivation is usually controlled: often attempts are made to satisfy all the basic needs except one, which is used by the experimenter to channel the behaviour. In nature, as we have seen, such a situation is unusual. Most of the time causal factors for more than one type of behaviour are present, and often the balance between them is a fine one. In this chapter we shall consider various types of behaviour which occur in conflict situations. The categories used are useful for purposes of discussion, but it will be apparent that they overlap in a number of ways. Discussion will be limited to immediate responses: the longer term effects of exposure to conflict situations have recently been discussed by Caïn (1959), who reviews also the literature on animal neurosis.

17.1. Inhibition of All But One Response

Undoubtedly the commonest consequence of the simultaneous action of factors for two or more types of behaviour is the suppression of all but one of them. That behavioural inhibition of this type occurs is a matter of common observation. Thus the appearance of a flying predator causes a feeding Great Tit to dash for cover, abandoning its food. Since Great Tits do not usually fly off in this way unless alarmed, it is reasonable to presume that the Great Tit would have gone on feeding if the predator had not appeared. In other words, causal factors for feeding are presumably still present but overridden by the effects of the predator.

Behavioural inhibition is thus said to occur when the causal factors otherwise adequate for the elicitation of two (or more) types of behaviour are present, and one of them is reduced in strength because of the presence of the causal factors for the other.

In practice, since it is usual for causal factors for more than one type of behaviour to be present, some degree of behavioural inhibition probably occurs all the time. The amount of time an organism spends in many of its activities is thus restricted by the necessity for doing other things; and one of the most important consequences of a change in one of the motivational variables discussed in Chapters 10 to 15 is an influence on the order of prepotency among the organism's possible activities. For instance, the proportion of the day Blue Tits spend feeding rises from about 70 per cent in the summer to nearly 90 per cent in midwinter when food is scarce, temperatures are low and the days short: there is a correlated decrease in the time spent resting and preening (Gibb, 1954). Thus a consequence of winter conditions is to increase the priority of feeding behaviour relative to the others. A more detailed example on a different time scale is provided by Cotton's (1953) study of the influence of different periods of deprivation on the speed with which rats run down a runway for food. Over all test trials, running speed was found to decrease with increasing deprivation time. However, if trials in which the animals showed other types of behaviour, such as sniffing in the runway, were excluded, running speed was little affected by deprivation. Apparently the most important effect of deprivation was to increase the priority of running to food (*see also* Prechtl, 1953).

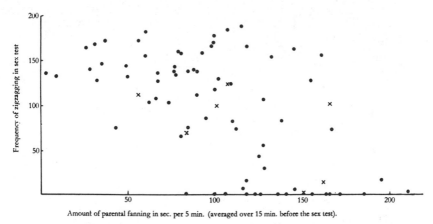

Amount of parental fanning in sec. per 5 min. (averaged over 15 min. before the sex test).

Fig. 17.1. Relation between amount of parental fanning and frequency of zig-zag courtship shown in a subsequent sex test by Three-spined Sticklebacks. (*After Sevenster, 1961.*)

A similar point is made by Bindra (1961). Starting from the observation that every organism has a large repertoire of "acts" (e.g. walking, grooming, head-turning, sniffing), he suggests that the outcome of competition between these acts can be determined from a knowledge of their relative probabilities, those with a higher probability on the average occurring sooner. On this basis, Bindra describes performance in a learning situation in terms of the elimination of irrelevant responses (e.g. sniffing, sitting, and grooming, in a task involving running along an alley), and an increase in the relative probabilities of the relevant ones. Of particular importance in the test situations used in the laboratory are the various responses to novelty—freezing, fleeing, exploring—which compete with those necessary for the solution of the problem. Pre-exposure of the animal to the situation reduces these novelty responses (Claus *et al.*, 1960). A similar hypothesis to account for the effect of earlier experience on fighting in mice has been advanced by King *et al.* (1954) and supported by Banks (1962) (*see also* pp. 368–70).

Just because behavioural inhibition involves the suppression of an activity, and because that suppression may be partial rather than absolute, detailed analysis may be necessary to reveal it. Some examples are provided by the experiments of van Iersel (1953) and Sevenster (1961) on the interaction of sexual and parental behaviour in the Three-spined Stickleback. The number of zig-zag courtship dances given to a standard female, and the proportion of time spent fanning, were among the dependent variables chosen for study. In fanning, the fish takes up a position in front of the nest and pointing towards its entrance, and moves its tail as though swimming forwards while moving its

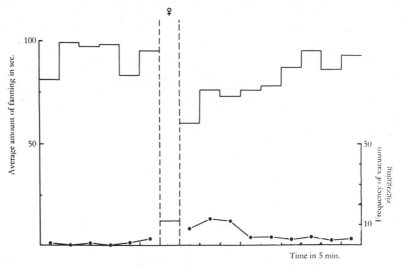

Fig. 17.2. The effect of a sex test (with more than 20 zig-zags) on the parental fanning of male Three-spined Sticklebacks. A female was present for the period between the vertical discontinuous lines. (*After Sevenster, 1961.*)

pectoral fins as though swimming backwards. As a result a current of water is directed towards the nest and the eggs are aerated. Considering first some short-term experiments, the relation between fanning during a 15-minute observation test and the number of zig-zags given in a test immediately following is shown in Fig. 17.1. This indicates considerable independence between the two tendencies, but also a degree of negative correlation; low numbers of zig-zags are found only with large amounts of fanning. This suggests that a strong tendency for fanning is associated with an inhibitory effect on zig-zagging. That the reverse effect also occurs was demonstrated as follows. If two zig-zag tests are given in succession, the number of zig-zags in the second is usually greater than in the first. This indicates that the initial exposure to the standard female (and/or performance of the zig-zag response) has a positive effect on the tendency to show zig-zags which persists to the second test (cf. pp. 213–9). Comparison of the amount of fanning before and after the sex test gives an indication of the effect of this increased courtship tendency on fanning: if the number of zig-zags in the sex test is considerable, the subsequent fanning is decreased (Fig. 17.2).* Thus an increase in the courtship tendency is accompanied by a decrease of fanning even after the sex stimulus has been removed.

Behavioural inhibition involves suppression of one or more activities while another predominates, but what are the consequences of the conflict for the behaviour which does appear? This depends in part on the criteria by which it is assessed, but in terms of frequency measures it too usually suffers a decrement. Indeed, an acute conflict may result in the inhibition of all possible responses. The paralysis of fear is well enough known in human subjects: a comparable phenomenon has been studied by Rigby (1954). He trained rats to obtain food by performing one response in the presence of a light, and to avoid shock by another response in the presence of a buzzer. When both light and buzzer were presented simultaneously, many of the animals sat motionless.

In some cases, however, there is evidence that the behaviour not suppressed may actually be augmented. If Sticklebacks are fed in only one part of their aquaria, and are then given one or two electric shocks there, they subsequently spend less time in the danger area, but while there they feed more intensively (cf. p. 151). These changes are not a consequence specific to electric shock: similar increases in intensity of feeding combined with a reduction in time spent feeding were shown by fish in conflicts between feeding and migratory behaviour or feeding and fleeing from rivals (Tugendhat, 1960b; *see also* pp. 149 –61).

The concept of behavioural inhibition is, of course, a loose one, and diverse types of mechanisms may be involved. One may fail to leave one's room to go to a meeting when the clock strikes because of failure to notice it or refusal to respond appropriately: both would qualify as behavioural inhibition. Competition for the mechanisms of selective attention, as discussed in Chapters 5 and 6, competition for the effectors, and perhaps competition for more than one type of intervening mechanism, may all be involved. Where selective attention is the issue all responses associated with the relevant object may be possible and all responses associated with others suppressed. Thus a Great Tit behaving territorially may show any of the sorts of aggressive behaviour elicited by other Great Tits, but will ignore nest-holes. At the other extreme, competition for effectors may result in inhibition only of particular responses or components of responses (*see* below).

---

* In practice the depression of fanning is even greater than is apparent from the results of the experiments, for it overrides a tendency towards an increase in fanning due to its interruption by the sex test (*see* p. 303).

17.2. Intention Movements

Behavioural inhibition is often not complete, so that the behaviour is reduced in intensity or frequency or appears in an incomplete form. This may consist of the initial phases of movements or movement sequences, usually referred to as "intention movements". For instance, the take-off leap of a bird before flying consists of two phases: first it crouches, withdraws its head and raises its tail and then reverses these movements as it springs off (Fig. 17.3). These incomplete movements may be repeated several times before take-off when

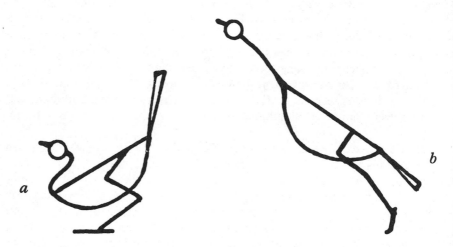

Fig. 17.3. The first and second phases of the take-off jump by a bird. (*After Daanje, 1950.*)

the bird is about to fly up from rest. In conflict situations they (or a modified form of them) may occur repeatedly for much of the time that the bird remains in the situation (Daanje, 1950).

17.3. Alternation

We have seen that, just before copulation, a male Chaffinch has conflicting tendencies to approach and avoid the female. He does not, however, stay still at the point of balance, but alternates between the two patterns, sometimes edging a little closer and then fleeing away. Another well-known example of such alternation is provided by the zig-zag courtship dance of the Three-spined Stickleback (Fig. 18.2, pp. 295–6). When a pregnant female enters a male's territory he swims in a zig-zag course. One leg of this course is an intention movement of attacking the female, the other of leading her to the nest (Tinbergen, 1951; van Iersel, 1953). Similar alternation behaviour is to be seen in a rat placed in an approach/avoidance conflict as described above: the animal vacillates about a point some distance from the goal.

17.4. Ambivalent Behaviour

Sometimes intention movements appropriate to the two tendencies are combined into a single pattern which contains components appropriate to both. Thus, a half-tame Moorhen (*Gallinula chloropus*) offered food may make incipient pecks towards it, and even swallowing movements, while simultaneously keeping its distance or even edging away: components of both feeding and fleeing are shown simultaneously. A number of examples of ambivalent postures have already been considered (Chapter 16): they are often a patchwork of components, each of which depends on only one of the conflicting tendencies. Since both tendencies are influencing the effectors, the primary competition between them cannot be for the mechanisms of selective attention, but must be nearer the final motor pathways: indeed such postures occur especially when both tendencies are elicited by the same object.

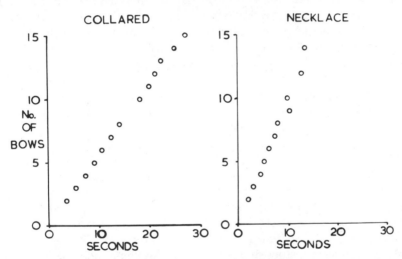

Fig. 17.4. The relation between the mean duration of bouts of bowing display and the number of bowing cycles in the bout for Collared and Necklace Doves. (*After Davies, 1965.*)

Although they depend on incompatible tendencies, there is reason to believe that some ambivalent postures may remain relatively unchanged over a considerable range of intensities of the associated tendencies. There is, of course, a methodological problem here. At the behavioural level of analysis "tendency" is implied from frequency measures—the frequency with which an activity occurs in given circumstances, or of what follows it. We have no direct method for measuring "tendency" at any particular instant, even if it were meaningful to do so. Nevertheless it seems reasonable to assume that at some level the causal factors for a particular activity change over a continuous range. The threat and courtship postures which an animal shows, however, often do not. If an animal has two or three postures, it is usually possible to say at one instant which one it is showing, and intermediates are rare. For instance, the Blackheaded Gull (*Larus ridibundus*) uses both "oblique" and "forward" threat postures. Analysis of ciné-frames shows that the postures themselves are much more frequent than intermediates (Tinbergen, 1959): it thus seems reasonable to suppose that each posture is shown over a range of values of the associated conflicting tendencies. This view is also supported by the observation that in many cases practically the same threat posture may be shown when the animal is both edging slightly towards and slightly away from its rival.

Another line of evidence that the form of such postures may be constant over a range of strengths of the underlying causal factors comes from a simultaneous assessment of form and frequency. Whereas some ambivalent postures change in form as they become more frequent, others are similar over a wide range of frequencies. An example is the courtship posture of the male Cut-throat Finch (*Amadina fasciata*): whether it is given at low or high frequency its form is almost identical. In other words, the increase in the causal factors which give rise to the increase in the frequency of the posture make little difference to its form (Morris, 1957b). A slightly different case is illustrated in Fig. 17.4: the frequencies of the bow-coo displays of the Collared Dove (*Streptopelia decaocto*) and Necklace Dove (*Spilopelia chinensis*) do not vary with the length of the bout of displaying (Davies, 1965).

In practice, many movements other than those occurring in conflict situations show a constancy of form which is independent of frequency. While "fanning" the eggs in the nest the Three-spined Stickleback moves its fins with a fairly constant frequency and amplitude which vary little with the length of the bout or the proportion of time spent fanning (van Iersel, 1953). By contrast, the fanning movements of the River Bullhead (*Cottus gobio*) vary considerably in frequency and amplitude (Morris, 1954b). Morris (1957b), who first called attention to such relationships, described it as the development of "typical intensity".

Morris (1957b) apparently regarded the ruffled courtship posture of the Cut-throat Finch as not ambivalent, and used the term "typical compromise" to refer to ambivalent postures which remain constant in form over a wide range of the conflicting tendencies. Comparative evidence would, however, suggest that this posture, like so many other courtship postures, is ambivalent, and in any case there seems no justification for the use of two terms.

Typical intensity in ambivalent postures often seems to be the result of natural selection acting to increase the efficiency of the posture as a social signal. A signal which is constant from one occasion to the next is more easily recognized than one which varies. Other ways in which ambivalent postures have been modified in evolution to this end are considered in Chapter 27.

17.5. Common Components—Compromise Behaviour

When a hungry bird wishes to fly towards a food source, which it also has a tendency to avoid, it flicks its tail vigorously. This tail-flicking is an intention movement of take-off which would be appropriate to both approach and avoidance. This has been called "compromise behaviour" (Andrew, 1956a) —the animal shows elements common to both tendencies.

Compromise behaviour, as used here, thus differs from ambivalent behaviour in that the one element expresses both tendencies, whereas ambivalent behaviour is a patchwork of elements from both. However, the two intergrade. Thus the bunting *Emberiza schoeniclus* has a call "eee" which expresses fear and is given during flights, and a female soliciting call "ti-ti-ti". When attacked by her mate the female may give "eee" calls which change into "ti-ti-ti" calls as she alights. At the moment of changeover she gives a call in which the individual notes resemble the fear call but the repetitive sequence resembles the soliciting call. In Andrew's opinion this could be described either as compromise behaviour, or ambivalent behaviour. It will be apparent that compromise behaviour, like ambivalent behaviour, involves competition for effector rather than receptor mechanisms.

It must be added that the term "compromise behaviour" suggested by Andrew, though now used widely, is not altogether a happy one. The cases he cites involve the appearance of components or characteristics common to the two otherwise incompatible patterns: this selection of "common components" hardly comes within the meaning of compromise in its everyday sense.

"Compromise" is more appropriate when the behaviour shown is in some sense intermediate: for instance, when gravity and the dorsal light response conflict for the control of the orientation of a fish the result is an intermediate position (Figs. 7.6 and 7.7, p. 113), the precise nature of the compromise depending on various aspects of the internal state (von Holst, 1950a). The approach/avoidance conflicts involved in courtship or threat often result in a circling movement round the object of the display, another example of compromise. That the result of conflict between orientational mechanisms is not always a compromise is shown by Birukow's (1958) experiments on the beetle *Geotrupes silvaticus*: this species orients to either light or air currents, but does not take up an intermediate position when both are present.

17.6. Autonomic Responses

Perhaps because so many cases of conflict are associated with agonistic tendencies, they are frequently accompanied by autonomic responses. Defaecation and urination in situations involving conflict or frustration are indeed often used as measures of "anxiety" or "emotionality" (*see* p. 385). In other cases, however, the autonomic basis of the behaviour observed is less easily recognized. For instance, many species of bunting show "cooling responses", i.e. panting, feather-sleeking and wing-raising as normally used with high environmental temperatures, after fleeing. This could be due to the muscular exertion of fleeing, but such an explanation cannot hold in all instances: for instance as part of courtship, the male flies rapidly after the female in "sexual chases" at a stage when he has, in fact, a considerable tendency to flee from her. During the chase male and female undergo similar degrees of muscular exertion, but after it is over the male, but not the female, shows cooling responses. Furthermore, if the male attacks the female despite his strong fear of her, the attack is usually followed by cooling behaviour. At other times buntings show warming responses in fear, as indeed does man. Andrew (1956a) has suggested that the occurrence of such temperature regulatory responses in fear is to be ascribed to the changes in peripheral circulation consequent upon autonomic activity, and the resultant warming or cooling of the temperature receptors (Morris 1956). Like other types of behaviour given in conflict situations, these autonomic responses may become ritualized in evolution to serve as social signals (*see* Section 4).

17.7. "Displacement Activities"

Animals in conflict situations sometimes show behaviour which appears to be irrelevant to any of the tendencies which are in conflict. For instance, in many aggressive or sexual situations passerine birds may wipe their beaks or preen their feathers, show drinking or feeding behaviour, or engage in some other activity which seems unrelated to the context. Such activities were clearly not evolved for use in aggression or courting, and their occurrence requires explanation in causal terms. Comparable examples have been described in many other groups, including arthropods, fishes and mammals (e.g. Tinbergen, 1940, 1952; Kortlandt, 1940; Crane, 1957). First labelled by Kirkman (1937) as "substitute activities", they are now usually grouped under the heading of "displacement activities".*

It was originally suggested that such apparently irrelevant activities depend on causal factors quite different from those which produce the same activities in their normal functional contexts. It is of course plain that the total set of circumstances which obtain when a starling preens his wet plumage is different from that when he preens during a fight, but more than that was claimed. The displacement activities were distinguished as depending on motivational factors other than those normally activating them, the suggestion being that the factors denied their normal expression because of thwarting or conflict "sparked over" to activate another type of behaviour. Such an explanation depends on an energy model of motivation, and its deficiencies have been discussed by a number of authors (e.g. Kennedy, 1954; Hinde, 1956a, 1960; van Iersel *et al.*, 1958; Bindra, 1959).

* The term displacement is thus used here in a sense different from that found in the psychoanalytic literature. Psychoanalytic "displacement" is discussed here as "redirection".

Even when the "sparking over" explanation was still in vogue, it became apparent that the occurrence of any particular displacement activity was influenced by the presence of those same factors which determine its occurrence in its normal functional context. Thus in an approach/avoidance conflict fighting turkeys may drink if water is available, but feed if food is there (Räber, 1948; Armstrong, 1950; Tinbergen, 1952). Even the posture of the animal could influence its subsequent behaviour (Tinbergen, 1952; Lind, 1959). Subsequently, further evidence along the same lines accumulated; for instance van Iersel *et al.* (1958) found that rain increases the frequency of both "normal" and "displacement" preening in terns.

Not only external factors, but also internal ones may influence the occurrence of displacement activities; for instance most of them are activities which the organism performs frequently and are elicited fairly easily (Bindra, 1959).

If the occurrence of an apparently irrelevant pattern of behaviour is influenced by the same causal factors which influence it in its normal context, are such factors sufficient to explain its occurrence, and what is the significance of the conflict? These questions became relevant as soon as the shortcomings of an energy model of motivation were being recognized: if the displacement activity is not motivated by "sparking over", does the thwarting of other patterns play any role in its causation?

Three ways in which the conflict might influence the occurrence of the displacement activity have been suggested:

1. *Autonomic Activity*

In some cases the displacement behaviour is a consequence of autonomic activity aroused by frightening stimuli or other aspects of the external situation. We have already seen an example of this in the cooling responses shown by buntings in sexual chases. The autonomic activity engendered by the conflict situation may also provide stimuli for somatic activities which appear at first sight to be irrelevant. For example, vasomotor or pilomotor activity may provide skin stimuli which, in turn, elicit scratching or preening, and dryness of the throat may elicit drinking (Andrew, 1956a; Morris, 1956).

2. *The Disinhibition Hypothesis*

In some cases the conflict plays a more permissive role. When mutual incompatibility prevents the appearance of those types of behaviour which would otherwise have the highest priority, patterns which would otherwise have been suppressed are permitted to appear. This suggestion, now known as the "disinhibition hypothesis", was first made by Andrew (1956a): the "displacement" preening which buntings show in conflict situations can be regarded as a consequence of peripheral stimuli which normally induce preening but whose effect is easily suppressed by factors for other activities. In a conflict situation these other activities cannot occur, and preening is possible.

A similar hypothesis was put forward independently by van Iersel *et al.*

(1958) on the basis of a quantitative study of preening by terns (*Sterna* spp.). They showed that intensive incubation inhibited preening: preening during incubation occurred only when the incubation tendency was relatively weak. Preening which occurred in association with aggressive or escape behaviour they labelled as "displacement" on the grounds that it was associated with conflict and was often frantic or hurried. Van Iersel *et al.* assessed by independent means the strengths of the conflicting tendencies, and found that displacement preening was most likely to occur when they had a certain relation

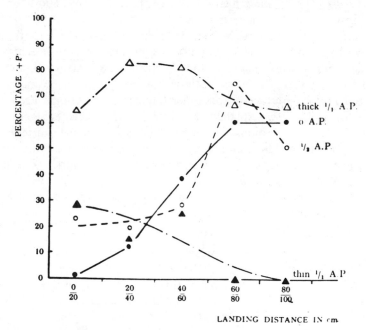

LANDING DISTANCE IN cm

Fig. 17.5. "Displacement preening" by terns. The relationship between the probability of preening by birds approaching their nests and the distance away from the nest at which they land. (*After van Iersel and Bol, 1958.*)

The four sets of data are for birds showing increasing alarm, as indicated by their posture, in the order o A.P., ¼ A.P., thick ⅓A.P., thin ¼A.P.

to each other. For instance, when returning to incubate after an alarm the distance at which the bird lands from the nest can be regarded as a consequence both of its tendency to incubate and its tendency to flee. The latter is also indicated by its posture, four qualitative grades of which were distinguished. When birds were only weakly alarmed, displacement preening was most likely to occur when the bird landed far from the nest, i.e. when the tendency to incubate was also weak (Fig. 17.5). On the other hand, strongly alarmed birds were most likely to show preening when they landed near the nest. With an intermediate degree of alarm displacement preening was most likely to occur at an intermediate landing distance: in other words, the displacement activity was most likely to occur when the conflicting tendencies were both very strong, both weak, or both of intermediate value. On the basis of these and other observations, van Iersel and Bol argued that when the conflicting tendencies are "effectively equal", they are mutually inhibited, and this results in a removal of their inhibitory action on other activities such as preening.

C. H. F. Rowell (1961), studying the preening shown by Chaffinches in an approach/avoidance conflict, confirmed the essential elements of this disinhibition hypothesis. The Chaffinches flew to and fro between perches, occasionally showing a few preening movements as they stopped there. The tendencies to approach and to fly away, when not in conflict, were correlated with a low frequency of preening: during conflict preening occurred when there was equilibrium between the two tendencies. As with the terns, Rowell found that "displacement" preening was increased by wetting the plumage. He also found that it increased with the duration of equilibrium between approach and avoidance (as measured by the time spent on particular perches), that is, with the opportunity for the external stimulation to produce its effect.

Whereas van Iersel and Bol ascribed the occurrence of preening primarily to a constantly present though fluctuating "preening drive", Andrew loc. cit. and Rowell loc. cit. laid more emphasis on external stimulation. All these authors, however, assume that some degree of external stimulation for preening is constantly present. Of course, the argument here easily becomes circular, for the presence of external stimulation for preening is normally revealed only by the occurrence of preening: preening is, however, augmented by increasing the external stimuli.

Even more detailed evidence in support of the disinhibition hypothesis has been given by Sevenster (1961) in a study of the Three-spined Stickleback. One activity involved in the male's care of the eggs is "parental fanning", an activity which, as we have seen, serves to aerate the eggs. Fanning also occurs, however, before the eggs are laid—in particular, during the sexual phase which occurs after the nest is completed but before eggs are laid, and during courtship at any time. This latter "displacement fanning" seems not to serve any useful function, and was formerly ascribed to the sexual "drive", when "thwarted", finding "outlet" through parental activities.

When Sevenster counted the number of zig-zag (courtship) dances and the number of bites given during tests in which the male was presented with a female or another male (see p. 272), he was able to show that the male's sexual or aggressive tendency is raised for some minutes after the model is removed. By further observations during this period Sevenster showed that the sexual tendency has a strong inhibitory effect on parental fanning, and the aggressive tendency a weak one (see pp. 271–3).

The relations between the sexual tendency, the parental tendency and the amount of "displacement" fanning shown were then investigated as follows. Using males in the parental phase, the amount of fanning in a standard period was used as an index of the parental "drive". The fish were also given a "sex test": a female was presented and the number of zig-zag dances and period spent fanning assessed. Figure 17.6 shows that at low levels of zig-zagging the average amount of "courtship fanning" was correlated with the amount of parental fanning. This is consistent with Sevenster's finding that displacement fanning is influenced by the same factors that influence parental fanning (van Iersel, 1953), namely, the number and age of eggs in the nest, the presence of CO_2 in the water, and certain internal factors. Figure 17.6 also shows that the average amount of courtship fanning was negatively correlated with the

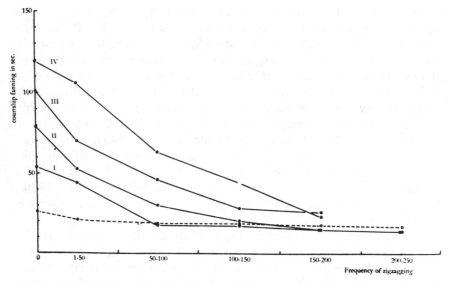

Fig. 17.6. Relation between the average amount of "courtship fanning" and the frequency of zig-zag dances shown by Three-spined Sticklebacks in sex-tests during the parental phase of the breeding cycle. (*After Sevenster, 1961.*)

The data are separated according to the strength of the parental tendency (as indicated by the proportion of time spent fanning): I 0–500 seconds/30 minutes; II 500–1000 seconds/30 minutes; III 800–1200 seconds/30 minutes; IV 1000–1500 seconds/30 minutes. The equivalent relationship during the sexual phase is shown by the discontinuous line.

number of zig-zags: this is ascribed to an inhibitory effect of the sexual drive on the parental activities (*see* p. 272). At high levels of zig-zagging the average amount of courtship fanning decreased only so far as the minimum value found in the sexual phase, about 15 seconds/5 minutes courtship. Sevenster concluded that, at this point, the sexual factors were not inhibiting the parental activities: if they had been, the amount of fanning would have been correlated with the strength of the parental factors, and an increase in sex drive would have resulted in a further decrease in fanning. In other words, for those 15 seconds the parental fanning is temporarily disinhibited. In fact, both sexual and aggressive factors can inhibit fanning: the greatest amount of disinhibition occurs when both have intermediate strengths (Fig. 17.7).* For instance, this displacement fanning fluctuates in a cyclical fashion, the cycle being associated with changes in the balance of sexual and aggressive tendencies: at the stage in the cycle at which the sexual tendency reaches predominance, fanning falls off abruptly.

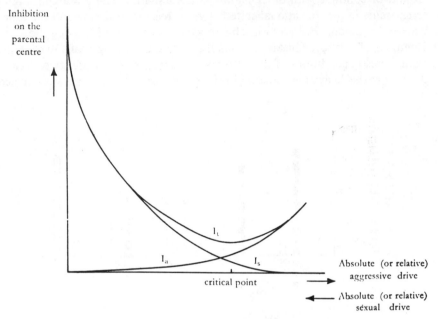

Fig. 17.7. Schematic representation of variation in total amount of inhibition on parental fanning as a result of interaction of sex and aggression. (*After Sevenster, 1961.*)

I_s represents the inhibition due to sexual factors, I that to aggressive factors, and I^t the total. The mechanism controlling fanning is termed the "parental centre".

In other cases there is suggestive evidence that the strengths and relative strengths of the tendencies which are in conflict influence which displacement activity is shown. In his study of Junglefowl (*Gallus gallus*) Kruijt (1964) compared the incidence of various displacement activities in the winners of fights with their incidence in the losers. A number of differences were found,

* This view, it may be noted, differs slightly from that of van Iersel and Bol. The latter showed that effective equality between the conflicting tendencies is more probable the greater the absolute strengths: when it occurs, it results in a negation of the inhibitory effect on preening. On Sevenster's view, if one tendency is strong its inhibitory effect on the "displacement" activity is bound to be large: the total inhibition due to both tendencies will be minimal when both have intermediate strengths. The views could be reconciled by making certain assumptions about the strengths of the tendencies in the two studies; for instance that Sevenster was working with a range which included "stronger" tendencies than van Iersel and Bol.

and are presumably to be ascribed to the different attack/flee ratios in the two cases (Fig. 17.8).

That the disinhibition hypothesis may also be applied to mammals has been shown by Fentress's (1965) study of grooming in voles. After a frightening stimulus, these animals flee and/or freeze, groom their fur, and then walk around or continue with other maintenance activities. The grooming, therefore, occurs in the transitional state between freezing or fleeing and the other types of behaviour. Fentress was able to vary the amount of freezing shown in a number of ways; for instance by manipulating the strength of the stimulus or the rearing conditions of the animals. The stronger the tendency to freeze, the greater the delay after the stimulus before the transitional state was reached

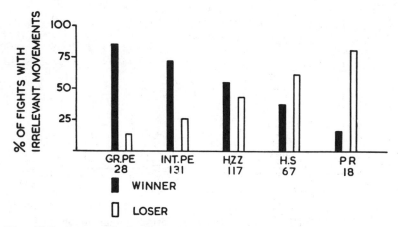

Fig. 17.8. Apparently irrelevant movements made during fighting by Burmese Red Junglefowl. The distribution of different movements between winners and losers. (*After Kruijt, 1964.*)

GR.PE = ground pecking; INT.PE = intention ground pecking; H.ZZ = head zigzagging; H.S. = head shaking; PR = preening.

and grooming appeared. A particularly interesting comparison was that between *Microtus agrestis* and the more timorous *Clethrionomys britannicus:* as shown in Fig. 17.9, grooming was much slower to appear in the latter species. However, the total amount of the apparently irrelevant activity of grooming shown in the standard time of 12 minutes was greater in the conflict situation than in a comparable control period for *Microtus*, but less for *Clethrionomys*. This would not be predicted from the disinhibition hypothesis without additional assumptions. Furthermore, when individual records were analysed, there was a number in which grooming was not followed by walking: these can be accounted for on the disinhibition hypothesis only on the assumption that some activity other than walking was in conflict with freezing and inhibiting grooming. Thus Fentress suggests that the disinhibition hypothesis accounts for the overall occurrence of grooming, but may need to be supplemented by further considerations.

The disinhibition hypothesis has elements in common with the view advanced earlier by Kennedy (1954) that displacement activities were analogous to the phenomenon of positive induction, as described by Sherrington (1906), in which the reciprocal inhibition of two spinal reflexes lowers the threshold for a third. This comparison must not be pressed too far, however, because of the obvious differences in complexity between the mechanisms (*see* p. 303).

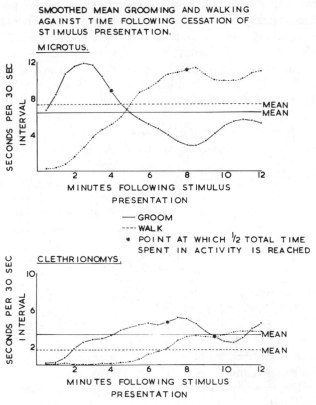

Fig. 17.9. The effect of a fear-eliciting stimulus on grooming and on locomotion in two species of vole. Ordinate—Time spent in each activity per 30-second interval after stimulation. (*After Fentress, 1965.*)

Von Holst *et al.* (1963) also advanced a similar hypothesis in describing the behaviour of a cockerel with two electrodes in the brain-stem, stimulation of one causing fleeing and the other sleep. When hungry, the elicitation of a slight fleeing tendency causes the bird to stop eating. If the sleeping stimulus is then given, it may feed briefly before sleeping. They ascribe this to the liberation of feeding when sleeping inhibits fleeing.

All these authors thus agree that "displacement" activities are not to be sharply distinguished from the same activities appearing in their normal functional context, though Sevenster points out that displacement fanning is characterized by an almost complete dependence on the interaction of sex and aggression, while normal fanning is not. In all these cases the so-called "displacement" activity occurs at a point of balance between two other tendencies which would otherwise dominate the scene. Rowell *loc. cit.* emphasizes that preening occurs not only at the points of balance in an approach/avoidance conflict, but is also especially probable at other changeover points; for instance between resting and feeding (*see also* Fentress, cited above). Data pointing to a similar conclusion are available for grooming in the rat (Bindra *et al.*, 1958; Bolles, 1960), and comfort movements in sticklebacks (Tugendhat, 1960b) and various other activities (Räber, 1948; Armstrong, 1950; Tinbergen, 1952; Moynihan, 1955; Schmidt, 1956; Andrew, 1956a and b; van Iersel *et al.*, 1958; C. H. F. Rowell, 1961).

3. *Possible Effects of Non-specific Arousal*

Another possible basis for displacement activities is that the conflict influences the occurrence of the apparently irrelevant behaviour in a non-specific manner. Miller *et al.* (1936) noted that when rats, previously trained to run down an alley for food, were given a number of trials without food, such activities as sniffing and grooming increased, and were often given in an explosive manner. They suggested that absence of reward led to conflict between the learned response of eating and that elicited by the empty food dish, and that conflict produced proprioceptive stimulation which facilitated the apparently irrelevant activities. Essentially similar hypotheses were subsequently put forward by a number of other learning theorists (e.g. Brown *et al.*, 1951; Hull, 1952; Amsel, 1958), the implication usually being that a "general drive" (*see* p. 149) was augmented. The literature has been reviewed by Brown (1961). Later, it was suggested that conflict might be associated with a positive effect on the apparently irrelevant behaviour in a non-specific fashion, perhaps mediated by the reticular system (Bindra, 1959; Hinde, 1959a).

Furthermore, in many situations in which displacement activities occur the degree of "arousal" (p. 155) is high, and it is possible that this could influence which activities occur, and, perhaps, the intensity with which they are shown. Bindra (1959) has suggested that only activities with high habit strengths are likely to occur when the degree of arousal is high, and this is consistent with the frequency with which activities like feeding and preening occur in conflict situations.

However, the evidence that the intensity of an activity is affected by all the motivational variables acting at the moment is far from conclusive (*see* Chapter 9). Furthermore, many apparently irrelevant activities are characteristically incomplete (Tinbergen, 1952): if they were influenced by motivational factors determining strong incompatible tendencies the opposite would be expected.

There are thus at least three different explanations for the occurrence of activities outside their usual functional contexts, in circumstances in which they appear irrelevant. The evidence that at least two of these hypotheses (autonomic activity and disinhibition) are valid in some cases is substantial, and these explanations do not invoke new principles additional to those already in use for behaviour not classed as "displacement". What then remains of the category of "displacement activities"?

In part this depends on the level and type of analysis in which it is to be employed. For the field worker, concerned with the initial descriptive phase of the behaviour of a previously unstudied species, it will undoubtedly continue to be useful. The student of the evolution of behaviour, interested in the evolutionary sources of display movements (Chapters 27 and 28), will also continue to employ it. But for causal analysis, the term can no longer be used to imply a category of instances of behaviour whose causation involves principles not shared by other types of behaviour. Their common feature is that they occur in conflict situations. Conflict, however, is almost ubiquitous; and the difference between activities occurring as "displacement" activities and those occurring as "transitional" activities (*see* both Rowell and Fentress, quoted above) is only one of degree. In the detailed causal analysis of a particular case, the utility of the concept fades away.

This view is emphasized strongly by Beer (1963a, b) on the basis of his study of the occurrence of nest-building behaviour during the incubation phase of Blackheaded Gulls. Previous authors had shown that such nest-building activities were associated with situations in which sitting on the eggs is hindered, or in which the eggs or nest provide the "wrong" feedback for sustained sitting. On the basis of such observations the nest-building had been ascribed to frustration of the incubation behaviour (Kirkman, 1937) or inadequate consummatory stimulation (Bastock *et al.*, 1953). Now the types of nest-building behaviour shown are "sideways building" and "collecting", and the incubation activities "settling" and "shifting" the egg in the nest. By analysing the sequences of behaviour shown, Beer found that the evidence for common causation drawn from analysing sequences of behaviour cuts across this grouping based on function. For instance, "sideways building" was more closely linked in time to "rising and settling" than to "collecting", and "settling" was more closely linked to "sideways building" than to "shifting". It is thus not useful to talk about the interaction of drives labelled in terms of their functional consequences, and judgements made about what is "irrelevant" or "out of context" from a functional point of view may have no causal validity.

17.8. Redirection Activities

Here the motor patterns appropriate to one of the conflicting tendencies are shown, but are directed on to an object other than that which initially elicited them. This is often seen in winter flocks of birds: one individual is supplanted at a food source by a superior, and, instead of retaliating, turns its aggressiveness on to an inferior bird. Similarly male Blackheaded Gulls, whose tendency to attack their mates is inhibited, may attack other birds (Moynihan, 1955). In Herring Gulls, pecking during aggressive encounters is often redirected on to objects in the environment (Tinbergen, 1959).

The distinction between redirection activities, displacement activities and responses to suboptimal stimuli is not always clear-cut. Thus redirected pecking, as described for the Herring Gull, occurs also in Junglefowl: in the early stage of the development of fighting behaviour the ground-pecking during fighting is indistinguishable from that during normal feeding, but later it has the vigorous quality characteristic of aggressive pecking. Thus it seems that irrelevant feeding and aggressive pecking occur in combination with each other. The vigorous ground-pecks in aggressive situations often result in swallowing, and when the bird is fighting a coloured stick it pecks more at food particles of a similar colour to the stick than at those of a different colour. In such cases the categories of "displacement", "redirection", and "responses to suboptimal stimuli", seem to merge (Kruijt, 1964). Ficken et al. (1960), describing cases of redirected copulation in passerine birds, also suggested that redirection was a special case of reaction to subnormal stimuli.

Such findings would perhaps have been expected in terms of the conceptual scheme elaborated by Miller (1959) to account for the way in which the new target of the behaviour is determined. He postulates that the inhibited response generalizes on to other objects according to their similarity with the one which originally aroused it. The inhibiting response generalizes in the same way, but with a steeper gradient. The inhibited response is thus most likely to generalize on to an object of intermediate likeness to the original one.

17.9. Sexual Abnormalities

Certain types of sexual inversion among animals appear characteristically in conflict situations. Among birds, species vary widely in the extent to which the behaviour patterns of courtship and copulation are characteristic of both sexes, and sexual "inversion" is a matter of degree. The adoption of the female copulatory posture by males can, however, reasonably be described in this way. It occurs when the female is unresponsive to the male's courtship in the Zebra Finch (Morris, 1954a) and after copulation attempts in carduelines (Hinde, 1955/6 and references cited). This can be understood on the assumption that sexual arousal in either sex involves an increased tendency to show both male and female patterns, though male patterns normally have a higher priority in males and vice versa. If the behaviour of the characteristic type is thwarted, the other may be shown. Similar principles apply to other species (Morris, 1955, and references cited; Barraud, 1955).

17.10. Regression

The literature on regression in animals is now fairly extensive, but there has been little attempt to analyse the processes underlying it. Indeed, the phenomena commonly lumped under this heading are probably physiologically heterogeneous: there is no *a priori* reason for thinking that reversion by an adult animal to a more juvenile form of behaviour has anything in common with trying again a solution found to be successful earlier in a problem situation. Some cases of juvenile behaviour in adults imply that the mechanisms controlling the juvenile pattern remain present but latent in the adult, and become active when the adult pattern is thwarted (e.g. Holzapfel, 1949).

17.11. Immobility Responses

When wild-caught Great and Blue Tits are held in the hand, they sometimes lie on the outstretched palm for a minute or longer, their eyes open but bodies limp. They fly immediately at a sharp noise, or if they are thrown into the air. Similar responses to handling or stroking occur in a wide range of animals, and are often accompanied by analgesia: they have been ascribed to frustration or conflict (e.g. Armstrong, 1947; Ratner *et al.*, 1960). The relation of such responses to the "freezing" postures used when escaping from a predator has not been investigated.

17.12. Aggressive Behaviour

Many students of mammalian behaviour have proposed that aggression is not elicited by specific stimuli, but is rather a response to frustration. McDougall (1923), for instance, supposed that aggression was instigated by interference with some other form of activity. This view has been worked out in detail by Dollard *et al.* (1939) (*see also* Miller, 1959). At first sight it seems incompatible with the views of most students of lower vertebrates, who regard aggressive behaviour as elicitable in each species by fairly precisely defined stimulus characters, such as the red belly of the Three-spined Stickleback (*see* p. 45). The difference in viewpoint is not so great as might appear, however, since Miller amended the original hypothesis to suggest that frustration produced instigation for a number of responses, one of which was aggression. Frustration is thus regarded as increasing the likelihood of aggressive behaviour, though the actual appearance of aggressive behaviour might depend on other factors— external stimuli, inhibitory factors, and so on. Furthermore, the definition of what constitutes "frustrating conditions" can be somewhat flexible (e.g. Berkowitz, 1963), and it would be easy to coin a definition such that a territory-owning Great Tit was "frustrated" by an intruder. The inclusion of incompatible response tendencies as a source of frustration (Brown *et al.*, 1951) indicates that aggression should be mentioned as a possible response to a conflict situation, though the evidence for its importance in animals other than man is largely anecdotal.

17.13. Responses to Frustration

When an animal, engaged in a sequence of behaviour, is unable to complete it because of a physical barrier, the absence of an appropriate stimulus link, or for similar reasons, its behaviour may take a number of forms. One possibility is the appearance of investigatory behaviour or trial and error, which may lead the animal into a situation which makes possible the completion of the chain. Another is a response to a normally inadequate stimulus situation, making possible the completion of the sequence albeit possibly in a nonfunctional manner. In other cases the animal may show one of the types of behaviour already discussed as appearing in conflict situations, such as displacement or aggressive behaviour.

One feature which seems more frequent in frustration than in conflict situations is an increase in the vigour of the behaviour which is being shown at the time. This is well exemplified in an experiment by Marzocco (1951). Rats were trained to obtain food by depressing a bar in a Skinner box. After preliminary habituation and training in bar-pressing, the animals were given three rewarded trials followed by a series of unrewarded ones. The mean force exerted on the bar rose from 28 gm. in the first four trials to 35·9 gm. in the responses following the first unrewarded one. The force exerted then fell off gradually, but remained above the mean level in the initial four trials for about 10 trials after the first unrewarded one. The increase in force was found to be related to the length of food deprivation at the time of frustration.

17.14. Summary

1. Various types of behaviour occurring in conflict situations are discussed.
2. The usual outcome of the simultaneous action of factors for two or more types of behaviour is the suppression of the activities appropriate to all but one. This is called "behavioural inhibition".
3. Sometimes one or both of the conflicting tendencies are expressed in incomplete patterns of behaviour—intention movements, alternation, ambivalent postures or compromise behaviour.
4. Autonomic activity often occurs in conflict situations.
5. Sometimes, in a conflict situation, an animal shows an activity which appears to the observer to be irrelevant to either of the conflicting tendencies. Such "displacement activities" do not require new principles for their explanation: some examples can be ascribed to autonomic activation, others to "disinhibition".
6. In some conflict situations, the motor patterns appropriate to one of the conflicting tendencies is "redirected" on to another object.
7. Other categories of behaviour occurring in conflict situations include sexual abnormalities, regression, immobility responses and aggressive behaviour.

18

Integration

The categories of behaviour shown by an animal can be labelled in terms of a physical description of the movements involved, or in terms of their consequences (Chapter 2). In the repertoire of any organism the number of discrete types of behaviour, as differentiated in one or other of these ways, is usually large. They do not, however, occur at random, but in integrated sequences which, for the most part, lead to biologically adaptive consequences. After a Stickleback has made a zig-zag dance to a female, it will often swim towards the nest, and this is likely to be followed by other courtship activities which lead to fertilization of the eggs: when a Great Tit sings, it is especially likely to show functionally related activities; for instance to fly from tree to tree on its territory, and to attack intruders. The aim of this chapter is to examine the ways in which discrete items of behaviour are integrated into functional sequences.

There are two basic procedures by which temporal relations between items of behaviour can be assessed. One method is to record the frequency with which activity A is preceded or followed by activities B, C, D etc: if the frequency exceeds the chance level, the two activities are said to show sequential association. The data can be subjected to factor analysis, so that it is possible to assess the extent to which correlations between a large number of activities can be ascribed to a small number of common factors (*see* Chapter 16).

Alternatively, certain items from an animal's repertoire can be recorded over standard periods of time, and the relations between their frequencies examined. Some examples were given in Chapter 17. Two further examples, drawn from the non-reproductive behaviour of the Bitterling, are shown in Fig. 18.1 (Wiepkema, 1961). The more frequently "chafing" occurs in a given minute, the less likely is "snapping" and the more likely is "finflickering" to appear. In other cases the relationship between two activities may be more complex; there may for instance be an S-shaped or U-shaped curve.

The lengths of the time units in such analyses is of crucial importance. The use of day-long observation sessions to count how often a Great Tit sings, examines a nest-hole, and threatens other Great Tits with the head-up threat

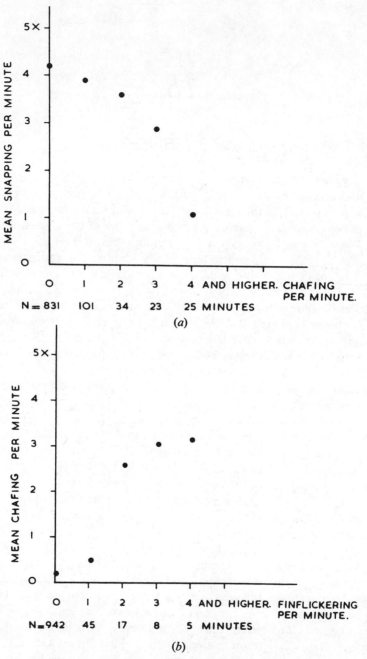

Fig. 18.1. Non-reproductive activities of the Bitterling. Relationship between (*a*) snapping and chafing; (*b*) chafing and finflickering. (*After Wiepkema, 1961.*)

posture, would indicate that all these activities are positively correlated—all are more frequent in the spring. If, however, their frequency was examined during 1-minute periods taken at intervals during the first few hours after dawn in early April, negative correlations would appear.

If such methods show that two activities are positively or negatively correlated to a significant extent, we must search for relationships, direct or indirect, between the factors or mechanisms controlling them. Thus, on the basis of the data summarized in Fig. 18.1, it would seem that chafing and finflickering are in some way positively causally related, while snapping and chafing are negatively so.

The limitations of deductions made in this way must be recognized. Apart from the difficulty of the time units employed (on different time scales chafing and finflickering might be negatively or snapping and chafing positively correlated), it is important to recognize that the correlations are derived from behavioural data, and inferences about underlying physiological mechanisms must be made with caution. A positive correlation between two activities A and B could arise in a number of ways, and we must now examine some of these.

18.1. Common Causal Factors

In Chapter 3 we saw how more and more of the different components of a fixed action pattern may appear as the causal factors specific to that pattern become more intense. The components all depend on the same causal factors (this is our definition of a fixed action pattern), but differ in the threshold levels at which they appear.

In the same way, but at a more complex level of integration, different activities may share causal factors. A particular experimental manipulation— it may involve the presentation of an external stimulus or an alteration to the internal state—alters the probability of some activities, but has relatively little effect on others. For instance, administration of male sex hormone to a male Chaffinch influences whether it will show courtship to a female, the extent and the nature of its aggressive response to a male, the frequency with which it sings, and so on: androgens act as a causal factor common to many different activities, though, of course, all are not affected equally. Similarly, deprivation of food may influence the intensity of a rat's response to food when it is presented, the speed with which it will run down a runway at the end of which it has previously found food, the amount of time it spends searching its cage, and so on. The same is also the case with external factors—stimuli from a baby mouse increase the probability of retrieving, nest-building, licking and adoption of the lactation position in an adult (Beniest-Noirot, 1958). Similarly, stimuli from the eggs of the Herring Gull influence a number of different activities concerned with incubation (Baerends, 1959b).

The multiplicity of consequences produced by an apparently simple change in an independent variable can arise in a number of ways:

(*a*) The change in the independent variable may not be so simple as it appears, for it may entail separate but correlated changes which influence different responses. Such a situation arises when the stimuli for two responses consist of separate features of the same object, or when they are associated in space (*see* e.g. Chapters 6 and 15). The various stereotyped movements used by canaries in nest-building appear in temporal association partly because they are all elicited by stimuli encountered when the bird is in the nest.

(*b*) A common factor could act more or less independently on the mechanisms controlling two types of behaviour. Thus when a hormone influences more than one type of behaviour, it may do so by action on different brain sites rather than (as has previously been suggested) through a super-ordinated mechanism. Since the action of one hormone on one type of behaviour may be mediated through more than one mechanism (*see* p. 171), it is even more likely that effects on two activities are. In the case of the nest-building of female canaries, for instance, stimuli from the nest-cup influence a number of aspects of behaviour through both central and peripheral mechanisms (*see* pp. 169–70 and 301–2).

(*c*) A single factor could act on a mechanism which, in turn, influences the occurrence of more than one response. The appearance of a predator may evoke autonomic activity and thus a number of different responses which all depend on the autonomic system.

(*d*) The independent variable could exert an inhibitory effect on other activities leading to an apparent association between activities not so affected. Thus many activities which an animal shows at night are correlated just because they are the only activities not inhibited by darkness. Similarly, activities may be associated because they share a low priority among the organism's activities and can occur only in the absence of response tendencies of greater priority. This may be one reason why different "toilet" or "comfort" movements tend to be associated together: they rarely interrupt other types of behaviour already in progress, but are themselves easily interrupted (p. 255).

Whatever the mechanisms by which a common causal factor produces its effects, a difference in threshold between the various activities is usually to be observed. Thus with increase in the quantity of oestrogens injected into female canaries they first hop about over nest material and occasionally pick it up, then pick it up and carry it about inconsequentially until they drop it, and finally gather it, carry it to a nest site and place it there. Similarly, when a hawk flies over, a passerine bird may respond with anything from a momentary glance to a sudden dash to cover, depending on (among other things) the intensity (size, proximity, etc.) of the stimulus. In such cases the early phases of the sequence require a lower level of motivational factors, or a weaker eliciting stimulus, than the behaviour which brings it to an end.

18.2. Chain Responses

In a chain response, each movement or activity brings an animal into a situation where the next is evoked. The principle is well known at the reflex level: the alternating movements involved in walking, nystagmus and so on depend in large part on the first phase of the movement inducing the second. A case discussed in some detail by Sherrington is that of the chewing movements of a decerebrate cat. If its jaw is touched with a piece of meat, it drops sharply. The muscles which close the jaw are thereby stretched, their proprioceptors stimulated and their motor neurones caused to fire. As the jaw closes through the meat, the pressure causes stimulation of receptors in the periodontium. The muscles which close the jaw reflexly cease to contract. The jaw-opening muscles, already tensed, can then open the jaw. The proprioceptors of the closing muscles are thereby stimulated again, and the process is repeated (Sherrington, 1917). Of course, the intact cat's chewing movements are not solely dependent on this simple mechanism. Similarly, with more complex activities, the proprioceptive input from one response may play a part in eliciting another (Lind, 1959).

More obvious, perhaps, are cases in which the stimuli for the later responses are external stimuli which the animal encounters as a consequence of its earlier behaviour. In such cases the chain nature of the sequence may be revealed when sudden breaks are correlated with the absence of a particular external stimulus, or when the presentation of a limited stimulus situation elicits only some of the links in the chain. Two examples have been analysed in detail by Tinbergen (1935, 1951). The wasp *Philanthus triangulum* preys on bees. When hunting, it flies from flower to flower in search of a bee. It is responsive to visual stimuli from any moving object of about the right size, but at this stage indifferent to the scent of bees. When the visual stimuli are perceived, it turns towards the prey and hovers 10–15 cm. to leeward of it. The wasp is now sensitive to bee-scent; dummies without it are at once abandoned, but the wasp seizes with a sudden leap ones that smell appropriately. The further responses, including the stinging of the bee, depend on additional as yet unanalysed stimuli which are not provided by simple dummies.

A comparable case in vertebrates is provided by the mating behaviour of the Three-spined Stickleback (Fig. 18.2). The zig-zag dance of the male is elicited by certain stimuli from the female (pp. 45–6). When the female swims towards him, he turns and leads her to the nest. She follows, and this stimulates the male to point his head at the nest entrance. His behaviour causes the female to enter the nest. Stimuli from the female elicit "trembling" from the male (*see inset* Fig. 18.2), which induces the female to spawn. The male is then stimulated to fertilize the eggs (Tinbergen, 1951), and stimuli from the eggs produce a decrease in his tendency to show further sexual behaviour (Sevenster-Bol, 1962).

Many other cases of social behaviour in which two individuals respond

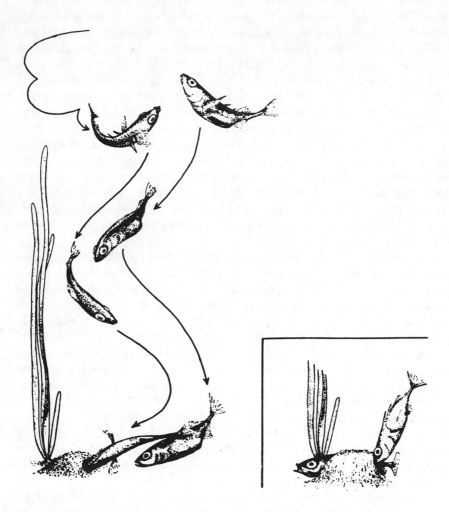

Fig. 18.2. Schematic representation of the sexual behaviour of the Three-spined Stickleback. (*After Tinbergen, 1951.*)

The female, with a swollen belly (top right) enters the territory of the male, swimming in a special posture. The male courts her, and when she responds he leads her to the nest. If she follows, he adopts a special posture by the nest entrance. When she enters (inset), a trembling movement by the male elicits spawning. Subsequently the male enters the nest and fertilizes the eggs (not shown).

reciprocally to each other similarly depend in part on a chain sequence. In most cases (including that of the Stickleback), however, the chain is far from rigid: links may be missed, or the behaviour may continually revert to an earlier stage in the sequence even though the stimuli for the next stage are available. As an example of this, Fig. 18.3 shows the sequences of courtship activities observed by Baerends et al. (1955) in *Lebistes reticulatus*, the thickness of the lines indicating the frequency with which each transition was observed. (*See* Aronson, 1949; Hinde, 1953a, 1954c; Morris, 1958a, b; Dane et al., 1964). This implies that the sequence is largely controlled by internal factors as well as by the external stimuli. In such cases a given act by one individual may produce any of several (but usually not all) of the responses from the other. Thus Fig. 18.4 shows first the "ideal" sequence of responses in the courtship of the fish *Badis badis*, and underneath the extent of "stimulus overlap" (Barlow, 1962b). Another example is given in Fig. 16.6.

Indeed, most instances in which responses appear in a regular sequence do not depend solely on the chain reaction principle, but also on common causal factors for the various responses. Often, as we have seen, the later activities in the sequence require a higher intensity of these factors than do the earlier ones: if they are inadequate, behaviour reverts to an earlier point in the sequence. This is undoubtedly the case with the Stickleback's sexual behaviour, where all the activities of each sex depend both on common endocrine factors and on a short-term state of heightened responsiveness, as well as on the external stimuli. Similar principles apply to the courtship of *Drosophila melanogaster* (Bastock et al., 1955), the feeding of Sticklebacks (Tugendhat, 1960a), the fighting of ants (Wallis, 1961) and the hunting of Salticid spiders (Tugendhat Gardner, 1964).

The changeover from one activity to the next when stimuli for the second activity appear depends not only on an increased tendency to perform the second activity, but also on the overriding of the first; it is, in fact, a matter of relative priorities. These may depend not only on the stimulus situation, but also on the level of the motivational factors for both activities. In addition, performance of one of the two activities may produce a differential effect on the tendencies of both, as discussed in Chapter 13. An example of such interaction is provided by the nest-building of female canaries. The activities involved can be subdivided into those involved in gathering material, in carrying it to the nest-site and in building it into the nest. Their integration depends in part on motivational factors which they share (endocrine factors) and a more short-term central state revealed in a nest-building "mood". Changeover from one activity to the next depends in part on stimuli encountered during the course of the first: the female cannot "carry" unless she has gathered material, and does not usually visit the nest unless she is carrying. The presence of the adequate stimulus situation, however, is not in itself sufficient to bring about a change-over; the female may carry material to and fro between perches for a long time before visiting the nest. One factor here is that the three groups of activities

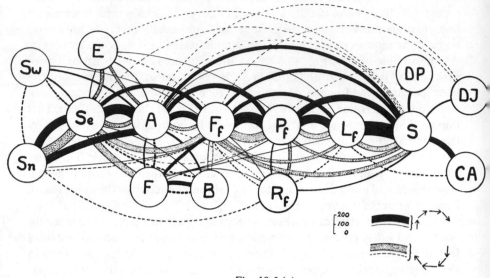

Fig. 18.3 (a)

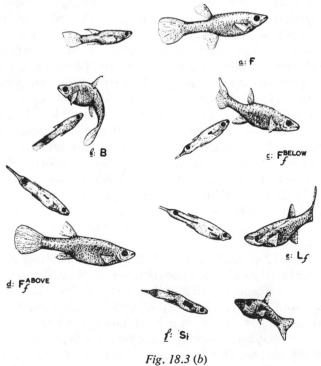

Fig. 18.3 (b)

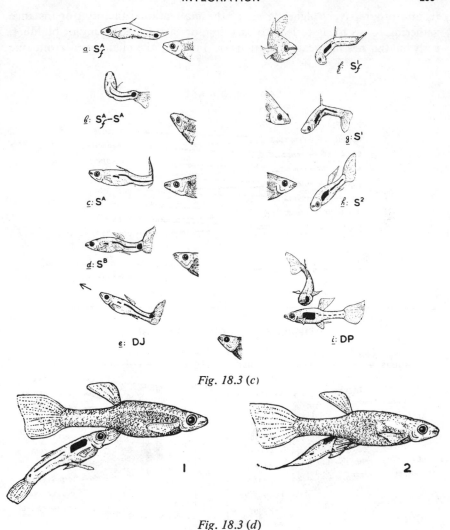

Fig. 18.3 (c)

Fig. 18.3 (d)

Fig. 18.3. (a) The sequence of courting activities shown by male guppies. (b) Preliminary courting activities. (c) Advanced courting activities. Various variations of the sigmoid posture, S, are shown. (d) Copulation attempt. (*From Baerends, Brouwer and Waterbolk, 1955.*)

The thickness of the lines in (a) indicates the frequency with which one activity is followed by the one to which the line leads. Block lines should be read from left to right, hatched bands and dotted lines from right to left. The activities are illustrated in Fig. 18.3 (b) (c) and (d), and Fig. 3.4. The abbreviations are as follows: A = approach; B = biting; CA = copulation attempt; DJ = display jump; DP = display posturing; E = evading; F and F_t = following; L_t = luring; P_t = posturing; R_t = retreating; S = sigmoid posture; Se = searching; Sn = snapping; Sw = swimming about. The male's coloration changes according to his internal state.

require progressively higher levels of the motivational factors: for instance gathering is less likely to lead to carrying, or carrying to sitting or building, early in the nesting season than later. Further, the changeover from one

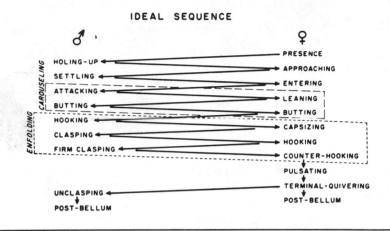

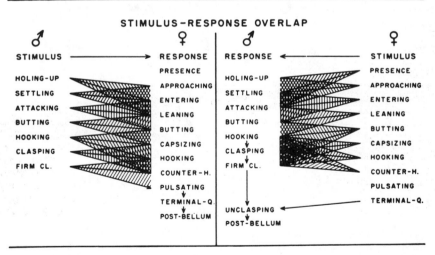

Fig. 18.4. The courtship behaviour of the fish *Badis badis.* (*After Barlow, 1962b.*)

    The upper diagram shows a hypothetical scheme in which the sequence of behaviour shown by male and female is regarded as a chain response. The lower diagrams represent the actual stimulus response relations which occur.

activity to another depends in part on decremental effects consequent upon the performance of the first activity, as discussed in Chapter 13 (Hinde, 1958a; *see also* comments by Cane, 1961).

Canary nest-building serves to illustrate another point. So far we have considered only chain responses in which the later responses were immediate reactions to stimuli encountered as a consequence of the earlier ones. The concept can, however, be extended to cases where the earlier response leads the animal to encounter a stimulus situation which influences its endocrine state, and thus causes a longer-term change in behaviour. In many avian species changes in the environment cause changes in the female's endocrine state, as a result of which she associates with a male. Stimuli from the male accelerate her gonadal development and this results in nest-building behaviour. In the course of this activity she receives stimulation through her ventral surfaces from the nest cup. These stimuli, in turn, may both accelerate egg-laying and produce further endocrine changes, causing her to be ready to incubate eggs (*see also* pp. 169–70).

A study of the reproduction of female canaries has shown that the relationships are in practice more complicated than this (Fig. 18.5). In the first place stimulation from the nest-cup has both short- and long-term effects on behaviour. Immediately, it elicits certain of the nest-building movements. Over a period of minutes, it influences the frequency of the female's visits to the nest and the nature of the nest material which she selects. Over a longer period, it results in endocrine changes: birds receiving adequate stimulation of this sort lay earlier than those which do not (*see* p. 302). Stimuli from the nest and eggs also have immediate and long-term effects on incubation behaviour. In addition, the endocrine changes result in an increase in the stimulation received from the nest-cup in two ways. First, they cause the female to visit the nest more often. Second, they result in the formation of a brood patch (*see* pp. 169–70): the female's ventral surfaces become defeathered, vascular, and more sensitive to tactile stimulation. She thus becomes more responsive to stimulation from the nest she has built. The integration of the female's reproductive activities thus involves complex interactions between the external stimuli to which she is exposed, her internal (endocrine) condition, and her behaviour (references on p. 173).

18.3. Inhibitory Relations

At any one moment, causal factors for many types of behaviour are likely to be present. A male Stickleback may, for instance, be on its territory, in reproductive condition, in the presence of food, a ripe female, and nest material. Yet animals usually do only one thing at a time: at some stage the causal factors for the other activities fail to produce their effects. We can describe this by saying that there are inhibitory relations between the activities concerned. This is a statement in terms of behaviour, and carries no implications about whether the inhibition occurs by direct negative effects in the central nervous system, or by competition for receptors or effectors. Various mechanisms involved have already been discussed in the contexts of selective

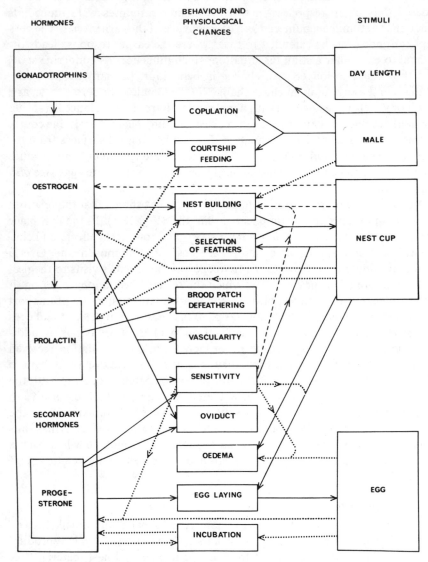

Fig. 18.5. The relations between external stimuli (right-hand column), internal hormonal condition (left-hand column), and various aspects of the reproductive development and behaviour of female canaries. (*Modified after Hinde, 1965.*)

The continuous lines represent experimentally established positive effects, the discontinuous ones negative effects. The dotted lines indicate probable relationships not yet established with certainty. Where the extent to which an effect may be indirect has not yet been established, only the direct effect is shown.

attention (Chapters 5 and 6) and responses in conflict situations (Chapters 16 and 17).

18.4. Antagonistic Induction

There is some evidence to suggest that activities may be linked centrally in such a way that the performance of one increases the probability of the subsequent performance of the other, even in the apparent absence of peripheral effects or change in the external situation. Comparable phenomena have long been known at simpler levels of integration. The undulatory movement of the dorsal fin of a Sea Horse can be inhibited by peripheral stimulation: when the latter ceases, the movements of the dorsal fin continue with an increased amplitude (von Holst, 1936). Earlier, Sherrington (e.g. 1906), from a study of spinal reflexes, had suggested that, after the withdrawal of inhibition, the excitation of previously inhibited units is likely to develop ("successive induction"). The opposite effect also occurs: the swimming movements made by a medullary goldfish are increased when a current of water is directed against the body, but subsequently fall below the normal level.

Phenomena which appear similar, though the time scale and thus the mechanism may be quite different, have been studied at the level of the whole animal. *Aphis fabae* flies for a while after becoming adult, and then settles. Kennedy (1958) and Kennedy *et al.* (1963, 1964) have shown that during the first phase the threshold for locomotory behaviour is low, while that for responding to host-stimuli is high. After flight the reverse is the case. The longer the period of flight, the stronger is the response of the aphid to a leaf suitable for settling; that is, the longer it settles, and the more young it leaves. Kennedy concludes that settling is positively "primed" while being inhibited by flight, and names the process "antagonistic induction" by analogy with the "successive induction" of simpler reflexes. He supports this interpretation with evidence compatible with the view that there is a reciprocal effect of the host reflexes on flight (*see also* p. 285). It is worth noting that here, as in most other cases, more than one method of integration is involved. Flight not only lowers the threshold for the host responses, it also brings the animal into the appropriate stimulus situation.

Kennedy's interpretation of this result in terms similar to those of Sherringtonian successive induction does not imply a similarity of mechanism; he himself points out that the time scale and level of complexity are quite different from the phenomena which Sherrington studied. What is important is the reciprocal influence of each of these activities on the other, and the demonstration that flight is not appetitive to settling and feeding in the sense that both are caused by the same factors, for it is flying which creates a state in which the insect is ready to feed.

Another example, though the author does not choose to interpret it in terms of successive induction, concerns the "rocking" movement made by Hemileucid moths on assuming the resting position after preceding activity (Bastock *et al.*, 1958; Blest, 1958, 1959). The number of "rocks" given increases with the length of a preceding flight according to a simple linear relationship, the relationship changing somewhat with age from eclosion. Since the duration of flight controls the subsequent strength of the rocking response, it must be registered in some way. This registration appears not to depend on exteroceptive or proprioceptive feedback resulting from flight, or by change in metabolic reserves. In the absence of plausible alternatives, it thus seems that the control of rocking depends directly on activation of the central nervous mechanisms involved during flight, and not on its peripheral consequences.

It is possible that a similar description could be applied to the sudden increase in aggressive or fleeing behaviour which is seen immediately after copulation in many vertebrates. As discussed in Chapter 16, the preceding courtship involves tendencies for a variety of incompatible types of behaviour, such as attack, fleeing and behaving sexually. At copulation the first two are suppressed, but may find expression as soon as it is over.

18.5. Consummatory Stimuli and/or Goals

A missile tracking a moving target is controlled by information indicating its own position relative to the target. In the same way when an animal varies its behaviour so as to achieve a goal, responding appropriately to variations in that goal, its behaviour may be controlled by stimuli indicating the discrepancy between the present situation and the goal. The interpretation of such cases, however, is a subject on which extreme views have been expressed. When the "purposive" drives of the early twentieth century were countered by the reflexes and tropisms of the pioneer behaviourists, the use of words like "goal" or "directiveness" was regarded by many as disreputable. But now that it is recognized that even machines with negative feedback can be regarded as teleological mechanisms (Rosenblueth *et al.*, 1943), it has become respectable to interpret animal behaviour as goal-seeking. And since Craik's (1943) suggestion that thinking can be regarded as a form of symbolism of the same kind as that which goes on in a computer, it has become less difficult to postulate in animals a "Schema", "cognitive map", "neuronal model" or Sollwert with which the external situation can be compared. However, we must not forget that animals are diverse: they not only achieve the same thing in different ways, but also have capabilities which differ markedly from phylum to phylum and species to species. We must therefore ask just how broad are the generalizations which can be made here: in seeking to analyse the causal mechanisms which underlie adaptive behaviour, should we regard all animal behaviour as "directive" (Russell, 1943), and can we discriminate between degrees of directiveness?

Some of the consummatory stimuli discussed in Chapter 10 have a short-term effect which is merely inhibitory. Even when the consummatory situation influences a number of different types of behaviour, as when the stimulation from a nest-cup decreases the probability of all types of nest-building behaviour by a female canary, the integrative function may be no more than that of a common causal factor: the probability of some activities is lowered relative to that of others, and thus the likelihood that some activities occur in temporal association is increased and that for others decreased. For given activities a particular consummatory situation produces a maximal inhibitory effect, and the effectiveness of any other stimulus situation depends on its difference from this optimal one. But this could imply merely that the behaviour depends on the balance between positive and negative (consummatory) factors: if the positive factors predominate, it appears; if the negative factors, it does not. In such a case there is need to postulate a process of summation of positive and negative causal factors, but not a process of internal comparison between the input at the moment and a Sollwert.

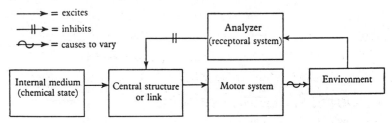

Fig. 18.6. Deutsch's conception of the feedback system underlying motivation of eating, etc. (*After Deutsch, 1960.*)

Further complexity is, however, indicated when the direction of the change in behaviour is influenced by the direction of the discrepancy. Several examples have been cited in preceding chapters; for instance the corrections made by a singer attempting to maintain a note of constant pitch (p. 39), or the optomotor (pp. 74–9) and orientation (Chapter 7) movements of insects. Such cases often imply a process of comparison, and can legitimately be described as goal-seeking: the behaviour varies in a manner which optimizes the input. Where the Sollwert changes from time to time, we have seen that it is more economical to postulate a goal-setting mechanism than a separate goal-seeking mechanism for each possible goal (pp. 122–32).

More complex still are cases where the goal-seeking behaviour involves the achievement of a succession of sub-goals. This can be illustrated by Deutsch's (1960) model of maze-running by rats. Deutsch argues that the learning of a maze involves not the learning of a series of responses (*see* p. 295), but of a succession of sub-goals which, if achieved in turn, lead to the ultimate goal of the food box. We shall discuss the nature of this "cognitive map" later (Chapter 26): here we are concerned primarily with the rat's behaviour once it has been acquired. To account for this Deutsch has produced a conceptual scheme, based on a feedback model of motivation and utilizing also the principles of common causal factors, chain responses and inhibitory relations, which accounts for many of the facts of maze running. His motivational model is shown in Fig. 18.6 and indicates the role played by feedback. Deutsch further supposes that, underlying the performance of a complex task (like the correct running of a maze) is a series of units each consisting of an analyser (or sensory/perceptual mechanism capable of selective responsiveness), a link and a motor unit. The links are connected together in such a way that when the primary link (referred to in Fig. 18.6 as the "central structure") is activated by a change in the medium, all the other links are initially also activated (i.e. principle of

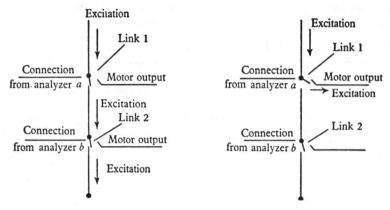

Fig. 18.7. Deutsch's scheme for the mechanisms underlying goal directed behaviour. (*After Deutsch, 1960.*)

In the first diagram neither analyser is stimulated and excitation is conducted through the links. On the right, stimulation of analyser (*a*) switches the excitation to the corresponding motor output, cutting off the link 2.

common causal factors). As soon as an analyser is stimulated, excitation is no longer passed to units more remote from the primary link, but is directed to the motor mechanism (Fig. 18.7). That unit then acts as a goal-seeking mechanism, moving so as to optimize its own stimulation. When this is achieved, the next analyser is stimulated (chain response principle), and stimulation through it is optimized by the activity in its motor mechanism. The process continues until the activity in the primary link is inhibited by the appropriate consummatory stimuli. With additional assumptions about changes in resistance in the connections consequent upon performance, Deutsch's scheme describes a mechanism which will learn to run through a series of goals in turn, and stop when it gets to the end. It will avoid blind alleys, and take short cuts, but cannot make detours. The ability to take short cuts is of particular interest as it implies that the machine will, if opportunity arises, pursue goals nearer (in some sense, spatial or otherwise) to the final consummatory one, instead of going through its routine: in other words, selection from among the possible goals is not random, nor dictated entirely by the environment. It is thus goal-seeking, both in the sense that sub-goals are sought by each motor mechanism in turn, and in the sense that some ability to select appropriate sub-goals is present. Such a scheme would appear to be of wide applicability outside maze-running.

Discrepancy between present input and a goal situation can thus effect behaviour in a number of ways. It may determine the intensity of the behaviour, or its direction, or its nature or even the sub-goal towards which it is directed. In view of this, general terms like "goal-directed" are of little value for discriminating between types of causal mechanism underlying behaviour.

In the past some authors have labelled behaviour as "directive" or "goal-directed" on the sole criterion that variable means are used to achieve a consummatory situation (e.g. Russell, 1945). Some of the examples quoted are susceptible to simpler explanations than the label implies. For instance, Jennings' classic observations on *Stentor*, the protozoan which may "try" several different courses of action when exposed to a stream of carmine particles until it avoids them, was cited by Russell as implying, "a power of varying behaviour according to the result of previous action, a power which is essentially a psychological one, a power of relating events and acting in accordance with the situation". This, however, is an over-interpretation: each type of behaviour is stereotyped, and its cessation could be due merely to inhibitory effects consequent upon performance (Chapter 13), rather than to response to error signals.

Another case, cited by Russell in the same context, is of quite a different order. As discussed in Chapter 26, if rats are subjected to spinal or cerebellar operations so as to interfere with their motor coordination, they may nevertheless use quite novel movements to make errorless runs through a maze (Lashley *et al.*, 1929). The essential point here is that the new movements are not stereotyped, but selected from variable patterns in such a manner as to bring the animal nearer the goal. Furthermore, the new patterns are "directly and efficiently substituted without any random activity".

Contrasting these examples we may draw two conclusions. First, persistency with varied action cannot be taken as evidence of "goal direction" in any useful sense unless the actions are selected from a large repertoire of stereotyped movements, or from variable movements, in a non-random manner in such a way that they bring the animal nearer a goal. Second, the most sophisticated goal-directiveness implies selection of the most economical course from starting point to goal, and thus, for any given starting point, lack of variability. When a monkey given a mechanical puzzle bites, bangs, pushes, pokes, jiggles and jogs it in an apparently infinitely variable fashion, the behaviour is goal-directed only in the sense that solution of the puzzle will bring the behaviour to an end, and not in the sense that it is guided by error-signals. Far from being an indication of goal-directiveness, variability in the types of behaviour shown may even indicate the opposite, for it implies little selection from all possible activities. Efficient goal-directed behaviour is variable only in the large number of starting points (relative to the goal) from which the goal can be reached.

Thorpe (1963a) also uses complexity and variability in behaviour as evidence for goal-direction. He cites a number of accounts of nest-repair behaviour in wasps and other invertebrates which demonstrate a surprising flexibility in both the type of behaviour shown and the manner in which it is organized into sequences. As yet, however, there has been no analysis of the precise stimuli eliciting the several responses, and thus no conclusive proof that (for instance) the response of a wasp to a hole in its nest is a response to a discrepancy between mutilated and complete nest, rather than to the edges of the hole.

Another case discussed in detail by Thorpe (1963a) is the nest-building of the Long-tailed Tit (*Aegithalos caudatus*). Citing a descriptive account by Tinbergen, Thorpe shows that this involves thirteen motor patterns and responsiveness to eighteen different releasers. He suggests that such complexity provides evidence of goal direction, arguing that it must indicate that the bird has some "conception" of what the completed nest will look like, and that "the addition of a piece of moss or lichen here and there will be a 'help' towards the ideal pattern, and that other pieces here and there would detract from it". There are in fact three points here. First, evidence from other avian species does indeed show that the intensity of building behaviour is influenced by stimuli from the nest (pp. 233–6): by itself, however, this does not necessarily imply comparison with a Sollwert. Second, it is at least likely that the orientation of particular building movements is influenced by irregularities, gaps, or excrescences in the existing structure; but even if this can usefully be said to involve comparison with a Sollwert, it is at most a matter of the elicitation of the individual movements, and quite a different issue from comparison between present structure and completed nest. Crook (1964b), studying the nest-building of weaver-birds, found no evidence for a process of comparison between the stimuli provided by the nest and a goal situation. When nests were mutilated, the repair behaviour was essentially a stereotyped repetition of earlier phases of building, and was successful only so long as the orientation of the nest was not changed. If the orientation was changed, a new initial ring was built, and from that a new nest which did not conform to the old.

A third point is that Thorpe, in his discussion of this and other cases of nest-building, suggested that error-signals contribute to integration in a second way. Not only are movements elicited and orientated by discrepancies between the present structure and the completed nest, but movements which reduce that discrepancy, even though not achieving the goal immediately, are more likely to be repeated. This would bring nest-building into line with a number of cases of the development of motor patterns (*see* Chapter 20), but the evidence for it is as yet meagre. Such evidence as is available indicates that the efficiency and orientation of the movements depends more on the level of motivational factors than on experience (*see* p. 190).

Where such an effect is of importance it tends to operate against the negative feedback principle. Behaviour which produces reafference involving a closer approximation to the Sollwert will result in both an increase in the probability that the same movement, rather than any other, will be performed in the same context; as well as, perhaps, a decrease in the probability that the animal will respond at all. Human subjects often work hardest at a task as it approaches completion. This is the opposite of what would be predicted on simple cybernetic grounds, which would suggest that "motivation" would be greatest when discrepancy between present state and goal was greatest (Welford, 1962). But achievement is rewarding, so that actions which lead to a diminution of the discrepancy will be reinforced.

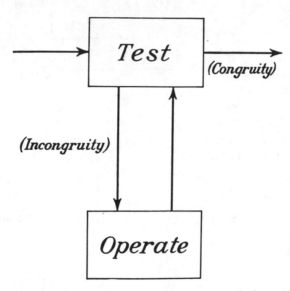

Fig. 18.8. The TOTE unit. For explanation see text. (*After Miller et al., Plans and Structure of Behavior, Holt, Rinehart and Winston, Inc., New York, 1960.*)

At this point it therefore becomes important to emphasize that behaviour may be goal-directed at one level of integration, but not at another. In the early stages of nest-building, the movements used by a weaver-bird in stitching may be oriented and coordinated to produce a perfect stitch, but the stitches are not oriented in such a way that a nest is produced. The lower levels are goal-directed, but there is no direction of behaviour towards the completion of a nest. Eliot Howard's classic field studies of bird behaviour provide many other examples of the manner in which species-characteristic movements are performed in an incomplete, disoriented and functionless manner when motivation is low. Even when motivation is at full strength, biological consequences may be achieved without the operation of teleological mechanisms guiding behaviour towards them: in nest-building the goal-directed mechanisms controlling the part-activities may be integrated by stimuli from the growing structure to produce a finished nest (*see* Figs. 15.2 and 15.3).

Such cases can be accommodated in the scheme devised by Miller *et al.* (1960) to embrace the goal-directedness of human behaviour. These authors suggest that the basic unit of behavioural organization (the TOTE unit) de-

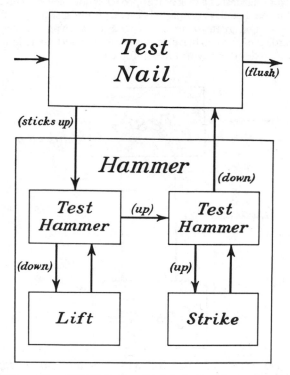

Fig. 18.9. Hierarchy of TOTE units which describes the hammering of nails. (*After Miller et al., Plans and Structure of Behavior, Holt, Rinehart and Winston, Inc., New York, 1960.*)

pends on negative feedback as illustrated in Fig. 18.8. The test unit serves to compare the input with some criterion established in the organism, the response occurring as a result of incongruity. After the response, a further test may or may not reveal congruity. If it does, action ceases. The sequence is thus Test-Operate-Test-Exit.

Such a scheme can be applied at many levels, from the reflex, where the diagram may represent nervous impulses passing along the neurones, to more complex behaviour, where it may be information or control. Such TOTE units, they suggest, may be arranged in an hierarchical manner, which they illustrate by the mechanism which might underlie hammering a nail (Fig. 18.9). Hammering has two phases—lifting the hammer and striking the nail. It must continue until the head of the nail is driven down flush. The sequence of events is thus as follows:

Test nail. (Head sticks up.) Test hammer. (Hammer is down.) Lift hammer. Test hammer. (Hammer is up.) Strike nail. Test hammer. (Hammer is down.) Test nail. (Head sticks up.)... Test nail. (Head flush.) Control transferred elsewhere.

We need not dwell here on the many ways in which such a model can be used to clarify the structure of human behaviour. Important for our present purpose is the emphasis laid on hierarchical organization, for this permits the possibility that behaviour can be goal directed (in some sense) at one level but not at another. Miller *et al.*'s insistence that even the simplest reflex is based on a TOTE structure is both not necessary and misleading. Indeed, it is a major task for comparative psychologists to specify at just which levels and which stages such a model is applicable, and at which it is not (cf. Chapter 3).

18.6 Summary

1. The mechanisms whereby the various types of behaviour in an organism's repertoire are organized into functional sequences are discussed.
2. The sharing of causal factors by a number of types of behaviour may assist in their functional integration.
3. In a chain response each movement or activity brings an animal into a situation where the next is evoked. Usually such chains are far from rigid.
4. Inhibitory relations, as discussed in Chapter 17, play an essential role in integration.
5. Antagonistic induction, with properties similar to the "successive induction" studied at the spinal level, may also play a role.
6. Behaviour sequences may also be integrated through the consummatory situations or goals towards which they are directed. "Goal directedness" as a term has, however, been used to refer to mechanisms of greatly differing complexity, and has little explanatory value. It is necessary to distinguish between cases in which:
    (*a*) The goal situation is merely consummatory, bringing the behaviour sequence to an end.
    (*b*) The difference between the perceived stimulus situation and the goal situation influences not only the intensity of the behaviour, but its direction or nature.
    (*c*) The goal-seeking behaviour involves the selection of a succession of sub-goals.
7. Variability in behaviour is not a useful criterion of goal-directiveness.
8. Some mechanisms showing goal-directiveness are discussed.

SECTION 3

The Development of Behaviour

19

The Study of the Development of Behaviour

So far, in studying the immediate causation of behaviour, we have been concerned with an artificially limited span of time. For each unit of behaviour we have searched for events, processes or conditions, internal or external to the animal, which are present about the same time as the behaviour in question. The identification of causes in this way immediately opens up further questions, for each cause must have a cause. The following chapters, therefore, are concerned with the development of behaviour in the individual.

A descriptive account of the ways in which behaviour changes with age might seem to be a necessary preparation for an analysis of the factors which influence those changes, but in fact really detailed descriptions of the development of behaviour over even a small part of the life span are rather rare.* Most research has been concerned with selected problems or aspects of behaviour, and the species used has simply been the most suitable for the task in hand. This concentration on the development of one type of behaviour at a time inevitably carries with it the risk of thinking of each different type as depending on a distinct mechanism, isolated from the mechanisms which underlie other types of behaviour, and differentiating independently of them. This danger has been repeatedly stressed by Schneirla (e.g. 1946, 1952, 1956) and his pupils. However narrow the problem may be, it is essential to remember that development involves a nexus of causal relations, with action, reaction and interaction, both within the organism and between organism and environment, at every stage.

Having recognized complexity, however, it is also necessary to abstract and simplify in order to analyse the processes involved. Here lies another danger, for until recently most of the questions asked about the development of behaviour have been in the form of dichotomies—is a given piece of behaviour

---

* There are, of course, exceptions, among which the studies of Kuo (1932) on the chick embryo, Nice (1943) on the Song Sparrow (*Melospiza melodia*), Eibl-Eibesfeldt (1951a) on the Red Squirrel (*Sciurus vulgaris*), Sauer (1954) on the Whitethroat (*Sylvia communis*); Messmer *et al.* (1956) on the Blackbird (*Turdus merula*); Kruijt (1964) on the Burmese Junglefowl (*Gallus gallus*); Hines (1942) on the Rhesus Macaque (*Macaca mulatta*); Gesell (1954) on the human infant, Bolles *et al.* (1964) on the rat, and Schneirla, Rosenblatt and Tobach (1963) on the kitten, exemplify diverse approaches.

"instinctive" or "intelligent," "innate" or "learnt"? That such dichotomies are not only false but sterile, has now been pointed out by a number of authors (e.g. Schneirla, 1951, 1952; Hebb, 1953; Lehrman, 1953; Beach, 1955; Hinde, 1959b; Tinbergen, 1963), but the matter merits consideration in some detail.

In the first place, the innate/learnt type of dichotomy can lead to important environmental influences on development being ignored. This can occur if it is assumed that the factors influencing the development of behaviour are of two types only—genetic, and those associated with learning. Such a view has recently been re-asserted by Lorenz (1961) and Thorpe (1963b), the latter author taking it as a prime aim of ethology "to differentiate between complexity coded in the germ plasm (the truly innate components) and that impressed by the environment (imprinted or otherwise learnt)". Now environmental factors can influence the course of development in many ways, some of which do not come within any generally accepted meaning of learning. To take an extreme example, a given genetic strain of *Drosophila melanogaster* may be capable of full normal flight, or of erratic flight, or incapable of flying at all, depending on the temperature during development (Harnly, 1941): the difference can hardly be ascribed to learning. If all environmental influences on development are said to operate through learning (as could be inferred from some definitions of learning), then the concept of learning becomes so broad as to be valueless.

A second objection to such "either–or" classifications is that in practice innate behaviour is defined solely in negative terms: a response is said to be innate or unlearned just so long as no learning process (or other environmental influence) has been identified in its ontogeny. Often, indeed, behaviour is labelled as innate on the basis of a "deprivation experiment"—animals which develop in an environment lacking some factor believed to be important are compared with animals living normally. But no series of deprivation experiments can exclude *all* environmental influences. The difficulty here is not merely the theoretical one of proving a null hypothesis: to repeat a truism, all development depends on both nature and nurture. Just as a bird's egg develops only if kept within certain limits of temperature, for any organism there are critical ranges of environmental variables outside which development is distorted or absent. Similarly, there are limits to the environmental conditions under which any pattern of behaviour will develop: in some cases these may be coincident with those in which life itself is possible, so that the behaviour appears after any conceivable deprivation experiment which the animal survives, but usually they are narrower. For this reason, it is sometimes useful to characterize items of behaviour according to their stability or lability under environmental influences (Hinde, 1959a). The form of some movements is so stable that it cannot be modified by any environmental conditions within the viable limits: in particular, modifications cannot be effected by learning (Lorenz, 1961; *see* pp. 17–20). In other cases the form or nature of a movement is labile, varying greatly according to environmental influences, human speech being an extreme example.

Thirdly, dichotomies between learnt and innate behaviour involve the assignment of units of behaviour into one or the other category, rather than an analysis of the factors and processes involved in their development. Since the appearance of any response depends on *both* nature and nurture, attempts to classify responses according to one source or the other are doomed to failure.

If attention is concentrated on *factors or processes*, as opposed to units of behaviour, it is often convenient to distinguish the consequences of "maturation" (tissue growth and differentiation) from those of "experience" (the contributions of stimulation from the developmental medium), although even this is useful only so long as we do not forget that it is only a convenient abstraction (Schneirla, e.g. 1965). The distinction depends, in fact, on the extent of the universe which is being considered. Processes of maturation by definition occur in, and depend on, the intraorganismic environment: they are not influenced by extraorganismic factors only because the environment relevant to them is maintained constant by homeostatic mechanisms. Furthermore, the consequences of maturation may vary with the experience of the individual: even when processes of tissue growth and differentiation have led to the development of an eye, that eye may not be functional until it has been exposed to the light (*see* p. 345).

However, even when processes, rather than units of behaviour, are considered, a dichotomous distinction runs into considerable difficulties. One of these is that it implies opposed or incompatible categories, whereas in practice the factors concerned constitute an interacting and reacting system: as we shall see, learning depends upon the genetic constitution of the animal; and behaviour may not be learnt, and yet depend on learning processes at an earlier stage in ontogeny (Lorenz, 1961).

In spite of these difficulties, it remains true that the determinants of the characteristics of the organism come from only two sources: the zygote, and the environment of the developing individual (e.g. Pringle, 1951; Lorenz, 1961; Thorpe, 1963b). For instance, Lorenz *loc. cit.*, who regards any environmentally induced modification in the mechanisms determining behaviour as learning (*see* p. 316), emphasizes that an organism acquires "information" from only two sources, its genetic structure and its environment. In his view, therefore, "innate" and "learned" are defined "by the origin of the information which is the prerequisite for adaptedness to any one among the givens of the environment". Thorpe (1963b) emphasizes this point even more strongly, suggesting that it should be possible to determine quantitatively how much of the information necessary to specify an adult characteristic comes from the environment and how much was genetically encoded.

There seem at present to be three difficulties in the way of using information theory to assess the contributions of gene and environment to particular patterns of behaviour. The first is a theoretical one: there is a possibility of interaction between genetic and environmental information. As mentioned above, development depends on interaction between organism and environment. Hebb's (1953) argument, that it is as meaningless to ask how much a given piece of behaviour depends on genetic factors and how much on environmental, as it is to ask how much the area of a field depends on its length and how much on its width, is still cogent.

A second, practical, difficulty concerns the use of information theory in such contexts. To measure the information required to describe a given state or a given pattern of behaviour, we must know the number of states or patterns of behaviour possible. Calculations of the information content of an egg start from knowledge of the proportions of the various atoms present. These, however, are already a selection from those which *might* have been incorporated. Even more so in the adult organism; we can say that to specify a Chaffinch's song, say, certain parameters must be defined, but who can assess the number of possible parameters which it might have had? And how can we equate the assumptions made in assessing the information content of the pattern of behaviour with those made in assessing that in the zygote or the environment?

A third difficulty is discussed in some detail by Thorpe himself. Estimates of the information content of the organism indicate an enormous increase from zygote to adult, even in such simple cases as plants which can be grown indefinitely in relatively simple homogeneous media. Neither the hereditary material nor the environment seems to be able to provide the increase in information present in the adult organism. In Thorpe's view, "This seems to push us to a new form of the old vitalist position which assumed that in living organisms purely physical laws no longer operated", though he regards the difficulty as at present unresolved. Thus, in practice, it seems that considerable difficulties beset an information theory approach to the task of obtaining quantitative measures of the extent to which an adult character is determined by the genes and the extent to which it is determined by the environment.

Whether or not it will ultimately be possible in theory and in practice to separate the contributions of zygote and environment in terms of information, the immediate problem is to disentangle a pattern of changes occurring through time. Each stage in the development of an organism depends on preceding stages, and results from interactions between the organism or part of the organism and its environment. The behaviour of the mature organism is thus not the consequence of a series of straight-line developmental processes leading from gene to adult pattern, modified in some instances by the environment. Rather, we must think in terms of a web of causal relations such that each part may interact with other parts and with the environment at every stage. What then are the relevant and useful questions to ask?

First, given two organisms that differ in behaviour, we can ask if the difference can be traced to a genetic difference, or if it is due to environmental factors. It is in the study of *differences* that the quantitative methods advocated by Thorpe (1963b) are most likely to be fruitful (Hinde *et al.*, 1958; Jensen, 1961).

Evidence that a difference in behaviour is to be ascribed to genetic differences must come ultimately from the rearing of animals, known to differ genetically, in similar environments (*see* e.g. Caspari, 1958). For instance, adult Great Tits use their feet to hold particles of food, but adult Chaffinches never do so, even when they have been reared from eggs by Great Tits in a Great Tit's nest. We can therefore conclude that the differences between the post-hatching environments of the two species are not responsible for the difference, and the operation of genetic factors seems likely. However, such evidence must not be over-interpreted. The occurrence of a behavioural difference between inbred strains or between species is evidence for a genetic influence on the behaviour, but does not imply that environmental factors are not also important. It remains possible that the intra-egg environment is responsible for the above difference between Chaffinches and Great Tits, and further work would be necessary to discover the manner in which this, in its turn, is genetically determined. In addition, we are not entitled to conclude that learning does not enter into the development of the behaviour in the adult Great Tit—the occurrence of learning may depend on a certain genetic constitution, present in Great Tits but not in Chaffinches. In fact, both observational (Hinde *et al.*, 1958) and experimental (Vince, 1964a) evidence indicate that learning does play a part in the development of this skill (*see* p. 331).

Evidence for an environmental influence is the converse of the above: if we take two animals of the same genetic constitution, or two samples from the same strain, and rear them under different conditions, differences in behaviour can be ascribed to those in the environments. If, for instance, we rear some domestic chicks in groups and others in visual isolation from each other, and find that the latter follow a moving model when the former do not, we can associate this difference with that in the rearing conditions (Guiton, 1959). If we can find no difference, we cannot of course conclude that the conditions of rearing have no influence, but only that that range of conditions tested is equally suitable (or unsuitable) as assessed in terms of the criterion used. Nor, from such an experiment, can we conclude much about how the environmental factors operate. Guiton's view that the socially reared birds do not follow the model because they have already learnt to follow each other is only one of a number of possible explanations.

This brings us to the second type of question that can be asked about the development of behaviour—how development occurs. We must ask how the differences in genetic constitution influence the behaviour of the adult, what environmental factors are involved, and how they produce their effects.

Since the organism is an integrated system, any change in its heredity may have diverse consequences. We must thus expect behavioural characters to be influenced by more than one gene substitution, and gene substitutions to influence more than one behavioural character. Although there is considerable variation between characters in this respect, some having a considerable degree of stability and being influenced by few gene changes while others are influenced by the majority of gene substitutions, it is indeed found that most behavioural differences have a polygenic basis (e.g. Keeler *et al.*, 1942). However, the number of genes involved in behaviour differences between strains is often small, and even single gene differences between strains may be associated with marked differences in behaviour. Thus the reduced mating success shown by "Yellow" mutant males of *Drosophila melanogaster* is due to courtship of reduced intensity, resulting from the single gene substitution (Bastock, 1956).

Whether the genetic difference involves one or many genes, its effect on behaviour may occur in diverse ways: there may, for instance, be changes in sense organs, effectors, body proportions, or general excitability, as well as in neural organization. Furthermore, the basic difference between two selected strains may not be that implied by any single response measure; for instance Searle (1949) showed that the differences between two strains of rats which had been selected for maze learning ability was rather one of "timidity", the low learning capacity of the "dull" strain being due to their anxiety in the experiment.

Where the young are dependent on maternal care, the route by which genetic differences produce behavioural ones may be very indirect. Ressler (1963) studied the behaviour of two strains of mice which were reared during infancy by foster parents of the same strains in all four possible combinations. Off-spring of both strains showed more visual exploration at 60 days of age, weighed more and had a higher expectancy of survival, if reared by parents of one strain than if reared by the other. The author points out that the differences could be due to the amount of handling given by parents to young. This, however, is influenced by the strain of the offspring as well as that of the parents: as a result, even this cross-fostering technique cannot completely separate genetic from post-natal parental influences. But Ressler's claim (made also by Broadhurst, 1961) that the finding of strain differences does not in itself justify the view that such differences are due to genetic factors, even when the physical environment is constant, is not valid: it is a question of how directly the genetic factors act.

Just as differences in genetic constitution can affect development in diverse ways, so also can environmental factors. They may, for instance, influence developmental processes directly, produce a change in hormone balance, or provide an opportunity for learning. The student of the development of behaviour must aim at discriminating between these and other possibilities.

In the following chapters some problems concerned with the development of various aspects of behaviour will be considered. While acknowledging the complexity of developmental processes, it is necessary to make an analytical approach, and consider first the development of isolated fragments of the behaviour machinery. Their integration will be considered later. The techniques most used in the study of behaviour have been variants of the deprivation experiment, in which the question asked is: "How does behaviour develop if this or that factor, believed to be important in normal development, is eliminated?". Much of our discussion will therefore be concerned with the extent to which development is stable under changed environmental conditions. Having found that a given experimental factor affects the behaviour under study, we can then ask how it acts.

Summary
1. A dichotomous division of behaviour into "innate" and "learnt" components is not fruitful because
   (a) It neglects effects of the environment other than those produced by learning.
   (b) The category of "innate" is, in practice, defined solely in negative terms.
   (c) It involves the classification of units of behaviour rather than the processes upon which development depends.
2. The possible use of information theory in assessing the contributions of genotype and environment is considered.
3. The most useful questions to ask about the development of behaviour are concerned with differences. Given two organisms that differ in behaviour, is the difference to be ascribed to genetic or experiential factors? And how do those factors exert their effects?

20

Development : The Form and Orientation of Movement Patterns

If a pattern of movement differs recognizably between the individuals of a species, we can attempt to relate the differences to variations in either genotype or environment, and thus begin an analysis of the factors controlling its development. Usually, it is environmental variations which are pertinent, and we can then try to assess how the environmental features in question produce their effects. The language a child speaks is determined by the language spoken in its home: we have little hesitation in ruling out any important genetic influence, and can set about analysing the nature of the "imitation" that occurs. More rarely, individual differences in the form of a movement pattern can be traced to genetic differences, and here, too, we can attempt to trace how the effects are produced: an abnormal gait in mice, for instance, may be due to abnormalities in the effectors, or in the middle ear.

If a movement pattern does not show consistent differences between individuals, identification of the factors influencing its development is more difficult. Its constancy of form tells us little except that the range of genotypes and range of environments are adequate for it to develop normally. One possible next step is to assess the effects of depriving the developing organism of environmental influences likely to be important. We can do this by a deliberate deprivation experiment, but some types of environmental influence can be ruled out by direct observation. If, the first time a movement appears in its usual context, it does so in its characteristic form, we can be sure that practice reinforced by the proper functional consequences is not essential. We may consider some examples.

20.1. Movements whose Form is Not Determined by "Practice" or "Example"

The motor movements used in flight by the White Butterfly (*Pieris napi*) are already developed when it emerges from the pupa, and such improvement in flying ability as occurs during the first few days is probably related solely to the hardening of the wing cuticle, and not to changes in the movements themselves (Petersen *et al.*, 1956–7). Practice thus plays little part in the development of the form of the movements. Similarly, young axolotls show swimming movements even before they have left the egg (Coghill, 1929); and characteristic prey-catching movements can be elicited from newly metamorphosed specimens of the toad *Xenopus laevis*, a species which is a filter-feeder in the tadpole stage (Eibl-Eibesfeldt, 1962). Young nidicolous birds beg before they have been fed by their parents, make preening movements before their feathers are fully grown, and show the species-characteristic freezing position on the first occasion that they hear their parents' alarm call (e.g. Nice, 1943; Barraud, 1961). Many of the signal movements (p. 437) used by lower vertebrates have been seen in individuals of known history on the first occasion they were exposed to the appropriate stimulus situation (e.g. E. Cullen, 1960); though in gulls (Moynihan, 1959) and Goldeneye ducks (Dane *et al.*, 1964) such movements are at first more variable than when their signal function is developed.

Although the bulk of the evidence refers to invertebrates and lower vertebrates, similar examples are well known in mammals. Eibl-Eibesfeldt (1951a, c, 1953) found that the movements used in display and brood-rearing by both squirrels (*Sciurus vulgaris*) and hamsters (*Cricetus cricetus*) reared in isolation are normal in form. He also listed sixty-five movement patterns in the Desert Mouse (*Meriones persicus*), which seem to be independent of experience in their normal functional context. Gauthier-Pilters (1959) recorded that the following motor patterns of the Dromedary appear "spontaneously" at the following intervals in minutes after birth: chewing 10, rolling on the ground 74, jerking of the head 120, yawning 160, tail beating 198, shaking 304, grinding and headshaking 100, sucking 100, kicking 156, urinating 185, rubbing of neck against mother 294. The three phases of rising occurred at 10, 87 and 95 minutes after birth, and standing upright at 100 minutes. Although many of these movements may have been made prenatally, and some may even have been functional then, the majority appeared without preceding practice in their normal functional context. Many other comparable examples are known.

The human baby has a number of stereotyped movement patterns which appear at birth, and can be seen even in infants born prematurely. One example is the lateral head movement which, though not specific to feeding, is used in finding the nipple and sucking. Another is the Moro reflex given on stimulation of the vestibular organ and/or the muscles in the neck, which is almost certainly a phylogenetic remnant of the movement whereby other young primates cling to their mothers (Prechtl, 1965).

Turning to some experimental studies, Grohmann (1939) prevented young pigeons from carrying out their incipient flight movements by rearing them in narrow boxes, so that they were partially prevented from using their wings. When the control (normally-reared) birds could fly a certain distance, the confined birds were released. Their flight performance was almost as good as that of the controls, indicating that they had not been handicapped by the period during which they had been restrained from making full flying movements.

Another case concerns the development of swimming movements in amphibian larvae (Carmichael, 1926, 1927). The movements first appear in an incipient form while the larva is still in the egg capsule, and gradually improve both before and after hatching. In an experimental group the movement was prevented by rearing the larvae under continuous chloretone anaesthesia from a stage prior to the development of the peripheral nervous system. When a control group, reared under normal conditions, was swimming well, the experimental animals were transferred to fresh water. Carmichael found that, as soon as the effects of the anaesthesia wore off, they were swimming as well as the controls. Although, in repeating this work, Fromme (1941) found some quantitative deficiencies in his anaesthetized groups, there seems no doubt that the main features of the swimming coordination do not depend on practice of any sort.

Surgical interference provides another type of evidence that the development of some fixed action patterns is independent of at least their normal functional consequences. Weiss (1941a, b) interchanged the left and right forelimb rudiments of salamander embryos at a stage when the antero-posterior axes of the limbs were already determined. Normal limbs developed, but they faced backwards instead of forwards. When the nerve connections had been established, the grafted limbs moved just as they would have done if they had been left in their original positions, working to move the animal backwards when the movements of the rest of the body were causing forward locomotion, and vice versa. A year's experience did not change this reversed movement of the grafted legs. Weiss has produced evidence that such motor patterns develop in the same way in the absence of sensory innervation, and that they persist after cord transection down to levels just in front of the tail segments (Weiss, 1950). Comparable results have been obtained in fishes (Sperry et al., 1956).

Although these experiments are concerned primarily with spinal cord/limb mechanisms, which are known to be relatively unmodifiable, they do serve also to illustrate that many movements not only develop independently of learning, but cannot subsequently be modified by it. Even in mammals there is apparently an early loss of embryonic plasticity, so that rearrangement of central-peripheral relations is subsequently compensated for only with the greatest difficulty, if at all. Monkeys in which the motor nerves to biceps and triceps had been interchanged learnt to inhibit the resultant reversed elbow movement, but made little positive correction (Sperry, 1947).

That the precise form of many species-characteristic movements is independent of the achievement of their normal functional consequences is shown also by the study of hybrids between species which themselves show different movement patterns. Unfortunately, few such cases have been studied in detail, as species showing markedly different movements are usually too distantly related to hybridize. The Lovebirds (*Agapornis*), however, provide an interesting case. In this group some species (e.g. *A. roseicollis*) obtain nest material by cutting long strips of paper, bark or leaves. The strip is grasped at one end in the bill and then tucked into the feathers of the lower back and rump for carrying to the nest. The feathers are raised as the material is tucked in, and subsequently lowered, holding it in place. Other species (e.g. *A. fischeri*) cut material in the same way, but carry it back to the nest in their bills. Hybrids between these two species were studied, from the time when they first started to cut material, by Dilger (1960). Although the hybrids were not successful in carrying material by tucking it into their feathers, they almost invariably tried to do so before carrying it off in the bill. The tucking movements were sometimes incomplete, but more often the movements themselves were normal, the failure being due, for instance, to the bird failing to let go of the strip with its beak after placing it among the feathers, tucking the material into an inappropriate part of the body, or grasping the material in the centre instead of at one end. Thus in many cases the full tucking movement appeared, even though inadequacy in orientation or selection of material prevented it from being successful.

Where coordination develops with little or no practice, processes of growth and differentiation in the nervous and effector systems, occurring in the homeostatically controlled internal medium, must play a major role in its development. These processes were followed in some detail in Coghill's (1929) classic studies of larval axolotls. The successive stages in the development of swimming movements—reflex flexure, coiling, S-bending—were found to proceed synchronously with the development of new connections in the nervous system, which thus probably mediate them (*see also* Harris *et al.*, 1954). This opens the further problem of the processes directing the growth of nervous connections. These are certainly diverse, but a number are well known; for instance, there is the tendency of growing fibres to veer towards organs in a stage of rapid proliferation, and the stimulating effect of ingrowing fibres on dendrite growth within a nuclear field. In the growth of peripheral nerves, mechanical guidance and chemical affinity seem to play a leading role (review by Sperry, 1951). However, the outgrowth of amphibian spinal axons seems to be largely nonselective. Although the termination of a given axon is determined in part by the proximo-distal sequence of development within the limb, considerable freedom remains. Since normal muscular coordination is achieved even under conditions in which the axon outgrowth appears to have been highly unusual, it seems that the central relations must be adjusted in accordance with the peripheral connections (*see above*, p. 324). The motor neurones must somehow be distinguishable centrally on the basis of the muscles they innervate: just how this occurs is not yet known (e.g. Wiersma, 1931; Weiss, 1941a, b; Sperry, 1941, 1951, 1963).

Even if the motor neurones are fired according to pre-established patterns, the mechanisms of central coordination pose further problems. Until relatively recently, much of the research in this field was concerned with a controversy as to whether the more complicated patterns of behaviour are built up by the integration of simpler ones; or whether the larger "total" patterns are primary, the simpler forms being "individuated" from them. Coghill's work on *Amblystoma* indicated that the first movements to be shown are simultaneous mass movements of the trunk somites. These subsequently differentiate into local patterns, the components of which gradually become distinct from the behaviour as a whole. For instance, the limbs are at first capable only of moving synchronously with, and in the same way as, the neighbouring trunk somites. Later they are able to move independently. In mammalian embryos, however, discrete reflex responses appear very early, and are not preceded by a "total pattern" stage (e.g. Windle, 1944), though the response depends in part on the intensity of stimulation. It seems possible that the resolution of this controversy depends on the nature of the response studied—individuation from a total pattern seems to occur in the development of responses related to the axial musculature, but not in those cases where the appendicular musculature develops independently from the axial system (Barron, 1950). In any case it is now becoming clear that the processes involved in the development of even quite simple movements are so complex that "individuation versus integration" is hardly a fundamental issue (Kuo, 1963).

It is natural to emphasize neural growth in discussing the development of movement patterns, but the development of the effectors is, of course, of equal importance. This is especially apparent in the development of vocalizations. The threat noises of the Elephant Seal (*Mirounga angustirastris*) develop from those of the pup, the progressive changes being correlated with an increase in the size of the animal. Similarly, the occurrence of the "clop threat" in this species depends on the development of the male's proboscis (Bartholomew *et al.*, 1962). The role of anatomical features in determining the characteristics of sounds used in vocal communication has also been stressed by Rowell (1962) in her study of the agonistic noises of the Rhesus Macaque.

Although many species-characteristic movements develop without practice in the usual functional context, it is still possible that experience involving incomplete performance plays a role. Often the appearance of the full movement is preceded by incomplete movements, and feedback from these could influence the course of development (Schneirla, 1956). One possibility is learning resulting from a comparison between this feedback and a Sollwert. Casual observation of the efforts of a human infant to attain the standing position, or to walk, suggest such a mechanism. That such a process of comparison occurs in the development of some vocal utterances we shall see later; but in most other cases it is an unnecessarily complicated hypothesis, and only puts the problem a stage further back, since the development of the Sollwert and comparator mechanism remain unaccounted for.

Nevertheless, the possibility that proprioceptive feedback from incomplete movements may be important in other ways in the development of fixed action patterns must not be neglected. This point has been stressed especially by Schneirla (1952, 1965) and Lehrman (1953), who discuss particularly Kuo's (1932) studies of the development of behaviour in chick embryos. Kuo described how, as a consequence of early postural changes, the chick's head comes to rest against the thorax and is passively lifted and dropped with the heart beats. Within a few days an active nodding movement appears, which could be a conditioned response to gentle pressure from the thorax each time it is raised. After the sixth day, the head movements occur in relation to a wider range of stimuli, such as pressure from the yolk sac, or contact of the head with the toes. At around this time the beak begins to open and close as the head nods, and after the ninth day fluid enters the mouth as the bill-clapping occurs. On the seventeenth day the head, now much more mobile, occasionally lifts and thrusts forward, and this is followed by beak-opening and closing. The elements of pecking thus appear gradually in the egg (*see also* Gottlieb *et al.*, 1965).

Opinion is divided as to the significance of these observations. Schneirla and Lehrman suggest that early interactions of the embryo with its immediate environment, and the movements which occur, may play an essential role in the development of the post-hatching pecking response. For instance, Schneirla (1965) suggests that the "gustatory and other afferent effects of these actions can function as agents reinforcing a progressive neural control of the head and bill actions by extrinsic stimuli". He also suggests that the reactivity of the head increases first to low intensity contact with soft yielding tissues in the egg, but later its movements come under optic control when "diffusion of impulses from aroused optic centres reaches and activates somatic afferent centres, exciting functions controlled by the latter in embryonic states" (*see also* p. 362).

Such suggestions have been greeted with ridicule by a number of writers (e.g. Lorenz, 1961; Eibl-Eibesfeldt, 1961; Thorpe, 1963a), but it is difficult to see why. True, they rest largely on observational evidence and are without experimental support, but the processes which Schneirla suggests are similar to those well known to occur in other contexts. In the first place there is evidence that the activity of an organ, even in the embryo, may help to bring it into a functional state; Peters *et al.* (1958) have shown that repeated stimulation facilitates retinal responsiveness in embryo chicks. Second, the importance and ubiquity of interoceptive conditioning, of just the type suggested by Schneirla and Lehrman, has been demonstrated by much recent Russian work (Razran, 1961). Third, hatching is not a zero-point for the development of behaviour: chicks do "behave" before hatching; they respond for instance to the warning call of the cock by remaining quiescent (Baeumer, 1955, *see also* Vince, 1964b):

Reflex pattern in 18 newborns after breech-foot presentation

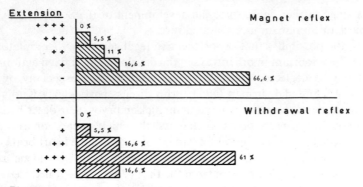

Flexion

Reflex pattern in 116 newborns after uncomplicated vertex presentation

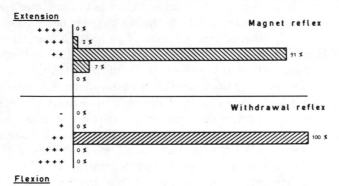

Flexion

Reflex pattern in 35 newborns after breech presentation with extended legs

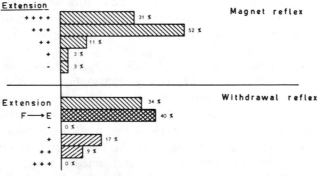

Flexion

Fig. 20.1. Reflex responses to stimulation of the sole of the foot of new-born babies. (*H. F. R. Prechtl, personal communication.*)

The magnet reflex is an extension of the lower limb in response to mild stimulation, and withdrawal indicates flexion in response to a pinprick or scratch. The intensity of the response is indicated by the number of crosses, the lengths of the lines indicating the number of infants in each category. (*a*) After breech-foot presentation. (*b*) After uncomplicated vertex presentation. (*c*) After breech presentation with extended legs.

if environmental factors can influence their behaviour, they are likely also to influence their development. Fourth, it is not possible to make *a priori* assumptions about what sorts of experience will affect behaviour. For instance, Reyniers (1953) claims that young rats delivered by caesarian section are unable to urinate until they have received gentle tactile stimulation of the genitalia, as normally provided by the licking of the mother. Such an observation would certainly not have been predicted.

Finally, there is strong evidence for the human baby that experiences before parturition can influence later behaviour. Prechtl (1965) found a direct correlation between the position of the legs during the last week before delivery and their post-natal posture and pattern of reflex behaviour (Fig. 20.1). Thus, a normal infant withdraws his legs to a pinprick on the sole of the foot, but extends them to mild stimulation. Breech babies with extended legs keep their legs in abnormal extension spontaneously, and may extend them after sharp stimulation of the sole. In babies born in a breech presentation with flexed legs, however, the reverse is found—extension to mild stimulation is diminished and the withdrawal reflex is exaggerated. Breech babies with one leg flexed and the other extended showed the patterns corresponding to the leg position. In cases diagnosed as breech presentation in the seventh or eighth month of pregnancy, but turned successfully during the last few weeks and born with a vertex presentation, leg posture, mobility and reflex patterns are normal. It thus seems that there must be an influence of the intra-uterine proprioceptive input on post-natal postural and reflex patterns.

In view of these facts, it is safer at least to consider Schneirla's view that the intra-egg environment and activity may have some effect on the ontogeny of pecking in chicks, than to presume that it does not. The constancy in form of the movement between individuals, and its apparent environmental stability in development, may thus be consequences of the constancy of the intra-egg environment rather than an indication of a lack of environmental influences on development. Such a view is in no way incompatible with the view that there is a "pre-stabilized harmony between organism and environment" (Lorenz, 1961): if the response of pecking is adaptive, so must also be the mechanisms by which it develops. Although it seems improbable that the precise coordinations involved in pecking can depend on the relatively unstructured intra-egg environment, as yet we know very little about how far the intra-egg environment could be altered without development being affected.

In spite of the controversy over this issue during the past ten years it remains unresolved: clearly the present need is for an experimental approach.

20.2. The Role of Learning

So far we have been concerned with movements whose development is stable over a wide range of developmental conditions. Now we must turn to more labile patterns. Environmental conditions can influence the form of a movement in diverse ways: in human babies suffering from rickets the effectors are influenced directly, while in certain human anxiety states a hostile environment may result in the superposition of a cringing posture which affects nearly all movement patterns (Barlow, 1959). Most commonly, however, the environment acts through individual learning in specific contexts, and this must be our principal concern.

When a particular pattern of movement is common to all members of a species, the importance of learning may be difficult to assess: it cannot be assumed from the mere observation of changes in the movement during development. Many movements are made first in an incomplete form, and observation alone cannot decide whether the gradual improvement that occurs is a consequence of practice, or merely correlated with it. For example, the development of sniffing behaviour in the rat has been studied in some detail by Welker (1964). In the adult, sniffing involves an integrated and precisely timed sequence of contractions in four groups of muscles which produce (a) bursts of polypnea, (b) recurrent protraction and retraction of the vibrissae, (c) repetitive retraction and protraction of the tip of the snout, and (d) a rapid series of discrete head movements and fixations. Development of this pattern occurs gradually, and during the first five days of life only the first of these components is apparent. Synchronous retraction of the vibrissae appears on the fourth day and protraction on the seventh. Repetitive movements of the nose and nostrils appear on the seventh day, and associated head movements on the eighth. At first the polypnea frequencies are only slightly higher than those of normal respiration, but they increase during the next two days, and again from the tenth to eighteenth days. As each type of movement appears it becomes synchronous with those already present. The length of sniffing bouts increases with age, especially between the eighth and tenth days, at which time the sniffing movements become associated with the locomotor components of exploratory behaviour. After about 18 days of age the sniffing pattern changes little. As yet we have no precise information as to the role of experience in the development of this pattern, but it is known that its coordination is maintained in the absence of olfactory feedback in the adult. It is thus at least possible that its development does not depend on learning in any ordinary sense (see also Eibl Eibesfeldt et al., 1958).

Furthermore, lack of individual variation does not indicate absence of learning: the course of learning may be determined, in part, by the structure of the species, so that individual variation is minimal. An example is provided by the behaviour of birds with abnormal beaks. Individuals with gross abnormalities may obtain their food with "scooping movements", or other bizarre patterns apparently quite foreign to the normal repertoire of the species (Fox, 1952; Pomeroy, 1962). Since the development of such unusual patterns clearly involves learning conditioned by the abnormal structures, the development of the corresponding normal patterns may also involve learning similarly conditioned by structure: lack of individual variation in the motor pattern could thus be ascribed, in part, to lack of variation in the relevant effectors (Hinde, 1959a).

Another example is provided by the movements used by some passerine birds in the course of holding an object down with one or both feet. This pattern of behaviour is characteristic of all members of some passerine species (e.g. tits and chickadees of the genus *Parus*) and never seen in others (e.g. Chaffinches). Nevertheless, learning plays an essential role in its development in those species where it occurs: the initial attempts of a young tit to hold a mealworm under its feet are clumsy, and are perfected only after some time (Hinde *et al.*, 1958). The development of this movement was studied in detail in hand-reared Great Tits by Vince (1964a). All her hand-reared birds, whether reared with or without objects which could be held with the feet, showed some approximation to the normal patterns as soon as they were given objects to hold: indeed birds reared initially without access to seeds responded to them in this way more readily than birds which had previously not been restricted. But Vince also found that the rates at which the movement patterns became perfected and stabilized varied with the opportunity for practice with suitable objects: this is consistent with the view that learning plays a major part in its detailed development.

Of course, the learning of new motor patterns always contains a species characteristic element, in the sense that members of a species will tend to produce movements more similar to each other's than to those of other species. This could be a consequence of similarities in the structure of nervous system or effectors.

In addition, many of the motor patterns characteristic of individual vertebrates are modifications of species-characteristic ones. Thus before take-off most birds show a series of "intention movements" of jumping into the air (Fig. 17.3, p. 274). Andrew (1956d) has described how some buntings, kept in a cage in which the perches were placed too near the roof, showed highly peculiar intention movements of flight: after an initial crouching phase, the body was moved upwards until the bill was vertical, while the legs and neck remained in the same posture as before. These movements, derived from a normal take-off by a change in the association of its components, became extremely stereotyped and persisted when the birds were moved into a larger cage.

A similar building-up of individually characteristic movement patterns from species-characteristic components is seen in the so-called superstitious behaviour of pigeons. If a pigeon is given food on an arbitrarily chosen time schedule, without reference to its behaviour at the time, it begins to repeat certain acts which happen to coincide with the reinforcement. The probability that one of these will coincide with the next reinforcement is thereby increased, and its frequency then increases. Bizarre movements, like turning quickly in a small circle, or tic-like movements of the head, may be learnt in this way

(Skinner, 1948). Individually characteristic stereotyped movements are especially common in caged animals (e.g. Holzapfel, 1939a) and it is probable that a number of factors contribute to their development (Hinde, 1962c, *see* p. 389).

The development of the skilled movement patterns used by primates raises a number of problems which cannot be discussed here. There is, however, considerable evidence that each skilled movement depends on the elaboration of pre-existing patterns and thus, ultimately, on species-characteristic factors (Schiller, 1957). In man, comparison of the movement with a "model" or Sollwert of the required movement often plays an essential role in its elaboration (Guillame, cited by Paillard, 1960).

Finally, it is worth emphasizing that the development of a movement pattern involves changes not only in the outward form of the movement, but in the mechanisms by which it is controlled. For instance, we saw earlier (p. 39) that introduction of a delay into the auditory feedback causes human speech to become incoherent. The speech of 7–9-year-old children is more adversely affected by delayed auditory feedback than that of 4–6-year-olds, a finding probably related to the increase in control over speech with age (Smith, K. U., 1962; Yates, 1963). The adult type of response to delayed feedback is present from an age of about 12 years (Ratner *et al.*, 1964).

As another example, the extent to which a skilled movement depends on *exteroceptive* stimuli may depend on practice. Thus Poulton (1952) studied the performance of subjects in following a pointer which oscillated in a regular way: after training they could follow with fair accuracy even if the target was momentarily obscured. Broadbent (1958) points out that a consequence of training is that performance of the movement comes to interfere less with other activities: if the pattern of movement is repeated often in the same order, the first part of the stimulus contains almost as much information as the whole sequence, the remaining input becomes redundant, and the neural mechanisms are set free for other tasks.

20.3. Avian Vocalizations

The ontogeny of bird vocalizations raises problems of particular interest. Progress in their analysis has been greatly accelerated by the development of the sound spectrograph, which is an instrument that produces a graph of the frequency of a sound plotted against time, and makes it possible to record the forms of sounds more precisely than those of any other behaviour pattern. Each avian species has a repertoire of sound signals: often there are as many as 15–18 types, each appearing in a distinct functional context, with some of these types having considerable variability (Thorpe, 1961b). These signals are characteristic of the species, and interest has been focused chiefly on whether or not individuals are able to produce them without previous example from other members of their species.

Little work has been done on non-passerine species, but the available evidence suggests that, with a few possible exceptions (e.g. Goethe, 1954), the species-characteristic repertoire is developed independently of example (Lanyon, 1960; Baeumer, 1962; Lade et al., 1964). The adult calls often develop by elaboration and restriction from those of the chick (e.g. gulls, Moynihan, 1962; domestic chicks, Andrew, 1963a). That some species, such as the parrots and mynahs, can learn by imitation is beyond doubt, but there is as yet no evidence that this ability is used outside captivity, let alone that it is necessary for normal development (Thorpe, 1963a).

Among passerine birds the call notes, which are normally relatively simple sound patterns, also usually develop independently of example (Messmer et al., 1956; Sauer, 1954, 1955; Lanyon, 1957; Marler, 1956a; Blase, 1960; Thorpe, 1961b). In a few cases, however, certain call notes either fail to develop, or develop abnormally, in birds reared in isolation (Poulsen, 1954; Messmer et al., 1956; Marler, 1956a; Lanyon, 1957). Whether or not the crucial factor in these cases is absence of example is so far unproven.

The more complex songs of passerine birds, which usually function in pair-formation or territorial defence and occur in the breeding season, provide the most interesting material. Here again there are many cases in which the species-characteristic song develops in individuals brought up in isolation, and the song often develops from, and may even include, call-notes otherwise used in other contexts. Sauer (1954) made a detailed study of the development of song in Whitethroats (*Sylvia communis*) isolated in sound-proof rooms either as eggs or within a few hours of hatching. In this species, the song of the male begins as a continuous reiteration of one note, comparable to the begging call of the fledgling. Gradually other notes are added, and the song develops synchronously in auditorally isolated individuals and wild birds. One isolated bird started to sing belatedly, but its song then corresponded to that of other birds of the same age. It therefore seems that the maturation is in some degree independent of practice. (*See also* Konishi, cited on p. 337.)

Many passerines, however, are known to be capable of imitation, and in some the development of the normal song depends on it. A particularly interesting case is that of the Chaffinch, which has been analysed in detail by Thorpe (e.g. 1954, 1958). The full song of this species lasts about 2·5 seconds, and consists of notes ranging from 2–8 kilocycles/second. It is divided into three main phrases, of successively lower frequency, followed by a terminal flourish (Fig. 20.2 (a)). Individuals usually have a repertoire of one to six songs of this type, differing in their details. This song develops from a rambling sub-song, which has no definite duration, a wide range of notes, and no terminal flourish.

Chaffinches hand-reared in isolation from a few days of age develop only a very simple type of song (Fig. 20.2 (b)). This is of about the right length and number of notes, but is not divided into phrases and lacks the terminal flourish. This, then, is the song pattern produced when opportunity for imitating other individuals is denied. If such birds are brought up in groups, still in auditory isolation from adult Chaffinches, they produce spring songs more elaborate than those of birds isolated individually. This is presumably a consequence of the stimulating effect of counter-singing with other individuals. Such songs may be divided into phrases, though the structure of the notes is often abnormal (e.g. Fig. 20.2 (c)). The song patterns are usually similar in the members of a group, but differ markedly between groups. This indicates that learning by imitation is occurring within each group.

However, isolated Chaffinches will not learn any song pattern they hear. Using a tape recorder to play back songs at frequent intervals, Thorpe showed that isolated Chaffinches did not modify their song as a result of exposure to an artificial Chaffinch song in which the notes had a pure tonal quality, and were thus unlike those in normal Chaffinch song, but did after exposure to patterns made by modifying Chaffinch song; for instance by playing it backwards or with the order of the phrases changed. Figure 20.2 (d) shows the song of a Chaffinch reared in isolation but exposed to a recording of Chaffinch song re-articulated so that the end was in the middle. Thus, although Chaffinches occasionally incorporate foreign notes into their subsong, these isolated birds will imitate only a limited range of sound patterns in the full song. It is possible that this limitation is in part peripheral and depends on structural features of the syrinx or its nerve and muscle supply; this explanation is rendered less likely by the wider range of notes which occur in the sub-song. Autumn-caught birds, which have heard normal songs during the first few months of life, are even more restricted in the variety of patterns they will learn from the song tutor than are birds isolated from the fifth day. This greater selectivity was presumably acquired during their first few months, before they themselves were singing.

In fact, there is further evidence that some learning of the song, which could lead to greater selectivity, does occur during the first few months of life. Unlike the birds reared from five days in groups, autumn-caught birds kept in such isolated groups produce songs which fall within the range found in normal birds.

Since some of the characteristics of the adult song are learnt long before the bird itself starts to sing, song learning seems to involve both the acquisition of a model or Sollwert, and also the gradual approximation of motor output to match this pattern. Yet, since even the individually isolated birds produce a song with some characteristics in common with normal song, either this simple song does not require adjustment of output to a model, or these aspects of the model do not depend on example from other individuals. The differences between isolated and autumn-caught birds indicate that some further aspects of the song are learnt in the first few months of life; the similarities

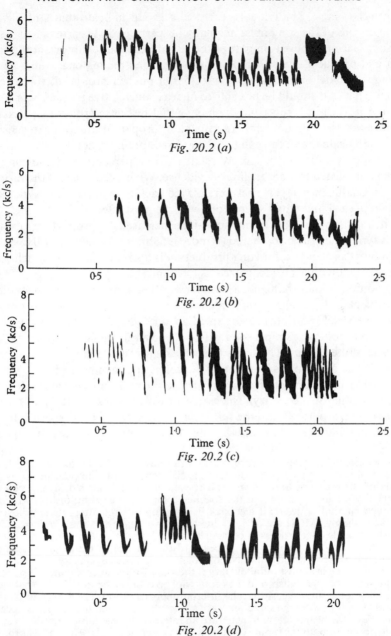

Fig. 20.2 (a)

Fig. 20.2 (b)

Fig. 20.2 (c)

Fig. 20.2 (d)

Fig. 20.2. Chaffinch song. (*After Thorpe, 1961b.*)

(*a*) A characteristic normal song. (*b*) Song of an individual reared in isolation. (*c*) Song of an individual from a group reared in isolation. (*d*) Song produced by a bird reared in isolation, after tutoring with a disarticulated chaffinch song with the ending in the middle.

between the songs of individuals reared in a group indicate that still further characteristics of the song must normally be learnt in early spring.

If song learning consists in part of the adjustment of the motor output until the sound produced matches a previously acquired model, one would expect hearing the model or normal song (whether or not self-produced) to be reinforcing. That is, it should be possible to increase the relative frequency of some response in the bird's repertoire by having that response produce a playback of a full adult song. Preliminary experiments in an operant situation (Stevenson, in press) indicate that a full song does have reinforcing effects.

That song production is closely related to the perception of the song as uttered is indicated by another line of evidence. When recordings of the various songs in Chaffinches' repertoires were played back to them, the song type most frequent in each individual's repertoire was the most effective in eliciting song from it, and the playing of any one song-type increased the proportion of songs of that type which the bird uttered (Hinde, 1958b). It thus seems probable that the Sollwert as acquired for song production is also the model by which song from other individuals is recognized as Chaffinch song.*

In addition to the Chaffinch, a number of other species have been studied. In the Blackbird (*Turdus merula*; Messmer *et al.*, 1956; Thielcke-Polz *et al.*, 1960), and Meadowlark (*Sturnella* sp.; Lanyon, 1957) individuals brought up in isolation produce a simple song with only general similarities to that characteristic of the species. The songs of such isolates show individual variations in detail, but if the birds are reared in groups the members of each group conform to a common pattern. For the development of full song example from other individuals is necessary. The extent to which notes or phrases of other species are incorporated into the full song varies between these species. In the Red-backed Shrike (*Lanius collurio*) the ability to mimic persists throughout

---

* At a quite different level of complexity, this finds a parallel in human speech. As we have already seen (p. 39), coherent speech depends on the perception by the speaker of the sound of his own voice: if the auditory feedback is delayed, speech is disturbed. We must suppose that the speaker compares the sound of his own voice with some internal Sollwert: if feedback is inappropriate, he attempts to adjust his voice accordingly. M. Halle and K. Stevens have suggested that understanding similarly depends on a process of comparison: the input is accepted and interpreted as a sentence to the extent that it appears to the listener to match some internal representation. However, the number of possible sentences against which the input could be matched is almost infinitely large: there are for instance about 10^{20} possible 20-word sentences in English, and they could not possibly all be stored in the listener's brain. They therefore suggest that the internal representations are generated as they are needed by following the same generative rules that are used in producing speech. On this view, the hearer starts to generate an internal representation on the basis of some hypothesis about the input. The mismatch is reported and used as a basis for the next hypothesis, which will be a closer one, and so on. The successive hypotheses are generated on the basis of the rules the listener uses for generating speech when speaking himself. The rules of language need be assimilated only once—not once by the ear and again by the tongue. Speaking and understanding are thus both manifestations of a single *faculté de langage* (G. A. Miller, 1964).

life, but appears to be seasonal (Blase, 1960). Similarly in the canary, which does not have to learn its song but can include imitations, learning can occur in the first few months of life and again every autumn when the bird is singing its subsong (Poulsen, 1959).

Auditory isolation of single individuals does not rule out the possibility that learning plays some role in the development of the simple song produced. The possibility remains open that the simple Sollwert is independent of example, but the young bird may still have to tailor its own motor pattern to fit it. Some evidence on this point is available: Messmer *et al.* (1956) deafened Blackbirds at 18 days of age and found that motifs similar to those of control birds reared in auditory isolation were developed, though there were some differences in tonal quality. Konishi (1963) obtained a similar result with chickens, but points out that deafening does not exclude non-auditory feedback. Nottebohm (personal communication) followed this up to show that when deafening is followed by section of the recurrens branch of the vagus, which carries afferent fibres from the syrinx, crowing is still unchanged. In a later paper, Konishi (1964) reports more detailed experiments with Juncos (*Junco oreganus* and *phaeonotus*). The birds were taken from the nest when 5–8 days old and kept in auditory isolation until they were deafened by extirpation of the cochlea. The normal song of *J. oreganus* consists of a simple trill, and this appeared in the deafened individuals. The song of *J. phaeonotus* is more complex, usually consisting of three or more parts, each consisting of trills or phrases: this multipartite character was absent in the deafened birds. In both species the form of the syllables tended to be abnormal, and unstable between songs and from song to song, in the deafened individuals. This could be due merely to a role of auditory feedback in maintaining the stability of the syllables (cf. p. 39), but Konishi regards this as improbable in view of evidence from another species that the form of the song is unchanged by deafening even though it was originally acquired through the ear. More probably, therefore, the defects were a consequence of songs never having reached the terminal point of "crystallization" into a more rigid form which occurs in normal development. Since Juncos raised in acoustic isolation but not deafened develop normal songs, it appears that motor mechanisms producing normal song develop only in the presence of auditory feedback: possibly there is a central mechanism which is capable of recognizing the normal song without previous experience of it.

In other species, by contrast, the characteristics of the species song which mark it as appropriate to be learnt are themselves acquired in early life. Nicolai (quoted by Lanyon, 1960) claimed that young Bullfinches (*Pyrrhula pyrrhula*) learn their song by preference from the male which reared them. A young Bullfinch reared by a canary but permitted to hear Bullfinches learned the motifs of the canary.

The observation that young Chaffinches reared in groups without example from adults elaborate more complex songs than do individuals reared in isolation raises the question of the role of generalized auditory input on the elaboration of the song. Marler *et al.* (1962) hand-reared male Oregon Juncos (*Junco oreganus*) in various degrees of acoustic isolation. The birds raised in the richer auditory environments had more song types per individual and a more elaborate syllable structure: this was apparently a consequence not of imitation but of unspecific stimulation to improvise.

Improvisation involving both the rearrangement of phrases and the invention of "new" ones occurs in a number of species (Messmer *et al.*, 1956, and references in Thorpe, 1961b), and can lead to a surprisingly large repertoire. A detailed description of the improvisation, elaboration and crystallization occurring in the song of the European Blackbird is given by Hall-Craggs (1962). Marler (1959) recorded a Robin (*Erithacus rubecula*) which produced 57 different songs, and cites comparable cases in other species.

It may be that something akin to this improvisation plays a role in normal song development in many species, for we have seen that syllable or song structure may be variable prior to a process of crystallization.

The role of experience in the ontogeny of mammalian vocal signals has so far been little studied, but anecdotal observations of animals reared by hand strongly suggest that the majority of (non-human) mammalian vocalizations develop normally even when the individuals have not heard them from others. Gauthier-Pilters (1959) describes how a young dromedary gave the humming contact note as soon as its head appeared at its mother's vulva, and uttered nearly all the sounds normally observed in dromedaries within the next hour. Learning, however, may play a part in local differences in species characteristic calls, and certainly plays a part in the "instrumental" noises made by Rhesus Macaques. These animals, especially the males, shake branches as a challenge: in captivity each individual male develops his own techniques of noise production, such as rattling wire netting or bouncing on wooden boards (Rowell *et al.*, 1962).

20.4. Orientation of Movements

So far we have considered the development of the form of a movement pattern independently of the question of its orientation. In Chapter 3, however, we saw that the orientation of a fixed action pattern may be controlled by stimuli different from those which release the movement itself: it may also depend on different ontogenetic factors. The orientation of most of the movements of invertebrates discussed in Chapter 7 is probably independent of experience, but in the menotaxis involved in the orientation of an ant's track (p. 124), the foraging of honey bees (pp. 127–8), and the recognition of its hole by a hunting wasp (p. 116), the mechanism is clearly set by experience. Similarly, in vertebrates some orientation mechanisms are probably independent of previous experience in the particular context: examples are given by the begging of passerine nestlings (p. 104) and the pecking of young Herring Gulls (pp. 46–7, *see also* Chapter 21). Of course, this does not mean that the mechanisms underlying such movements do not have a developmental history involving interaction with the environment.

Frequently, however, the learning of an orientational component plays an important role in the development of functional sequences of behaviour. For instance, Braum (1963) studied the first prey-catching movements of larvae of the fish *Coregonus* and pike (*Esox lucius*) by analysing ciné films. Many stereotyped components like binocular fixation, approaching, pushing forward and snapping were present, but skill improved later: the precise nature of the improvement is not yet known. Eibl-Eibesfeldt's observations on a number of species indicate that in the species-characteristic activities of mammals it is often only the small units of stereotyped movements that are independent of practice. Thus inexperienced squirrels may bury a nut at the first opportunity: the sequence of digging, depositing the nut, pushing it down with the snout, covering it over and stamping often occurs even when the animal is unable to dig, e.g. in the corner of a room. But the sequence is improved by learning, which affects largely the orientation of the movements: an inexperienced animal may dig a hole, but cover in the wrong place, and sight of the nut then releases covering again.

The movements used by squirrels in opening nuts show similar improvement in the orientation component with practice. These movements include gnawing and splitting with a movement whereby the nut is rotated around different axes. At first furrows are gnawed in many directions round the nut, and only gradually do the squirrels develop the more efficient technique of gnawing a furrow right round. The precise method used varies between individuals (Eibl-Eibesfeldt, 1951a).

Among other examples cited by Eibl-Eibesfeldt (1963) is the prey-catching of polecats, where shaking, turning over the prey, and so on, occur on the first occasion prey is given to a naive animal. The orientation of the bite in the back of the neck, however, is learnt, a learning process in which playing with the litter-mates helps. Play probably also plays a role in perfecting the orientation of sexual mounting in mammals, which is often inadequate at first (e.g. mice, McGill, 1962a, b; Rhesus monkeys, Harlow, 1963; personal observation).

It is worth emphasizing that mere observation of improvement with practice is insufficient to establish that the orientation component has been modified by learning. For instance the pecking of young chicks at grain consists of pecking, seizing and swallowing. Close observation shows that the early attempts are frequently unsuccessful, only about 15 per cent of the pecks leading to swallowing (Breed, 1911). If chicks are given their first opportunity to peck at different ages (1–5 days), being kept in the dark and fed by hand meanwhile, it is found that the accuracy of striking improves with age. This cannot be due to learning and must be related to growth: perhaps postural

stability and general improvement in neuromuscular coordination is responsible. With every age group, however, there is further improvement with
practice, so that birds which have been pecking for some time are more accurate
than naive birds of the same age (Fig. 20.3 and Cruze, 1935). Thus the improvement which accompanies practice in the normally reared chick may be
a consequence of increased postural stability as well as learning.

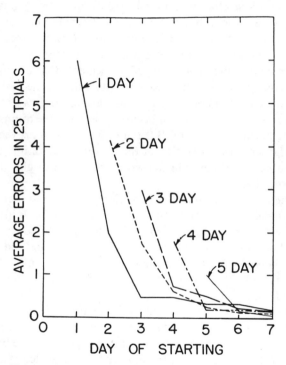

Fig. 20.3. Changes in the accuracy of pecking by chicks. The ordinate
shows the number of misses made by chicks allowed to begin practice at the
intervals indicated after hatching. (*After Cruze, 1935.*)

20.5. Summary

1. Many species-characteristic movements appear in near-perfect form on the first
   occasion they are elicited in their normal context. Practice reinforced by the normal
   functional consequence is thus not essential for their development. This does not
   show, however, that previous experience is of no significance in the development of
   the movement: in particular, it is quite possible that intra-egg or intra-uterine
   experience can influence the form of movement patterns.
2. A number of cases in which the form of movement patterns more or less characteristic of a species are influenced by learning are discussed.

3. Avian vocalizations provide particularly interesting material for study. Although the calls and songs of many species appear in individuals brought up in isolation, in others the song has to be learned. In some of these the learning involves first the acquisition of a Sollwert in early life, and then an adjustment of the motor output to approximate to this pattern.

4. Often improvement in a species-characteristic movement occurs as a result of modification to the orientation component.

21

Development of Perceptual Abilities

For information about what an animal perceives we depend on observation of overt behaviour (*see* p. 64). If physically diverse stimuli always elicit the same response from an animal, we say that it does not discriminate between them. An explanation of this could be that the ability to discriminate is present but lacking in the mechanism specific to the response: however, when a wrong response has painful consequences and results, for instance, in falling off a cliff or in missing a prey, a more probable explanation is that there are inadequacies in the sensory/perceptual apparatus itself (Chapters 5 and 6). It is with such cases that this section is primarily concerned. To what extent does the development of perceptual abilities depend on experience? Discussion here is limited to two problems: the perception of spatial relations and the discrimination of shapes.

21.1. Spatial Orientation in *Sepia* and Lower Vertebrates

Perfect performance on the first occasion that an animal makes a response shows that correct orientation is independent at least of previous practice of that response. Thus the cuttlefish *Sepia* catches its prey by first turning towards it and then striking at it with its long tentacles. The strike is made only when the *Sepia* is at the correct distance from its target and, even in a newly hatched *Sepia* feeding for the first time in its life, is nearly always successful (Wells 1962a). Thus the assessment of the distance of the prey must be more or less independent of previous experience in the prey-catching situation. Presumably the prey-catching mechanism is modified later, for the correct distance for the strike must change as the animal grows (see also von Frisch, 1962).

More detailed studies have been made of spatial orientation in vertebrates. The surface of the retina is connected in a more or less orderly fashion with the visual areas of the brain, mesencephalon or telencephalon according to the phyletic level. In a detailed series of experiments, Sperry (e.g. 1950, 1951) has used various visual responses of salamanders to study how these connections are established. The normal animal strikes in the correct direction when prey objects are presented at various locations with respect to its body axes, and shows an optokinetic following response (*see* p. 75) if a cylinder painted with vertical stripes is rotated round it. If the eyeball is rotated on its optic axis

through 180 degrees, leaving the optic nerve intact, it heals in its new position. The retina is then upside down and back to front. As might be expected,
the visuo-motor responses are then reversed—the prey-catching movements
are directed towards the opposite side of the visual field from that in which
the prey is located, the optokinetic responses to movement of the visual field

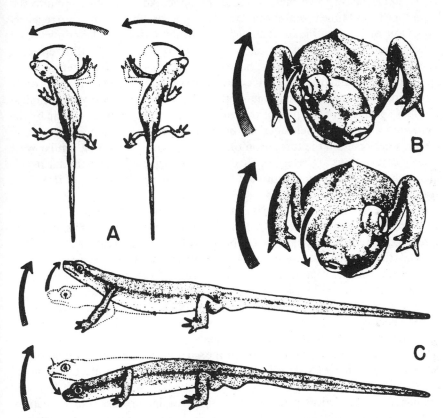

Fig. 21.1. Visuo-motor responses of salamanders with normally orientated
and inverted eyes. (*By permission from R. W. Sperry, Mechanisms of neural
maturation* in *Handbook of Experimental Psychology, John Wiley & Sons
Ltd., London, 1951.*)

Concurrent arrows indicate normal reactions; arrows in opposite directions, reversed
reactions.

around the dorso-ventral or rostro-caudal axes are made in the direction opposite from normal, and so on. These reversals persist indefinitely
(Fig. 21.1).

It is also possible to rotate the eye after severance of the optic tract. The optic
fibres slowly regenerate and establish connections with the brain, leading to a
restoration of vision. As in the previous experiment, all visual responses are

reversed. Thus, although the axons are tangled in an apparently random fashion in the scar region, orderly relations between the retina and the brain have been re-established. If, in addition, the eyes are transplanted to the opposite orbit, only one of the optic axes is reversed. On recovery, the animal shows distorted visual responses only in this plane. By these and other experiments, Sperry has shown that, whether the optic axons are growing into the brain for the first time in embryonic development, or whether they are regenerating from an adult retina, the functional central relations are laid down in an orderly way. Clearly, then, the axons from the retina must be differentiated from each other; each axon must have a qualitative specificity determined by the part of the retina from which it comes. Sperry thus suggests that the orderly patterning of synaptic associations in the brain is determined by biochemical affinities specific for each part of the retina; of the many contacts made by the ingrowing axons with neurones in the central nervous system, only certain specific ones result in the formation of synaptic connections. In a similar way, orderly connections are re-established after severance of the vestibular nerve, cutaneous nerves, proprioceptive fibres, and so on (Sperry 1951, 1958; Franzisket, 1959; Wiemer, 1955).

In Chapter 5 we saw that there is not merely a point-to-point correspondence between the retina and the optic tectum in the amphibian brain, but that optic fibres of different functional types connect with different layers in the tectum. Lettvin *et al.* (1959) have confirmed Sperry's finding that, after severance of the optic nerve, regeneration results in a restoration of the point-to-point correspondence as indicated by visuo-motor performance, and have also established that the connections are formed with the correct layers. Furthermore, Parriss (1963) has shown that learned shape discriminations are retained after severance and regeneration of the optic nerves in toads.

Sperry (e.g. 1958, 1963) has thus proposed that the detailed course of the development of many parts of the nervous system depends on specific chemical affinities between different classes of neurones. Neuronal and synaptic specificity is regarded as a refinement of the cruder processes of induction, embryonic fields, and other basic processes known from the experimental embryology of organ systems; and the neuro-chemical differentiation of the nervous system which is involved is seen as a refinement of that revealed by the selective action of stains, drugs, poisons, and so on.

It is worth adding that even after Sperry's elegant analysis we cannot say that the visual responses of the Salamander are independent of the influences of all visual experience: in other amphibians proper retinal functioning is known to depend on exposure to light (Knoll, 1953). It must also be emphasized that though the principle of specific chemical affinities may have wide applicability throughout the vertebrates, the particular manner in which the sensory-motor system develops varies between phyla. Regeneration does not occur to the same extent in higher vertebrates: the adaptability found more in early stages than later, and more in lower vertebrates than higher, parallels the evidence for tissue plasticity in regeneration.

21.2. Perception of Space and Pattern Vision in Birds and Mammals

The role of experience in the development of perceptual abilities has also been studied by rearing animals in the partial or total absence of sensory input. This work, which was stimulated largely by Hebb (1949), has been concerned especially with the perceptual abilities of mammals and birds reared in darkness or without patterned visual stimulation. Such studies are not always easy to interpret since the deprivation may result in a degree of retinal degeneration which, though significant, is too subtle to detect histologically (Brattgård, 1952; Weiskrantz, 1958; Riesen, 1958). This necessity for the retina to have adequate exposure to light for it to function appropriately is not limited to the higher mammals, but holds also for amphibian tadpoles (Knoll, 1953). The deprivation may affect other functions in addition to perception, the consequences being difficult to separate (*see* below). If these difficulties are borne in mind, however, some interesting conclusions can be drawn.

After birds are reared under such conditions of sensory or perceptual deprivation simple reflex responses which do not require localization in space, such as the pupillary reflex, may be unaffected. Mowrer (1936) sewed together the eyelids of pigeon squabs before they had opened. When the lids were opened at six weeks, these birds showed normal pupillary responses, but their optokinetic nystagmus, visual startle responses and ability to avoid objects, were impaired. Their behaviour became normal after 3 days in the light. In this case retinal degeneration was at least a possibility: Siegel (1953a, b) found no deficiencies in the optokinetic responses of doves reared for two months with their eyes merely covered by translucent hoods.

Space perception in birds has been studied by using the pecking response as an indicator of the bird's ability. Chicks reared in darkness for a few days after hatching show a rapid improvement in pecking accuracy, which soon reaches the level of controls (p. 340). Only if the period in darkness is as long as a fortnight, and the birds are fed meanwhile from a spoon, does the pecking movement fail to develop at all (Padilla, 1935): this could be due to the interference of other responses, rather than to sensory/perceptual deficiencies.

Hess (1956b) used a more sophisticated technique than complete visual deprivation. Newly hatched chickens were fitted with hoods, some of which had prisms which displaced the visual field 7 degrees to right or left, while in the control animals plane glass was used. In tests of pecking accuracy, the control animals pecked in a pattern centring round the target, while the patterns of the experimentals were displaced laterally by 7 degrees. There was little evidence for improvement in lateral accuracy with practice over the first 3–4 days of life. In another experiment, Hess allowed chickens normal use of one eye or the other on alternate days, but never both together. Their pecking behaviour was tested when the chicks were 2–3 months old and were wearing binocular prisms. The prisms were such that, if the chick was to use binocular clues to estimate the distance of objects at which it was pecking, it would peck short of the object. Since all nine animals tested did in fact peck short, the use of binocular clues for assessing distance seems not to depend upon binocular experience (but *see* p. 347). As always, we must bear in mind the limited nature of such negative conclusions. We still know nothing about the role of other types of experience through the same or other modalities in the development of the chick's powers of visual perception.

That the distance perception of chicks is largely independent of visual experience has also been shown by a quite different method. On the assumption that depth perception is a special case of distance perception, Gibson *et al.* (1960), Walk *et al.* (1961), and Walk (1965) confronted the young of various species with an apparent cliff, and assessed whether or not they would move in such a way that, had it been real, they would have fallen over it. Their "visual cliff" apparatus consisted of glass raised above the floor, across the centre of which was laid a board. On one side of the board a sheet of patterned material was placed immediately underneath the glass (the "shallow" side), while on the other side a sheet of similar material was placed on the floor (the "deep" side). The animal was placed centrally on the board, and the number of occasions on which it moved out on to each side counted. Chicks tested 24 hours after hatching—and chicks do not normally move far from their mother before this age—invariably left the board on the shallow side, turning away from the deep side. The same result was obtained when the chicks were reared in darkness for 24 hours and tested on exposure to light immediately afterwards (Shinkman, 1963).

Of the other species tested on the visual cliff, nearly all were found to avoid the deep side when tested at the age when they normally begin to move about freely—kids and lambs at one day, kittens at four weeks, human babies at 6–14 months. Rats also showed a clear preference for the shallow side, but only if the board was raised so that the glass was out of reach of their vibrissae. Even after being reared for the first 90 days in darkness rats performed as well as normally reared controls on the visual cliff apparatus. Rhesus monkeys showed a preference for the shallow side from 3 days of age (Rosenblum *et al.* 1963), and human infants from the age at which they first started to crawl. Only turtles failed to show a near-100 per cent preference for the shallow side.

In chicks, at any rate, binocular vision is not essential for discrimination between "deep" and "shallow" sides (Schiffman *et al.*, 1963). The two most probable sensory features on which this depth perception could depend seem to be pattern density, distance decreasing the retinal size and spacing of the pattern elements, and motion parallax, near elements moving more rapidly across the field of vision than distant ones. Gibson *et al.* (1960) concluded for both day-old chicks and rats that motion parallax is of primary importance. However, when rats were tested on a visual cliff apparatus with $\frac{1}{4}$-inch squares on one side and $\frac{3}{4}$-inch squares on the other, the patterns being placed immediately under the glass in each case, light-reared animals went only on to the large pattern. Dark-reared animals showed no such preference at first, but did so after 24 hours' experience of light. Thus pattern density also can provide a basis for depth discrimination, but the response is apparently acquired by experience (cf. Lashley et al., 1934; see also Shinkman, 1962). The position is far from clear, however, for Schiffman et al. (1963) could find no support for the view that the preference for the larger of two patterns is due to a learned association between largeness and closeness. Furthermore, Shinkman (1963), working with chicks, has shown that cues requiring focusing are critical for discriminating between the deep and shallow sides, while binocular and motion parallax cues are not. Kittens can perform correctly on the visual cliff when using only one eye, provided that eye has previously received adequate use during active self-produced locomotion: if the eye has been used only during passive movement it fails to mediate normal visually guided behaviour. From this observation Held and Hein (in press) argue that the kittens can discriminate deep and shallow sides during self-induced movement, the relationship between movement and displacement of the retinal image being interpreted as distance of the object from the eye. Other experiments are discussed in detailed reviews by Gibson et al. (1960) and Walk (1965).

Although chicks with only very brief visual experience show a preference for the shallow side, pre-exposure to the deep side can reduce the extent to which the chicks avoid it (Tallarico et al., 1964). In other species, however, experience plays a much greater role. As noted above, rats choose the larger of two chequered patterns in a visual cliff apparatus only after a day's exposure to light. When reared in the dark and tested on the visual cliff apparatus at 27 days, kittens show no side preference: only after a week of visual experience does their performance equal that of normally reared controls (Gibson et al., 1960).

The amount of visual experience necessary for distance perception by kittens has been determined with some accuracy by Munro et al. (in Riesen, 1961), using a different response. When a kitten is held in the hands and lowered towards a surface, the forepaws are extended before bodily contact with the surface occurs. Under normal conditions of rearing this "visual placing" first appears at 22–28 days. In this study litters were divided between experimental and control groups, all being allowed normal indoor lighting for the first 18 days of life. Both groups were then placed on a daily schedule of 23 hours darkness and 1 hour light. During this hour in the light, the experimental kittens wore hoods which diffused the light. The controls were tested daily for visual placing. On the day following the appearance of visual placing in a control animal (27–29 days) its experimental litter-mates were unhooded and tested during the hour of light. Every one of the 15 animals tested gave its first visual placing response after 5 hours in the patterned light, even though in some cases the 5 hours was given continuously instead of at 1 hour per day.

The development of visual responsiveness and of visuo-motor control thus depends on light more in kittens than in chickens. In Chimpanzees visual deprivation has even more severe effects. Riesen (e.g. 1958) found marked visual deficiencies in a Chimpanzee which was reared in darkness except for 90 minutes light each day. At $7\frac{1}{2}$ months it was given slowly increasing periods in daylight for 10 days. During this period there were frequent episodes of nystagmus and squint, lack of eyeblink to movement in the visual field, and also deficiencies in visual fixation and pursuit. Eyeblinks were first observed on the 9th day of normal exposure to visual stimuli, and fixation and pursuit responses were first seen on the 11th: the deficiencies subsided during the following weeks. Comparable data were obtained from a number of other animals suffering various degrees of visual deprivation. Of special interest was an animal confined in a supine position during the daily 90-minutes period when it was allowed to see the room. Although more advanced in these responses than animals reared in diffuse light only or in total darkness, it was less advanced than an animal given an equal period of light but allowed to move around freely (cf. pp. 351-7).

Turning to studies specifically of pattern discrimination, some experiments suggest that early perceptual deprivation has only a minor effect in birds and lower mammals. Pastore (1958, 1959) reports that ducklings develop abilities for form perception, as well as for size constancy and brightness constancy, independently of visual experience. Siegel (1953a, b) reared doves with trans-lucent goggles and found that they subsequently took rather longer to learn to discriminate shapes than did normally reared controls. Early rearing in dark-ness has only a slight effect on rats (Hebb, 1937a, b). These results must be considered together with others mentioned later on the effects of richness of the early environment (pp. 393-4).

In higher mammals, being reared under conditions of sensory deprivation may result in marked deficiencies in form vision. Just as the performance of cats on the visual cliff apparatus is impaired by rearing in darkness, so also do they take longer than normally reared animals to discriminate patterns: discrimina-tion of light intensities is, however, not affected (Riesen, 1960; Riesen *et al.*, 1959). Similar effects have been found in primates (Chow *et al.*, 1955, Riesen, 1958, 1961; refs. in Fantz, 1965). Although form perception in Rhesus Monkeys depends on processes which are completed in the first 3 weeks of life (Zimmermann, 1961), Chimpanzees subjected to visual deprivation develop pattern and form vision more gradually. The animal referred to above learnt to discriminate horizontal from vertical striations rapidly, but discrimination of human faces took much longer: unlike normally reared infants of similar age, it was not upset by being fed by a stranger during the period after it was first exposed to the light.

The relevance of visual deprivation experiments for the development of perception in normal animals has, however, recently been questioned by Fantz (1965). He argues that visual deprivation does not prevent visual development, but alters its course, leading not only to neural deterioration but also oculo-motor abnormalities, excessive arousal with novel stimulation, the development of abnormal competing habits, and disturbance of visual preferences. Instead, Fantz used the relative duration of visual fixation on different targets to assess visual preferences: where preferences occurred, they were taken to indicate discrimination. His experiments indicated that infant Rhesus monkeys, Chimpanzees and humans can discriminate patterns without opportunity for visual learning, and show strong preferences for particular visual targets from birth (e.g. Fantz, 1958). Although it has been argued that these results could be due in part to intensity discrimination at a retinal level (Sackett, 1963), they certainly demand re-examination of the results of visual deprivation experiments.

In any case, there is no dispute that pattern vision normally improves progressively (Fantz et al., 1962), differential fixation experiments revealing an increasing interest in complex patterns and solid objects. Congenitally blind human subjects whose sight is restored in adulthood show grave disturbances in spatial orientation. It is clear, therefore, that many aspects of visual perception in man depend on visual experience (von Senden, 1932; Gregory et al., 1963). There is also evidence that stimulation through other modalities, such as that provided by handling, may influence the development of visual abilities and visuo-motor skills (White, 1963).

The functional equivalence of the two eyes can be assessed by training an animal on a visual discrimination task with one eye covered, and then testing it with that eye exposed and the other eye covered. In ducks there is evidence that inter-ocular transfer does not require previous joint experience with both eyes in patterned light (Moltz et al., 1961, 1962): this is presumably related to the complete decussation at the optic chiasma and the absence of a corpus callosum in birds. In higher mammals, which have a corpus callosum, complete and immediate transfer does not occur unless both eyes have had considerable simultaneous exposure to patterned light (e.g. Riesen, 1958). Monocularly deprived cats and Chimpanzees show marked deficiencies on the deprived side, even though performance with the other eye is normal: the usual equivalence between the two eyes does not develop, a discrimination habit learnt with one eye remaining specific to that eye. Since performance through the non-deprived eye was not impaired, these results incidentally also show that the form blindness produced in deprivation experiments is not an artefact of motivational origin.

In order to assess the effects of deprivation in another sensory modality, Nissen et al. (1951) kept a Chimpanzee with its arms and legs enclosed in cardboard cylinders for 30 months, starting at the age of 4 weeks. When the cylinders were finally removed the animal showed marked tactile-kinaesthetic disabilities in spatial orientation; for instance only after considerable fumbling and exploration was it able to touch a stimulated point on its skin. Walking and sitting postures were also abnormal, grooming was absent, and when picked up the animal did not cling to the keeper. Its abilities for visual discrimination were normal.

Another experimental approach to this problem, which avoids the disadvantages of drastic sensory deprivation, depends on controlling the complexity of the environment. As stressed by Hebb (1949), early experience might be expected to have more beneficial effects, the greater its diversity. A number of workers have therefore assessed the importance of the richness of the early environment for the development of perceptual abilities and the learning which depends on them. In some of these experiments fairly complex tests, like maze learning, have been used. For instance, rats reared in a spacious environment subsequently perform better than rats kept in a restricted environment when tested in a maze: young rats reared for a period in a large space are superior to rats kept at first in a small cage and then placed in a larger cage for a similar period at a later age (Hymovitch, 1952). This question is considered further on pp. 393-4.

Of more interest in the present context are studies in which the effects of early experience are assessed by rather simpler tasks; for instance by a test of discrimination learning. Such studies have revealed an effect of early visual experience on the ability to discriminate between patterns, which is often ascribed to "perceptual learning" (Gibson et al., 1955). Thorpe (1963a) has stressed its possible importance at all phyletic levels.

Perceptual learning appears to be independent of conventional reward. Although rats reared in darkness up to 96 days of age can learn to discriminate between a circle and a triangle (Gibson et al., 1959), early experience of the forms without differential reinforcement increases the ease with which learning occurs (Gibson et al., 1956). The effect is not very consistent, and depends closely on the experimental conditions. In particular, experience of forms made from metal cut-outs is effective, but when the same forms are merely painted on a rectangular background, the early experience has little influence on subsequent discrimination learning. Gibson et al. (1959) suggested that the difference lies in the "attention-getting" properties of the stimulus, the cut-outs having depth at their edges. Gibson also found that prior exposure to only one of the test patterns led to an improvement in discrimination learning. The treatment was at least as effective if the previously exposed pattern was the negative one in the discrimination as if it was the positive (Gibson et al., 1958). The effect thus seems more easily described in terms of a learning of the properties of the stimulus than in terms of the formation of a positive stimulus-response association.

An experiment by Michels et al. (1958) goes further than this in suggesting that experience may involve a degree of abstraction of stimulus properties. They studied the effects of different types of visual experience on the ability of rats to discriminate the magnitude (successively, but in varying order, brightness, area and height) and form of different stimuli. Animals reared in the dark and given visual experience only during testing showed a gradual improvement on the magnitude problems, but were inferior to the light-reared animals on all tests of visual discrimination. The improvement in the magnitude problems, each of which was essentially novel, was interpreted by the authors as indicating that the animals responded not simply to a brightness, size or light difference, but to differences in stimulus magnitude as such.

The view that perceptual learning involves a learning of the various properties of the stimulus is also supported by experiments in which access to some aspects of the stimulus is controlled. For instance, Meier *et al.* (1959) studied the performance in a tactile-visual discrimination between three-dimensional forms (a cross and a triangle) of rats reared in different ways. Four groups differing in the cages in which they were reared for the first 155–162 days of life were used in this study:

1. Visual-tactual experience group. The cage had sides of grey plywood, with a number of three-dimensional figures.
2. Visual experience only. As Group 1 but the forms were placed behind plate glass.
3. Minimum experience group. As Groups 1 and 2, but free of regular stimulus forms.
4. Control group. The cage had continuous visual access to the laboratory.

In testing, which was started after a few days in standard laboratory cages, Group 1 was superior to Group 2, and Group 2 to Group 3. Group 2 was indistinguishable from Group 4. These results are explained on the hypothesis that the animal must first learn to differentiate the stimuli, qua stimuli; that is, to differentiate tactual and visual cues related to the edges and angles of the forms. They must then learn which of the objects was associated with food and which was not. Group 1 had already accomplished the first phase at the time of testing, and thus had to complete only the second. Group 2 could distinguish the objects only visually, and thus had to learn the tactile differentiation in addition to the second phase. Group 3 had to accomplish both phases. Presumably, the visual stimuli from the room permitted Group 4 to reach a stage similar to that of Group 2. The authors believe that the first stage of learning is independent of reinforcement. This matter is referred to again in Chapter 26.

An indication that *mere* exposure to the stimuli itself is not enough for perceptual development is contained in one of Riesen's experiments with Chimpanzees, mentioned above: an animal which was not permitted to move about in a visual world was deficient by comparison with animals which were (*see* p. 348).   Riesen *et al.* (1959) showed that locomotion or manipulation was essential for perceptual development. Kittens reared in holders but permitted visual stimulation in a patterned environment showed deficiencies in visually guided behaviour compared with normally reared littermates. Comparable deficits were found in kittens allowed free movement but wearing light-diffusing hoods over their eyes. However, such deficiencies in animals reared with patterned visual stimulation but limited mobility may not occur if the discrimination task does not involve a visually guided response (e.g. Meyers *et al.*, 1964; *see also* Epstein, 1964).

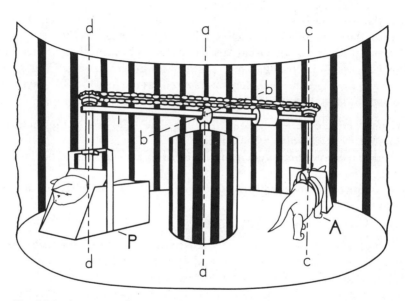

Fig. 21.2. Apparatus for equating motion and the consequent visual feedback for an actively moving, *A*, and a passively moved, *P*, kitten. (*After Held and Hein, 1963.*)

Such experiments are open to interpretation in two ways. Riesen (1961), following up Hebb's earlier suggestions, supposes that patterned visual stimulation is important in the development of visually guided behaviour because of the opportunity it offers for developing sensory-sensory associations, both within and between sensory modalities. On this view, the environment of the confined kittens, though patterned, provided insufficient variation in visual stimulation. Another possibility is that it is not merely the magnitude of the stimulus variation that is important, but whether or not it is self-induced. To investigate this, Held *et al.* (1963) equated the variation in stimulation between the confined and non-confined groups. The groups thus differed primarily in the cause of the variation: in one case it was a consequence of the animal's own locomotion, while in the other it was not. This was achieved by using the apparatus shown in Fig. 21.2. The movements of the confined cat B about the axis of its own box d—d and about the main axis a—a were controlled by the movements of the restrained but unconfined cat A: visual stimulation was a feedback consequence of its own movement for A, but largely the result of equivalent passive movement for the other. The kittens were reared initially in the dark and placed in the apparatus for a daily exposure period beginning between 8 and 12 weeks of age. Subsequently the kittens were tested on a visual cliff apparatus (*see* p. 346) and for visual paw placing (p. 347). The actively moving animals were uniformly superior. In a later experiment Held and Hein (in press) showed that this difference in abilities for space perception between kittens reared under conditions of active and passive movement could be induced also between the two eyes of the same kitten. When kittens were reared with one eye open in active locomotion, and the other impassive, the "active" eye was found to mediate normal visually guided behaviour but the "passive" eye failed to do so. Such results suggest that the role of experience in the development of visual perception cannot be interpreted solely in terms of S-S associations, as suggested by Hebb (1949) and Riesen (1958): S-R-S sequences seem also to be involved (Held, 1961; *see also* Meyers, 1964).

This view is consistent with observations on the development of behaviour in human children by Piaget (1952, 1955) and Gesell (1954). For instance, Piaget found that for a child of three or four months there was no integration of the stimuli presented by an object through different sensory modalities. At 5–6 months the visual and tactile aspects of objects began to be coordinated, and Piaget describes the differentiation between "near space" which can be touched and "distant space" which cannot. Throughout this and later stages in the development of visuo-motor behaviour the role of interaction between the child and its environment by movement of eyes, limbs and body is constantly apparent.

At this point we may refer again to the discussion of the role of feedback stimulation in the perception of relative motion (p. 74). Even simple organisms behave differently to relative movement of the environment which is caused by movement of their own bodies and that which depends on movement of objects in the environment. To account for this, von Holst *et al.* (1950) suggested that the consequences of movement (reafferent stimulation) are compared with a representation of the required movement (efference copy or corollary discharge) centrally, further action depending on the results of this comparison (*see* p. 77). But here a further question is raised. How is it that the corollary discharge from the efferent system resulting from a command to, say, move the eyes 10 degrees to the right, and the reafference from a shift of 10 degrees of the image on the retina, exactly balance each other? Do the growth processes of the organism determine the coding of the messages in each case in such a manner that they do just balance?

That this is not the case in human subjects can be demonstrated quite readily by experimental methods which disturb the reafference. These fall into three main groups (Held, 1961; Teuber, 1960, 1961; Hein *et al.*, 1962; and references cited).

1. *Rearrangement*. If the retinal image is shifted by a wedge prism, there is an apparent displacement of objects in the visual field. This results in various types of sensory-motor discoordination; for instance the subject is unable to put his finger accurately on an object which he sees. With prolonged exposure, however, there is considerable readjustment, and in a matter of hours most of the errors disappear. Readjustment occurs, at any rate to some degree, even when the subject wears spectacles which produce complete inversion of the retinal image (Stratton, 1897; Köhler, 1951).

This readjustment depends on a comparison between the intended movement (Sollwert) and reafferent stimulation, that is, the subject must make voluntary movements and witness their results. For instance, if subjects wear prisms which displace their visual field laterally, considerable readjustment occurs if the subject is allowed to walk about for an hour, but not if he is pushed about for a similar period in a wheelchair. Similar results are obtained when hand-eye coordination is assessed in subjects wearing prismatic spectacles. Considerable readjustment occurs if they are allowed to move their arms themselves, but not if their arms are moved passively an equivalent amount (Held *et al.*, 1958; Held *et al.*, 1961).

2. *Disarrangement*. In the experiments described above the rearrangement results in a regular relation between the reafference actually received and the reafference which would have been received without experimental interference. Under these conditions readjustment occurs. It is possible, however, to arrange for the discrepancy not to be predictable in this way. Cohen *et al.* (cited by Held, 1961) used a prism which varied continuously in power, so that the image was displaced over a range of positions, and at any particular time the deviation produced by the prism was unpredictable. The prism produced larger displacements in the horizontal than in the vertical dimension. Under these conditions measures of hand-eye coordination showed no readjustment, with very considerable errors in the horizontal dimension but much smaller ones in the vertical dimension.

3. *Deprivation*. In these experiments a marked reduction in sensory input is produced. Typically subjects are confined in soundproof an-echoic chambers or in small rooms with a continuous masking noise. The conditions are stabilized, and the subjects may be required to lie down while wearing translucent spectacles and cardboard cuffs to reduce tactile stimulation (e.g. Bexton *et al.*, 1954; Doane *et al.* 1959; Solomon *et al.*, 1961 and references cited). We have already considered some aspects of the results of such experiments (p. 157): here we may note that they produced marked perceptual after-effects which

lasted for minutes or hours. It is characteristic of these effects that they are variable and disorderly: not only is there loss of perceptual constancies and dysfunction of colour vision, but shapes are distorted and unstable, with straight edges or lines appearing curved and wavering (Freedman, 1961). The results of deprivation experiments thus contrast with those of rearrangement experiments, for the after-effects of the latter are relatively regular and predictable. In both cases, however, the time courses of recovery are about the same (Held, 1961).

Such results can be interpreted in terms of a body-schema (Head, 1920), an integrated consequence of previous perceptions and memories concerned with the relations between the parts of the subject's body and its relations to the external world (*see* critical discussion by Oldfield *et al.*, 1942a, b). We may suppose that the organism's operations with respect to the external world are guided in accordance with such a schema. In rearrangement experiments like those described earlier the new sensory field is isometric with the old one, but shifted along one or more dimensions. Adjustment occurs as a result of modifications of the schema to fit the new conditions. Under conditions of deprivation, however, regularities in the sensory input are reduced; the organism has a more or less undifferentiated and homogeneous environment. That the important factor is the absence of regularities in the sensory input, rather than a reduction in the level of input itself, is indicated by the finding that similar perceptual disturbances occur with diffuse light, no light, and randomly flashing lights. Since we cannot suppose the schema to be forgotten during a few hours of deprivation, the degeneration which occurs may well be the consequence of attempts, inevitably unsuccessful, to fit the schema to the new conditions (Freedman, 1961).

Using the language of control systems, Held (1961; Hein *et al.*, 1962) has produced an elaboration of the von Holst/Mittelstaedt model (Fig. 21.3) which encompasses the results of these experiments. This involves the addition to the reafference model of a "correlation storage unit" where traces of previous combinations of concurrent efferent and reafferent signals are retained. The correlated discharge of the efferent system is supposed to select from the correlation unit the trace combination containing the identical efferent part and to activate the corresponding reafferent trace. This is sent to the comparator for comparison with the current reafferent signal. The outcome of this determines perception and/or further performance.*

Under conditions of rearrangement, more than one efferent correlated discharge/reafferent combination will be available for selection from the storage

* There is a certain formal similarity here to Tolman's "means-end-readinesses". He writes: "When an *instance* of an *S* is presented, there tends to be released an expectancy . . . that an instance of the kind of performance symbolized by *r*, will lead to an instance of *s*. . . ." (Tolman, 1959).

unit by any particular effector discharge. Since readjustment occurs, selection is presumably weighted by how recently the combinations were stored. With constant rearrangement, selection of the old combinations gradually ceases. Under conditions of disarrangement or deprivation, however, a number of combinations of equal weight will be available for selection from storage. Thus any one of a number of reafferent signals may be sent to the comparator, whose result will be ambiguous. The model thus accounts for: (1) the possibility of readjustments under conditions of stable rearrangement, (2) the lack of readjustment under unstable or deprived conditions, and (3) the necessity for reafference if readjustment is to occur (*see also* Held and Freedman, 1963).

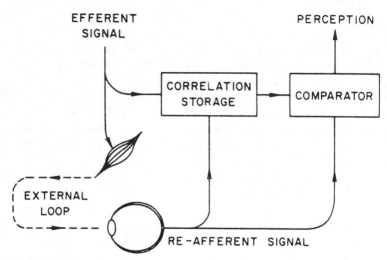

Fig. 21.3. Schematized process assumed to underlie the consequences of neonatal development, rearrangement, disarrangement and deprivation. (*After Hein and Held, 1962.*)

These experiments have been concerned largely with humans, however, and we know very little about the extent to which such readjustments are possible in the adults of other higher vertebrates. It may well be that, for most species, there is no need to postulate a correlation storage unit: much of the available information for invertebrates (e.g. Mittelstaedt, 1949; Wells, 1962b) and lower vertebrates (e.g. Sperry, 1943, 1950, 1951) indicates that little readjustment occurs after rearrangement of the sensory-motor systems (p. 324). However, some fish show gradual readjustment to disturbances of the sensory inflow used in orientation to gravity and light (von Holst, 1950b), and others show progressive changes in orientation with growth which must be due to a progressive change in the gravity feedback system (Braemar *et al.*, 1958; *see also* p. 125). The effects of rearing mammals under conditions of sensory deprivation indicate that in many species at least sensory-motor coordination is influenced by early experience: adjustment may thus be possible in adult life in the same way as in man.

In these studies the role of experience in the integration of motor output with sensory feedback, including that involved in space perception, is clear. Nevertheless, as we have seen (p. 349), a limited degree of form vision may be present independently of experience. Held and Hein (in press) thus suggest that form vision in higher mammals may depend on more than one mechanism. There may be both an analyser system whose functioning is relatively independent of experience and which is responsible for a rudimentary form vision, and a more modifiable mechanism whose functioning involves the integration of visual feedback with motor output. They suggest further that the latter is important when the orientation of the animal to the environment plays a role. A particular case is the recognition of objects despite change in perspective (shape constancy), which depends on an assessment of spatial relationships between object and eye.

In conclusion, we see that there are great differences between lower and higher vertebrates in the role of early experience in the development of perceptual abilities. In the lower forms many of the patterns of orientation in visual space can be accounted for in terms of the maturation of nervous connections, though some exposure to light may be necessary for proper retinal functioning. In the higher forms not only does early experience have far-reaching effects, but perception is also adjusted in the light of immediately preceding experience: at any one moment perception must be a consequence of many and diverse effects from the remote and recent past. Presumably, the maturational processes of nerve growth are basically similar in the higher and lower species: just why (causally and functionally) there is this difference in plasticity is not clear.

21.3. Summary

1. The orientation of visuo-motor responses in lower vertebrates depends on orderly connections between retina and brain. After severance of the optic tract, rotation of the retina, and subsequent regeneration of the optic pathways, the visuo-motor responses of salamanders are appropriate to the point on the retina stimulated, and not to the location of the prey in space. This indicates that neurones re-establish functional connections similar to those existing before the operation. A mechanism involving specific chemical affinities between neurones has been suggested. Similar findings have been made with other responses and other sensory modalities.
2. Visual experience is not essential for the development of space perception in chicks, as shown by pecking accuracy or performance on the visual cliff.
3. In kittens, and even more in primates, distance perception does depend on visual experience.
4. Simple pattern discrimination is affected only slightly by lack of visual experience in pigeons and rats, but markedly in Chimpanzees.
5. Binocular equivalence depends on binocular experience in cats and Chimpanzees, but not in ducks.

6. The richness of the early environment affects the subsequent performance of rats in form discrimination and maze running. The "perceptual learning" by which early experience influences later ability for pattern discrimination is independent of conventional reward.

7. In kittens, the experience necessary for the development of perceptual abilities does not involve merely the development of S–S connections, but requires active participation by the subject. The learning is best described as S–R–S.

8. Perception of space in human subjects can be upset by a number of techniques which disturb the feedback stimulation received from self-initiated movement. The data from such experiments can be described by a modification of the von Holst-Mittelstaedt reafference model.

22

Development of Stimulus-Response Relations

Although some responses can be elicited by a very wide range of stimuli and some only by very specific ones, in each case it is possible to delimit the effective ones with some degree of precision (Chapter 4). In vertebrates these stimulus-response relations may be strongly influenced by preceding experience. Since a detailed discussion of the learning processes involved is beyond the scope of this book, attention will be focused on stimulus-response relations in which learning initially plays only a minor part, and on the manner in which those seen in the adult animal develop from them.

22.1. Appropriate Responsiveness Independent of Experience in that Context

In the first place, there are many cases in which stimuli are responded to appropriately the first time that they are perceived. If, for instance, the high-pitched whistle given by adult Great Tits on the approach of a flying predator is heard by 12-day-old nestling Great Tits which have been reared by hand away from their kind, they will immediately crouch and freeze (Barraud, 1961). A Chaffinch 30 days old, which has never seen an owl, will give the mobbing response on the first occasion that an owl is presented to it (Hinde, 1954a). Such cases are not limited to very young individuals. The red breast of the male Chaffinch is important in intra-species fighting. Females, whose breasts are the natural grey-brown, are dominated by females whose breasts have been dyed red. A similar avoidance of females with dyed breasts is shown even by females reared by hand away from males, so it is not acquired as a result of social experience (Marler, 1955; *see also* E. Cullen, 1960).

It is, of course, not a complete explanation of the developmental problem to say that, in such cases, the appropriate response is "unlearnt". The observations merely delimit the problem—previous experience in the specific situation is not essential for the appropriate response.

22.2. Extent of Initial Diversity of Effective Objects

In some cases not only does the naturally occurring object evoke the appropriate response on the first occasion it is presented, but experiment reveals a considerable degree of stimulus specificity in responsiveness. For instance, Hess (1956a) measured the frequency with which young chicks and ducklings would peck at differently coloured chips. Although they had had virtually no previous visual experience, and were not rewarded for pecking, clear preferences for certain of the chips were shown. These were related to the wavelengths of the colours on the chips rather than to their reflectance or purity, the chicks showing a bimodal preference in the orange and blue regions and the ducklings a single sharp peak in the green (Fig. 22.1). In each species, therefore, there was differential responsiveness to colour.

On the other hand, it is important to emphasize that the range of effective stimulus situations is usually greater for a naive animal than an experienced

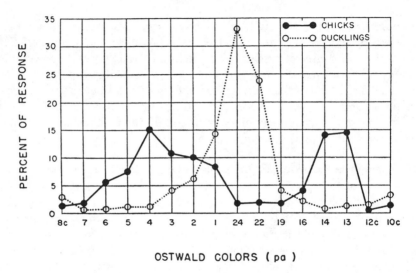

OSTWALD COLORS (pa)

Fig. 22.1. Percentage of total pecks delivered by chicks and ducklings to each of 16 colours. (*After Hess, 1956a.*)

one. The species-characteristic prey-catching response of the newly-metamorphosed Clawed Toad (*Xenopus laevis*) is elicited even by a jet of water directed against the side of the body, or a small moving dot of light (Eibl-Eibesfeldt, 1962). Similarly, while Tinbergen *et al.*, in their study of begging in young thrushes (p. 104), analysed the essentials of the stimulus situation eliciting begging, it is also known that when a young passerine first opens its eyes it will in fact beg to a very wide range of objects, including a spatula or a pair of forceps. A few days later the response can be elicited only by the object to which the bird is accustomed (*see also* Schaller *et al.*, 1961). Many of the behaviour patterns used subsequently in reproduction by passerine birds appear erratically in fledglings a few weeks old in response to stimulus situations which would be quite inadequate in the adult (personal observation).

Similarly, some of the responses of the human baby can initially be elicited by diverse stimuli. The case of smiling has been studied by Ahrens (1954). After an initial stage in which the baby smiles "spontaneously", there is a period during which two black dots on a white oval background, and a wide variety of masks, are at least as effective as a human face. Later, other features such as eyebrows, mouth and so on, become necessary; and, later still, masks become ineffective and only a human face will elicit smiling. By the middle of the first year only one or two familiar faces, such as that of the mother, will elicit smiling, though, when yet older, the range of individuals to whom the baby will smile is again extended (Ambrose, 1960). A comparable example is provided by the sucking behaviour of kittens. Up to four days of age a kitten will suckle from any receptive mother, but after 6 days it will suckle only from its own mother, unless it is made extremely hungry. At 20–25 days, however, it will once again suckle from strange mothers (Rosenblatt, personal communication). In such cases it is often difficult to determine whether the diversity of stimulus situations eliciting a response in a young animal is due to its inability to distinguish them (i.e. lack of development of the sensory/ perceptual apparatus), or to a lack of specificity in the stimuli pertinent to the particular response, or to response to a common feature of stimulus situations divergent in other respects.

In line with this last possibility, Schneirla (1959, 1965) has suggested that the essential aspects of the stimulation for many responses of young organisms are quantitative rather than qualitative. They tend to approach, with part or all of the body, sources of stimulation which are quantitatively low, regular and limited in range of magnitude, and withdraw from those which produce inputs which are high, irregular and of extensive ranges (*see also* Andrew, 1964b). On this view, as the intensity of stimulation is increased from zero it first becomes more effective in eliciting a full approach, but, beyond a certain intensity, withdrawal becomes more likely. The important aspect of the stimulus is thus a quantitative one, qualitative differences becoming significant only later.

For instance, newly hatched chickens are attracted by a wide range of repetitive sounds (Collias *et al.*, 1953) as well as by moving objects and visual patterns (e.g. Smith, F. V., 1962), and are caused to withdraw and give distress calls by a wide range of intense stimuli through various modalities, including temperature (e.g. Collias, 1952; Salzen, 1962; Kruijt, 1964). Similarly, in many amphibians such as the toad (*Bufo bufo*), small stimulus objects elicit tongue-flicking, and somewhat larger objects a body lunge as well, but objects larger still induce withdrawal (Eibl-Eibesfeldt, 1951b). Again, many of the stimulus characters important in eliciting pecking from nidifugous birds seem to involve primarily quantitative features. Thus, in addition to colour (*see* above) the results of Rheingold *et al.* (1957) suggest that brightness of the reflecting surface may also be an important variable. Some (Engelmann, 1941;

Fantz, 1957) but not all (Curtius, 1954) workers find that rounded shapes are more effective in eliciting pecking than other shapes: differential responsiveness is maintained if pecking experience is unreinforced. Since round shapes are known to be especially conspicuous to a wide range of vertebrates, these characters may be effective through their quantitative contribution to visual stimulation rather than their particular qualitative characters (Schneirla, 1965). Curtius, *loc. cit.*, however, also found that newly hatched Lapwings (*Vanellus vanellus*), chicks, and turkeys showed size preferences in their pecking response to models, and that these size preferences were related to their bill sizes, a result perhaps less easy to explain in simple quantitative terms. Again, as we saw earlier (p. 63), Schneirla interprets the various stimulus characters which Tinbergen *et al.* (1950) found to elicit pecking from Herring Gull chicks (*see* pp. 46-7) on the same principle, namely, that they owe their effectiveness to the quantitative intensity of visual stimulation they produce. He also interprets withdrawal responses in the same way: the effectiveness of a dark object moving overhead in eliciting fleeing from nidifugous birds is regarded as due not to any qualitative characters of shape (Schleidt, 1961; Müller, 1961), but to the sudden change in retinal stimulation (*see also* p. 82 and Melzack *et al.*, 1959; McNiven, 1960).

On the basis of such examples, Schneirla conceives of the mechanisms underlying approach responses in the young organism as depending on a system activated by weak sensory input and involving both central and autonomic nervous systems. The continuing "tonic" activity in these systems forms the basis of normal functioning. When weak stimuli are encountered in pre- and early post-natal development the system is further but briefly aroused and there is a "phasic" response. This phasic response has the same character as the tonic one, and, with repetition, phasic responses become tied to the tonic background. Thus at an early stage the neural mechanisms underlying approach come under the control of low intensity mechanical and visual impulses. Through tactual-proprioceptive and other feedback mechanisms, the phasic approach responses of head-advancing and turning-towards develop. At hatching or birth the control is extended to optic or other exteroceptors by a diffusion of neural impulses from these newly excited sensory systems, so that approach is elicited by a broad range of extrinsic stimuli which are equivalent in terms of their quantitative neural input. For example, the head-advancing movement of a chick embryo is at first elicited by mild tactile stimulation, but is later controlled visually, the generalization, in Schneirla's view, resulting from similar quantitative characteristics of the two types of stimulation. At this stage, through feedback effects, approach movements become phasic, and further experience leads to stimulus differentiation and response specialization.

Schneirla suggests that the withdrawal system, aroused by strong stimulation, does not have a tonic basis since by nature it interrupts the ongoing activity. Arousal of the withdrawal system produces only a phasic response, though this too may become tied to the tonic system as responses come to be elicited by qualitative rather than quantitative features of stimuli. The with-drawal system, aroused by strong stimulation, arises later than the approach system, perhaps because strong stimulation is encountered less frequently.

Just how far Schneirla's generalizations can be taken remains to be seen: in many of the examples he cites, some qualitative differences between stimuli seem to be important in addition to quantitative ones. But Schneirla's theoriz-ing will certainly initiate an attack on the hitherto neglected early development of stimulus-response relations, and stimulate the collection of information to supplement the meagre data now available.

22.3. The Narrowing of the Range of Effective Stimuli

The lack of specificity in responsiveness does not persist. The range of stimuli eliciting each type of response becomes narrowed in the course of development (cf. James, 1892). Often the process is extremely rapid. Newly hatched domestic chicks and ducklings will peck at any spots which contrast with their backgrounds (although they prefer some colours to others; *see* above): they quickly learn, however, to deliver the majority of their pecks at potential food objects and to neglect others. Similarly, the gaping response of young Blackbirds is given initially to a very wide range of auditory stimuli, but becomes narrowed by learning so that, under natural circumstances, it is elicited only by the feeding notes of the bird's own mother (Messmer *et al.*, 1956). Tschanz (1959) has shown that young Guillemots (*Uria aalge*) learn to respond selectively to the calls of their own parents during the first few days of life, and Sladen (1955) has described how individual young Adelie penguins (*Pygoscelis adelias*) are called out from among the thousands in the crêche by their parents.

A narrowing in the range of effective stimuli is most likely to occur on the first occasions on which a response is given, but this does not mean that such effects are confined to early development. Dilger (1962) has shown that once some Lovebirds (*Agapornis*) have had experience in rearing their own young, they will not rear the young of other species with a differently coloured down. If, however, the eggs of another species are substituted for a female's first clutch, she will subsequently rear only nestlings of the species of her foster young. Similar data for some Cichlid fishes are given by Myrberg (1964): in some of these cases there is a greater facility for learning the characteristics of their own species than for learning those of others.

In many cases habituation plays an important role in narrowing the range of effective stimuli. If, as a consequence of frequent exposure to some of the initially adequate stimuli, these cease to be effective, others may remain so. The fleeing response of young nidifugous birds, normally elicited by flying predators, appears initially to be elicited by quite generalized stimuli, though the relationship between size and speed of movement, and also the sudden increase in apparent size which characterizes a swooping model, are important issues (McNiven, 1960; Müller, 1961). Later, shapes which are often seen lose their effectiveness. The earlier view that young turkeys respond differentially to a model shaped like a hawk (Fig. 4.5) and not to one shaped like a goose (e.g. Tinbergen, 1951) was apparently due to pre-experimental habituation to geese (Schleidt, 1961).*

Reciprocally, a narrowing of the range of effective stimuli can often be ascribed to the reinforcement associated with some stimuli and not others. Chicks continue to peck at stimuli which subsequently release the actions of grasping and swallowing, and cease to peck at those which do not. Young finches (Carduelinae and Fringillidae) at first show only a limited degree of preference between seeds, but after a while take mostly that kind of seed which they can de-husk most efficiently, obtaining the greatest kernel weight in the least time. Since the different species have beaks of different sizes, they come to prefer different sorts of seeds (Kear, 1962).

Habituation and reinforcement are also important in determining the range of stimuli effective for eliciting sexual behaviour. Hagamen *et al.* (1963) found that once a male cat had mated with a normally inadequate object such as a rabbit or a teddy-bear, it would continue to do so with no need even for occasional reinforcement with a real female. In their experiment no cat which had shown three complete mountings on one of the objects ever failed in a subsequent test (*see also* Valenstein *et al.*, 1957). Similarly, male Chaffinches which mounted a sub-optimal dummy usually continued to do so on successive days, while males which failed to mount showed progressively less interest in the model (Hinde, 1959c).

Another issue of importance in limiting responsiveness is the fear induced by strange situations; the range of objects which will elicit begging from a young passerine is reduced in part because those objects, with which it does not become familiar, subsequently induce avoidance responses.

Avoidance of strange situations implies a background of familiarity against which the strangeness is recognized. The role of experience in establishing this has been stressed especially by Hebb (e.g. 1946). Chimpanzees show signs of autonomic disturbance, aggression and fear when confronted by parts of a Chimpanzee's body, or by an anaesthetized Chimpanzee, and young Chimpanzees are disturbed by strangers. Both Chimpanzees which have been reared in darkness (*see* p. 348) and congenitally blind human patients who have had their vision restored (Dennis, 1934) initially show no such fear responses to strangers: the responses depend on previous learning. Similarly, kittens who

---

* Although Melzack *et al.* (1959) found a differential response to a hawk model in one of a series of tests on Mallard ducklings tested from 25 days of age, this could have been a consequence of preceding tests, and provides no substantial support for the view that young birds respond more to hawk-shaped models.

have been removed from their home cage for a while hiss and show clear evidence of fear of their mother and litter mates when returned (Rosenblatt *et al.*, 1961). Such cases are by no means confined to higher mammals (e.g. Thorpe, 1963a).

The influence of previous experience on avoidance behaviour is, however, complex. Fear induced by the unfamiliar depends on previous experience to build up a knowledge of the familiar, but by further experience the unfamiliar by definition ceases to be so. In addition, experience in a diverse environment may result in a reduction in the fear shown to strange objects. Thus 2-year-old Chimpanzees reared in captivity are timid in the presence of novel objects, and do not investigate or manipulate them to the same extent as do wild-raised Chimpanzees of a similar age. The difference is greater, the more severely restricted the conditions under which the laboratory-reared Chimpanzees are reared. It cannot be ascribed to deficient arousability, motor ability or discriminatory ability, and disappears if the animals are exposed to a richer environment (Menzel *et al.*, 1963).

22.4. Imprinting

This limitation of the range of stimuli capable of eliciting a response has been studied especially in the context of the following response of nidifugous birds. A newly-hatched gosling or duckling will follow practically any moving object it sees, in the same way that it would follow its own parent (Spalding, 1873; Heinroth, 1911; Lorenz, 1935). For ducklings, the diversity of effective objects is at least sufficient to include a matchbox and a walking man (Fabricius and Boyd, 1954). This does not mean, of course, that all objects are equally likely to evoke following; some (for instance, round objects) are better than others (e.g. Hess, 1959a; Schaefer *et al.*, 1959; Gray, 1961; Smith F. V., 1962). Within limits, the effectiveness of an object increases with its conspicuousness. Of the models used by Hinde *et al.* (1956) to elicit following from Moorhens (*Gallinula chloropus*) and Coots (*Fulica atra*), a large conspicuous canvas hide carried over the shoulders of one of the experimenters was more effective than a life-sized model of a bird. Similarly, Bateson (1964c) found that a significantly higher proportion of day-old chicks approached a conspicuous static pattern than two less conspicuous patterns. But if the object becomes too conspicuous it elicits fleeing rather than approach. Young ducklings approach a human being if he sways his body from side to side, or walks slowly away (Weidmann, 1958), but flee from him if he moves too vigorously. Such findings are consistent with Schneirla's hypothesis that mild stimulation elicits approach and more intense stimulation avoidance (*see* p. 361).

After a certain period new objects cease to be effective in eliciting the response; the range of adequate objects becomes restricted to ones similar to those already experienced. The learning process involved is known as "imprinting". Though there is now no reason for thinking that imprinting is fundamentally different from other forms of learning (e.g. Hinde, 1955, 1962b; Thorpe, 1963a; Bateson, 1963 and references cited), as Lorenz (1935) and Hess (1959a) believed, it has properties which make it of particular interest. One of these is that the period during which it can occur is limited to a "sensitive period", which may be only a day or two in duration. Thus domestic chicks will not follow a novel moving object when only a few hours old, nor when they are several days old, but only during the intervening period (Fig. 22.2). After the sensitive period, not even the natural object (i.e. the hen) is effective. The earlier limit to the sensitive period is related to the development of loco-motor ability: Hess (1959b) found that the curve of increase in speed of loco-motion of chicks with age corresponds closely with the curve showing the onset

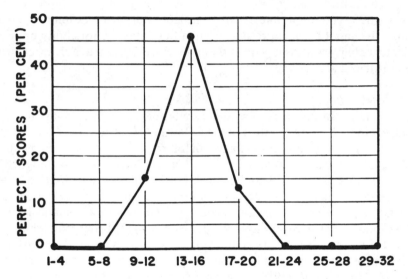

Fig. 22.2. The sensitive period for imprinting. The ordinate gives the scores of birds tested at the ages shown in hours along the abscissa. (*After Hess, 1959a.*)

of the sensitive period (Fig. 22.3). This, of course, does not demonstrate that locomotor ability is itself the operative factor: many perceptual and motivational changes are correlated with it. Gottlieb (1963), however, has shown that the beginning of the sensitive period is related to developmental age, and little affected by post-hatching experience.

There has been more disagreement over the factors limiting the end of the sensitive period. The first suggestion was that the sensitive period is limited by a waning of the tendency to follow (Lorenz, 1935; Fabricius, 1951). This carried with it the assumption that, in imprinted individuals, the specific cues learnt during the sensitive period are sufficient to elicit following later. This view was earlier associated with the assumption that the decrease in the tendency to follow was inherently determined, a hypothesis not easily subject to experimental verification. Later authors who postulated a decrease in the tendency to follow (e.g. Jaynes, 1956, 1957, 1958a, b; Weidmann, 1958) either did not specify its cause, or ascribed it to experiential factors. However, for Coots at least, this theory is inaccurate, since they will generalize their following response to new objects up to at least 60 days of age, provided they are tested in a familiar environment (Hinde *et al.*, 1956). In any case, evidence for such a decrease in the tendency to follow has not yet been produced for any species:

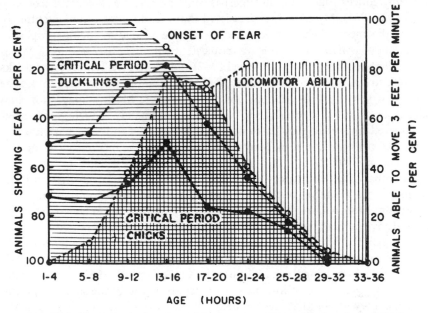

Fig. 22.3. Hypothetical and empirical curves of the critical period of chicks and mallard ducklings. (*After Hess, 1959b.*)

The two discontinuous lines (with open circles) show the increase with age in the proportion of birds moving more than 3 ft./minutes in a standard situation, and in the proportion of birds showing fear responses (the latter plotted from above downwards). The area under both lines (cross-hatched) is the hypothetical sensitive period on the assumption that these two factors are the limiting ones. The empirical period for chicks is shown by the continuous line, and for ducks by the discontinuous one.

the end of the sensitive period is marked by a decrease in the proportion of individuals following, rather than weaker following by those which do (Bateson, 1963).

A second possibility is that the end of the sensitive period is set by the inhibition of following by other types of behaviour which had not previously appeared, fear responses in particular having been suggested (Hinde *et al.*, 1956; Hinde, 1955b; Guiton, 1959; Hess 1959a). In support of this view Hess (1959b) showed that the proportion of experimentally naive birds which would follow a model decreased at the same age as the proportion of birds giving "distress" calls in a standard situation increased (Fig. 22.3). This view left open the problem of the role of experience in the development of the fear responses.

Moltz (1960) extended this hypothesis in an attempt to account not only for the end of the sensitive period, but also for why the young bird follows models at all. He suggested that the stimuli perceived during the first day or two of life, before "anxiety" responses have appeared, acquire anxiety-reducing properties. They are therefore followed later, especially in anxiety-producing situations. In support of this hypothesis, it was shown that habituation to the test run reduces following, and increase in "anxiety" augments it (*see also* Pitz *et al.*, 1961). Moltz further suggested that the more attention-catching an object, the more likely it would be to acquire anxiety-reducing properties during the sensitive period: this was consistent with the observations of James (1959, 1960a, b), F. V. Smith (reviewed 1962) and Moltz (1963) that young chicks will be attracted by and form attachments to flashing lights, and to a wide variety of stationary or moving objects. However, Moltz's suggestion that objects are followed because they have acquired anxiety-reducing properties is rendered improbable by cases in which a model is followed within a few moments of its presentation. Moltz (1963) has now modified his views on this point (*see* p. 370).

A number of experimenters have shown that the end of the sensitive period is not fixed rigidly in terms of developmental age, but depends on the conditions of rearing. Moorhens and Coots reared in groups in pens shielded from the general environment hardly follow models at all, though birds reared in groups in more exposed pens follow readily (Hinde *et al.*, 1956). In chicks the sensitive period is extended by rearing them in isolation (Guiton, 1961; Sluckin, 1962) and in ducks by rearing them in diffuse light (Moltz *et al.*, 1961). Since the decline in the tendency to follow the test object at the end of the sensitive period is correlated with an increased tendency to flee from it, this influence of the environment on the length of the sensitive period could be due to an influence on the development of fear responses.

As already discussed (p. 242), objects which are strange to an animal are likely to elicit fear responses, though responsiveness to strangeness depends on previous learning of the familiar. It seems probable, therefore, that the sensitive period is one in which the bird learns the details of the environment in which it is reared. Only when this is accomplished are strange objects recognized as such, and only then do they elicit fleeing (Sluckin *et al.*, 1961; Sluckin, 1962; Salzen, 1962; Bateson, 1963; Moltz, 1963). After the sensitive period, only enforced proximity to a strange object can result in habituation, and thus a cessation of the attempts to flee.

In a study of the development of fear responses in young chicks, Salzen (1962) showed that drastic alterations in the environment produce fear responses at almost any age. However, chicks reared in isolation, with no experience of moving objects, respond with "pleasure behaviour" to a moving cardboard cylinder even when 7 days old; though chicks which have lived in a social group for 24 hours show fear of the cylinder. This is not easy to understand, but Salzen interprets it on the view that the mobile stimulus can induce positive social behaviour (contentment calls, nestling movements, approach and following) provided it is not responded to as strange; and that the latter is rendered more likely if previous experience of moving objects has provided a familiar moving object percept. This, of course, need imply no absolute distinction between static and mobile objects: we have already seen that chicks may be attracted to static objects, and Thorpe (1945, 1963a) has emphasized that attachment to an environment may be akin to imprinting (p. 368).

Further, Bateson (1964a) has shown that the persistence with which chicks avoid a mobile object is reduced if the object is coloured in a pattern similar to that of the static walls of the pen in which they had been reared. This shows that, within a few days after hatching, chicks learn the characteristics of the pens in which they are reared, and discriminate objects sufficiently dissimilar from those to which they are accustomed. The ability of the chicks to discriminate was shown to be related to the conspicuousness of the pattern with which the walls of the home-pen were painted: with a more conspicuous (and therefore presumably more easily learnt) home environment, avoidance of differently painted models in the test-pen persisted for longer (*see also* Matthews *et al.*, 1963; Klopfer *et al.*, 1964).

This line of argument thus suggests that imprinting during the sensitive period consists largely of the development of familiarity with the moving object. Under natural conditions chicks become familiar with at least two types of moving object—the mother and the siblings—and under experimental conditions Coots similarly can learn to follow several different objects (Hinde *et al.*, 1956). If familiarity is the issue, then imprinting would seem to have much in common with "perceptual learning" (*see* p. 350), for in both cases the responsiveness to a stimulus is influenced by previous experience of that stimulus independently of its association with any reward (Sluckin *et al.*, 1961; Hinde, 1962b; Sluckin, 1962; Bateson, 1963). Thorpe (1956, 1963a) has already emphasized the importance of imprinting as a tool for investigating the genesis of the perceptual side of behaviour.

Bateson (1964b) has produced evidence in support of this view by showing that the learning during the sensitive period can be revealed in contexts other than that of the following response. Thus the performance of chicks in a discrimination problem was augmented when one of the patterns to be discriminated was the same as that on the walls of the home-pen. This is exactly the sort of test used in studies of perceptual learning (*see* p. 350).

There remains the question of why the newly hatched bird approaches conspicuous or moving objects in the first place. At least, however, this is a phenomenon not peculiar to the young of nidifugous birds. As mentioned above, Schneirla (1959, 1965) has emphasized that the young of many species tend to approach stimulation of low intensity and flee from that of high intensity, and this is precisely what happens in the imprinting situation. Since the "distress calls" of chicks are associated with the absence of various types of stimulation to which the chick becomes accustomed before and just after hatching (e.g. contact, warmth), and since the moving object produces a reduction in the distress calling which occurs when a chick is placed alone in a strange environment, the view that approach and following are responses adopted to maintain a low level of stimulation such as that provided by a familiar object is at least a reasonable one (*see also* Salzen, 1962).

It remains possible that the familiarity of a stimulus may give it reinforcing properties (cf. pp. 98-9) which augment the following. From a quite different point of view, and working with a quite different experimental situation, Marx *et al.* (1963) regard their data on the development of a light-contingent bar-pressing response by rats as partial support for the proposition that familiarity *per se* is a sufficient condition for a stimulus to become reinforcing. Further, Campbell *et al.* (1961) showed that the object on which chicks had been imprinted for 4 days had reinforcing properties as indicated by performance in a T-maze (*see also* Peterson, 1960). Such a view would be consistent with many of the findings of imprinting experiments, e.g. that readiness to follow an object, and to respond to it selectively, increases with experience; and moreover that an imprinted bird will show searching behaviour when the object is absent. It is also consistent with the facts that reward is unnecessary, that models which evoke fear may later (after habituation and the establishment of the "neuronal model") elicit following, that new models are more likely to elicit following if presented in the same situation as a model on which the bird has previously been imprinted, and so on (Salzen, 1962).

In discussing imprinting of the "following" response, we have so far neglected interspecies differences. In practice, of course, species differ considerably in the length of the sensitive period, in the amount of experience required for imprinting, in the range of objects effective in eliciting following, and so on. An issue of particular interest concerns the relative roles of auditory and visual stimuli. In most species they may both be effective in eliciting following: auditory stimuli can be conditioned as a consequence of exposure to visual characteristics of the object, or vice versa. After training with an object which provides both visual and auditory stimuli, the relative importance of each varies with the developmental age and experience of the individual concerned, and also with the species (Gottlieb *et al.*, 1962). In ducks which nest on the surface of the ground, the young will approach a wide range of rhythmical sounds, but imprinting to a particular sound occurs only if it is associated with visual stimulation from an appropriate object. In the Wood Duck (*Aix sponsa*), on the other hand, there is no initial tendency to approach repetitive sounds, but exposure to a sound signal, in the absence of correlated visual stimulation, can produce a subsequent preference for that sound. This is to be understood in relation to the Wood Duck's nesting behaviour: the nest is in a hole in a tree, and auditory stimuli may be more important than visual ones in governing the ducklings' early responses to its mother (Klopfer, 1959a, b; Gottlieb, 1963). Domestic chicks are attracted by sounds similar to those which they themselves emitted in the egg (Collias, 1952; Kruijt, 1964) and sound signals play an important part in inducing following (Smith *et al.*, 1964a, b; *see also* Gottlieb, 1965).

22.5. Adult Social, Sexual, and Parental Behaviour

Another area in which the stimulus-response relations characteristic of the species are influenced in large part by experience is that of post-juvenile social and reproductive behaviour. Although in many species, for instance the European Cuckoo (*Cuculus canorus*), the stimuli eliciting pair formation and mating behaviour must be determined independently of experience with con-specific individuals, there are many cases in which such experience plays a major role. As Thorpe *et al.* (1937) showed, this is the case even among insects. The response to odours made by female ichneumon flies (*Nemeritis canescens*) while laying their eggs is influenced by the larvae on which they were reared. Some adult females which had been reared on Wax-moth larvae were attracted to the odour of Wax-moth larvae in preference to the odour of the normal host (Meal-moth larvae), which was not the case with any of the females reared on the normal host. The extent to which such host-conditioning occurs in other insects appears to vary considerably between species (Monteith, 1962; Thorpe, 1963a).

Examples of the effects of early experience on the stimuli eliciting later social or sexual behaviour are known for nearly all vertebrate groups. Adult males of certain Cichlid fish normally direct their courtship only towards females, but males reared in isolation attempt to mate initially with both sexes (Noble *et al.*, 1935–6). Social behaviour also may be influenced by the colour of the parent (Noble *et al.*, 1939). Gregarious behaviour in the chicken (Baron *et al.*, 1960) and rat (Angermeier, 1960) depend on earlier social experience. In the latter species the use of tactile receptors in a social situation is responsible for the effectiveness of visual social reinforcement later.

In ungulates, early experience plays an even more important role in "socialization". Lambs reared by hand tend not to graze with the flock when turned out to pasture (Scott, 1945), and early experience has profound effects on their subsequent social behaviour (Hersher *et al.*, 1963). The effects of early experience have also been extensively studied in dogs (Scott *et al.*, 1950; Scott, 1954) and monkeys (Harlow *et al.*, 1965).

Particular interest has centred around the influence of early experience on mate selection in birds. One of the reasons given by Lorenz (1935) for considering imprinting distinct from other forms of learning (*see* p. 365) was that the early experience appeared to have long-term effects, determining not only the objects towards which the young bird directed its filial responses, but also those to which its adult sexual responses were directed. The imprinting thus seemed to have a latent influence on responses not yet in the repertoire of the organism. In addition to the examples given by Lorenz (1935, 1937), the case described in some detail by Räber (1948) may be cited. This was a hand-reared domestic turkey cock which, as an adult, courted most men walking through the park in which it lived, but attacked women. As a consequence of the early imprinting, the turkey behaved as though humans were fellow members of its species. The differentiation between men and women, however, appeared not to be related to the early experience, but to correspond to species-characteristic responsiveness to hanging or flapping accoutrements (e.g. in this case skirts) as indicative of maleness: under normal conditions these are provided by the wattles and drooping wings of a displaying male turkey.

Other examples of adult birds directing sexual responses towards objects similar to those towards which they previously had directed their early filial responses have been cited by a number of authors (references in Thorpe, 1963a; Hess, 1959a). The majority of these accounts have been anecdotal, and care is necessary in generalizing from them. If early experience were indeed all important in determining sexual responsiveness, it would be reasonable to expect the evidence to be much more abundant. Hens are, in fact, frequently used as foster parents for a wide variety of species, but abnormalities in mate selection among the adults reared thus are relatively rare (Fabricius, 1962). There are, however, some precisely controlled studies which show that the sexual or social responses of *young* chickens or turkeys, induced where necessary by testosterone treatment, are directed preferentially towards objects which the birds had been trained to follow (Schein *et al.*, 1959; Guiton, 1961). Comparable data are also available for guinea-pigs (Shipley, 1963).

This, however, does not show that juvenile experience is in itself sufficient to determine mate selection in *adulthood*, for adolescent experience has rarely been controlled. Under natural conditions the establishment of sexual bonds follows a period of social interactions with other members of the species lasting throughout the whole of adolescence, and it is likely that these have an important influence on mate selection (Hinde, 1962b). For instance, in the Bullfinch, juveniles (usually from the same nest) normally form "betrothed" pairs which are subsequently dissolved in favour of new mates by the beginning of the first breeding season. If a Bullfinch is reared by hand, in isolation from its kind, it first treats its human keeper as a parent, and then as a substitute for a "betrothed" mate. If, during the autumn or winter, the bird is given opportunity to pair with a member of its own species and the opposite sex, its relation to the human gradually dissolves. If, on the other hand, it is kept in the society only of human beings, it later accepts one of them as its mate and the imprinting becomes irreversible (Nicolai, 1956). Similarly detailed studies by Schutz (1965) have shown that sexual imprinting occurs later and requires longer than the imprinting of the following response: when ducks were kept with their own species for 1–3 weeks, and then with another species for 5–6 weeks, about one-third of them proved to be sexually imprinted on the other species as shown by their subsequent choice of a sex partner. Again, Red Junglefowl cocks reared without normal social experience will show normal copulatory behaviour provided they are brought into contact with a female at a sufficiently early age: after this period the social behaviour patterns become fixated in abnormal ways and are difficult to change (Kruijt, 1964).

That adolescent experience is important even in the domesticated species usually used for imprinting experiments is shown by an experiment by Guiton (1962b). Cockerels were reared in visual isolation from each other for 13 weeks, and then penned in a group together with females. At 11 weeks, after androgen treatment, they mated with a yellow glove in preference to a stuffed pullet mounted in a crouching position. At 5 months, however, the preference was reversed, though they would still court humans if they had had recent opportunity for courting hens. Thus, in this case, although the early experience certainly influenced adult sexual behaviour, it was largely overruled by the effects of adolescent experience.

So far, in fact, there have been no controlled studies showing that juvenile social experience with an object leads to a preference for that object as a sex partner in adulthood whatever the adolescent experience may be. Schein (1963) compared the sexual behaviour of three turkeys, isolated from other turkeys but exposed to people for their first 32 days of life, with that of three birds kept in groups for some or all of this period. All birds were then kept in social groups until adulthood. At 5 years of age all six birds would court humans in the absence of turkeys or turkeys in the absence of humans, but when offered a choice the first three courted humans and the second three courted turkeys. It was unfortunate that the number of birds available for use in this experiment was so small. Another study which comes near to satisfying the requirement of controlled adolescent experience is that by Warriner *et al.* (1963), in which it was shown that male (but not female) pigeons tended to mate with birds of the same colour as the adults that reared them. Even here, however, the young were left with their (foster) parents until 40 days old, and were thereafter confined in visual isolation until the mating tests. Their parents were thus the only adult birds they had seen previously (*see also* Schutz, 1963a, b). Further studies in which experience at different ages is carefully controlled are urgently needed, especially as inter-strain and inter-species differences in the role of experience may be considerable (Guiton, 1962a).

Thus we see that experimental evidence for the unique importance of early experience in determining later choice of a sex partner, as was claimed by Lorenz, is so far lacking, and that in most species pair formation occurs only after an extended period of social experience. The most economical hypothesis is that the influence of previous experience on later choice of a sex partner is only a special case of greater readiness to respond to a familiar stimulus. Thus experience in early development is merely one of the factors determining choice of a sex partner. Bateson (1964b) has already shown that early experience influences not only the "following" response of domestic chicks but also discrimination learning for a food reward, and there seems to be no reason why sexual behaviour should not also be influenced in this way (see p. 370). On this view then, adolescent experience is also likely to influence the subsequent choice of a sex partner, and the influence of experience very early in life is not a peculiarity of imprinting, but another example of the role of perceptual learning and familiarity (Bateson, 1963).

22.6. Extension of the Range of Effective Stimuli

Imprinting, as we have seen, involves a decrease in the range of stimulus situations effective for a given response. Sometimes, however, the development of the adult stimulus-response relation involves processes of the opposite kind. Newly hatched *Sepia* will attack only living *Mysis*, a small crustacean which is probably their normal food in the sea. If they are allowed to attack *Mysis*, however, the latency of attack decreases with successive attacks independently of whether the attacks are rewarded with prey, and there is a concomitant increase in the probability of attack on a variety of other moving objects that were at first rarely or never attacked. Thus a cuttlefish which has attacked mysids a few times is much *less* selective than an animal attacking for the first time. The situation is, however, temporary, and the animal later becomes able to learn not to attack patterns which do not result in a food reward (Wells, 1958, 1962a).

Some such cases can be interpreted in terms of generalization or conditioning to the circumstances of the experiment. Thus a poor model of an owl may elicit a more intense mobbing response from Chaffinches which have had previous experience of a more effective one than from experimentally naive birds (Hinde, 1954a); and after a series of presentations involving copulation with dummies of a soliciting female, male Chaffinches will mount a normally ineffective male dummy (Hinde, 1959c). Similarly, a Polecat will attack a stationary rat only after previous experience with a moving one (Eibl-Eibesfeldt, 1963). As a more extreme example, male Siamese Fighting fish normally extend their gill membranes in threat as a response to visual stimuli from another male, but this response can be conditioned to an electric shock (Adler *et al.*, 1963).

That such long-term incremental effects may interact with decremental ones has already been illustrated in the discussion of the mobbing behaviour of Chaffinches. Another case is provided by a study of the maternal and aggressive behaviour of the Golden Hamster (*Mesocricetus auratus*). Females, which had not as adults previously encountered young, were presented with either a 1-,

6- or 10-day-old pup, and then later with a 6-day-old one. The extent to which the 6-day-old pups were attacked on the second test tended to be appropriate to the pups experienced on the first. One-, 6- and 10-day-old babies induce a successively smaller incidence of attacks from naive animals, and experience with such babies has corresponding effects on subsequent attacks on the standard 6-day-old baby (Noirot and Richards, 1966). Similar results are well known in human subjects (Welford et al., 1950).

Noirot's (1964a, b, c; 1965) studies of the maternal behaviour of mice have already been mentioned in several contexts. Here it seems improbable that a total explanation of the incremental effect of experience with a live baby can be found in terms of common stimulus characters between the initial and test exposure. Naive adult mice show maternal behaviour (retrieving, licking, etc.) when presented with a 1-day-old living baby, but are much less likely to respond to the weaker stimulus of a 1-day-old drowned baby: there is strong evidence that the difference is due to the supersonic cries emitted by the former. However, responsiveness to a drowned baby is markedly increased by previous exposure to a live baby, the effect being at least as great when the interval between the two exposures is several days as when it is one minute. The increased responsiveness in retrieving does not depend on the performance of the full response during the initial test with the live baby. If the live baby was placed in the nest of an inexperienced female, who thus had no opportunity for retrieving, the female was nevertheless more likely to retrieve a dead baby than animals without previous adult experience of live babies. Furthermore, Noirot (personal communication) has shown that only the auditory (and perhaps olfactory) stimuli from the live young enhance subsequent responsiveness to the dead young. In this experiment not only was it impossible for the adult to retrieve, lick or show the lactation position to the baby in the initial exposure, but there would seem to have been no stimuli, except possibly olfactory, in common between the two situations. It thus differs from conditioning, and "priming" might be a better term (see also p. 219).

It will be apparent that the processes leading to the stimulus-response relations found in the adult organism are diverse. In general, very young animals respond to quantitative features of stimulation, qualitative aspects are of less importance, and responsiveness is lacking in specificity. Later response occurs to qualitative features, and subsequent experience may either narrow or broaden the range of effective stimuli.

22.7. Summary

1. The stimuli eliciting many responses are responded to appropriately the first time they are encountered. Usually, however, the range of effective stimulus situations is greater for a naive animal than for an experienced one.
2. This lack of specificity in the stimuli eliciting the responses of very young animals may be due to the essential aspects of the stimulation being quantitative rather than

qualitative. Schneirla has suggested that pre- and early post-natal animals tend to approach sources of weak stimulation and withdraw from strong ones.

3. Later, the range of effective stimuli becomes narrowed as a result of experience. Habituation and reinforcement play important roles.

4. Responsiveness is also limited to the fear induced by strange situations. Here experience plays a dual role, because fear of the unfamiliar depends on previous experience to build up a knowledge of the familiar, but further experience renders the unfamiliar familiar.

5. The learning process whereby the range of stimuli eliciting the following response of nidifugous birds becomes narrowed has been termed "imprinting", but this is not a special form of learning. It is limited to a sensitive period: this period comes to an end, in part, because the bird begins to flee from strange objects. Its responsiveness to strangeness depends partly on perceptual learning during the sensitive period.

6. In many species experience plays an important part in determining the objects towards which adult social, sexual and parental behaviour is directed, but the earlier claim that juvenile imprinting determines the object of the sexual responses of adult nidifugous birds, independently of adolescent experience, has not yet been substantiated.

7. In some cases experience leads to a widening of the stimuli effective for a given response. Not all of these can be accounted for in terms of generalization.

23

Developmental Aspects of Motivation

The activities of young animals are often not related to the motivational contexts in which they will appear in adulthood (e.g. Holzapfel, 1939b, 1949). For example, when a fledgling Great Tit first starts to peck at small objects which contrast with their background, it is most likely to do so when it is not hungry: when it is hungry it begs from its parents. A week or two later it shows fragments of reproductive behaviour—snatches of subsong, nest-building and copulatory behaviour—which seem unrelated to the motivational factors which control such activities in the adult. Similarly the play activities of young animals—fighting, hunting, nesting—are largely independent of those motivational factors which will later be associated with them. Indeed, in the study of development the functional categories of behaviour, such as eating, fighting, and sexual behaviour, can be even more misleading than in the study of motivation.

The development of aggressive behaviour in Red Junglefowl illustrates the diverse stages through which the motivation of species-characteristic patterns may pass in development. When chicks are about one-week old the hopping which occurs in the course of general locomotion sometimes becomes oriented towards other individuals, and a few days later such hops may be followed by incipient threatening. Later still (9–12 days) this is followed, in turn, by directed leaping, the two birds bumping their breasts against each other. Aggressive pecking does not appear until about 3 weeks, and kicking still later. Only at about 4 weeks does the pattern come to be elicited from the start by the proximity of another individual. At this stage the motivational factors associated with aggressive behaviour are complex. It still often accompanies locomotory behaviour, and is also especially likely to occur after alarming stimuli and after the chick has been engaged in "comfort" and feeding activities. Furthermore, some, but not all, aspects of fighting are influenced by the factors controlling feeding behaviour: aggressive pecking is more frequent in the fighting of hungry chicks than in that of satiated ones, though the frequency of fighting itself is much the same. In the adult, aggressive behaviour becomes more independent of factors such as locomotor activity, with which it was associated in the chick.

In this development social experience plays a complex role. It is apparently important in acquainting chicks with the stimuli appropriate for eliciting fighting: chicks raised in isolation come to fight their own tails, perhaps because these are the only moving objects in close proximity to them. On the other hand, social experience also has a negative role: week-old chicks reared in isolation show more advanced fighting behaviour than do socially reared birds. Further development entails changes in the relative preponderance of the tendencies to attack, to flee from, and to mate with other individuals, and the extension of the conflict between these tendencies from the fight itself to the locomotory behaviour which succeeds and precedes it (Kruijt, 1964; *see* Andrew, 1964b, for additional data on domestic chicks).

Such cases pose a host of developmental problems. What precisely are the processes whereby activities like eating, fleeing, fighting and mating come to appear in the appropriate motivational contexts as well as in the presence of the appropriate stimuli? The relationships with which we are concerned here are mostly characteristic of the whole species, and thus the changes involved in their development are likely to be determined by common features of structure or environment. For this reason, they are difficult to investigate experimentally, and as yet only scattered facts which cannot be pieced together into a coherent story are available.

Indeed, even descriptive data about what happens in development are scarce and usually inadequate for assessing the relevance to early development of processes known to occur in adults. To cite one example, the use of operant techniques has shown not only that the frequency of species-characteristic patterns, such as a Budgerigar's calls, can be increased by food reinforcement (Ginsburg, 1960), but also that experience with the visual stimuli which elicit fighting is itself reinforcing for domestic cocks and Fighting fish (Thompson, 1963). The relationship of such experiments to development in young animals urgently requires investigation (*see also* p. 336 and Stevenson, in press).

Furthermore, it is worth stressing that no easy assumption can be made about which characteristics of a response are influenced by any particular type of experience and which are not. During the period 105 to 138 days of age, various characteristics of sex behaviour of male rats change (e.g. frequency of ejaculations/hour increases, number of intromissions before ejaculation decreases, post-ejaculatory latency decreases). The last of these is influenced by mating experience, but all the others are a function of age and not of mating experience (Larsson, 1959a).

In the following pages we shall confine our attention to a few functional categories of behaviour in order to indicate the nature of the problems.

23.1. Feeding

The extent to which the feeding movements of neonate mammals are controlled by motivational factors associated with food deprivation is not clear. For instance, some studies of sucking by puppies have indicated that it is at first largely independent of hunger. Puppies fed from bottles with nipples having large holes, who thus satisfied their nutritional needs easily, sucked more at objects outside the feeding situation than did puppies fed through small holes (references in Beach *et al.*, 1954; *see also* Ross, 1950; James 1957). The amount of sucking activity thus appeared not be be related to the satisfaction of hunger.

On the other hand, consummatory stimuli from the stomach may affect sucking behaviour from a very early age. Satinoff *et al.* (1963) assessed the effect of stomach loading by a tube on the amount of nutritional sucking behaviour shown by puppies. Even with 1-day-old puppies the non-loaded animals spent more time sucking and drank more milk than did the pre-loaded ones, and the effect varied little with age over the 11 days of testing. Satinoff and his co-worker regard the negative results obtained in earlier studies as due to the less sensitive procedures used or to insufficient pre-loading (*see* Stanley *et al.*, 1963). James (1963), however, regards the positive results of these authors as due to overloading beyond a normal day's nutritional intake.

Various lines of evidence indicate that, while the feeding behaviour of mammals may be very largely dependent on visceral factors at a certain stage of development, it later becomes much less so, external factors playing a progressively greater role (Anderson, 1941). One of the most intangible factors here is the time schedule on which the animal has been accustomed to eat. A rat does not run well in a maze until it has been on a regular feeding schedule for some time: only when it has had repeated experience of hunger followed by eating will it work well for food (Verplanck *et al.*, 1953; Reid *et al.*, 1955; Birch *et al.*, 1958). The relationship between a given degree of deprivation and feeding behaviour is also a product of experience (*see also* Lawrence *et al.*, 1955; Ghent, 1957; Dufort, 1964). This same point is illustrated in a different way by the effects of infantile food deprivation on the rate of eating in adulthood. Marx (1952) restricted recently weaned rats to two brief feeding periods per day. They were then fed *ad lib.* for 30 weeks. On subsequent testing for rate of eating after deprivation the experimental animals fed more rapidly than did control animals who had had food *ad lib.* throughout (*see also* Mandler, 1958). Effects of experience on eating are not limited to mammals: the diversity of environmental variables influencing eating in chicks is discussed by Shreck *et al.* (1963).

Further problems are raised by the relations between the acceptability of a food substance and its reinforcing value. For instance, saccharin, although non-nutritive, is well known to have a reinforcing effect in some species (Sheffield *et al.*, 1950). There is, however, evidence that the effect of saccharin is greater if it is experienced in the presence of need reduction. Rats preloaded by stomach tube with sugar and then allowed to drink saccharin showed an increase from day to day in the amount ingested, while rats preloaded only with water did not (Capretta, 1962). Such a result is, of course, consistent with the evidence for the multiple nature of the consummatory stimuli for eating, as discussed in Chapter 10.

The development of hoarding behaviour in rats is closely related to that of feeding, and shows similar complexities. Some of these may be mentioned here. Wolfe (1939) reported that rats hoarded more if they were reared on pellets than if reared on powdered food, and Rosenblatt (1950) found that rats reared on a liquid diet carried pellets to the home cage but left them scattered over the floor, though normally reared rats placed them in piles. Wolfe, *loc. cit.*, also found that rats hoarded more if they were deprived of food prepuberally than if they were not. This effect does not occur if the animals are deprived for a period starting 12 days after weaning, and is apparent only if the hoarding tests are preceded by a period of deprivation (Hunt, 1941; Hunt *et al.*, 1947). Even the effects of infantile deprivation are more complex than would appear from the studies just cited, for they are more marked in males than females, and infantile food deprivation affects the hoarding of food by adults but water deprivation does not affect the hoarding of water-soaked cotton (McKelvey *et al.*, 1951). Infantile food deprivation may affect adult hoarding in part because it results in a higher rate of eating, allowing more time for hoarding pellets in the test (Marx, 1952).

23.2. Sexual Behaviour

The course of development of sexual behaviour is similarly complex, involving both hormonal action on the mechanisms of mating behaviour and experiential factors. With regard to the former, the most detailed studies have used guinea-pigs and rats (e.g. W. C. Young, 1961b), where changes occurring in at least three different periods of development are important:

1. Gonadal hormones from the mother have a prenatal organizing action on the tissues mediating sexual behaviour. For instance, if pregnant guinea-pigs are given testosterone propionate, the genitalia of the female offspring resemble those of males: if the young are ovariectomized and treated with gonadal hormones, their behaviour is much more male-like than that of similarly treated controls whose mothers did not receive testosterone (e.g. Young, 1961b and references cited; Young *et al.*, 1964; Rosenblatt, in press).

2. During the neonatal period the tissues mediating mating behaviour probably become more sensitive to gonadal hormones, since exogenous hormones then become effective.

3. At puberty the increase in endogenous gonadal hormones produces a readiness to show sexual behaviour. This is apparently a result of action by the hormones on mechanisms which become organized even in animals castrated during the prepuberal period (Beach *et al.*, 1946; Riss *et al.*, 1955; Rosenblatt *et al.*, 1958a, b). In male hamsters some aspects of the sexual pattern develop even in animals castrated and adrenalectomized before puberty, indicating that such sexual activity as castrates show is not due to androgens from the adrenal cortex (Warren *et al.*, 1957).

The mode of action of hormones after puberty is discussed in Chapter 10.

Although sex hormones are considered to have usually a rather specific effect on sexual behaviour, this is not necessarily the case during development. The most detailed work here concerns the influence on chick calls (Andrew, 1963a). Injections of testosterone during the first week or two of life led to the production of higher intensity variants of all calls, and to a more persistent use of the calls already present in the repertoire. Andrew believes the most likely mechanism to be a non-specific effect on a control system on which all vocalizations depend, the various calls being as yet not organized into groups such as aggression and sex. Indeed, facilitation of the constituent responses by testosterone may be one of the factors necessary for the organization of such groups.

Although gonadal hormones are of fundamental importance in the control of sexual behaviour in most adult vertebrates, young animals often show mating patterns when their gonads are showing at most slight endocrine activity (*see* p. 172). In chicks of the Red Junglefowl, Kruijt (1964) believes that copulatory activity occurs when the tendencies for aggressive and fleeing behaviour are low and balanced, a conclusion supported, for instance, by the observation that it depends strongly on the dominance rank of the male and the size of the group, and is directed to lower-ranked birds.

In addition to the various actions of hormones, experiential factors also play an important role in the mechanisms underlying sexual behaviour. In the first place, the social conditions of early rearing may influence sexual behaviour in a number of ways.

In birds, males reared in isolation may fail to mate with females because they show more fear than group-reared controls. When sexually mature male Chaffinches, hand-reared in isolation from others of their kind, were presented with females stuffed and mounted in the soliciting posture, they showed some courtship but would not approach the model. The same model elicited copulation from a high proportion of normally reared birds. Under ordinary circumstances Chaffinches become habituated to the proximity of other individuals, but to the isolate the soliciting female was a strange object, and therefore elicited an unusually strong tendency to flee as well as sexual behaviour (Hinde, 1959c). Fisher *et al.* (1956/7) similarly found that male domestic fowl reared in social isolation courted female chickens but would not mount a crouching bird: this is in marked contrast to the behaviour of normally reared cocks, for whom crouching readily elicits mounting attempts. After experience of live females some of these males attempted to copulate by force with standing females rather than with crouching ones. Kruijt (1962) also found that Junglefowl cocks reared in isolation for ten months were unable to perform normal copulatory behaviour, and suggested that this was due to deficiency in the integration of aggressive and escape behaviour in early life: the agonistic behaviour was abnormal from quite an early age, the birds showing fits of very strong escape behaviour alternating with periods of extreme aggressiveness. Normal mating behaviour was shown by cocks which had been reared in isolation but had been placed with females before they were 10 months old.

In rats, the evidence about the role of early social experience on later sexual behaviour is rather contradictory. Beach (1942a, 1958) found that male rats reared in isolation were more responsive to females and more likely to copulate than males reared with females: this was attributed in part to the greater excitement engendered in the isolates by contact with a second animal. Kagan *et al.* (1953) also found that males kept in isolation from the 37th to 100th day of life were more likely to show the complete copulatory pattern in a mating test than were animals which had had weekly contact with a male or a female during the same period of isolation. They attribute this difference to patterns of social behaviour formed by the latter groups which partially reduced the sexual responses.

Zimbardo (1958), however, obtained conflicting results. Male rats reared in part-time cohabitation showed better performance in mating tests than males reared in isolation. This result is in agreement with data on the guinea-pig, where experiments by Valenstein *et al.* (1955), with several genetic strains, showed that males reared in a social situation scored better in sex tests than males reared in isolation. Moreover, male cage-mates were adequate for the organization of sexual behaviour in other males: males reared with spayed females were inferior to males reared with either intact females or with other males, apparently because of the lack of sexual stimulation these females provided (Valenstein *et al.*, 1957). The social experience produced its effect before the animals were 25 days old (Young, 1961b). That social experience through the whole of this period is not necessary is indicated by Dieterlen's (1959) finding that individuals isolated when 4–10 days old respond appropriately to olfactory stimuli from other individuals, and mate normally even when completely inexperienced.

Gerall (1963) has obtained data on the sexual behaviour of the guinea-pig not wholly consistent with that of Valenstein *et al.*, *loc. cit.* His data indicated that practice in mounting behaviour is not an important issue, for guinea-pigs separated from the social group only by a wide mesh screen, which permitted visual, olfactory and some tactual contact but no mounting behaviour, showed no deficiency. Gerall (1963) suggests that the sexual inadequacies of the isolates were due to interference by other types of behaviour (e.g. play responses, *see* above) and inadequate responsiveness to the relevant stimuli from the female, but the precise nature of the deficiency remains obscure.

A detrimental effect of isolation on sexual performance has also been found in female guinea-pigs (Goy *et al.*, 1956-7).

These experiments indicate that experience with companions plays an important part in the organization of the sexual behaviour of rodents. Since incipient mating behaviour may occur at a very early age, the experience may operate in part through effects of incomplete sexual behaviour (McGill, 1962a), though this is not the only issue. Experience gained in early (pre-adolescent) mounting attempts also has an important influence on later sexual behaviour in the higher mammalian groups (Whalen, 1961, 1963a): in Chimpanzees and Rhesus Monkeys learning during mating attempts is essential for the organization of the components of sexual behaviour into a functional system (Nissen, 1954; Harlow, 1962).

Experience during puberty or early adulthood also plays an essential role in the organization of the mating pattern. Rosenblatt *et al.* (1958a) castrated thirteen male kittens at the age of 4 months. As adults they showed little sexual behaviour when tested with oestrous females. Eleven of these were subsequently treated with testosterone propionate. Six of these were given sexual experience during the period of hormone administration, four showing the complete sexual pattern. The other five were kept isolated from females during the period of hormone administration, but tested subsequently. Three showed no increase in sexual performance over the pre-androgen level: the other two showed some increase during the period of testing, suggesting that experience in the tests soon after hormone withdrawal was important. The organization of sexual behaviour thus requires appropriate environmental stimulation while the animal is in an adequate hormonal condition. Rosenblatt *et al.* (1958b) also showed that the sexual behaviour of cats persists after castration only if the male has had some sexual experience before castration, a result again pointing to the necessity for a combined action of hormonal state and external stimulation for the organization of the mating pattern. Once this organization has occurred, however, mating behaviour may continue even with very low hormone levels in this species. Beach (1947, 1948) had earlier pointed out that the extent to which sexual behaviour may become independent of its normal hormonal background increases in the higher mammals, and is greater in males than in females.

23.3. Avoidance, Anxiety and Emotionality

We shall consider here the complex of behaviour which includes fear and escape responses in strange situations or from rivals or predators, "anxiety" or "emotionality" in a strange situation, and so on. That these are grouped together carries no implications as to their precise developmental relationships with each other (*see* footnote, p. 242). Indeed, there are problems here whose complexity has only recently become apparent. For instance, Junglefowl chicks show escape responses to intense tactile and auditory stimuli immediately after hatching, but visually elicited escape responses develop only later. Furthermore, the escape responses elicited through the three modalities differ in nature; for instance, fast silent running is not elicited by tactile stimuli, and at most rarely by visual ones; and running in response to sounds, unlike the others, is often not directed away from the source of stimulation (Kruijt, 1964).

Sensory and perceptual deprivation early in life may influence an animal's ability to learn to avoid noxious objects. A dramatic instance is given by Melzack *et al.* (1957). Dogs were reared to maturity under conditions which severely restricted their sensory experience and screened them from noxious stimulation. Such animals learned to avoid various types of painful stimulation (nose-burning, electric shock, etc.) much more slowly than did controls reared under more normal conditions. At first the restricted animals showed no avoidance responses at all, walking repeatedly into lighted matches, striking their heads against water pipes, and so on. Social isolation may also affect aggressive behaviour. Rosenblatt (personal communication) reared two cats in isolation from birth to sexual maturity: both became unpredictably ferocious, and attacked on the slightest provocation. In Deermice (*Peromyscus*) the effect of early social isolation varies with the sub-species: post-weaning isolation decreases dominance in *P. maniculatus bairdii* but not in *P.m. gracilis* (Rosen *et al.*, 1963).

Unlike the dogs studied by Melzack *et al.*, birds brought up in a restricted environment are usually more prone to give avoidance responses to strange objects or situations than individuals brought up with a wider range of experience (e.g. Hinde *et al.*, 1956; Schaller *et al.*, 1961). Kruijt (1964) found that Junglefowl reared in visual isolation from conspecific individuals went through a stage in which they showed excessive escape behaviour, but later the males became very aggressive towards their tails and towards humans. As yet little is known of the precise way in which the early experience produces its effect in such cases (*see also* Salzen, 1962, cited on p. 368).

As previously mentioned in several other contexts, experience determines the stimuli which will elicit avoidance behaviour. Since avoidance responses may be elicited by a discrepancy between the perceived stimulus situation and that which is familiar, habituation plays a major role. This, in turn, may have profound effects on other behaviour: for instance, individuals reared in partial or total isolation are not only more afraid of others of their kind than are normally reared individuals (e.g. Katz, 1937), but also show quite different social behaviour. The rate of distress calling by 3-day-old domestic chicks placed alone in a strange situation is decreased by the presence of a mirror in group-reared birds, but increased in chicks reared in isolation (Kaufman *et al.*, 1961). Similar data are available for puppies (Fredericson, 1952) and kittens (e.g. Rosenblatt *et al.*, 1961).

In addition to habituation, positive conditioning also plays a role. If young mice are exposed to attack by more aggressive individuals, they develop withdrawal responses in fighting situations. These persist the longer, the younger (within limits) the mouse when first defeated (Kahn, 1951; *see also* Bevan *et al.*, 1960).

These effects of early experience on later emotional behaviour come within a broad but generally acceptable definition of learning. Recent studies of the development of behaviour in mammals, however, have shown that apparently trivial aspects of early experience may have profound effects on later behaviour which, though revealed in learning tests, are probably mediated in a quite different way.

Bernstein (1952) found that the mere handling of juvenile rats improved their subsequent performance in a T-maze. Hunt *et al.* (1955) assessed the effects of various treatments given in infancy—daily handling alone or with food deprivation, daily electric shock, etc.—on the readiness of adult rats to emerge from their cages on to an open runway when hungry: a control group of animals was not handled. While no differences among the experimental groups were found, the control (non-handled) group emerged from the cages less readily than did any of the experimental groups. It thus seemed that the noxious stimulation in infancy produced a reduction in "emotionality" among the adults.

In subsequent experiments with rats, Levine (e.g. Levine *et al.*, 1956; Levine, 1962a, b) showed that, "stimulation in infancy results in the capacity for the organism to respond more effectively when confronted with novel situations, or, in other words, to exhibit a diminished emotional response to such novel stimuli...". In the early experiments the stimuli used were handling for a few minutes a day, or mild electric shock, administered from birth to weaning (about 21 days). Response measures included the amount of defaecation and freezing shown in an open field test, the amount of water drunk after a period of deprivation, and so on. Later, other behavioural indices, as well as measures such as length of survival with total food and water deprivation (an unnecessary, cruel procedure), or survival with known pathogenic agents, were used by other investigators. The most effective age for the stimulation lies during the first weeks of life, though the optimum period varies somewhat with the intensity and conditions of stimulation (Denenberg *et al.*, 1960; Meyers, 1962; Spence *et al.*, 1962; Denenberg, in press; *see also* below). Although there have been some reservations (e.g. Broadhurst, 1961; McMichael, 1961) these results have now gained general acceptance.

Many of the results obtained have been interpreted in terms of an effect of the early experience on "emotionality", a concept not always clearly defined but usually assessed in terms of defaecation and lack of mobility in an open field. The concept is, in fact, a loose one, and the various measures by which it is assessed are not always highly correlated (e.g. Paré, 1964). In addition, developmentally controlled studies show that defaecation may increase or decrease in a disturbing situation according to the subject's own developmental history (Tobach *et al.*, 1962). When used in this context it must not be taken as more than a descriptive term, but it then has some value in coordinating data: for instance, mice stimulated in infancy were more aggressive than non-handled mice, but this was because the latter showed more "emotional" behaviour (i.e. freezing) in the test situation, which was incompatible with fighting. Similarly, such pre-weaning treatment seems to have no direct effect on perception or problem-solving behaviour: if these are affected, it is through an influence on emotionality (Denenberg *et al.*, 1962).

In a number of experiments on rodents (e.g. Denenberg *et al.*, 1963a) it was shown that a few minutes handling each day during infancy produced effects indistinguishable from those of noxious electric shock. Other studies suggest that the resultant temperature change, rather than handling itself, may be the crucial variable (Hutchings, 1963; Schaefer, 1963). Yet other studies show that mere shaking of the cage, or moving it about the laboratory, is as effective as handling in reducing "emotionality". This led to the view that quality and quantity of stimulation are unimportant. However, very intense stimulation in infancy leads to an increase rather than a decrease in subsequent emotionality (Lindzey *et al.*, 1963). Bell *et al.* (1963), working with infant mice and studying the effects of infantile shock on avoidance learning and performance in an open field, showed that an intermediate amount of stimulation in infancy leads to the best performance on certain learning tasks in adulthood. The optimum amount of shock administered in infancy, however, varies with the age at which it is administered, so that there seem to be different sensitive periods depending on the intensity of stimulation and other variables.

More recently Denenberg (in press) has suggested that the amount of stimulation in infancy reduces subsequent emotionality in a monotonic fashion, but is related in an inverted U-fashion to adult performance in tasks involving noxious stimulation and of moderate difficulty. For tasks which are easy or difficult he suggests that the relationship between intensity of infantile stimulation and adult performance is monotonic, though opposite in slope.

Since infantile stimulation affects responsiveness in novel or fear-producing situations, where the response is known to involve autonomic activity and release of adrenocorticotrophic hormone, Levine (1957, 1961, 1962b) compared the adrenocortical response of rats stimulated and not-stimulated as infants to stressful situations. In general, the results confirmed the view that the non-stimulated animals are more reactive to the unpleasant situations used, for when measured 24 hours later their adrenals were heavier. Paradoxically, however, the stimulated animals showed as adults a more rapid rise in circulating corticosteroids after electric shock, and a greater output in the first 15 minutes after the shock. Thus it is the pattern of response to stressful situations which seems to be affected by stimulation in infancy. The non-stimulated animal's response to unpleasant situations seems maladaptive in that it is less vigorous to painful stimuli like electric shock than that of a stimulated animal, but greater to relatively non-noxious situations like the open field.

The consequences of infantile stimulation in rats are, however, more widespread than this. In stimulated animals the eyes open earlier, hair growth is more rapid, weight at weaning is greater, there is an earlier maturation of the hypothalamic-hypophyseal-adrenal system, a heavier subcortical brain, and earlier myelinization of the central nervous system, than in non-stimulated animals (Levine *et al.*, 1959; Levine, 1962b and c; Tapp *et al.*, 1963). In human infants visual attentiveness appears to be influenced by previous non-specific stimulation (White, 1963).

The effects of infantile stimulation on subsequent emotionality could be due to disturbance of the mother rather than a direct action of the stimulation on the infant: most experiments have confounded the two. It has been known for some time that the temperament of rats can be affected by that of the mother (Rasmussen, 1939). Ressler (1963) has shown that genotype correlated characteristics of a (foster)-parent exert a post-natal influence on visual exploration, body weight and viability of two strains of mice; and Thompson (1957) has shown that subjecting mothers to stressful experiences in pregnancy leads to greater emotionality in the offspring, the effects being controlled by fostering the young with mothers that have not been stressed during pregnancy (*see also* Doyle *et al.*, 1959; Hockman, 1961; Thompson *et al.*, 1962). Denenberg *et al.* (1963b) therefore assessed the effect on adult emotionality of a variety of environmental and social variables applied during infancy. They found that the adverse effects on adult emotional behaviour of lack of early stimulation can be offset by providing a fairly diverse environment after weaning, but are accentuated by rearing the animals in company with stimulated, non-emotional controls. Furthermore, the more emotional mother rats (like human mothers, e.g. Ottinger *et al.*, 1964) tended to rear more emotional offspring. Experiments in which infants were switched between mothers showed that while the effect was not a genetic one, the mother's influence was exerted both pre- and post-partum. In fact, the effect is also reciprocal, the mother's emotionality being affected by that of her young. It is thus clear that although stimulation as applied through daily handling by an experimenter is effective in reducing adult emotionality primarily during a few days after birth, emotionality can be affected by other environmental factors before and after this period. In addition, Denenberg *et al.* (1963a, b) found that the experiences which a mother rat received in infancy had an effect on her offspring's body weight at weaning and open field behaviour in adulthood. The effects were mediated both through the pre-natal mother-foetus relationship and in the course of post-natal mother-infant interaction.

Most of the experiments on the effects of infantile handling have been carried out with rats or mice. Comparable effects are known in other species; for instance dogs and cats (Meier, 1961; and references in Levine, 1962a). However, great care must be exercised in generalizing from one strain or species to another. Adult mice stimulated in infancy, for instance, show *less* rather than more resistance to total food and water deprivation than unstimulated controls (Denenberg *et al.*, 1959). King *et al.* (1959) subjected two species of Deermouse (*Peromyscus*) to infantile stimulation. Adult avoidance learning in a Skinner box situation was improved in one species as a consequence of the infantile stimulation, but impaired in the other. Similar genetic influences on the effects of infantile stimulation have been found by other workers (review by Levine, 1962a). In some cases genetic differences in the effects of infantile stimulation may be related to correlated differences in rates of development. Further studies are listed in a comprehensive review by Bell (1965). In spite of the inter-species differences, these studies indicate new ways to examine the effects of the nature of the mother-infant relationship, and of maternal deprivation, on subsequent behaviour characteristics in man (Bowlby, 1960) and monkeys (Harlow, 1962; Spencer-Booth et al., 1965).

A more extreme example of a general influence of early experience is given by the solitary and migratory phases of the locust (Schistocerca gregaria). These differ in colour, morphology and behaviour, and were once classified as separate species. Individuals reared in isolation do not become migratory, but their offspring develop into the migratory type if reared under crowded conditions (Faure, 1932; Ellis, 1953, 1963).

A final point about avoidance responses must be made. Stimuli eliciting them produce not only an overt behavioural change, but also a complex of internal changes, involving the autonomic system, which have a relatively long-lasting influence on behaviour. This complex of overt and autonomic changes, loosely termed fear, is of special interest since responses which reduce fear are easily learnt. Miller (1948b), for instance, has shown that rats will learn to rotate a wheel or press a bar in order to escape from a compartment in which they had previously been shocked. Assessing the usefulness of a drive-reduction hypothesis in accounting for this, Miller suggests that stimuli from the compartment elicit fear as a result of previous conditioning. The reduction in fear produced by escape reinforces the wheel-turning or bar-pressing (see also Brown et al., 1949; Kalish, 1954). Internal fear or anxiety responses have been similarly postulated to explain the acquisition of many types of behaviour ranging from the tics of neurotics to complex higher human activities. To cite but one example, Brown (1961) suggests that an empty wallet arouses a state of anxiety which provides the basis for money-seeking responses (see Mowrer, 1939).

23.4. Maternal Behaviour

Motivational aspects of the development of maternal behaviour will not be considered in any detail here, but two controversial studies on the rat must be mentioned. Birch (1956) prevented pregnant rats from licking themselves by placing wide rubber collars round their necks, and found that most animals treated in this way did not attend to their young at birth or establish effective maternal behaviour. He therefore supposed that the pre-parturient grooming behaviour of the female played a role in the establishment of maternal behaviour. Subsequent detailed data by Roth et al. (1964) show that self-licking does in fact become concentrated along the nipple lines and in the anogenital region as parturition approaches (see also Steinberg et al., 1962; Rosenblatt et al.

1963). However, Coomans (in Eibl-Eibensfeldt, 1958) obtained quite different results and concluded that such deficiencies in maternal behaviour as he found could be accounted for in terms of mechanical interference. As Rosenblatt *et al.* (1963) point out, the strains of rats and methods used differ in the two cases, so that an attempt to reconcile the two studies is urgently needed.

A parallel case is given by Riess's (1950) finding that female rats, reared in cages containing no food or other objects which could be picked up and carried about, failed subsequently to build nests, or even to establish a proper nest-site in a test cage. He concluded that, in the course of carrying food about, rats learn to pile up warm nest material in one corner of the cage. Eibl-Eibesfeldt (1961) however, produced evidence that the failure of Reiss's rats to build nests was due to a deficiency in the experimental conditions. In a new environment rats show mainly exploratory behaviour, and thus do not form the attachment to a particular part of the cage necessary for nest-building.

23.5. Nest-Building by Chimpanzees

Another complex species-characteristic pattern, the development of which depends on experience, is the nest-building of Chimpanzees. Under natural conditions a quite complicated nest, constructed by bending over and intertwining the branches of a tree, is built every evening, and sometimes another is built during the day time. In the field young animals start to build nests when a few years old, but, of course, they have daily opportunity for watching nests under construction by adults before that (Goodall, 1962). As far as the available evidence goes (Bernstein, 1962), it appears that most Chimpanzees born in captivity do not build nests if first given the opportunity to do so when adult: the few which do make some attempt to do so usually have some history of being supplied with material at a younger age. It must be noted, however, that the conditions in which the Chimpanzees used in Bernstein's study were kept were extremely unnatural, and the nest materials provided (burlap strips, newspaper, 5 ft. lengths of hosepipe) were very different from the living branches used in nature.

23.6. Stereotypes—Functional Autonomy

It often seems as though with repetition some activities become progressively more independent of the external stimuli and/or internal conditions with which they were associated initially. In captivity animals often develop behaviour stereotypes or tics which are repeated monotonously. They may walk repetitively to and fro, or show movements resembling incomplete locomotor or feeding patterns (Holzapfel, 1939a; Hediger, 1950). These movements often consist of the early stages of a behaviour sequence which has become fixed and modified to a varying degree. Thus the flying to and fro of a bird in an aviary develops from attempts to fly out of the aviary, though it may be so stereotyped that the bird flies on a constant track from side to side, perching in the same place each time. Such behaviour often becomes more or less divorced from the conditions which initially evoked it. The stereotyped flying to and fro may occur in the absence of any of the stimuli which normally elicit fleeing: apparently the bird shows this behaviour in the absence of fear whenever there is no overriding tendency to behave in other ways. A comparable case has been studied experimentally by Datel *et al.* (1952). These authors assessed the amount of ear-scratching shown by two groups of rats–one group in which the ears were treated with collodion for five days and a control group not so treated. The collodion caused a large increase in ear-scratching, some of which persisted for at least 16 days after the last application. Since the difference between the amount of scratching shown by experimental and control groups did not diminish during these 16 days, it seems improbable that the greater amount of scratching shown by the experimentals was merely due to diminishing after-effects either of the collodion or of the excessive scratching during the collodion period on the tissues themselves (*see also* Earl, 1957).

Since such responses persist even though the factors which originally gave rise to them are no longer present, there has, presumably, been some change in their motivational basis. This has been described as the acquisition of "functional autonomy", though this is only a descriptive label (Woodworth, 1918; Allport, 1937). Bindra (1959) has pointed out that autonomy is never complete, but occurs with respect to a limited set of conditions, and can be understood to some extent at least in terms of processes known to be important in other contexts. First, cues frequently associated with the response may become substitute cues, capable of eliciting the response in the absence of those factors which were necessary initially. Second, as a result of repeated performance, fewer of the original cues are necessary to elicit the response—individual cues become increasingly effective. Third, Bindra suggests that activities acquired on the basis of one reinforcer are maintained in its absence because something else comes to reinforce the same activity—possibly the performance of the activity itself may have reinforcing value. There is, of course, a danger of circular argument here.

Since such stereotypes are especially liable to develop in monotonous environments, the stereotype may persist because it provides a source of stimulation, exteroceptive and proprioceptive. Such an explanation may well apply to the rocking and other stereotyped movements shown by children in hospitals (Hinde, 1962c).

The general principle that the performance of a response leads to an increase in the probability that the response will be given on subsequent occasions may be of wide applicability. Male grasshoppers reared in isolation, while able to sing the various songs of their species quite normally, do so very infrequently until placed in a singing group. The frequency of stridulation then increases markedly and permanently (Haskell, 1957).

23.7. Summary

1. The activities of young animals are often not related to the motivational factors associated with them in adulthood; and the motivational bases of apparently simple activities often have a complex developmental history.
2. Evidence on the relations between the feeding movements of young mammals and the stimuli resulting from food deprivation are contradictory.
3. The feeding behaviour of adult mammals shows considerable independence of tissue needs: the time schedule of eating to which the animal is accustomed may be an important issue.
4. Infantile food deprivation influences adult feeding and hoarding behaviour.
5. Motivational aspects of sexual behaviour are markedly influenced by hormones at a number of stages in development.
6. Sexual behaviour may also be much affected by the social conditions of rearing.
7. Sensory, perceptual or social isolation may affect emotional, aggressive and fear behaviour.
8. Non-specific stimulation in infancy, such as that produced by handling or mild electric shock, may have profound influences on a wide variety of juvenile and adult characteristics, and especially on "emotionality" and other related aspects of behaviour.
9. Some problems concerned with the development of maternal behaviour in rats, nest-building in Chimpanzees, and the formation of stereotypes, are mentioned briefly.

24

Developmental Aspects of Learning

Learning abilities, as measured by changes in performance, change with age. For instance, adult cuttlefish given prey-objects which are inaccessible inside glass tubes learn more rapidly than do young animals not to attack them: it seems to be impossible to train *Sepia* of less than 3 or 4 weeks old not to attack their prey under conditions in which adults learn rapidly (Wells, 1962a, b). In chicks, the ability to acquire an active response (moving from a cold place to a warmer place where there is some food) is present on the day of hatching, but a passive avoidance response (absence of approach) cannot be acquired until the third day (Peters *et al.*, 1963). This experiment involved the use of a thermoregulatory response which changes markedly with age, but a similar finding under more stringently controlled conditions has been reported by Fischer *et al.* (1964).

The retention of a conditioned fear response is much better in older rats than in younger ones: animals conditioned at 18 days show practically no retention 21 days later, but rats conditioned at 100 days show near-perfect retention 42 days later (Campbell *et al.*, 1962). On the other hand, these authors found that the rate of extinction of a fear response does not vary with age in rats, though it does in mice (Denenberg *et al.*, 1958). A similar relation between age and the retention of conditioned responses is found in Rhesus Macaques (Mason *et al.*, 1958): detailed information on age changes in learning in a number of contexts are available for this species (Harlow, 1959a, b; Harlow *et al.*, 1962, 1965; Zimmermann *et al.*, 1965). It is possible here to indicate only briefly some of the processes which influence such changes in learning ability with age.

In the early stages, learning may be limited by growth and differentiation in the nervous system or the effectors. The ease with which conditioned responses can be established in puppies is paralleled by the progress of myelinization (Harman, cited by Scott, 1954), and in the human infant learning to walk or control micturition clearly requires a certain degree of muscular development. The poor ability of *Sepia* to learn not to attack prey during the first few weeks of life is probably related to the late development of the vertical lobe of the brain (Wells, 1962b).

In other cases the ease of learning may be affected by the development of perceptual abilities as discussed earlier (Chapter 21), or by changes in the response repertoire. Tinbergen (1942) records that immature Eskimo dogs, which do not defend territories, seem incapable of learning the territories of others: but when they begin to show territorial behaviour, they learn to avoid the territories of others very quickly.

Another issue is the difference in inquisitiveness and persistence between young and older animals in many species. We have already had cause to mention the complex way in which experience may affect responsiveness to novel objects, and this will, in turn, affect learning ability in many situations. Welker (1956) found that young Chimpanzees (1–2 years) are more cautious in approaching or touching small stationary objects than are older ones. The initial responsiveness of 3–4-year-olds was similar to that of 7–8-year-olds, but in the latter case it waned more quickly. Vince (1961a) found changes of this sort to have an important influence on the ability of passerine birds to pull up food suspended from a perch by a piece of string. Juveniles were more successful than adults, in part because of the greater time they spend responding to the bait in each test, and in part because of the greater variety of methods they tried. By means of detailed studies Vince (1960) showed that age changes in learning ability cannot be interpreted in terms of a unitary learning capacity, but must be analysed in terms of a number of characteristics, each of which has its own developmental history. In these birds both responsiveness to new stimuli and the stability of unreinforced responses rise to a peak and then fall,

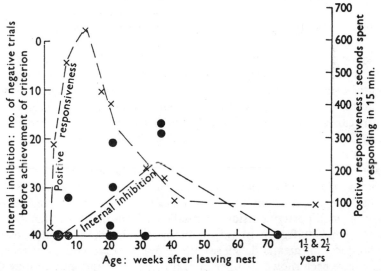

Fig. 24.1. Changes in positive responsiveness and negative responsiveness of hand-reared Great Tits to small coloured objects with age. (*From Vince, 1960.*)

but at different rates (Fig. 24.1; Vince, 1961a, b). In both birds and primates responsiveness to novel stimuli is much influenced by the conditions of rearing (*see also* Menzel *et al.*, 1963).

Stimulated by Hebb (1949), a number of authors have studied the effects of rearing conditions on later learning ability (cf. p. 350). Rats and dogs reared unrestricted in a rich environment perform better on maze learning tests than those reared under restricted conditions (e.g. Bingham *et al.*, 1952; Forgays *et al.*, 1952; Hymovitch, 1952; Thompson *et al.*, 1954; Woods, 1959). No doubt several factors are involved. One is the greater novelty of the test situation for the restricted animals, resulting in a greater amount of exploratory behaviour (Zimbardo *et al.*, 1957, Woods, 1959). Retardation in the development of perceptual abilities produced by the restricted environment is probably also an issue. This is suggested by the finding that the age at which access to the richer environment is permitted is important: rats reared in a large space at an early age are superior in maze performance to rats placed in the large space later. Forgays *et al.* (1962) similarly found that 3 weeks experience in a more complex environment given just after weaning was more effective in enhancing subsequent maze performance than when given either earlier or later: it is, of course, hardly surprising that the group placed in the complex environment for the first 21 days of life did not profit much from it, since during much of this time they would not have been mobile.

Although experience at a relatively early age is thus most beneficial, Woods (1959) found that the detrimental effect of early sensory and motor deprivation was reduced by subsequent exposure to an enriched environment. Moreover the relation between the nature of the early experience and the subsequent test conditions is an important issue. Walk (1958) compared the performance on an elevated maze of two groups of rats: one had been reared in a large cage with opportunity to see and have commerce with objects placed round it (visual-motor group), while the other had been restricted to the centre portion of a similar cage by transparent plastic sides (visual group). Tested in the light, the former group was superior, but no differences were found when tests were carried out in the dark. (This experiment replicated an earlier one by Forgus (1955), but obtained different results. *See also* Forgus (1958).) Other relevant studies are cited in Chapter 21.

Rearing conditions have also been shown to influence the deficit resulting from brain lesions and the nature of brain function. A large anterior cortical lesion has a greater effect on the performance of cage-reared rats in a learning test than a small posterior lesion, as predicted from the law of mass action. With rats reared in a free environment, on the other hand, the smaller posterior lesion produces the greater deficit (Smith, 1959). More recently, rats reared in isolation have been shown to differ in brain chemistry and morphology from those reared in a more complex environment (Rosenzweig *et al.*, 1962; Krech, 1965).

One way in which breadth of early experience may enhance subsequent learning has been studied in laboratory experiments on "learning to learn". This is discussed in Chapter 27.

24.1. Sensitive Periods for Learning

The concept of sensitive periods during which organisms are especially susceptible to particular environmental influences is of wide applicability, being useful to embryologists, clinicians (Kalter *et al.*, 1959), psychologists and many others. A particular instance concerns sensitive periods for learning, and we have already come across two examples. The imprinting of the "following" response of young nidifugous birds is normally limited to the first few days of life (p. 366), and some species of song-birds cannot add new songs to their repertoire after their first breeding season (pp. 332-8).

In general, it is a useful working assumption that no particular case of learning would occur with equal facility at all stages of the life cycle. In cases where a learnt modification to behaviour occurs most readily in a fairly restricted stage of development, we can refer to that stage as a sensitive period. Viewed in this way, the sensitive period refers not to a sharply defined period during which the learning can occur and outside which it cannot, but to the result of a gradual change in the ease or probability of learning. Furthermore, the period during which any specified type of learning can occur most readily is not rigidly determined but may itself be influenced by experience. The term "sensitive period" is thus to be preferred to "critical period", sometimes used in this context.

The latter term has in any case been used in a quite different sense (e.g. Scott *et al.*, 1950; Scott, 1958; Williams *et al.*, 1953) to refer to periods of an organism's life in which diverse aspects of its behaviour are particularly susceptible to modification. This is misleading, for the various types of behaviour in an organism's repertoire are susceptible to modification at different stages. The sucking behaviour of human babies is much influenced by what occurs on the first few occasions they are given the breast: whatever is learnt then is resistant to subsequent modification (Gunther, 1955). The learning of the characteristics of the mother's face which elicit smiling occurs somewhat later (Ambrose, 1960), and that involved for instance in toilet training, reading and many aspects of social and sexual behaviour progressively later still (e.g. Gesell, 1954; Piaget, 1952; Bowlby, 1952). Furthermore, sensitive periods are not characteristic solely of young animals. In mother goats and sheep there is a brief sensitive period after parturition during which the characteristics of the young are learnt: any infants which approach after that time are repelled (Collias, 1956, Blauvelt, 1956). Goats separated from their young for an hour after birth fail to show normal individual-specific maternal behaviour (Hersher *et al.*, 1958), though a dam will sometimes accept a kid after this sensitive period if forcibly confined with it (Hersher *et al.*, 1963). Thus, although the general learning abilities of an organism undoubtedly change with age (Harlow *et al.*, 1962; Welford, 1962), the concept of sensitive period is most usefully applied to specified items of behaviour, and not as a global term to the organism as a whole.

Scott's use of the concept of sensitive period has also been criticized on rather different grounds by Schneirla and Rosenblatt (1963). These workers found that the social approach made by a kitten to its mother before feeding undergoes a course of development in the litter situation which is different from that found in isolated kittens fed from an artificial mother. Isolation of kittens for specified periods at different ages showed that the isolates behaved differently from controls who remained with the litter, at whatever age the isolation occurred: experiences in the litter situation must thus be continuously modifying the approach behaviour (Rosenblatt *et al.*, 1961). Such a finding is not compatible with Scott's picture of critical stages in which learning occurs, but is compatible with the view that the particular characteristics of the natural approach behaviour are shaped by a continuous interaction between organism and environment which changes in nature as development progresses.

Even when used in this way, the term "sensitive period" may involve a considerable simplification. We have already seen how the responsiveness of Great Tits to small brightly coloured objects at first increases with age, reaches a maximum at about 15 weeks, and then declines. These changes are influenced by experience (Vince, 1960): the age at which the learning involved in this response occurs most readily also varies with experience. Sensitive periods therefore do not occur at fixed stages in an animal's development, and it is necessary in every case to search for those factors which change with age and influence the ease with which learning can occur. This may involve a detailed analysis of the ontogeny of behaviour, and a study of the interactions between the organism and its environment at each moment in its development (Schneirla, 1956).

Another complication is suggested by an experiment by Denenberg *et al.* (1960), though it is concerned not with a sensitive period for learning, but with a sensitive period to an environmental influence which later affected learning. They studied the effects of stimulating mice at 2–3 days, 8–9 days and 15–16 days, with various strengths of electric current, on avoidance learning in adulthood. The age at which the stimulation was administered was clearly important, but the age at which the stimulation had the most marked effect varied with the current strength. Studies such as this (*see also* e.g. Denenberg, 1962, in press) suggest that even to consider each type of behaviour to have a sensitive period for each kind of environmental influence is an oversimplification: nevertheless "sensitive period" remains useful as a descriptive term.

The factors which limit sensitive periods for learning are as diverse as the types of behaviour involved. Some factors which may set the earlier limit to a sensitive period were mentioned on p. 366: of more interest are those which bring it to an end. One is a change in the response repertoire of the organism. Razran (1935) has suggested that certain types of simple conditioning experiments on children become increasingly difficult with age because of the increasing self-consciousness and sophistication of the subjects.

We have already seen that the learning involved in the "following" response of nidifugous birds eventually becomes impossible because of the overriding fear of the strange object or environment used to elicit the response (p. 367). Here the sensitive period for learning is in fact brought to an end by the learning process itself—learning involves building up a schema of the familiar, and it is deviations from this which elicit fear (*see* Bateson, 1963 cited here on p. 370). Similarly, on the response side, the ability of a Chaffinch to learn new songs seems to be brought to an end by the learning of the songs used in its first breeding season (Thorpe, 1958), and the ability of chicks reared in darkness for a fortnight to learn to peck seems to be prevented by the intrusion of previously learnt incompatible responses (Padilla, 1935).

The problem of sensitive periods has recently been reviewed elsewhere (Thorpe, 1961a; Hinde, 1962a) and the examples cited here are intended to emphasize one point only, namely, that the problem of sensitive periods for learning is the problem of the ontogeny of behaviour itself. Only when the changing behaviour and abilities of the organism have been analysed in terms of its interaction with the environment at each stage can the factors limiting sensitive periods be understood. The problems involved are important not only from a theoretical viewpoint. Since development depends on an interplay between organism and environment, disturbance in the latter (and we may here include all forms of sensory input, proprioceptive as well as exteroceptive) may have far-reaching repercussions. Often there are regulating mechanisms to minimize such effects, but an environmental deficiency during a sensitive period may be difficult to correct. The disabilities of deaf children are likely to be cumulative as communication by language becomes more important, affecting diverse aspects of behaviour and personality, but the effects can be minimized if appropriate measures to establish such communication as circumstances permit are taken sufficiently early (Lewis, 1963).

24.2. Summary

1. Learning abilities change with age. The changes are related to motivation, the development of perceptual abilities, changes in inquisitiveness with age, and other factors. They depend upon experience.
2. No particular type of learning occurs with equal facility at all stages of the life cycle. When it occurs most easily at a particular stage of the life cycle, we can refer to that stage as a sensitive period. Sensitive periods are usually not sharply defined. Some of the factors which limit them are mentioned.

25

Interaction in Development

Earlier we noted that studies of development usually involve the isolation of particular aspects of behaviour, whereas in practice the development of each faculty and type of behaviour depends on the development of others in the course of a complex interaction between organism and environment. We may consider as an example one of the few cases where this has been worked out in detail—the continual and progressive interaction between cat and kittens which begins at or before parturition. Components of this interaction are the hormonal condition and related behavioural changes in the mother, and the motivational and perceptual development of the kittens; related changes in both mother and young are based upon experience in the litter situation. Unfortunately, it is not possible here to do more than hint at the intricate mosaic of factors which has been revealed by careful study under controlled conditions (Schneirla *et al.*, 1961; Rosenblatt *et al.*, 1961; Schneirla, Rosenblatt and Tobach, 1963 and references cited; Ewer, 1959, 1961).

Parturition itself involves both internal changes in the female (hormonal and muscular) and a change in her environment (appearance of neonate and birth fluids), and the female exhibits a number of different types of behaviour (self-licking, licking newborn or floor, eating after-birth, etc.). During parturition intervals of intense activity, which facilitate delivery, are interspersed with periods of exhaustion and rest, during which the kittens often initiate nursing. Throughout, the female directs much of her behaviour (for instance licking) towards the posterior part of her body: this may be induced by changes in cutaneous sensitivity, and contribute towards parturition.*

After birth, relations between mother and kitten are strongly influenced by the latter's attachment and orientation to the "home corner", a region of the cage which has been saturated chemically by the female. As early as a few hours after birth, odours from this site, as well as contacts with the female, have a quieting effect on the neonate. Initially the kitten orients to this corner on a tactuo-chemical basis, but later (about 5 days) visual orientation to the home region, and later still to the entire cage, is achieved.

* Particularly interesting observations on the parturition of the rodent *Acomys coharinus* have been given by Dieterlen (1962). This species, unlike most of its relatives, is relatively large when born. Obstetrical help is often given by other females present at the birth.

In the early days of feeding (in about the first 20 days), nearly all nursings are initiated by the female. She lies down around the kittens with her mammary surface against them. At first, the neonates gain the nipples only after much nuzzling and fumbling, but from the first day onward their suckling behaviour is influenced by experience. Individual methods of suckling, often involving specific nipple preferences, are soon developed (see also McBride, 1963; Ewer, 1961). Between days 20 to 30, feeding is initiated by either kittens or mother, the changes paralleling perceptual development (some aspects of which were discussed on pp. 348–57), increased efficiency in feeding and orientation by the kittens, and changes in their mobility, vigour, and so on. The feeding process provides a focus around which much of the learning involved in the establishment of the social relationship occurs, but during this period other responses (e.g. "play") appear. During the next period the initiation of feeding depends more and more upon the initiative of the kittens as they follow the mother about. The female actively repels and avoids the kittens, and the feeding periods become progressively shorter.

By rearing kittens from different ages in isolation on artificial mothers for periods of about two weeks, Rosenblatt et al. (1961) were able to show that kittens are guided to the nipple by their responses to the shape of the mother's body, and to analyse in detail the various types of adjustment between mother and infants, and the manner in which these depend on perceptuo-motor development in the latter. The temporary removal of kittens from mother and litter, and their subsequent return to the litter situation, emphasized "the necessity of a continued behavioural and functional interchange with female and littermates if the kitten is to develop an adequate suckling adjustment typical of its age group. Psychological processes concerning perceptual and behavioural organization are required in which organic factors underlying reciprocal stimulation play a basic, inextricable role" (Schneirla et al., 1961).

A comparable analysis of the maternal behaviour of the rat, in which the role of mother-infant interaction in influencing the mother's changing responsiveness to the pups, has been given by Rosenblatt et al. (1963, and references cited). In both these groups of studies emphasis has been laid on developmental and experiential factors. The importance of strain differences and of genetic factors has been emphasized in a series of studies of races of domestic rabbits (summarized Ross et al., 1963).

It will be apparent from this brief survey that an understanding of the development of social behaviour can be obtained only from study of the interaction between the developing organism at each stage, its companions and its environment. Similar principles apply to all other vertebrates.

26

Some Aspects of Learning

Learning, perhaps the most interesting, important and intensively studied group of processes involved in the development of behaviour, will not be discussed at length. An extensive review of work on submammalian species has recently been given by Thorpe (1963a), and the intensive work on rats, monkeys and pigeons carried out during the last few decades is reviewed in many text-books. Estes *et al.* (1954), Hilgard (1956), Koch (1959), and Hilgard *et al.* (1961) have given summaries and critical appraisals of the theoretical views to which the latter has given rise. Here, discussion is limited to a few issues which have been controversial among learning theorists, or which merit reconsideration in the light of contributions from workers outside the main streams of learning theory.

26.1. What is Learning?

While there is usually agreement as to whether any particular change in behavioural organization is an example of learning, there is no generally accepted definition. Differences between definitions largely reflect the pre-occupations of the authors. The psychologist uses the term with reference to a relatively permanent change in behaviour, the physiologist to an inferred change in neural substrate. The biologist may limit its use to "adaptive" change, while the psychopathologist uses it to include the acquisition of tics and motor stereotypes. Most definitions, however, utilize exclusion—learning refers to changes which cannot be understood in terms of maturational growth processes in the nervous system, fatigue, or sensory adaptation. Definition by exclusion is seldom wholly satisfactory, and here this is especially the case. For instance, maturation is difficult to define except either by exclusion of learning, in which case the argument becomes circular; or in terms of growth processes which may not be separable from the as yet unknown processes on which learning depends.

A second difficulty is that, although it is rarely stated explicitly, learning is usually taken to refer to changes in the central nervous system. Many behavioural adjustments involve both intraneural and extraneural changes which interact with each other, so that a change in behaviour produced by experience may entail both. Furthermore, while with higher animals it is convenient to restrict learning to cases believed to involve change in the nervous system, the question of whether modifications in behaviour shown by a single-celled animal are the result of learning then becomes partly a matter of definition.

Yet another difficulty with the learning concept is that it is often taken to refer only to relatively permanent effects on behaviour. We saw in Chapter 13, however, that it is sometimes difficult to separate decremental effects consequent upon exposure to a stimulus according to their degree of permanence. In addition, permanent changes may depend on short-term effects (Chapter 13).

In practice, this difficulty of definition is unimportant, except in one respect. When it is glossed over, there is inevitably a tendency to regard learning as homogeneous, a single category of changes requiring but one explanation and to be understood in terms of a single set of laws. As long as learning is defined by exclusion, the onus of proof rests with those who hold it to be a homogeneous category.

26.2. How many Kinds of Learning?

In discussing our own behaviour, the processes for which we use the term "learning" are diverse: we talk about learning to ride a bicycle, to judge distances, to recite a poem, to translate French, to find our way home. At the behavioural level of analysis, at any rate, these are pretty diverse. Since different animals achieve the same result in different ways, the diversity of learning processes is likely to be even greater when cross-species generalizations are involved. In spite of this, much effort has been made to relate all examples of learning to one or two basic types. The problem here is partly one of the level of analysis. All learning, however broadly defined in terms of behaviour, could depend on similar processes at a sub-cellular level. But since we know little about these processes, and since learning is in any case usually defined behaviourally, it is necessary to assess the degree of diversity of learning as studied at the behavioural level.

(a) Short-term v. Long-term Learning

In the first place, a distinction is often drawn between short-term and long-term or permanent learning processes. This distinction is based partly on the observation that a person who has been concussed loses his memory for events which occurred just before the accident, but not for earlier ones. This has been paralleled in the laboratory. Rats were given electroconvulsive shock at various intervals after each training trial on an avoidance conditioning task: those animals which received the ECS within a few minutes of the trial subsequently performed less well than those which received it later (Duncan, 1949; Gerard, 1961; McGaugh, 1965). Cooling to 2°C makes little difference to the subsequent performance (Mrosovsky, 1963), but the period during which memory can be eliminated by shock may be prolonged by cooling.

Such evidence has been used to support the view that the consequences of an experience first affect a short-term storage mechanism, thus producing a "short-term memory". Estimation of the period during which this decays vary from a few seconds to a few hours. It is, however, held to be distinct from the very short-term pre-perceptual trace which decays in about $\frac{1}{2}$ second: a number of studies on human subjects have shown that material must be responded to during its presentation or within this $\frac{1}{2}$ second period afterwards if it is to be subsequently available for recall (e.g. Averbach *et al.*, 1961; Mackworth, 1962).

Short-term storage is also held to be distinct from long-term storage. For instance, it involves activity in neural mechanisms which decays autonomously with time, and is susceptible to interruption by mechanical, electroconvulsive and other stimuli, as discussed above. Long-term storage, on the other hand, is believed either to be permanent or near-permanent, with the stored associations subject to only slow decay by disuse. It is usually held that long-term storage requires the preceding short-term neural activity for its consolidation (Hebb, 1949). Broadbent (1958) has emphasized that the mechanisms of short-term storage have a limited capacity which can be overloaded if the rate of presentation of information exceeds a certain level, while the long-term storage is effectively infinitely expandable.

The evidence on which the distinction between short-term and long-term storage depends has been drawn primarily from studies of rat and human subjects. That it may be valid even outside the vertebrates is suggested by some experiments with *Octopus*. A blinded *Octopus* soon learns to reject inedible objects by means of tactual cues. If the object is presented in a rapid series of tests to one arm, it comes to be rejected by that arm but not by other arms. If the tests are spaced, however, the effect spreads to other arms, none of which will accept the object. Wells (1959) thus suggests that the changes involved in learning related to one of the arms take some time to spread through the supraoesophageal lobes of the brain.

In addition, we have already seen in a wide variety of species that, when responsiveness wanes under conditions of constant or repetitive stimulation, it is often convenient to divide the waning into a short-term component, subject to fairly rapid recovery, and a long-term more or less permanent one (*see* Chapter 13).

Although a distinction between short-term and long-term memory traces has thus been valuable in a wide variety of contexts, its validity has been questioned in others: certain experiments on the storage of verbal material by adult human subjects suggest a continuity between short-term and long-term storage (Melton, 1963, in press). The question is thus not yet fully resolved.

(b) Other Classifications of Learning Types

Leaving aside the question of short-term learning, we may now turn to more permanent effects. Most theorists have been concerned with only one or two animal species, and some have worked with the assumption that all (long-term) learning is of one type. Watson (1919) and Guthrie (e.g. 1935), for instance, both use a single principle of conditioning or associative learning which is related to the Pavlovian conditioning experiment. Hull (1943, 1952) likewise made reference to only a single type of learning. Nevertheless by introducing intervening variables he was able to give descriptions of a surprising wealth of behavioural phenomena.

More commonly, however, at least two basic forms of learning are postulated (e.g. Schlosberg, 1937; Maier *et al.*, 1935). As an example, the distinction used by Skinner (e.g. 1938) may be considered. In the first place, Skinner recognized two kinds of responses: those which are immediately elicited by known stimuli (respondents), and those which, prior to conditioning, are not necessarily correlated with any identifiable stimulus (operants). The knee jerk is a respondent, the pressing of a lever by a rat an operant. Skinner relates this distinction between two types of response to different kinds of conditioning.

Respondents are susceptible to classical or Pavlovian conditioning, which is referred to as "Type S". Its occurrence depends on a temporal correlation between a to-be-conditioned stimulus (e.g. a tone) and an unconditioned stimulus (e.g. food). The choice of response is determined by the responses that the unconditioned stimulus will elicit; food will elicit salivation. With repeated presentations of tone followed by food, the tone alone will come to elicit the response of salivation. The paradigm is as follows, the arrow indicating the operations responsible for conditioning.

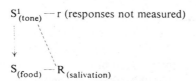

Operant responses, on the other hand, are held to be susceptible to Type R conditioning. If a response (e.g. lever-pressing) is followed by reinforcement (e.g. food), it appears more often. To begin with neither the lever nor the food elicit lever-pressing, but once the animal does press the lever, food is presented: if the animal has been deprived of food, the appearance of food increases the probability that it will press the lever again, and the following stimulus-response chain will be established:

$$S^1_{(lever)} - R_{(lever\ press)} \xrightarrow{\quad} S_{(food)} - r \text{ (responses not measured).}$$

Although, as conditioning proceeds, the lever will set the occasion for a bar press in a temporal sequence similar to the tone's elicitation of salivation, the ions which went into building up the two relations are quite different. in Type R conditioning, the operant response acts upon the environ- ..... to produce the reinforcement, it is often referred to as instrumental conditioning. An essentially similar distinction is made by Konorski (1948), though he labels Classical (Type S) Conditioning as "Classical Conditioning Type I" and "Instrumental (Type R) Conditioning" as "Classical Conditioning Type II".

One of the earliest examples of instrumental conditioning is provided by Grindley's (1932) work with guinea-pigs. The animal was placed in the experimental situation, which included an auditory signal. Whenever it made a certain movement (for instance, turning of the head), it was rewarded with food. Head movements then became more frequent in the experimental situation. Thus the stimuli indicative of the experimental situation set the occasion for the response, but did not elicit it in the same manner as, say, light elicits pupillary contraction.

Instrumental conditioning has been studied especially in the "Skinner box". This contains a mechanism which the animal can operate by a suitable response, usually pressing a lever in the case of a rat or pecking a disc in the case of a pigeon. Suitable reinforcement is delivered to the subject either with every response, or on a previously arranged schedule, e.g. every Nth response, or on the first response after an interval of n seconds from a previous response or reinforcement. This "schedule of reinforcement" (Ferster et al., 1957) is of crucial importance in determining the subsequent rate and pattern of responding. Removal of the reinforcement in either classical or instrumental conditioning results in a gradual decrease in responding. However, with suitable training, instrumental conditioning can occur when only one in a hundred or more responses are reinforced. Furthermore, the rate and pattern of responding in extinction depends on the previous schedule of reinforcement: in general, if the reinforcement presentations are spread out in the training schedule in any manner which makes the change to an extinction condition difficult to discriminate, resistance to extinction is high.

In most laboratory experiments on operant conditioning there is no initial relation between the cue stimulus and the response. The response becomes more frequent in the presence of the stimulus only as a result of the conditioning process. It seems likely that in nature the eliciting function of stimuli plays an important role, especially with responses of young animals (Clayton, personal communication). Two examples of such responses are the sucking of the human baby when a nipple is placed in the mouth, and the pecking of young nidicolous birds at a wide variety of objects which contrast with the background. Although, at the start, many pecks do not bring edible objects, long spells of pecking still occur, and enable a discrimination between food and non-food objects to be made. We actually know little about the development and maintenance of such responses of young animals. Further laboratory work with these types of stimuli and responses would be most profitable, both for the learning theorist and the ethologist.

The theorists mentioned so far have been concerned in the first instance with a limited range of animal types. From the point of view of economy, their attempts to interpret diverse instances of learning in terms of few principles have been very successful. When a wider range of animals is considered, however, the learning phenomena become more obviously heterogeneous. There is a virtue in not losing sight of this heterogeneity. Tolman (1932, 1959) met this point by including in his theoretical system a series of capacity laws. These may be listed as follows (*see* Hilgard, 1956):

(*a*) Formal means-end-capacities, that is, the ability to form an expectancy of a stimulus and act in accordance with it.
(*b*) Discriminative and manipulative capacities.
(*c*) Retentivity.
(*d*) Means-end-capacities needed for alternative routes, detours, etc.
(*e*) Ideational capacities, permitting, for instance, the comparison of alternatives.
(*f*) Creative instability.

Rather than postulate a basic number of types of learning, Tolman took three types of learning experiments—classical conditioning; trial and error learning, as studied in a maze; and inventive learning. He then interpreted each of these in terms of the capacity laws, using, in addition, other laws relating to the nature of the material and the manner of its presentation. The simpler cases of learning require fewer laws than do the more complex ones: thus, classical conditioning requires only capacity laws (*a*), (*b*) and (*c*). Trial-and-error learning requires also (*d*), though (*e*) enters into the more complex cases. Inventive learning requires also creative instability (*f*).

Thorpe (1956, 1963a), who has provided the most wide-ranging review of animal learning, has met this problem of diversity in another way. Using a descriptive classification of learning types, he accepts that the underlying mechanisms may be different in different species, and thus leaves open the extent to which examples of the same type drawn from different phyla depend on similar mechanisms. His types are as follows:

(*a*) *Habituation*. This is defined as: "The relatively persistent waning of a response as a result of repeated stimulation which is not followed by any kind of reinforcement." Habituation is further characterized as being specific to a particular stimulus: its relative permanence also distinguishes it from fatigue and sensory adaptation. A classical example is given by Humphrey's (1933) work on the snail's (*Helix albolabris*) withdrawal of its tentacles in response to mechanical shock. With repetition of the stimulus, the response gradually wanes. Comparable examples can readily be found in every phylum of the animal kingdom.

In so far as both involve a waning in response strength, there are resemblances between habituation and the extinction of an operant response. The distinction between them seems to depend only on the manner in which the response was acquired in the first instance, and it is perhaps for this reason that habituation was ignored by the earlier theorists. It must be noted, however, that extinction involves the removal of a reinforcing stimulus, while "habituation" is sometimes applied to cases of response decrement in which the absent reinforcement has not been identified.

Thorpe points out that, at any rate in the simpler cases, habituation involves merely a decrease in intensity or number of responses, and he thus regards it as the simplest form of learning. However, two types of evidence suggest that some cases of habituation may not be as simple as they appear. The first comes from Sokolov's (1960) work on the extinction of the orientation reflex in dogs discussed in Chapter 6. This comes within the above definition of habituation, but seems to imply some sort of central reorganization in the form of a "neuronal model". Whether such results could also be obtained with animals at a simpler level of organization, such as snails, remains to be seen: it is at least likely that the mechanisms underlying habituation differ considerably up the phyletic scale.

The second line of evidence has also been mentioned earlier. Studies of the mobbing behaviour of the Chaffinch show that response to a stimulus is accompanied by complex changes which may lead to both an increase and a decrease in response strength on subsequent occasions, and which decay at different rates (pp. 207–16). If habituation is defined in terms of the waning of the response, it is the resultant of these processes, and thus far from simple. If, on the other hand, habituation is held to refer only to the relatively permanent decremental processes, it cannot be measured directly.

A further difficulty, arising from the reference to absence of reinforcement in Thorpe's definition (*see* above), is discussed on p. 415. It will be apparent that the category of habituation calls attention to phenomena previously rather neglected, but is itself likely to include changes depending on mechanisms of differing complexity, some of which are less simple than they appear.

(*b*) *Classical Conditioning.* Thorpe, like other earlier writers, regards classical (Type S) conditioning, as investigated by Pavlov, as an artificially isolated part of the learning process, and feels that, as usually conceived, it is unlikely to form the fundamental unit out of which more complicated learning processes are constructed. Thus he emphasizes that the reflex is in any case an idealized concept; that stimuli are never in fact simple, for higher animals always respond to the situation as a whole with the stimulus presented by the experimenter differentiated against it; and that the conditioned response is always in fact "anticipatory", the animal behaving as if "expecting" the unconditioned stimulus rather than just attaching the unconditioned response to the new stimulus.

The conventional view of the conditioned reflex is, in fact, a simplification. It may not involve merely the association of a new stimulus with the unconditioned response, for the conditioned response is seldom the same as the unconditioned one, and often is only part of it (Hilgard et al., 1961). If the restrictions on the animal's freedom of movement usually imposed in conditioning experiments are removed, the conditioned response is accompanied by behaviour which appears to the observer to be appetitive to the arrival of the unconditioned stimulus.

Skinner was inclined to believe that Type S conditioning is limited to autonomic responses, but some workers doubt whether Type S, in Skinner's strict sense, ever gives a complete formulation if each reflex is considered in isolation. Thus it is argued that, in many of the situations in which classical conditioning is said to occur, the response studied (e.g. salivation) is accompanied by skeletal responses which may be conditioned according to the instrumental paradigm: where they seem to be absent, the conditioning is sometimes extremely difficult (Young, 1954), though it has been achieved (Solomon et al., 1962).

Conditioning as usually defined may cover changes in behaviour of markedly differing degrees of complexity. It is hard to avoid the view that conditioning in annelid worms involves little other than a change in stimulus response relations. Equally, however, it seems likely that the conditioning of (e.g.) salivation in man is more than a mere switching of connections, and involves a much more far-reaching reorganization of behaviour. Like habituation, therefore, classical conditioning, as defined behaviourally, covers changes which differ greatly in complexity (*see also* Zener, 1937; Hilgard et al., 1961).

(c) *Trial-and-error Learning.* This is defined by Thorpe as "The development of an association, as the result of reinforcement during appetitive behaviour, between a stimulus or a situation and an independent motor action as an item in that behaviour when both stimulus and motor action precede the reinforcement and the motor action is not the inevitable inherited response to the reinforcement" (Thorpe, 1956, 1963a). Learning to run mazes and open problem boxes provide classic examples. In practice, Thorpe regards trial-and-error learning as involving both classical conditioning, which modifies the external stimulus situation with which the response is associated, and instrumental conditioning. In his view, pure instrumental conditioning involves the "establishment of an association between a voluntary motor act as part of appetitive behaviour primarily as perceived by the animals' proprioceptive organs, and the normal reward or reinforcement...", and in its pure form is limited to some exceptional cases of the acquisition of skill. Thus Thorpe argues that all cases of instrumental conditioning must involve reference to a stimulus situation (external and proprioceptive) which sets the occasion for the response, and that there is therefore no good reason for distinguishing instrumental learning as a separate part of trial-and-error learning. At this point Thorpe does not allow the distinction made by Skinner between respondent and operant responses (p. 403), and the different relations between stimulus and response in the two cases. He holds, instead, that pure instrumental learning would be as much an isolated part of the learning process as he already believes classical conditioning to be.

Behaviour which comes within the category of trial-and-error learning may vary markedly in complexity. Thus Schneirla (1959) has emphasized the fundamental differences between the learning involved when an insect learns a maze, and that occurring in a rat in a similar situation. The insect first masters the individual choice points, and later integrates the habits thus formed in a stereotyped way, while the rat starts its local learning and its overall integration together on the first run.

Indeed, just as with classical conditioning, there is increasing evidence that generalizations about instrumental or trial-and-error learning may lead to over-simplification. In many cases the learning cannot be described in terms of new S–R connections but requires the postulation of quite complex intermediaries: this is discussed later (pp. 409–14).

(d) *Latent Learning*. Thorpe defines this as "The association of indifferent stimuli or situations without patent reward". Since the phenomena studied in this context are relevant to problems discussed later in this chapter, we must discuss them in some detail. In most maze-learning experiments, a reward is present in the goal-box throughout training. If rats are allowed daily access to a maze which has no reward in the goal-box, the number of errors they make falls only gradually by comparison with animals that are rewarded. If, after a number of days, the previously unrewarded animals are given a reward in the goal-box, their performance improves very rapidly to a level similar to that shown by animals which have been rewarded throughout. Thus the initially unrewarded group must have learnt something during their early trials—their learning was "latent" and did not show up in performance until activated by the reward. This has been described by saying that the rat initially learns "what leads to what", in the same way as it learns the relations between objects when exploring a novel spatial array (*see* p. 410). In more general terms this can be described more accurately by saying that the rat learns conditional probabilities of association between stimuli.

This classical latent learning experiment was the forerunner of many others which have been reviewed in detail by Thistlethwaite (1951) and MacCorquodale *et al.* (1954). These include studies in which the experimenter provided a reward, but one irrelevant to the animal's motivational state as controlled in the experiment. For instance, rats which are hungry but not thirsty are given forced runs through a T-maze leading to food in one arm and water in the other. If subsequently tested when thirsty, they will tend to choose the water side: learning thus took place under an irrelevant motivation. After a critical review of the literature, MacCorquodale *et al.* (*loc. cit.*) concluded that, although some experiments had given negative results, the majority of experiments on latent learning appear to demonstrate its occurrence.

The essential element in Thorpe's definition of latent learning is absence of reward. This in itself, however, cannot serve to differentiate it from trial-and-error learning. As we shall see, some theorists do not regard reinforcement as essential for trial-and-error learning, so the distinction from latent learning disappears. Even for reinforcement theorists there need be no distinction: Hull (1952) came to regard habit strength as acquired independently of the magnitude of the reinforcement, so any "latent" learning could occur in relation to some postulated minimal reinforcement, such as return to the home cage at the end of the maze: it is thus not separable from trial-and-error (but *see* Watson, 1961).

Thorpe also emphasizes that latent learning entails a transfer of behaviour learnt in one motivational context to another. This is partly a matter of definition, for it is experiments in which an animal learns under one motivation and is tested under another that are labelled as latent learning. In a situation identical except that the motivation was not changed during the test period, the learning would be called trial-and-error.

It will be argued later that the relationship between latent learning and trial-and-error learning is indeed close. In higher organisms, at least, the latter involves two processes: a learning of the characteristics of the situation, and a translation of this into performance. Latent learning involves only the former.

(*e*) *Insight Learning.* This involves "the production of a new adaptive response as a result of insight", where insight is defined as "the apprehension of relations". Thorpe includes here also "imprinting" (*see* p. 365). The controversy as to whether insight learning differs in kind or only in degree from trial-and-error learning is an old one. The argument has been prolonged largely because insight learning was held by some to involve "ideation", while trial-and-error learning could perhaps be explained in purely connectionist terms. We shall discuss this problem again in the next section.

Two points about this classification of learning types, both emphasized by Thorpe himself, must be repeated here. First, the categories intergrade; second, each contains examples of greatly differing complexity. The reasons are worth noting: each of Thorpe's categories may contain perceptual learning (*see* Chapter 21), and the extent to which this occurs varies between responses and between phyla.

26.3. Cognitive and S-R Theory

In higher animals, at any rate, learning rarely involves a mere shifting of relationships between external stimuli and responses. To understand all but the simplest types of behaviour, it is necessary to postulate events intervening between stimulus and response, but there has been considerable disagreement as to their nature. Behaviouristically oriented psychologists have regarded them as covert stimulus-response sequences, and have relied especially on kinesthetic stimuli as integrators of behaviour. "Cognitive" theorists, on the other hand, lay emphasis on the restructuring of central processes without regarding these central processes as basically similar to stimulus-response sequences. To put it at its simplest, a stimulus-response explanation of the learning of a maze would be given in terms of learning which responses must be made to which stimuli, while a cognitive explanation might be in terms of the learning of a "cognitive-map" of the maze such that the animal acquires a knowledge of "what leads to what", or of the probability that this stimulus will be followed by that. In practice, the results of most learning experiments can be interpreted in terms of either view, theorists of both types displaying remarkable ingenuity in accommodating the diverse data now available (Osgood, 1953).

The controversy is an old one, and all its ramifications will not be pursued here. It is worthwhile, however, to consider some experiments bearing on the nature of the central changes which occur in various types of learning situation.

An early experiment provides a convenient starting point. An auditory stimulus was given to dogs at intervals, followed in each case by a visual one. Any learning which occurred was at least not apparent. Subsequently a response was conditioned to one of the stimuli. It was then found that the response could also be elicited by the other stimulus (Brogden, 1939). The early presentations must therefore have led to some association between the stimuli. Although some of the early studies on this "sensory pre-conditioning" were inadequately controlled, the occurrence of learning under these circumstances has since been well established (review by Seidel, 1959). While such experiments appear to demonstrate the formation of direct associations between stimuli, they pose no real problem for the S–R theorist: covert S–R sequences could serve as intermediaries.

More recently a number of experiments have shown that variations in perceptual experience during development, although producing no effects apparent in behaviour at the time, may have consequences which can be revealed in subsequent testing. For instance, we have already considered evidence indicating that rats, if given early experience of a circle and a triangle without differential reinforcement, will subsequently learn to discriminate between them more readily than do rats without such experience (*see* p. 350). Such processes, by which an organism's readiness or ability to respond to variables of physical stimulation are improved, are often referred to as "perceptual learning" (Gibson *et al.*, 1955). The importance of perceptual learning in a wide range of species has recently been stressed by Thorpe (1956, 1963a). He argues that even the simplest stimulus is a relational one, so that perception always involves relational properties. On his view species which require perceptual experience (*see* pp. 356–7) are using it to build up, by various learning processes, the ability to respond to the significant patterns presented by the environment.

Whether or not perceptual learning differs from learning in a classical or instrumental conditioning situation in any absolute sense is not yet clear. One suggested criterion is that, as perceptual learning proceeds, the organism responds more and more selectively to the particular type of stimulus, the implication being that in conditioning, by contrast, the animal generalizes progressively more readily to other related stimuli. However no simple statement can be made as to whether continued training in the conditioning situation will increase or decrease the slope of the generalization gradient (e.g. Hilgard *et al.*, 1961). In any case, a conditioning situation which does not involve perceptual learning, and yet is operationally similar to the situations in which perceptual learning is studied, is hard to find—in part because attempts to define perceptual learning have been inadequate (Bevan, 1961) and not themselves operational.

The experiments on perceptual learning show that experience may produce changes in internal organization (and we can call it cognitive or neuronal organization according to our theoretical bias) which are not immediately revealed by changes in behaviour. We commonly talk about people learning the properties of stimulus objects or the relations between stimuli without reference to any immediate change in behaviour, and it is also legitimate to use this language for describing some animal experiments. This does not *necessarily* mean that the learning is not mediated by a response. We have already seen that, in higher mammals, the learning of the characteristics of visual space involves comparison of the feedback stimulation received as a result of a response with an expected feedback (pp. 353–7): learning is S–R–S rather than just S–S. Whether perceptual learning *always* requires mediation by a response (e.g. eye-movements) is not known.

Changes in central organization which are not immediately revealed in behaviour may accompany learning as studied in many conventional contexts. Lawrence (1949, 1950) showed that an acquired ability to discriminate between two stimuli had some measure of independence from the particular response which the animal was required to make to them. For instance, when rats learnt to discriminate between cues in one situation, the acquired distinctiveness of the cues was transferred to new situations even when the significance of the cues was reversed. Lawrence interpreted his results in terms of a hypothetical mediating response which made the cues more distinctive (*see also* Walker, 1942; Estes, 1942, 1948; Schoenfeld *et al.*, 1950).

More recently Sutherland (1959) has suggested that discrimination learning is a two-stage process: the animal first learns to respond to the quality by which the two stimulus situations are maximally differentiated—for instance it learns that the selection must be made in terms of brightness, or of shape—and then it learns to attach particular responses to the characters in question. This view accounts satisfactorily for various experimental results which pose difficulties for other theories; for instance mammals reverse a discrimination faster with over-training on the original task. This could be due to a more thorough learning of the types of characters relevant which is not revealed by the response scores during the over-learning period: this is, of course, still appropriate after the reversal (*see also* Mackintosh, 1964 and references cited). Similar results have been obtained with octopuses (Sutherland *et al.*, 1963).

Mackintosh (1963) likewise interpreted the extinction performances of non-overtrained and overtrained rats on the assumptions that discrimination learning involves two stages, and that with non-overtrained animals extinction affects mainly the first stage (isolation of the relevant stimulus dimension), while with overtrained animals it affects the second stage (attachment of responses to stimuli). Other experiments pointing to a similar conclusion were discussed in Chapter 21.

Evidence that some aspects of maze running can be understood more easily in cognitive than stimulus-response terms is provided by experiments on "place-learning". The cruder stimulus-response theories would suggest that an animal which has learnt a maze moves from start to goal according to a fixed sequence of movements. However in some experiments interference with the movement sequence does not prevent attainment of the goal. Rats which had learnt to walk through a maze subsequently demonstrated their learning when severe cerebellar damage caused gross abnormalities in their locomotor pattern (Lashley *et al.*, 1929).

If an elevated maze is arranged in such a way that rats have to learn either a spatial habit (i.e. always to go to the same place, irrespective of whether this involves turning to right or left) or a response (e.g. turning left), the former is the more easily learnt if cues from outside the maze are readily available (Tolman *et al.*, 1946, 1947). If such cues are not available, however, response learning is more important (e.g. Blodgett *et al.*, 1948). Maze-running may thus involve either the learning of spatial habits or that of responses or both: the relative importance of each varies with the cues available, and also with the stage in training reached (Kendler *et al.*, 1948). Other experiments have investigated the extent to which rats could make use of alternative paths when the main route to the goal was blocked: on the whole they favoured the place-learning hypothesis, though they also indicated that acquisition of the "cognitive map" is surprisingly influenced by such variables as "alley width", and that the map does not correspond in any very direct way with the maze (e.g. Keller *et al.*, 1936; Ritchie, 1948; *see also* Deese, 1951). Seldom cited in this context, the work on the abilities of birds to navigate (*see* Chapter 7) would also seem to stretch any theory couched in simple stimulus-response terms beyond the limits of credibility. Another line of evidence drawn from experiments on maze-learning is that, in certain types of mazes, rats appear to adopt systematic modes of solution which are tried in turn until success is achieved (Krechevsky, 1937). Such a finding is again more easily interpreted in cognitive terms.

From these experiments, it is reasonable to conclude that many of the phenomena of learning experiments cannot economically be described in simple stimulus-response terms. The theorist who would attempt to do so must concede that the covert responses have behavioural laws different from those governing overt responses: such a conclusion results in a loss of the logic of the stimulus-response approach. The evidence quoted has been drawn primarily from laboratory experiments on rats: we may now refer to some work on other species, mostly already discussed in earlier pages, which seems to demand explanation in terms of a central change that is (or can be) initially independent of any change in overt behaviour and cannot easily be interpreted in terms of covert S–R sequences.

(*a*) *Orientation.* Many orientational responses of insects involve either movement bearing a similar relationship to two sorts of stimulation (e.g. light and gravity) or movement whose relationship to one sort of stimulation varies with time. Such cases can be understood more easily in terms of a control system with variable Sollwert than in terms of multiple S–R mechanisms, each serving a different orientation, together with a mechanism to select between them (*see* Chapter 7). Although much simpler than the other examples discussed here, these cases of orientation in insects are of special interest in indicating the existence of a type of mechanism which both S–R and cognitive theorists might own.

(*b*) *Search image, reward expectancy and selective attention.* Much appetitive behaviour involves a scanning of the environment until a particular set of stimuli are encountered, and can be understood on the assumption that the animal is using a "search image". In other words, searching involves not only a change in behaviour, but also a change in responsiveness not immediately apparent in behaviour (*see* Chapter 5). Similarly, as we have seen, the phenomena of selective attention cannot be understood in terms of a passive and peripheral filter, but must involve central mechanisms sensitive to subtle categories of stimulation (*see* Chapter 6).

(*c*) *Habituation.* As discussed on pp. 98–9, some of Sokolov's experiments on the extinction of the orientation reflex seem to be explicable only in terms of some central restructuring. Sokolov referred to the process as the formation of a "neuronal model", a pseudo-physiological term which has the merit of implying a direction for future research, but does not explain the phenomena any more than does description in terms of a "cognitive schema".

(*d*) *Song-learning.* As discussed in Chapter 20, the development of the species-characteristic song by Chaffinches involves first the acquisition of a Sollwert and then the adjustment of the motor output until correspondence with it is achieved.

(*e*) *Imprinting.* The learning associated with the following response of nidifugous birds was discussed in Chapter 22. It involves a learning of the characteristics of the environment which has consequences on the birds' subsequent responsiveness to stimuli in other contexts. Bateson (1964a) has shown that the same early treatment which determines the effectiveness of stimuli for eliciting the following response in an imprinting experiment also influences the speed of learning when the same stimuli are used in a discrimination experiment, where the response is quite different. Clearly the learning is more easily described as involving first a learning of the characteristics of the object, rather than in crude S–R terms.

(*f*) *Conceptualization*. The extent to which sub-human animals are capable of concept formation has long been a matter for speculation, but has only recently been subject to experimental study. Herrnstein and Loveland (1964) trained pigeons to respond to the presence or absence of human beings in photographs. The people might be anywhere on the photograph, and were clothed or nude, adults or children, in varied postures, black white or yellow, in fact so diverse that simple stimulus characterization seems ruled out. These experiments thus suggest very considerable powers of conceptualization in pigeons. (*See also* Köhler, 1955; Millenson 1962.)

Faced with such facts, it is clear that learning which appears to involve only changes in stimulus-response relationships may, in fact, involve a central reorganization not immediately evident in behaviour. This does not necessarily mean that all learning is to be interpreted in this way. Any student of lower animals, familiar with the rigid forms of behaviour which they often show, must believe not only that for some examples of learning descriptions in stimulus-response terms are adequate, but also that anything else would be erroneous.

26.4. The Role of Reinforcement

Another dilemma which has divided learning theorists concerns the role of reinforcement in learning. Some hold that the only requirement for stimuli and responses to become associated is a certain temporal relationship between them —this is learning by "contiguity". Others believe that learning does not occur unless the response is followed by some "reinforcing" stimulus change, be it the satisfaction of a biological need (drive reduction), or the removal of stimuli associated with such need (drive-stimulus reduction), or the appearance of stimuli previously associated with them (secondary reinforcement).

Since connections are not established between all stimuli and all responses which occur in association, the contiguity theorists must explain why some things are learnt and not others. One way in which they have met this difficulty is by suggesting that the reward which appears after the response takes the animal out of the situation, and thus prevents the stimuli which were present just before the reward was obtained from becoming associated with any further responses (e.g. Guthrie, 1935). Another hypothesis is that the motivational state determines which stimuli the organism will attend to, and thus which become associated with each other or with responses (e.g. Tolman, 1959): in this case the reward acts by confirming expectancies about the nature of the environment. Estes (1959) proposes a stimulus sampling, so that only the stimuli being sampled at the moment the response is made get attached to the response.

In part because it provides an apparently ready explanation of why some things are learnt and not others, the concept of reinforcement has proved invaluable in the study of behaviour. Most drive reduction theorists recognize, however, that the drive reduction/drive-stimulus reduction paradigm must be modified in a number of respects. In the first place, many types of behaviour are brought to an end not by the removal of the eliciting factors, but by contact with additional ones, the consummatory stimuli (p. 176). These act as reinforcing agents. For instance, pre-feeding by stomach fistula reduces the amount that rats will eat (Kohn, 1951; Berkun *et al.*, 1952), and rats will learn a discrimination task which leads to their receiving food and water in this way (Miller *et al.*, 1952; Miller *et al.*, 1957). Intromission without ejaculation acts as reinforcement for instrumental learning by the male rat (Sheffield *et al.*, 1951; Kagan, 1955; Whalen, 1961), and liquid made sweet with non-nutritive saccharin is similarly effective (Sheffield *et al.*, 1950). Such experiments must not be over-interpreted to mean that reduction in drive stimuli or need reduction are of no significance. We have seen that eating comes to an end as a result of a number of different feedback mechanisms (Chapters 10 and 15), and the same is true of sexual behaviour (Chapter 15). Thus the several different consequences of responding, including need reduction, could play a role in reinforcement (e.g. Smith *et al.*, 1955, 1957), and may only be reinforcing in interaction with one another (Sterritt *et al.*, 1965).

Second, it is often impossible to predict which stimuli will have reinforcing properties and which will not. For instance Kish *et al.* (1961) found that the manipulation of a movable lever functions as a reinforcing stimulus, and interpret this as supporting the hypothesis that *any* environmental change may be reinforcing. Some other examples were given in Chapter 9.

Third, we have seen that the mobbing response of the Chaffinch is accompanied by both self-enhancing and self-suppressing effects. If enhancement of the response is associated with reinforcement, and response decrement with absence of reinforcement, how can both conditions obtain at once? Similarly Whalen (1961) notes that mounting without intromission has both positive and negative effects on the subsequent sexual behaviour of male rats, the performance on a later occasion being determined by the balance between them. In addition, "extinction with reinforcement" sometimes occurs in conditioning experiments when the conditioned stimulus is presented repeatedly even though it is accompanied by the unconditioned stimulus (Berlyne, 1960).

Fourth, in our earlier discussion of perceptual learning and related phenomena, a number of cases in which learning occurred without evident reinforcement were cited. Mere exposure of rats to various shapes facilitates their subsequent ability to learn to discriminate between them (p. 350). Mere exposure of a young Chaffinch to the species' song modifies its subsequent motor pattern of singing (pp. 332–8). Mere experience of a maze, without food or other obvious reward, modifies a rat's subsequent ability to run the maze correctly when a reward is introduced (p. 408). Such instances are consistent with Tolman's view that the reward may be important in emphasizing some stimuli rather than others, or in confirming "expectancies", but is not fundamental to the learning process itself.

A case of special interest is provided by exploratory behaviour. As we have seen, this cannot be explained in terms of the traditional biological drives like hunger, and is not merely an aspect of general activity (p. 239). Furthermore, the opportunity to explore a novel environment is reinforcing in the sense that a response which leads to such an opportunity tends to be repeated (*see* references on p. 241). Berlyne (e.g. Berlyne *et al.*, 1957) has suggested that some of these results could be accounted for in terms of a reinforcing effect not of the novelty of the stimuli which the rat explores, but of the spaciousness or complexity of the environment it encounters: the difference, however, seems to be only one of degree. Furthermore, in some experiments novelty has been shown to be reinforcing when complexity was controlled. Rats show a smaller latency before running to a novel card than before running to a familiar one (Stretch, 1960; *see also* Chapman *et al.*, 1957). Working with hamsters, Schneider *et al.* (1965) found that a constantly changing series of stimulus objects retained their reinforcing value, but similar objects lacking in novelty did not.

As discussed by Watson (1961), attempts to explain the reinforcing effects of novel stimulation run into the following difficulty. If we suppose that the novel stimuli increase an exploratory drive, we must suppose that their reinforcing effect is related to drive induction rather than drive reduction (Montgomery, 1954). If we do this, however, drive reduction loses much of its value as a unifying concept: the chief merit of the drive reduction hypothesis is that it permits prediction of when learning will occur. Alternatively, we could suppose that lack of novel stimulation initiates the exploratory drive. On this view novel stimulation could reduce the drive, and an animal exploring a novel environment which is unlimited in extent should show a gradual decrease in exploratory behaviour: again, such evidence as there is contradicts this view. On these grounds Watson *loc. cit.* concludes that drive reduction is an unsatisfactory explanation of the learning associated with exploratory behaviour.

Berlyne (1960) suggests that situations which a rat explores produce "arousal" (*see* p. 155), but encounters a similar difficulty in that such a view would require an increase in arousal level to be reinforcing. He suggests that in general a decrease in arousal is reinforcing, but that an increase is not necessarily punishing and may become reinforcing if moderate and followed by a reduction in arousal. Such a reduction occurs when the novel stimuli become familiar as a result of exploration. Berlyne also suggests that arousal may be increased by "anticipation" of the unknown, and then subsequently reduced by exploration. Yet another possibility is that, in monotonous conditions, an increase in arousal may provide the level of effective sensory input necessary for efficient functioning (*see* p. 157). It will be apparent that, with such a wide variety of possible mechanisms, it is possible for Berlyne's theory to explain practically any result.

One additional point must be made here. The tendency for rats to alternate at a choice point (*see* pp. 206–8) is often described as an example of exploratory behaviour. As we have seen, however (Chapter 13), the tendency to respond more vigorously to novel stimuli is by no means confined to exploratory behaviour. In any case the time courses differ, since the tendency to alternate falls markedly with increasing intervals between trials, while exploration of a stimulus results in a marked decrease in time spent exploring a similar stimulus 24 hours later.

We may thus ask whether it is possible to bring the reinforcing effect of novel stimulation into line with that of other known reinforcing situations. Now some of the controversy about the role of reinforcement in learning has arisen from attempts to formulate laws of learning applicable to all learning in all situations. We have already seen that the situations which bring behaviour to an end differ in nature according to the type of response considered. In vertebrates feeding behaviour ceases after the advent of a variety of consummatory stimuli. Sexual behaviour also depends on a change in the stimulus situation. Fear behaviour ceases with the removal of an external stimulus (or the internal state induced by it). In each case those same changes which bring the behaviour to an end are associated with a change in behaviour next time the eliciting stimuli are encountered—they have reinforcing properties (*see* Chapter 15).

Now exploratory behaviour, the orientation reflex and so on cease as a result of a change, not in the external stimulus situation, but in internal organization —the situation becomes "familiar", a "neuronal model" is formed. In feeding and sexual behaviour the consequences of responding which bring the behaviour to an end also make that behaviour more probable on a subsequent occasion. If the same is true of exploratory behaviour, then its reinforcement must come from the change in internal organization that occurs as a result of exploring. On this view, then, exploratory behaviour is evoked by novel stimuli, and is brought to an end when those stimuli cease to be novel as a consequence of central reorganization: behaviour which preceded such central reorganization is likely to be repeated (*see* p. 242).

The nature of the reinforcing situation for other types of behaviour remains to be defined. Under what conditions, for instance, is aggressive behaviour likely to increase in frequency? When the adversary fights back, remains passive, or flees? The data are fragmentary: aggression wanes more rapidly to a passive dummy than to an animal which fights back (personal observation on Great Tits; Clayton, pers. comm., on Fighting Fish); after a fight a victorious animal is more likely to be aggressive subsequently; and a mirror image of a male Fighting Fish is a stronger "reinforcer" for an operant response to a male Fighting Fish than is a stationary model (Thompson, 1963). It is not easy to extract a generalization from these observations, though an understanding of the conditions governing aggressive behaviour would be of at least as much practical importance as an understanding of maze-running in rats.

26.5. Summary

1. It is convenient to distinguish short-term learning from long-term learning.
2. Other classifications of long-term learning, including Skinner's distinction between respondent and operant conditioning and Thorpe's classification of learning types, are discussed.
3. To understand all but the simplest types of behaviour, it is necessary to postulate events between stimulus and response. Although attempts have been made to treat these events as covert stimulus-response sequences, a number of types of evidence indicate that such an approach is inadequate.
4. The role of reinforcement is considered. The nature of the reinforcing situation differs according to the type of behaviour, so that generalizations based on feeding behaviour may not have general applicability. In particular, while changes in the (consummatory) stimuli influencing the animal are important in feeding behaviour, changes in an internal schema to conform to the external stimuli encountered are important in exploratory behaviour.

SECTION 4

Evolution

27

Evolution and Behaviour

The increased interest in the study of animal behaviour which occurred around the turn of the century was due in no small part to the stimulus provided by the theory of evolution by natural selection. Darwinism immediately posed questions like: "Are the differences in behaviour between animal species and, more especially, between animals and man, of kind or of degree?", or "To what extent can the principles used to explain human behaviour be applied to animals, and vice versa?" Before such questions could be answered, further knowledge about the causation and development of behaviour was required: this raised problems which have continued to occupy the major effort in psychological research ever since. Attempts to specify the precise similarities and differences between the behavioural capacities of animals continued, however, and work on this problem has recently been considerably accelerated (Schneirla, 1952).

Such studies have been concerned largely with macroevolution, since closely related species differ little in their abilities:* the comparisons made have thus been mostly cross-phyletic. Research on microevolution and behaviour has been concerned with questions which, though rather different, also spring from the theory of evolution by natural selection; for instance, "Can behavioural characters be used in the study of systematic relations between species?" and "What has been the detailed course of the evolution of those characters?" These issues were raised early in the century by such men as Heinroth and Whitman, and have recently been pursued actively by Lorenz, Tinbergen, and others influenced by them.

If behaviour has evolved under the influence of natural selection, then the differences in behaviour between closely related species must have survival value. Why is it advantageous for this species to be social and not for that? Why does this species have one sort of courtship display, while its close relative has a superficially quite different one? This question of the adaptedness of behaviour has been the subject of speculation for some time, but only recently has it become a subject for experimental study. Further problems concern the role played by behaviour in evolution; for instance we must know how

* "Abilities" here is not intended to include sensory and motor capacities, which sometimes differ considerably even in closely related species.

behaviour contributes to speciation, and how those behavioural differences between populations which are important in speciation arise.

For a full understanding of behaviour, these groups of problems are as important as the questions of immediate causation and development considered so far in this book. Here they will be merely outlined, the aim being to introduce the problems and show their connection with those previously discussed rather than to provide an extensive review.

27.1. Qualitative and Quantitative Differences between Behavioural Characteristics at Different Evolutionary Levels.

That animals with different degrees and types of structural complexity show corresponding differences in the complexity of their behaviour is immediately apparent. To specify their precise nature, however, is a task of great difficulty. From the evolutionary point of view, interest must centre on how each species functions as a whole in the environment in which it lives. But for practical reasons comparison must be confined to particular aspects. Furthermore, comparisons between the abilities of animals require standard tests suitable for those abilities: since each species is adapted to meet different situations, any one test is rarely equally suitable for many animals (Tinbergen, 1951). Even if a species does appear to be deficient in some faculty, as defined by a particular type of test, we must still refer back to the natural situation to assess the extent to which this is compensated for by the development of other faculties.

In spite of these difficulties, the problem is an important one, since the student of behaviour seeks to make generalizations. A knowledge of differences in the organization of behaviour between phyletic levels is necessary not only to define the limits of applicability of these generalizations, but to indicate the language in which they should be couched (Schneirla, 1949).

We may take the evolution of learning abilities as an example. This is a problem of peculiar interest, but cross-phyletic comparisons run into many difficulties. Few tests are equally suitable over a wide range of species, for differences in test scores may reflect differences in sensory, perceptual or motor functioning, rather than in learning ability itself. Furthermore, learning processes are themselves diverse, so that different species may solve the same problem in different ways.

Four learning situations that have been used over a wide range of animal types may be mentioned. Habituation (*see* p. 405) to stimuli not associated with consequences significant to the organism occurs in every phylum, and its general characteristics are at least superficially similar in all. But since the underlying complexity which has been demonstrated in mammals (*see* pp. 98–9) has not so far been shown to occur at lower levels, it remains possible, and indeed probable, that the processes involved are in fact very different at different phyletic levels. Detailed analyses of habituation in a wider range of species are necessary before this point can be settled.

Classical conditioning experiments have been performed on a great variety of species, and at first sight there are few obvious differences in the rate at which conditioning occurs (e.g. Razran, 1933). However Voronin (1962), reviewing experiments on learning in a number of vertebrate species, points out that while the number of trials required for conditioned reflex formation differs little between goldfish and Chimpanzee, the rate at which extinction and differentiation occurs is slower in the lower species. Reversal learning occurs slowly or not at all in the lower forms, but rapidly in the primates. Voronin's review thus demonstrates clearly that, within the vertebrates, there are great differences in some aspects of this type of learning ability and little in others: analysis must therefore precede comparison.

Members of several phyla have also been tested in roughly comparable maze-learning situations. Warren (1957), reviewing a number of studies on the basis of crude learning scores, found an increase in the rate of learning and the complexity of problems which could be learnt among invertebrates, from worms to ants. A similar increase in learning ability occurs in vertebrates, but "Among the vertebrates, only mammals are clearly superior to insects with respect to maze learning". Again, however, superficial comparisons can be misleading. In a more sophisticated comparison of maze learning in ants and rats, Schneirla (1959) showed that there are marked qualitative differences in the ways in which a maze is learnt. A precise analysis of the learning process is thus necessary before comparisons can be significant.

A technique promising for the study of interspecies differences in higher forms is that of testing for the ability to "learn to learn" or "learning set". Typically, an animal is given six trials on an object discrimination problem involving a single pair of objects. Regardless of the animal's performance, a new pair of objects is then presented for six trials, and so on until several hundred pairs of objects have been used. Of the first trials with each pair of objects, when chance alone can operate, 50 per cent will on average be correct. In the early discriminations, trial 2 scores are little more successful than trial 1. With successive problems, however, trial 2 scores improve, and after two or three hundred problems Rhesus monkeys may be obtaining 80–90 per cent correct responses on the second trials of each discrimination problem. Squirrel monkeys and marmosets improve considerably less rapidly than this (Fig. 27.1; Harlow, 1959b). Comparison with sub-primate forms must carry reservations about differences in the suitability of the testing conditions, but rats, cats and raccoons appear to be markedly inferior to primates (e.g. Koronakos *et al.*, 1957). The performance of pigeons, however, is comparable with that of cats (Zeigler, 1961). Warren's (1965) review of comparative aspects of primate learning indicates that learning set experiments provides the principal and almost the only source of evidence of differences in learning ability between primates and other mammals.

These are, of course, not the only techniques available for comparisons of learning ability, but they are sufficient to demonstrate that direct comparisons of crude learning scores are of restricted value: they must be accompanied by analyses of the learning process. Largely owing to the work of Schneirla (e.g. 1949), and more recently Bitterman (e.g. 1960), the importance of making comparisons only after an appropriate analysis is now becoming widely recognized.

Interphyletic comparisons must, of course, take into account many other characteristics of behaviour besides learning. Sensory and perceptual abilities, motivational mechanisms and motor skills must all be analysed, related to structure and compared among a wide range of species. Some examples of species and phyletic differences in sensory/perceptual mechanisms were discussed in Chapters 4, 5 and 6. Interspecies differences in motivational mechanisms have been related to structure by a number of workers: for

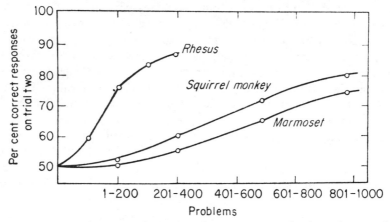

Fig. 27.1. Learning set performance of marmosets, squirrel monkeys, and rhesus monkeys. (*After Miles and Meyer, 1956.*)

instance Beach (e.g. 1948) has studied the role of the forebrain and of previous sexual experience in the mating behaviour of mammals, and Wünschmann (1963) has studied the relation between the complexity of central nervous organization and the development of exploratory tendencies. The relations between motor skills and brain structure are discussed by Paillard (1960): in herbivorous mammals the buccal organs of prehension have a relatively large cortical representation and the forelimbs a small one, while in the cat, and even more in the monkey, the cortical area concerned with the forelimb is enormously increased. Clearly such studies must be integrated with those of ability before a real understanding of evolutionary differences in the complexity of behaviour can be achieved.

27.2. The Use of Behavioural Characters in Taxonomy

Comparison of the behaviour of distantly related animals can give us a picture of the broad sweep of its evolution, but tells us little about its detailed course.

How can the small changes in behaviour, which must have accompanied the gradual evolution of species, be investigated? Here the student of behaviour is in a different position from the morphologist, for palaeontological data are not available, and ontogenetic evidence has so far been of little value. He must thus rely on the comparative method. This involves, first, the formation of hypotheses about the phylogenetic relationships between the taxonomic units (species, genera or higher categories) on the basis of a comparison of a large number of characters. These hypotheses are more likely to be reliable if the characters used are numerous and diverse, so that it is most profitable if morphological, physiological, biochemical and behavioural studies can be combined.* When the evolutionary relationships between the taxonomic units have been established with reasonable certainty, hypotheses about the course of evolution of the characters themselves can be formulated.

When the student of behaviour is concerned with groups whose relationships are already well known from other evidence, the first step is unnecessary, and comparison of behavioural characters can yield directly hypotheses about their evolution. But if the results of the behavioural study are not consistent with the previously accepted classification of the group, a reassessment of all characters may lead to its revision. We must thus consider first the use of behavioural characters for assessing phylogenetic relationships (Lorenz, 1935, 1950).

The first requirement is to select characters which are reasonably constant within groups but show moderate diversity between them. For instance all species of the genus *Parus* (most tits and chickadees) nest in holes and use moss for nest construction, differing in these characters from the other genera usually included in the family Paridae. These characters could thus be used to characterize the genus, but would be useless for elucidating relationships within it. For assessing relationships between species the most useful characters are fixed action patterns (p. 18). They are directly observable, they can be recorded on film, and their development is usually stable with respect to environmental influences. Indeed, fixed action patterns may be as characteristic of a species as any of its morphological characters. Among the detailed studies which exploited this were those of Heinroth (1911) and Lorenz (1941) on ducks and geese; Whitman (1919) on pigeons; Tinbergen (1959) on gulls; Crane (1949, 1952) on spiders and mantids; Baerends *et al.* (1950) on Cichlid fishes, and Jacobs (1953) and Faber (e.g. 1953) on grasshoppers.

Whatever the characters chosen, it is necessary to ensure that differences between the species (or other taxonomic groups concerned) are not environmentally determined. In principle this can be controlled by rearing them in the same environment: if the differences persist, then they must ultimately be of

* Such a comparative study shows the degree of resemblance between contemporary forms. It can be taken as indicating their phylogenetic relationships only with additional assumptions about similarities in the rate of divergence of different species. This assumption is known to be incorrect in some cases where a fossil record is available (Simpson, 1961), but is the only possible one in most cases.

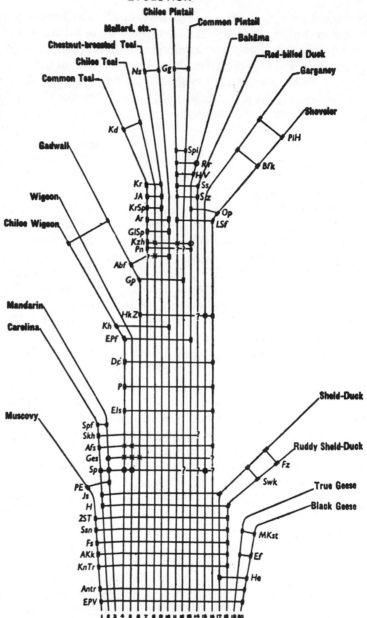

Fig. 27.2. The use of behavioural characters in taxonomy, as exemplified by Lorenz's study of the Anatinae. (*After Lorenz, 1941.*)

The vertical and oblique lines represent species and genera; each horizontal line a behavioural character present in the species whose lines it crosses. A cross indicates that the character is absent in the species in question; a circle indicates exceptional differentiation of a character.

genetic origin (*see* p. 319). In practice such a procedure is not often possible, and circumstantial evidence must suffice. As discussed in Chapter 19, the conclusion that the differences are ultimately genetic does not mean that the development of the characters is uninfluenced by the environment.

It is also necessary to assess the extent to which similarities between characters could be the result of independent evolution for a common function ("convergent evolution"), and the extent to which dissimilarities could be due to selection for divergence as such. Some examples of such characters, which could give a false indication of phylogenetic relationship, are mentioned on pp. 439–40.

Having selected the characters and established that the intergroup differences in them are genetically determined, it may then be possible to use them directly as taxonomic characters on a presence or absence basis. An example is provided by Lorenz's (1941) study of the ducks and geese. In Fig. 27.2 the vertical lines represent species, while the horizontal lines represent characters. Some characters, such as the monosyllabic piping of a lost chick, *EPV*, are common to all members of the group. Others, such as displacement shaking given as a form of display, *Js*, are common to nearly all ducks but not to the geese, while yet others are present only in particular groups of ducks. In some cases the unexpected presence or absence of characters in a particular species has led to a reassessment of its taxonomic position (*see also* Johnsgard, 1961).

When reasonably closely related species are compared, presence or absence may be a relative matter. The pivoting movement (Fig. 16.7), so characteristic of Goldfinch (*Carduelis carduelis*) courtship, is present to varying degrees in other members of the family, in some being represented only by occasional incipient movements (Hinde, 1955–56).

In other cases variations in the characteristics of a movement provide profitable material for comparison between the taxonomic units. When passerine birds move through foliage they flick their tails in a characteristic fashion. These tail-flicks vary in lateral displacement, spread and vertical amplitude. Although one of the types of flicking has been developed several times by insectivores feeding on the ground, the form of the tail-flicks has proved, on the whole, to be rather conservative within families, and provides useful evidence both for assigning genera to families and for assessing relationships between families. This is shown in Table 27.1 (Andrew, 1956d; *see also* Immelmann, 1962). Wickler (1960, 1961a, b) has used a similar method extensively in his studies of the fin movements of fishes, and of locomotory and other patterns in birds; these cover a wide range of species and relate movements to anatomy (*see also* Brereton *et al.*, 1962; Simmons, 1961).

Although the most useful behavioural characters for studies of systematics have been fixed action patterns, other aspects of behaviour are sometimes valuable; for instance Schutz (1956) found that the fright reaction, elicited in fishes by a substance from the injured skin of another individual, is not perfectly species-specific: the effectiveness of the substance produced by one species on the behaviour of another species varies with the distance of their phylogenetic relationship. Schutz was able to use the response to provide evidence on the systematic position of some species of Cyprinidae (*see also* Pfeiffer, 1960).

TABLE 27.1

Characters of the tail-flicks of certain Passerine groups useful in defining the groups and assessing the relationships between them. In D-U tail-flicks a downstroke is followed by an upstroke, and in U-D the opposite is the case (*After Andrew, 1956d*).

	Vertical Amplitude	Spread	Internal Displacement	Type
Richmondeninae	Large	Large	?	D-U (variable)
Emberizinae	Large	Large	Small	U-D
Ploceidae (excluding Estrildinae)	Small	Small	Small	Variable due to small size
Estrildinae	Small	Small	Large	Variable due to small size
Carduelinae	Large	Small	Small	D-U

In practice, of course, taxonomic relationships are never assessed on the basis of one character alone. Comparisons of many different characters— morphological, behavioural, physiological—are essential. When evidence from different sources conflicts, it is necessary to assess their relative value (e.g. Fiedler, 1964). But characters of behaviour have been of proven value in many groups (*see*, for example, review by Cullen, 1959; Lorenz, 1961), and in some cases have given the first clue to taxonomic distinctiveness (*see* Tinbergen, 1963).

27.3. The Microevolution of Behaviour Illustrated by the Evolution of Avian Displays

Once the phylogenetic relationships between the taxonomic groups have been reasonably firmly established, comparison of behavioural characters can provide evidence about the course of their evolution. Once again, the study of fixed action patterns has proved especially fertile.

The argument involves first the recognition of formal similarities between the FAP's of different but closely related taxonomic units (usually species). If the species are believed to be closely related on other grounds, and convergence (*see* pp. 439–40) can reasonably be ruled out, such similarities suggest that the movements have a common evolutionary origin.

Having established basic similarities between the movements of the different species, the next stage is to describe the slight differences which occur. If these are genetically determined, it is possible to erect hypotheses as to which variants are phylogenetically older. For this additional information may be used, such as knowledge about the distribution of the variants between species, and about their causation and function. Once some idea about which variant is more primitive has been gained, comparison of that variant with other movements of the same or other species permits further hypotheses about its probable evolutionary history. It will be apparent that there is a strong possibility of circular argument; behavioural characters can be used to assess relationships between species, and known phylogenetic relationships between species can be used as a basis for hypotheses about the evolution of behavioural characters. This danger can be avoided by the use of as many independent sources of evidence about the relationships between the species studied as possible.

The stereotyped movements used in the threat and courtship movements of birds and fishes have proved a rich source of material for studying the evolution of behaviour, the extent of interspecies diversity making them especially suitable for comparative study. These displays have already been discussed in some detail in Chapters 16 and 17, where it was shown that they are usually associated with some degree of ambivalence. Courtship displays, for instance, are often associated with tendencies to attack, flee from and behave sexually towards the mate. The relations between these tendencies and the components of the displays are qualitatively similar among closely related species (e.g. Stokes, 1962b).

Comparative study of display movements has led to the recognition of three fundamental evolutionary sources of displays (Daanje, 1950; Lorenz, 1935; Tinbergen, 1952, 1959 and references cited, 1962; Hinde et al., 1958):

1. *Intention Movements.* These are the incomplete or preparatory movements which often appear at the beginning of an activity (p. 274). Many avian displays are derived from intention movements of locomotion: for instance the displays shown in Fig. 27.3 are all derived from the take-off leap (*see* Fig. 17.3), though the relative extent and coordination of the components have altered in ways to be discussed later. Intention movements of biting or striking are a common source of the components of threat movements: the upright threat posture of the Herring Gull (*see* Fig. 16.8 and p. 258) provides several examples. In other cases intention movements of preening, nesting, self-protection, copulation and many other types of behaviour have given rise to display movements (e.g. Kunkel, 1959; Immelmann, 1962; Andrew, 1961e). As discussed in Chapter 17, in conflict situations movements elicited by one object are sometimes redirected on to another. The intention movements of such redirected activities may also give rise to displays (e.g. Moynihan, 1955).

2. *Displacement Activities.* As discussed earlier (pp. 278–87), the category of displacement activities is a causally heterogeneous one; nevertheless it is useful in the study of the evolution of display movements. Comparative study shows that many display movements have been derived, not from patterns associated with the major conflicting tendencies, but from apparently irrelevant activities

Fig. 27.3. (a)

Fig 27.3. (b)

Fig. 27.3. (c)

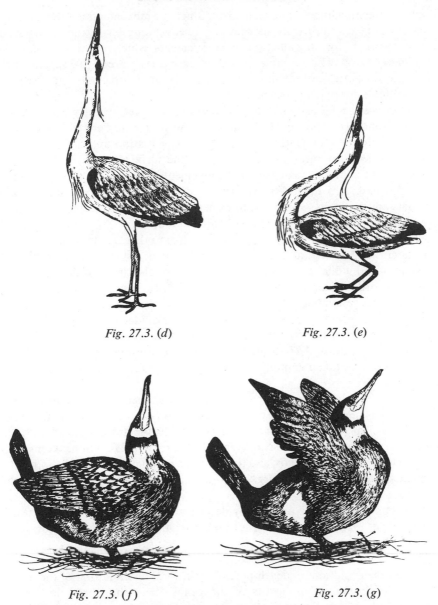

Fig. 27.3. (d)   *Fig. 27.3. (e)*

Fig. 27.3. (f)   *Fig. 27.3. (g)*

Fig. 27.3. Some examples of avian displays derived from the take-off leap (cf. Fig. 17.3). (*a*) *By permission of E. Stresemann (1927–1934) Aves in Kukenthal-Krumbach, Handbuch der Zoologie, Vol. VII. Walter de Gruyter & Co., Berlin. (b) After Bernhardt, 1940. (c) After Daanje, 1950. (d), (e) After Verwey, 1930. (f), (g) After Kortlandt, 1940.*

(*a*) Huddled and (*b*) stretching phase of display of male Goldeneye (*Bucephala clangula*); (*c*) Turkey cock; (*d*) and (*e*) Two phases of display of Blue Heron (*Ardea cinerea*); (*f*) and (*g*) Rhythmic wing-flapping of the Cormorant (*Phalacrocorax carbo*).

such as preening, incubating, and so on. Since the movements are incomplete, this category overlaps with the previous one. Among birds, the commonest examples are bill-wiping and preening movements, which in some species have become elaborated into complex displays (e.g. cranes, Lorenz, 1935). Similarly, in some fishes the movement used for shaking off ectoparasites has become part of male courtship (Fiedler, 1954).

3. *Autonomic Responses*. Many displays are derived directly or indirectly from autonomic responses; for instance those which are derived from movements of the hair or feathers, movements of urination and defaecation, or changes in skin coloration due to changes in the surface vessels, belong in this category. In addition, many somatic movements, such as those of grooming and preening, are in part responses to stimuli resulting from autonomic activity and could thus also be included here. A number of examples in birds are reviewed by Andrew (1956a, c) and Morris (1956).

In addition, some displays have evolved from other displays: for instance the lateral and horizontal displays used in finch courtship develop during the course of individual courtship, and presumably also in evolution, from the head forward horizontal threat posture (*see* Fig. 16.3 and p. 250).

Comparative studies of the evolution of signal movements in mammals are few, but recent studies have included the Equidae (Trumler, 1959) and primates (e.g. van Hooff, 1962), and indicate that many of them are derived from similar sources. As indicated in Chapter 16, however, such a generalization must not be taken to imply that *all* signal movements depend on ambivalence.

When the evolutionary origin of a movement has been identified, the changes which it has undergone in the course of evolution can be described. These are usually such as to improve its adaptive value in the functional context in which it appears. In the case of display movements, the principal function is communication with other individuals, and they become modified to this end, though the extent and nature of the changes may be limited by other factors, such as the need for crypticity.

The changes involved are usually described collectively as "ritualization" (Tinbergen, 1952; Blest, 1961). They include changes in the display movement itself, and the development of conspicuous structures by which it is enhanced. These two processes usually proceed in parallel, so that there is correlation between the evolutionary development of the structure and that of the movement. For instance, among tits of the genus *Parus* the "head-up" threat posture is elaborated most in those species which have a conspicuous throat and breast coloration (*see* Fig. 16.2 (*a*)). Furthermore, the Blue Tit (*Parus caeruleus*), in which the head-up posture is relatively inconspicuous, makes much use of a head-forward posture in fighting over territories: unlike many other species, it can raise the cheek feathers in a special way to make this conspicuous (*see* Fig. 16.2 (*b*); Tinbergen, 1937; Hinde, 1952).

In addition to changes in the form of the movement, there may also be changes in the relationship with the factors which elicited it. One of these is the development of "typical intensity" (pp. 275-6); the form or frequency of the movement remains constant over a wide range of intensities of the eliciting factors. This also no doubt enhances the signal value of the movement by making it more distinctive. To be effective, "typical intensity" must be characteristic of the species, though it may involve a considerably greater reduction in the variability of the displays of individuals than occurs in the species as a whole.

Other types of change in the relations between the movement and its causal factors also occur during ritualization. Sometimes, for instance, homologous displays in related species depend on different strengths of the associated tendencies. Baerends et al. (1963), comparing the agonistic and sexual displays of two closely related Cichlid fish (Genus Tilapia), found that each display was associated with a particular range of values of the ratio (tendency to attack)/(tendency to flee). The value of this quotient appeared to be higher in T. nilotica than that for the homologous display in T. mossambica. They thus suggest that the primary difference between the two species lies in a lower threshold for aggressive responses in T. nilotica. Similarly, differences in the displays between male and female of the same species can be understood in terms of threshold differences (see also McKinney, 1961).

It has also been suggested that there may be more marked motivational changes such that the movement comes to be governed by causal factors quite different from those which governed it originally. A well-known example of this is courtship feeding in birds: around the time of egg-laying and incubation the female of many species begs from the male with a posture used otherwise only by young begging food from their parents. Since courtship feeding is confined to a rather limited part of the reproductive cycle, it must depend on a fairly specific internal state which is presumably different from that of the begging juvenile. Lorenz (1951, 1960, 1961) has stressed that this sort of change occurs in many displays; for instance in many ducks displacement drinking and preening have become associated into a stereotyped sequence in which one always follows the other. The precise extent of the "emancipation" that has occurred in any one case is, however, difficult to establish: apart from anything else, it cannot be proved that none of the causal factors for the display are effective also for the movement from which it has been derived in evolution.

Although these generalizations about the origin and ritualization of the display movements of birds and fishes apply to a wide range of species including primates (Hinde, in press), the diversity of nature defeats practically any generalization. A final example illustrates this. The males of a mouth-breeding Cichlid fish (Haplochromis) have conspicuous orange or yellow spots near the base of the anal fin. These spots resemble the eggs of the species. During courtship, they elicit the response of snapping up the eggs, and make the male more attractive to the female. In spawning, the female snaps up the eggs before the male can fertilize them, but her response to the male's spots ensures that she also snaps up some sperm, and fertilization occurs in her mouth (Wickler, 1962).

Wherever ritualization occurs, there may also be corresponding changes in responsiveness such that the recipient of the signal responds to it optimally. As yet, however, these have been little studied experimentally.

27.4. Summary

1. Animals at different phyletic levels differ markedly in their behavioural capacities, but the task of defining the differences is one of considerable difficulty. Some examples from the study of learning abilities are given.
2. Behavioural characters can be used to provide evidence concerning the taxonomy of species.
3. Once the phylogenetic relationship between species is reasonably well known, hypotheses can be formed about the evolution of behavioural characters. The evolutionary origins of avian display movements are discussed. In the course of their evolution these displays have undergone evolution to adapt them for their signal function.

28

The Adaptedness of Behaviour and its Role in Speciation

28.1. The Adaptedness of Differences in Behaviour

The behaviour we observe is only one point in a nexus of cause-effect relations. So far we have been occupied in tracing these relations backwards in time by studying either the immediate causation of the behaviour, or the development of the behaviour and the mechanisms which control it in the life of the individual. We have also discussed evidence concerning the evolution of the behaviour, thereby relating it to the even more remote past. However, to gain a full understanding of behaviour we must treat it as a cause as well as an effect, for the behaviour itself has consequences. Some of these consequences may be of little interest to us, and we can treat them as incidental by-products. Others will affect the individual's behaviour if it returns to the same, or a similar, situation (e.g. Chapters 13 and 26). Yet others will influence the animal's chances of survival or reproduction, and will thus provide material for natural selection and affect later evolution. Thus, if one species is social while a relative is not, if one bird is a hole-nester while another is not, then the consequences of these differences are likely to be significant with respect to natural selection. We must thus ask precisely what the consequences of sociability or hole-nesting are, which of them are advantageous, and exactly why. As with morphological characters, the most significant questions are those which concern differences between characters rather than the characters themselves. To ask what the selective significance of this animal's legs or pecking response is, leads to less interesting answers than to ask why it has three toes and eats insects when most of its relations have four and eat seeds. Indeed, for the most part questions about adaptedness imply comparison even when it is not stated: "Why is it advantageous for this species to nest socially?" implies "When that species does not". Of even more interest, in that they lead to study of evolutionary changes actually in progress, are questions about the consequences of differences within a species: "Are the individuals which nest socially better off than those which do not, and why?" There is, of course, no reason why we should not ask similar questions about the selective significance of differences between individuals in learning ability or powers of perception, though such problems have not yet been tackled experimentally.

Questions about differences involve also questions about similarities. If we ask why this group differs from that, we are asking also why the members within the groups are similar. But when questions are posed by similarities in behaviour between distantly related species (convergence), it is the differences each shows from its own close relatives which pin-point the problem.

Progress in the study of the adaptedness of behaviour has been slow largely because it is only recently that the problems have been seen clearly. The clarification is largely due to the work of Tinbergen and his colleagues, who recognized problems which had previously been missed altogether. This is demonstrated by their work on egg-shell removal by the Black-headed Gull (*Larus ridibundus*). After their eggs hatch the adults of some species of birds leave the fragments of egg-shell in the nest, but others, such as the Black-headed Gull, remove them and drop them at a distance. This response takes about half a minute a year, and appears insignificant, yet the very fact that some species do it and others do not suggests that there is a problem in adaptedness. The further observation that in species nesting on open ground which do not remove the egg-shells, the young usually leave the nest very soon after hatching, and vice versa, also favours the view that the difference is adaptive and related to the life history of the species. In addition, the behaviour carries some disadvantages, for even the temporary absence of the parent from the nest required for egg-shell removal may expose it to a marauding predator. If the behaviour is potentially disadvantageous, there must surely be counterbalancing advantages.

Among the gulls and terns, those species with camouflaged young tend to show egg-shell removal, while those with conspicuous young do not. Since the broken egg-shells are themselves conspicuous, Tinbergen suggested that their removal was advantageous in that it reduced the conspicuousness of the nest site.

This suggestion was open to experimental testing. By laying out differently coloured eggs in a gull colony, it was shown that white eggs were taken by predators more rapidly than were those coloured naturally. The natural camouflage of the gull's egg is thus advantageous. Tinbergen also showed that this advantageous effect of camouflage could be reduced by the proximity of a conspicuous broken egg shell. Eggs were laid out in the colony, half of them with a broken shell nearby and half without. The former were taken by predators much more rapidly than the latter. There is thus strong reason for thinking that egg-shell removal has the advantageous consequence of reducing the conspicuousness of the nest.

This, however, turned out to be only the beginning of the problem. Comparisons with other species showed that Black-headed Gulls, which often do not remove the egg-shells for an hour or two after hatching, are more tardy than many other ground-nesting birds. Here, again, the finding of a difference has indicated a problem in adaptedness. Tinbergen has suggested that the difference is related to the fact that Black-headed Gulls themselves prey on newly hatched wet chicks, but not on dry ones. There may therefore be an advantage in delaying egg-shell removal until the parents' absence will not expose the chicks to intraspecific predation. This suggestion awaits experimental support, but does show that it is not only the occurrence of egg-shell removal which poses a problem in adaptedness, but also all its properties (Tinbergen, Broekhuysen *et al.*, 1962; Tinbergen, Kruuk *et al.*, 1962).

Only rarely is it possible to obtain evidence about qualitative changes in functional significance in the course of a movement's evolutionary history, but signal movements provide some examples. One case is the protective displays given by Saturnioid and Sphingid moths when disturbed. After studying respectively 35 and 6 species of these groups, Blest (1957) divided the responses to disturbance into the following types:

(*a*) Generalized escape behaviour.
(*b*) Rhythmic displays, involving coordinated movements of wings, legs and abdomen repeated many times.
(*c*) Sustained static displays, in which a posture may be maintained for several minutes.
(*d*) Mixed displays, in which the response to mild disturbance is a static posture and that to more intense disturbance is rhythmic.
(*e*) Vestigial displays, involving probably functionless remnants of any of the preceding types.
(*f*) Cryptic behaviour.

These displays are not distributed according to the systematic divisions of these groups of moths, but are correlated with coloration: for instance species showing generalized escape behaviour are cryptic, but those showing displays usually have conspicuous patterns consisting either of eyespots or mimetic patterns resembling harmful insects such as wasps. Experimental evidence shows that the displays are effective in eliciting escape responses from male passerines which prey on the moths. They thus have a functional significance.

The movements appear to have evolved from the intention movements of flight made by moths too cold to fly, and to have evolved in the order: inadequate flight movements, rhythmic displays, mixed displays, static displays. The efficiency of the displays in the various present-day species in scaring off predators increases in the same order. Thus the gradual evolution of these displays has been accompanied by a corresponding increase in efficiency.

The diversity of the signal movements shown by animals pose further problems in adaptedness. As discussed in Chapter 27, these movements have been elaborated in evolution in a manner which enhances their signal function. That they are in fact effective as signals is suggested in the first place by quite simple observations made under natural conditions. These show that the territorial song of a Robin will cause an intruder to fly away (Lack, 1939), or that the threat posture of a Great Tit is likely to cause a rival to flee. Examination of the efficacy of the components of display movements requires more sophisticated techniques, but leads to a similar conclusion. Stokes (1962a, b) assessed the extent to which certain components of the displays given by tits (*Parus* sp.) at a winter feeding station were followed by the displaying bird attacking, fleeing, or remaining where it was. Having established that certain components and combinations of components were associated with one or other type of subsequent behaviour (pp. 256–8), he then assessed the responses of other birds to these components, and found them to be appropriate. For instance, birds with erect body feathers usually escape and only rarely attack. The rivals of such birds are more likely to attack and less likely to escape than would be expected on a chance basis. Similarly, a bird which faces its rival is more likely to attack than a bird which does not: the rival is more likely to flee from birds in the former condition than the latter.

Additional evidence for the efficacy of these displays in communication is provided by dummy experiments which demonstrate that the structures used or postures given in a particular social context are, in fact, effective in eliciting the response appropriate to that context. For instance, Perdeck (1958) has shown that the species song is more effective in eliciting sexual approaches from certain grasshoppers than is that of related species, and Thielcke (1962) has shown that the species song is more effective in eliciting a reply from certain Tree Creepers (*Certhia*) than is the song of closely related species: this is of particular interest since the song probably promotes reproductive isolation. Some other examples were given in Chapter 4 (*see also* Lorenz, 1935).

Although signal movements have been selected for a signal function, there is no apparent trend towards some sort of "ideal" signal within each sensory modality. Nor could there be, for each species has a repertoire of signals which must be distinguishable from each other. Although Lorenz earlier regarded the form of each signal as a matter of mere convention, implying that it was more or less a matter of chance that, for instance, one species had one sort of greeting ceremony and another a different one, later study has shown that each signal is adapted to the particular context in which it is used.

In the first place, the different signal movements of any one species are distinct from each other, and are thus rarely confused. For instance, the submissive postures of passerine birds, which involve raising the feathers, a rather hunched position of the body and a generally rounded appearance, are in many respects the opposite of the horizontal sleeked threat posture (e.g. Hinde, 1952, 1953a). Further, submissive postures frequently involve a turning away from the more dominant animal. This is to be regarded as the ritualization of an intention movement of fleeing, which is efficacious in part also because it removes the sign-stimuli for aggression (Tinbergen, 1959; Baeumer, 1959).

(It has also been suggested by Chance (1962) that such postures "cut off" the incoming aggressive stimuli and thus reduce the tendency to retreat in the posturing individual. Grant *et al.* (1963) go so far as to regard catalepsy as a form of "cut off".) The necessity for displays to be distinctive may lead to "competition" between displays and to the extinction of some of them (Dilger, 1960): cases are known in which interspecies hybrids show display movements which are absent in both parents but present in various relatives (Lorenz, 1960).

In addition to intraspecies diversity, selection has acted to regulate the amount of interspecies diversity. The evidence here is mainly not experimental, but depends on the establishment of cross-species correlations between particular characteristics of the signals and the natural situations in which they occur.

Marler (1957b) has examined the circumstances in which selection will favour specific distinctiveness, or the lack of it, in signal movements and their associated structures. Where the signal plays a role in maintaining reproductive isolation from closely related forms, divergence is likely to occur. Thus in birds some aspects of the signals used in pair formation are usually markedly different between closely related species—in the Cardueline finches the displays used in the early stages of pair formation diverge to a greater extent than those which immediately precede copulation, which occurs after pair formation is accomplished (Hinde, 1955/6). The manner in which the form of bird songs is adapted to their function of mate selection has also been discussed by Marler (1960).

On the other hand, selection for convergence will occur in many displays given to predators—the prey species living in a given area will be better protected if they respond to each others' alarm signals. Marler (1959) has shown that the convergence shown by the alarm calls given by many passerine birds to a flying predator has an additional significance. The calls (*see* Fig. 28.1) all have just those properties which make them difficult to locate by the predator. They lack discontinuities and begin and end gradually, making binaural comparisons of time of arrival impossible; the frequency is too high for phase differences between the ears to be used for location, and too low for intensity differences to be appreciable.

This raises the further issue of the conflicting values of conspicuousness and crypticity. To be effective a signal must be conspicuous, but conspicuousness may bring danger from predators. A compromise must be effected, and the relative values of conspicuousness and crypticity will vary with the circumstances. Often this compromise is assisted by close adaptation of the signal to its functional context: thus the calls used by birds at close range need not be loud, and hence conspicuousness is reduced (Marler, *loc. cit.*). The nature of the environment in which the species lives also has a crucial influence on the nature of the display given: discussion of the variations with habitat in the "distraction displays" given by nesting birds to potential predators is given by Arm-strong (1954).

The nature of the display movements used in agonistic, social and sexual encounters thus suggest that they have been influenced by natural selection in adaptation to the circumstances in which they are used. That the nature of the signal movements can be influenced by selection for crypticity is an aspect of the important principle that all the characters of a species form part of an adaptive complex suiting it to its habitat and way of life. Change in one aspect

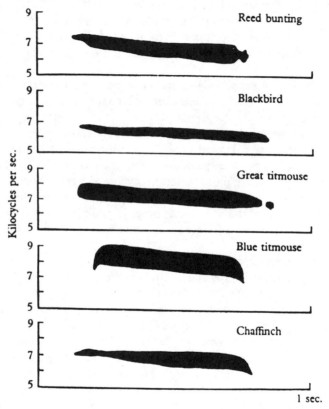

Fig. 28.1. Alarm calls of various passerine species, showing the similarities in their form. (*After Marler, 1959*)

can lead to other changes ramifying through the whole of the system. A classic example is given by the work of E. Cullen (1957) on the Kittiwake (*Rissa tridactyla*). This is the only gull species which nests on steep cliffs, a trait which protects it from both avian and mammalian predators. It differs in behaviour from other gulls in many respects, but many of the differences can be under-stood as adaptations either to the reduced predation pressure or to cliff-nesting.

Thus:

GROUND-NESTING GULLS	KITTIWAKE
High predation-rate in nesting colonies	*Predation pressure relaxed on cliffs*
Alarm-call frequent.	Alarm-call rarer.
Adults leave nest when predator some way distant.	Remain on nest until predator very close.
Vigorously attacks predator intruding in colony.	Very weak attacks at most at intruding predator.
Brooding birds disperse droppings and carry egg-shells away from nest.	Neither droppings nor egg-shells dispersed.
Young cryptic in appearance and behaviour.	Young not cryptic either in appearance or behaviour.
Clutch-size normally three eggs.	Clutch-size normally two eggs.
Suited to life in colony on ground	*Adapted to life on cliffs*
A. Several fighting methods.	More specialized to fighting in one way (grabbing beak and twisting).
	No upright threat.
Upright threat posture occurs, derived from preparation to peck down at opponent.	
Beak does not specially direct attacks. Not known if it is such a strong releasing stimulus as in the Kittiwake.	Beak releases and directs attacks.
Beak turned away in appeasement but not elaborately hidden.	Beak turned away in appeasement and elaborately hidden.
B. Young run away when attacked.	Young do not run when attacked.
No head-flagging in young.	Head-turning and hiding of beak in young when pecked and appropriate behaviour in attacker.
No neck-band.	Possess black neck-band.
C. Number of nest-sites probably less restricted and therefore probably less competition for nest-sites.	Number of nest-sites restricted, probably more competition.
Often first occupy pairing territories before nesting territories and pairs form away from nest.	Occupy nesting ledges at arrival in breeding area and pairs form on the nest.
Choking not normally used by unmated males as advertisement display.	Choking normal advertisement display of unmated males.
D. Copulation on the ground, female stands.	Copulation on the tiny ledge or nest, female sits on tarsi.
E. Nest-material collected near nest, building not synchronized, individual collecting.	Nest-material collected in unfamiliar places, synchronization of building and social collecting.
Little stealing of nest-material.	Birds very ready to steal nest-material.
Nests often unguarded before laying of first egg.	Nests guarded.
Nest-building technique relatively simple.	Nest-building technique more elaborate.

Mud not used.	Mud as nest-material.
Only one, or at most, very short series of depositing jerks.	Prolonged jerking of head when depositing nest-material.
Only traces of trampling on nest-material.	Prolonged trampling on nest-material.
Nest has relatively shallow cup.	Nest has deeper cup.

F. Young leave nest a few days after hatching.

Young have to stay on nest for long period.

Young fed by regurgitation on the ground.

Young fed from throat.

Nest-cleaning absent or less conspicuous.

Young and adults pick up and throw away strange objects falling into nest.

Parents have feeding call, probably to attract young.

Parents have no feeding call.

Hungry young make themselves conspicuous to parents by head-pumping.

Head-pumping absent in young.

Parents learn to recognize own young in a few days.

Parents do not recognize own chicks at least up to the age of four weeks.

G. Young face any direction. Vigorous wing-flapping in young.

Young face wall much of the time. Flight movements much weaker.

H. Weaker claws, cannot hold on so well.

Strongly developed claws and toe-musculature.

Comparable data are now available not only for other species of cliff-nesting birds (Cullen, J. M. *et al.*, 1963), but also for many other species (e.g. Crook, 1960c, 1962, 1963, 1964a; Haartman, 1957; Cullen, J.M, 1960; Hoogland *et al.*, 1956–7; Immelmann, 1962; Wickler, 1958, 1961a; and Brown, 1963). That apparently diverse characters may prove on examination to form part of an adaptive complex must be borne in mind when behavioural characters are used to assess systematic relations between species: if, during the course of evolution, selection for one character inevitably involves selection for several others, the group of characters will be of little more significance for systematics than will any one of them.

28.2. The Role of Behaviour in Speciation

The final group of problems to be mentioned here, the role of behaviour in evolution, is closely related to the others. Every question about the adaptedness of behaviour is also one about the role of behaviour in evolution. Here, however, discussion will be confined to the role of behaviour in speciation. When two species or incipient species inhabit the same area, their continued independent existence depends on the maintenance of some degree of reproductive isolation between them, and on the reduction of competition for biological essentials (e.g. Dobzhansky, 1941; Mayr, 1942, 1963; Huxley, 1942; Lack, 1947). Interspecies differences in the behaviour involved in mate selection, food selection, and in the selection of habitat, nest site and so on, are thus likely to be crucial. Some evidence for this view, relating principally to birds, will be reviewed briefly; more detailed references are given in Hinde (1959a).

1. *Mate Selection*

That interspecies differences in behaviour are in fact efficacious in ensuring reproductive isolation in nature is indicated by several types of evidence.

(*a*) Interspecies hybrids which can be bred readily in the laboratory are relatively very rare in nature. In captivity, when male and female are confined together in the absence of conspecific partners, the behavioural mechanisms normally involved in pair formation are unable to operate. Thus in captivity matings between Goldfinch (*Carduelis carduelis*) and Greenfinch (*Chloris chloris*) are almost as successful as those between pure species pairs, but wild hybrids are very seldom found.

(*b*) Closely related sympatric species usually differ markedly in some aspect of behaviour or structure which plays a part in courtship or pair formation. To cite but one example, two sympatric species of the warbler genus *Phylloscopus* are closely similar morphologically but have quite different songs. That such differences are of adaptive value in the maintenance of reproductive isolation is indicated by several types of evidence:

  (i) Divergence is most marked in characteristics which are important in pair formation.

  (ii) Divergence is often most marked where mating is otherwise possible; for instance in the overlap zone of partially sympatric species (*see* Thielcke *et al.*, 1963 for data on the *Phylloscopus* spp. cited above).

  (iii) The species characteristics in question often disappear on islands where no closely related species are present and thus no selection against hybridization operates.

  (iv) Divergence is usually more marked in males than in females. Since gamete loss is more serious for females than for males it is primarily female preference that will be selected for.

Some examples of the means whereby pair formation and mating are effected in birds and fishes have already been discussed in Chapters 16, 17 and 27. Clearly it is the differences between the signals used by closely related species that are likely to be important in the maintenance of reproductive isolation. These can be classified as follows:

(*a*) Differences in the strengths and relative strengths of the tendencies to attack, flee from, behave sexually towards, or behave in other ways in the presence of, the mate.

(*b*) Differences in the extent of sexual dimorphism in behaviour.

(c) Differences in display movements. Many of these are related to changes of the type referred to under (a).

(d) Differences in the structures or colours shown off by the display.

Selection for reproductive isolation between two populations will occur only if the populations have already diverged sufficiently for hybrid matings to be disadvantageous. The initial divergence is likely to occur when the populations are isolated from each other in some other way; for instance by a geographical barrier. However, some divergence in the behaviour involved in courtship and pair formation is likely to occur even in the absence of selection for divergence as such. As we have seen (pp. 440–2), the characters of a species must be regarded as an adaptive complex suiting it to the particular ecological niche which it inhabits. If the areas inhabited by the two populations differ ecologically, each will tend to become adapted to local conditions: the changes involved may have ramifying consequences through the adaptive complex, and thus affect the displays.

Among song-birds, for instance, local conditions will affect the extent of selection for territorial behaviour, and this may affect male song, the divergence between male and female behaviour and colour patterns, and the suppression of male aggressiveness in courtship: the courtship behaviour will thus be affected (Mayr et al., 1956).

Another example is provided by the relationship between nest-form and courtship behaviour in the Weaver-birds (Ploceinae). The primitive nest-form was apparently globular, with the entrance near the top: species with such nests perform a nest-invitation display while perched immediately below the entrance. Other species have added perches, tunnels, etc. to the entrance so that the hole is now underneath: this presumably provides better protection against weather or predators. In species with nests of this type the males still display in the same position with respect to the entrance, so that they now hang upside down (Crook, 1964).

Changes in courtship display can be of value in promoting reproductive isolation only if individuals of the new stock respond more strongly to the new pattern than to the old. It seems probable that there is a certain degree of plasticity in the stimuli eliciting sexual behaviour, and that learned tendencies to pair with conspecific individuals (see Chapter 22) may play an important role here.

2. Food Selection

When two closely related species inhabit the same area, they are likely to compete for biological essentials. Their continued coexistence will depend on the elimination of this competition. In this, behavioural mechanisms play an essential role.

Among birds, each species has a repertoire of fixed action patterns which are used in hunting for and preparing food (Chapter 3). The stimuli which elicit these movements, however, are often at first extremely generalized; for instance young passerines will peck at almost any spot which contrasts with its background, and only slowly come to restrict their pecking to food items (Chapter 22). This involves both positive learning and habituation.

The food items an individual learns to take will be those which it can find and prepare most efficiently. Among the seed-eating finches (Fringillidae and Carduelidae), for instance, the size of seeds taken by adults is related to the size of their bills: each species has a tendency to take seeds it can de-husk easily to obtain the maximum kernel weight in a given time spent feeding, though, of course, there are also other factors that influence the choice of seed. Young birds take more of the smaller seeds than do older ones, and only gradually learn to take the larger varieties. The course of this learning depends on which seeds can be opened most efficiently, which will depend, in turn, on the size of the beak and the behaviour patterns available (Kear, 1962).

Thus what a bird learns to eat will be determined in part by the structures and behaviour patterns available to it for feeding. These, however, become adapted in evolution to the food items which are locally abundant. Thus if two populations are isolated from each other, they will acquire methods of feeding and structures suitable to local conditions. If they subsequently come together in the same area, even though they do not differ genetically in responsiveness to food items, the individuals of the two groups may learn to feed on different items.

3. *Habitat Selection*

Differences in habitat preference between incipient species may be important in reducing both interbreeding and competition. The evidence for the latter is especially strong:

(*a*) Sympatric closely related species often occupy different habitats.

(*b*) Where they do not occupy different habitats, they differ in feeding habits sufficiently for competition to be avoided.

(*c*) When one of two closely related species which occupy different habitats within the same general area is locally absent, the other may spread to occupy both habitats.

(*d*) Individuals attempting to breed outside their normal habitats are rarely successful.

Habitat selection among birds usually depends on characters of the habitat which are not essential to survival, but which are visibly prominent characteristics of the landscape and which thus serve as sign stimuli (Chapter 4). Learning plays some role in habitat selection in many species (e.g. Klopfer, 1963). Selection of an abnormal habitat by some individuals may thus become perpetuated, providing scope for evolutionary adaptation to the new conditions.

It will be apparent from this brief summary of some of the issues raised by consideration of the adaptedness of behaviour and the role of behaviour in speciation that many of the problems discussed in the earlier sections of this book are of fundamental importance for the study of evolution. Conversely, a knowledge of the processes involved in speciation adds considerably to our appreciation and understanding of the interspecies differences in behaviour found in ethology and comparative psychology.

28.3. Summary

1. Behaviour produces consequences which may or may not be of significance for the survival or reproduction of the individual. Consequences which are of such significance provide material for natural selection. Some examples of the manner in which the adaptive significance of behavioural characters can be studied are given.
2. All the characters of a species, behavioural and morphological, form an adaptive complex. Evolutionary change in any one may have ramifying consequences.
3. When two species or incipient species inhabit the same area, their continued independent existence depends on the maintenance of some degree of reproductive isolation and on reduction of competition for biological essentials. Some behavioural mechanisms involved in mate, food and habitat selection are discussed.

References

Adler, H. E. (1963) Sensory factors in migration. *Anim. Behav.*, **11**, 566–577.

Adler, N. and Hogan, J. A. (1963) Classical conditioning and punishment of an instinctive response in *Betta splendens*. *Anim. Behav.*, **11**, 351–354.

Adolph, E. F. (1947) Urges to eat and drink in rats. *Amer. J. Physiol.*, **151**, 110–125.

Adolph, E. F., Barker, J. P. and Hoy, P. A. (1954) Multiple factors in thirst. *Amer. J. Physiol.*, **178**, 538–562.

Adrian, E. D. (1928) The Basis of Sensation. Christophers, London.

Adrian, E. D. (1931) Potential changes in the isolated nervous system of *Dytiscus marginalis*. *J. Physiol.*, **72**, 132–151.

Adrian, E. D. (1954) The physiological basis of perception. In "Brain Mechanisms and Consciousness", Ed. J. F. Delafresnaye, Blackwell, Oxford.

Adrian, E. D. and Zotterman, Y. (1926) The impulses produced by sensory nerve endings. Pt. 3, Impulses set up by touch and pressure. *J. Physiol.*, **61**, 465–483.

Ahrens, R. (1954) Beitrage zur Entwicklung des Physiognomie und Mimikerkennes. *Zeits. exp. und ang. Psychol.*, **2**, 402–454, 599–633.

Åkerman, B., Andersson, B., Fabricius, E., and Svensson, L. (1960) Observations on central regulation of body temperature and of food and water intake in the pigeon (*Columba livia*). *Acta physiol. scand.*, **50**, 328–336.

Akert, K. (1961) Diencephalon. In Sheer (1961).

Akimoto, H., Saito, Y., and Nakamura, Y. (1961) Effects of arousal stimuli on evoked neuronal activities in cat's visual cortex. In "The Visual System", Ed. Jung, R. and Kornhuber, H., Springer, Berlin.

Allport, G. W. (1937) Personality: a Psychological Interpretation. Holt, New York.

Ambrose, J. A. (1960) The smiling response in early human infancy. Ph.D. thesis, London.

Ammons, R. B. (1947) Acquisition of motor skill: II. Rotary pursuit performance with continuous practice before and after a single rest. *J. exp. Psychol.*, **37**, 393–411.

Amsel, A. (1949) Selective association and the anticipatory goal response mechanism as explanatory concepts in learning theory. *J. exp. Psychol.*, **39**, 785–799.

Amsel, A. (1950) The effect upon level of consummatory response of the addition of anxiety to a motivational complex. *J. exp. Psychol.*, **40**, 709–715.

Amsel, A. (1958) The role of frustrative non reward in noncontinuous reward situations. *Psychol. Bull.*, **55**, 102–119.

Amsel, A. and Maltzman, I. (1950) The effect upon generalized drive strength of emotionality as inferred from the level of consummatory response. *J. exp. Psychol.*, **40**, 563–569.

Amsel, A., and Work, M. S. (1961) The role of learned factors in "spontaneous" activity. *J. comp. physiol. Psychol.*, **54**, 527–532.

Anand, B. K., and Brobeck, J. R. (1951) Hypothalamic control of food intake in rats and cats. *Yale J. Biol. Med.*, **24**, 123–140.

Anderson, E. E. (1938) The interrelationship of drives in the male albino rat: II. *Comp. Psychol. Monogr.* 14.

Anderson, E. E. (1941) The externalization of Drive: I. Theoretical considerations. *Psych. Rev.*, **48**, 204–224.

Andersson, B. (1953) The effect of injections of hypertonic NaCl solutions into different parts of the hypothalamus of goats. *Acta Physiol. Scand.*, **28**, 188–201.

Andersson, B., and McCann, S. M. (1955) A further study of polydipsia evoked by hypothalamic stimulation in the goat. *Acta physiol. scand.*, **33**, 333–346.

Andersson, B., and Wyrwicka, W. (1957) The elicitation of a drinking motor conditioned reaction by electrical stimulation of the hypothalamic "drinking area" in the goat. *Acta physiol. scand.*, **41**, 194–198.

Andrew, R. J. (1956a) Some remarks on behaviour in conflict situations, with special reference to *Emberiza* Spp. *Brit. J. Anim. Behav.*, **4**, 41–45.

Andrew, R. J. (1956b) Normal and irrelevant toilet behaviour in *Emberiza* Spp. *Brit. J. Anim. Behav.*, **4**, 85–91.

Andrew, R. J. (1956c) Fear responses in *Emberiza* Spp. *Brit. J. Anim. Behav.*, **4**, 125–132.

Andrew, R. J. (1956d) Intention movements of flight in certain passerines, and their use in systematics. *Behaviour*, **10**, 179–204.

Andrew, R. J. (1957a) The aggressive and courtship behaviour of certain Emberizines. *Behaviour*, **10**, 255–308.

Andrew, R. J. (1957b) Influence of hunger on aggressive behavior in certain buntings of the genus *Emberiza*. *Physiol. Zool.*, **30**, 177–185.

Andrew, R. J. (1961a-d) The motivational organisation controlling the mobbing calls of the Blackbird (*Turdus merula*): I, II, III and IV. *Behaviour*, **17**, 224–246; **17**, 288–321; **18**, 25–43; **18**, 161–176.

Andrew, R. J. (1961e) The displays given by passerines in courtship and reproductive fighting: a review. *Ibis*, **103a**, 315–348.

Andrew, R. J. (1962) The situations that evoke vocalization in primates. *Ann. N. Y. Acad. Sci.*, **102**, 296–315.

Andrew, R. J. (1963a) Effect of testosterone on the behavior of the domestic chick. *J. comp. physiol. Psychol.*, **56**, 933–940.

Andrew, R. J. (1963b) The origin and evolution of the calls and facial expressions of the primates. *Behaviour*, **20**, 1–109.

Andrew, R. J. (1963c) Trends apparent in the evolution of vocalization in the old world monkeys and apes. *Symp. Zool. Soc. Lond.*, **10**, 89–101.

Andrew, R. J. (1964a) Vocalization in chicks, and the concept of "stimulus contrast". *Anim. Behav.*, **12**, 64–76.

Andrew, R. J. (1964b) The development of adult responses from responses given during imprinting by the domestic chick. *Anim. Behav.*, **12**, 542–548.

Angermeier, W. F. (1960) Some basic aspects of social reinforcements in albino rats. *J. comp. physiol. Psychol.*, **53**, 364–367.

Arden, G. B. (1963) Complex receptive fields and responses to moving objects in cells of the rabbit's lateral geniculate body. *J. Physiol.*, **166**, 468–488.

Armstrong, E. A. (1947) Courtship and Display amongst Birds. Lindsay Drummond, London.

Armstrong, E. A. (1950) The nature and function of displacement activities. *Sym. Soc. exp. Biol.*, **4**, 361–384.

Armstrong, E. A. (1954) The ecology of distraction display. *Brit. J. Anim. Behav.*, **2**, 121–135.

Aronson, L. R. (1949) An analysis of reproductive behavior in the mouth-breeding Cichlid fish, *Tilapia macrocephala* (Bleeker). *Zoologica*, **34**, 133–158.

Aronson, L. R. (1965) Environmental stimuli altering the physiological condition of the individual among lower vertebrates. In "Sex and Behaviour", Ed. F. A. Beach, Wiley, New York.

Aronson, L. R., and Noble, G. K. (1945) The sexual behavior of Anura: 2 Neural mechanisms controlling mating in the male Leopard Frog, *Rana pipiens. Bull. Amer. Mus. Nat. Hist.*, **86**, 87–139.

Autrum, H. (1950) Die Belichtungspotentiale und das Sehen der Insekten (Untersuchungen an *Calliphora* und *Dixippus*). *Zeits. vergl. Physiol.*, **32**, 176–227.

Autrum, H., and Stumpf, H. (1950) Das Bienenauge als Analysator für polarisiertes Licht. *Zeits. f. Naturf.*, **56**, 116–122.

Averbach, E., and Sperling, G. (1961) Short-term storage of information in vision. In "Information Theory", Fourth London Symposium (C. Cherry, ed.), Butterworths, London.

Ax, A. F. (1953) The physiological differentiation between fear and anger in humans. *Psychosom. Med.*, **15**, 433–42.

Baerends, G. P. (1941) Fortpflanzungsverhalten und Orientierung der Grabwespe *Ammophilia campestris* Jur. *Tidjschr. Entomol.*, **84**, 68–275.

Baerends, G. P. (1950) Specializations in organs and movements with a releasing function. *Sym. Soc. exp. Biol.*, **4**, 337–360.

Baerends, G. P. (1957a) The ethological analysis of fish behavior. In "The Physiology of Fishes", Ed. M. E. Brown, Academic Press Inc., New York.

Baerends, G. P. (1957b) The ethological concept "releasing mechanism" illustrated by a study of the stimuli eliciting egg-retrieving in the Herring Gull. *Anat. Rec.*, **128**, 518–519.

Baerends, G. P. (1959a) Ethological studies of insect behavior. *Ann. Rev. Entom.*, **4**, 207–234.

Baerends, G. P. (1959b) The value of the concept "releasing mechanism". *Proc. XVth Int. Cong. Zool., Lond.*

Baerends, G. P., and Baerends-van Roon, J. M. (1950) An introduction to the study of the ethology of cichlid fishes. *Behaviour, Suppl. No.* 1., 1–242.

Baerends, G. P., and Blokzijl, G. J. (1963) Gedanken über das Entstehen von Formdivergenzen zwischen homologen Signalhandlungen verwandter Arten. *Zeits. f. Tierpsychol.*, **20**, 517–528.

Baerends, G. P., Brouwer, R., and Waterbolk, H. Tj. (1955) Ethological studies on *Lebistes reticulatus* (Peters): I. An analysis of the male courtship pattern. *Behaviour*, **8**, 249–334.

Baerends, G. P. and van der Cingel, N. A. (1962) On the phylogenetic origin of the snap display in the Common Heron (*Ardea cinerea L.*). *Sym. Zool. Soc. Lond.*, **8**, 7–24.

Baeumer, E. (1955) Lebensart des Haushuhns. *Zeits f. Tierpsychol.*, **12**, 387–401.

Baeumer, E. (1959) Verhaltensstudie über das Haushuhn,—dessen Lebensart: 2 Teil. *Zeits f. Tierpsychol.*, **16**, 284–296.

Baeumer, E. (1962) Lebensart des Haushuhns, dritter Teil—über seine Laute und allgemeine Ergänzungen. *Zeits f. Tierpsychol.*, **19**, 394–416.

Baggerman, B. (1958) An experimental study on the timing of breeding and migration in the three-spined stickleback (*Gasterosteus aculeatus* L.). *Arch. Néerl. Zool.*, **12**, 105–317.

Baggerman, B., Baerends, G. P., Heikens, H. S. and Mook, J. H. (1956) Observations on the behaviour of the Black Tern, *Chlidonias n. niger* (L.), in the breeding area. *Ardea*, **44**, 1–71.

Baillie, P. and Morrison, S. D. (1963) The nature of the suppression of food intake by lateral hypothalamic lesions in rats. *J. Physiol.*, **165**, 227–245.

Bainbridge, R. and Waterman, T. H. (1957) Polarized light and the orientation of two marine Crustacea. *J. exp. Biol.*, **34**, 342–364.

Baldus, K. (1924) Untersuchungen über Ban und Funktion des Gehirnes der Larve und Imago von Libellen. *Zeits. wiss. Zool.*, **121**, 557–620.

Ball, J. (1934) Sex behavior of the rat after removal of the uterus and vagina. *J. comp. Psychol.*, **18**, 419–422.

Bambridge, R. (1962) Early experience and sexual behavior in the domestic chicken. *Science*, **136**, 259–260.

Bangert, H. (1960) Untersuchungen zur Koordination der Kopf-und Beinbewegungen beim Haushuhn. *Zeits f. Tierpsychol.*, **17**, 143–164.

Banks, E. M. (1962) A time and motion study of pre-fighting behavior in mice. *J. genet. Psychol.*, **101**, 165–183.

Bard, P. (1935) The effects of denervation of the genitalia on the oestrual behavior of cats. *Amer. J. Physiol.*, **113**, 5–6.

Bard, P. and Mountcastle, V. B. (1948) Some forebrain mechanisms involved in expression of rage with special reference to suppression of angry behavior. *Res. Publ. Ass. nerv. ment. Dis.*, **27**, 362–402.

Barlow, G. W. (1962a) Ethology of the Asian Teleost *Badis badis*: III. Aggressive behavior. *Zeits f. Tierpsychol.* **19**, 29–55.

Barlow, G. W. (1962b) Ethology of the Asian Teleost, *Badis badis:* IV. Sexual behavior. *Copeia*, **2**, 346–360.

Barlow, G. W. (1963) Ethology of the Asian Teleost, *Badis badis*: II. Motivation and signal value of the colour patterns. *Anim. Behav.*, **11**, 97–105.

Barlow, H. B. (1953) Summation and inhibition in the frog's retina. *J. Physiol.*, **119**, 69–88.

Barlow, H. B. (1961) The coding of sensory messages. In "Current Problems in Animal Behaviour", Ed. W. H. Thorpe and O. L. Zangwill, Cambridge University Press, London.

Barlow, H. B. (1963) Slippage of contact lenses and other artefacts in relation to fading and regeneration of supposedly stable retinal images. *Quart. J. exp. Psychol.*, **15**, 36–51.

Barlow, H. B., FitzHugh, R. and Kuffler, S. W. (1957) Change of organization in the receptive fields of the cat's retina during dark adaptation. *J. Physiol.*, **137**, 338–354.

Barlow, H. B. and Hill, R. M. (1963) Selective sensitivity to direction of movement in ganglion cells of the rabbit retina. *Science*, **139**, 412–414.

Barlow, W. (1959) Anxiety and muscle tension pain. *Brit. J. Clin. Practice*, **13**, 339–350.

Barnes, G. W. and Baron, A. (1961) Stimulus complexity and sensory reinforcement. *J. comp. physiol. Psychol.*, **54**, 466–469.

Barnett, S. A. (1958) Physiological effects of "social stress" in wild rats: I. Adrenal cortex. *J. Psychosomatic. Res.*, **3**, 1–11.

Barnett, S. A. (1963) A Study in Behaviour. Methuen, London.

Baron, A. and Kish, G. B. (1960) Early social isolation as a determinant of aggregative behavior in the domestic chicken. *J. comp. physiol. Psychol.*, **53**, 459–463.

Baron, A. and Kish, G. B. (1962) Low-intensity auditory and visual stimuli as reinforcers for the mouse. *J. comp. physiol. Psychol.*, **55**, 1011–1013.

Barrass, R. (1961) A quantitative study of the behaviour of the male *Mormoniella vitripennis* (Walker) (Hymenoptera, Pteromalidae) towards two constant stimulus-situations. *Behaviour*, **18**, 288–312.

Barraud, E. M. (1955) Notes on the territorial behaviour of captive Ten-spined Sticklebacks (*Pygosteus pungitius*). *Brit. J. Anim. Behav.*, **3**, 134–136.

Barraud, E. M. (1961) The development of behaviour in some young passerines. *Bird Study*, **8**, 111–118.

Barron, D. H. (1950) Genetic neurology and the behaviour problem. In "Genetic Neurology", Ed. P. Weiss, Chicago.

Barry, H. and Symmes, D. (1963) Reinforcing effects of illumination change in different phases of the rat's diurnal cycle. *J. comp. physiol. Psychol.*, **56**, 117–119.

Bartholomew, G. A. and Collias, N. E. (1962) The role of vocalization in the social behaviour of the northern elephant seal. *Anim. Behav.*, **10**, 7–14.

Bartlett, Sir Frederic (1953) Psychological criteria of fatigue. In Floyd and Welford (1953).

Bartoshuk, A. K. (1962a) Response decrement with repeated elicitation of human neonatal cardiac acceleration to sound. *J. comp. physiol. Psychol.*, **55**, 9–13.

Bartoshuk, A. K. (1962b) Human neonatal cardiac acceleration to sound: habituation and dishabituation. *Percept. mot. Skills.*, **15**, 15–27.

Bash, K. W. (1939a) An investigation into a possible organic basis for the hunger drive. *J. comp. Psychol.*, **28**, 109–134.

Bash, K. W. (1939b) Contribution to a theory of the hunger drive. *J. comp. Psychol.*, **28**, 137–160.

Bastock, M. (1956) A gene mutation which changes a behavior pattern. *Evolution*, **10**, 421–439.

Bastock, M. and Blest, A. D. (1958) An analysis of behaviour sequences in *Automeris aurantiaca* Weym (Lepidoptera). *Behaviour*, **12**, 243–284.

Bastock, M. and Manning, A. (1955) The courtship of *Drosophila melanogaster*. *Behaviour*, **8**, 85–111.

Bastock, M., Morris, D. and Moynihan, M. (1953) Some comments on conflict and thwarting in animals. *Behaviour*, **6**, 66–84.

Bateson, P. P. G. (1963) Filial and avoidance behaviour in chicks. Ph.D. thesis, Cambridge.

Bateson, P. P. G. (1964a) Effect of similarity between rearing and testing conditions on chicks' following and avoidance responses. *J. comp. physiol. Psychol.*, **57**, 100–103.

Bateson, P. P. G. (1964b) An effect of imprinting on the perceptual development of domestic chicks. *Nature*, **202**, 421–422.

Bateson, P. P. G. (1964c) Relation between conspicuousness of stimuli and their effectiveness in the imprinting situation. *J. comp. physiol. Psychol.*, **58**, 407–411.

Beach, F. A. (1940) Effects of cortical lesions upon the copulatory behavior of male rats. *J. comp. Psychol.*, **29**, 193–244.

Beach, F. A. (1942a) Comparison of copulatory behavior of male rats raised in isolation, cohabitation, and segregation. *J. genet. Psychol.*, **60**, 121–136.

Beach, F. A. (1942b) Analysis of factors involved in the arousal, maintenance and manifestation of sexual excitement in male animals. *Psychosom. Med.*, **4**, 173–198.

Beach, F. A. (1944) Relative effects of androgen upon the mating behavior of male rats subjected to forebrain injury or castration. *J. exp. Zool.*, **97**, 249–295.

Beach, F. A. (1947) A review of physiological and psychological studies of sexual behavior in mammals. *Physiol. Rev.*, **27**, 240–307.

Beach, F. A. (1948) Hormones and Behavior. Hoeber, New York.

Beach, F. A. (1951a) Instinctive behavior: reproductive activities. In Stevens (1951).

Beach, F. A. (1951b) Effects of forebrain injury upon mating behavior in male pigeons. *Behaviour*, **4**, 36–59.

Beach, F. A. (1955) The descent of instinct. *Psychol. Rev.*, **62**, 401–410.

Beach, F. A. (1958) Normal sexual behavior in male rats isolated at fourteen days of age. *J. comp. physiol. Psychol.*, **51**, 37–38.

Beach, F. A. (1965) Sex and Behavior. John Wiley, New York.

Beach, F. A. and Fowler, H. (1959a) Individual differences in the response of male rats to androgen. *J. comp. physiol. Psychol.* **52**, 50–52.

Beach, F. A. and Fowler, H. (1959b) Effects of "situational anxiety" on sexual behavior in male rats. *J. comp. physiol. Psychol.* **52**, 245–248.

Beach, F. A., Goldstein, A. C. and Jacoby, G. A. (1955) Effects of electro-convulsive shock on sexual behavior in male rats. *J. comp. physiol. Psychol.*, **48**, 173–179.

Beach, F. A. and Holz, A. M. (1946) Mating behavior in male rats castrated at various ages and injected with androgen. *J. exp. Zool.*, **101**, 91–142.

Beach, F. A. and Holz-Tucker, A. M. (1949) Effects of different concentrations of androgen upon sexual behavior in castrated male rats. *J. comp. physiol. Psychol.*, **42**, 433–453.

Beach, F. A. and Jaynes, J. (1954) Effects of early experience upon the behavior of animals. *Psychol. Bull.*, **51**, 239–263.

Beach, F. A. and Jaynes, J. (1956a) Studies of maternal retrieving in rats: I. Recognition of young. *J. Mammalogy*, **37**, 177–180.

Beach, F. A. and Jaynes, J. (1956b) Studies of maternal retrieving in rats: III. Sensory cues involved in the lactating female's response to her young. *Behaviour*, **10**, 104–125.

Beach, F. A. and Jordan, L. (1956) Sexual exhaustion and recovery in the male rat. *Quart. J. exp. Psychol.*, **8**, 121–133.

Beach, F. A. and Levinson, G. (1950) Effects of androgen on the glans penis and mating behavior of castrated male rats. *J. exp. Zool.*, **114**, 159–168.

Beach, F. A. and Rabedeau, R. G. (1959) Sexual exhaustion and recovery in the male hamster. *J. comp. physiol. Psychol.*, **52**, 56–61.

Beach, F. A. and Whalen, R. E. (1959a) Effects of ejaculation on sexual behavior in the male rat. *J. comp. physiol. Psychol.*, **52**, 249–254.

Beach, F. A. and Whalen, R. E. (1959b) Effects of intromission without ejaculation upon sexual behavior in male rats. *J. comp. physiol. Psychol.*, **52**, 476–481.

Beach, F. A. and Wilson, J. R. (1963) Mating behavior in male rats after removal of the seminal vesicles. *Proc. Nat. Acad. Sci.*, **49**, 624–626.

Beebe-Center, J. G., Block, P., Hoffman, A. C. and Wade, M. (1948) Relative per diem consumption as a measure of preference in the rat. *J. comp. physiol. Psychol.*, **41**, 239–251.

Beer, C. G. (1961) Incubation and nestbuilding behaviour of Black-headed Gulls: I. Incubation behaviour in the incubation period. *Behaviour*, **18**, 62–106.

Beer, C. G. (1963a) Incubation and nestbuilding behaviour of Black-headed Gulls: III. The pre-laying period. *Behaviour*, **21**, 13–77.

Beer. C. G. (1963b) Incubation and nestbuilding behaviour of Black-headed Gulls: IV. Nest-building in the laying and incubation periods. *Behaviour*, **21**, 155–176.

Bélanger, D. and Feldman, S. M. (1962) Effects of water deprivation upon heart rate and instrumental activity in the rat. *J. comp. physiol. Psychol.*, **55**, 220–225.

Bell, R. Q. (1960) Relations between behavior manifestations in the human neonate. *Child development*, **31**, 463–477.

Bell, R. Q. (1965) Development Psychology. *Ann. Rev. Psychol.*, **16**, in press.

Bell, R. W. and Denenberg, V. H. (1963) The interrelationships of shock and critical periods in infancy as they affect adult learning and activity. *Anim. Behav.*, **11**, 21–27.

Bellows, R. T. (1939) Time factors in water drinking in dogs. *Amer. J. Physiol.*, **125**, 87–97.

Beniest-Noirot, E. (1958) Analyse du comportement dit maternel chez la souris. *Monogr. Françaises de Psychol.*, **1**, C.N.R.S., Paris.

Bennet-Clark, H. C. (1963) The control of meal size in the bloodsucking bug, *Rhodnius prolixus*. *J. exp. Biol.*, **40**, 741–750.

Berkowitz, L. (1963) Aggression. McGraw Hill Book Company Inc., New York.

Berkun, M. M., Kessen, M. L. and Miller, N. E. (1952) Hunger-reducing effects of food by stomach fistula versus food by mouth measured by a consummatory response. *J. comp. physiol. Psychol.*, **45**, 550–554.

Berlyne, D. E. (1960) Conflict, Arousal and Curiosity. McGraw Hill Book Company Inc., New York.

Berlyne, D. E. and Slater, J. (1957) Perceptual curiosity, exploratory behavior and maze learning. *J. comp. physiol. Psychol.*, **50**, 228–232.

Bermant, G. (1961) Response latencies of female rats during sexual intercourse. *Science*, **133**, 1771–1773.

Bermant, G. (1964) Effects of single and multiple enforced intercopulatory intervals on the sexual behavior of male rats. *J. comp. physiol. Psychol.*, **57**, 398–403.

Bernhardt, P. (1940) Beitrag zur Biologie der Schellente (*Bucephala clangula*). *J. f. Ornith.*, **88**, 488–497.

Bernstein, I. S. (1962) Response to nesting materials of wild born and captive born chimpanzees. *Anim. Behav.*, **10**, 1–6.

Bernstein, L. (1952) A note on Christie's: "Experimental naïvete and experiential naïveté". *Psychol. Bull.*, **49**, 38–40.

Beusekom, G. van (1948) Some experiments on the optical orientation in *Philanthus triangulum* Fabr. *Behaviour*, **1**, 195–225.

Bevan, W. (1961) Perceptual learning: an overview. *J. Gen. Psychol.*, **64**, 69–99.

Bevan, W., Daves, W. F. and Levy, G. W. (1960) The relation of castration, androgen therapy and pre-test fighting experience to competitive aggression in male C57 BL/10 mice. *Anim. Behav.*, **8**, 6–12.

Bexton, W. H., Heron, W. and Scott, T. H. (1954) Effects of decreased variation in the sensory environment. *Canad. J. Psychol.*, **8**, 70–76.

Bindra, D. (1959) Motivation. Ronald Press Co., New York.

Bindra, D. (1961) Components of general activity and the analysis of behavior. *Psychol. Rev.*, **68**, 205–215.

Bindra, D. and Spinner, N. (1958) Response to varying degrees of novelty: the incidence of various activities. *J. exp. anal. Behav.*, **1**, 341–350.

Bingham, W. E. and Griffiths, W. J. (1952) The effect of different environments during infancy on adult behavior in the rat. *J. comp. physiol. Psychol.*, **45**, 307–312.

Birch, D., Burnstein, E. and Clark, R. A. (1958) Response strength as a function of hours of food deprivation under a controlled maintenance schedule. *J. comp. physiol. Psychol.*, **51**, 350–354.

Birch, H. G. (1956) Sources of order in the maternal behavior of animals. *Amer. J. Orthopsychiatr.*, **26**, 279–284.

Birch, H. G. and Clark, G. (1950) Hormonal modification of social behavior: IV The mechanism of estrogen-induced dominance in chimpanzees. *J. comp. physiol. Psychol.*, **43**, 181–193.

Birukow, G. (1951) Ermüdung und Umstimmung bei Gleichgewichtsreaktionen der Amphibien. *Verh. dtsch. Zool. Ges. Wilhelmshaven*, 1951, 144–150.

Birukow, G. (1954) Photo-geomenotaxis bei *Geotrupes silvaticus* Panz. und ihre zentralnervöse Koordination. *Zeits vergl. Physiol.*, **36**, 176–211.

Birukow, G. (1958) Zur Funktion der Antennen beim Mistkäfer (*Geotrupes silvaticus* Panz.). *Zeits f. Tierpsychol.*, **15**, 265–276.

Birukow, G. (1964) Aktivitäts- und Orientierungsrhythmik beim Kornkäfer (*Calandra granaria* L.). *Zeits f. Tierpsychol.*, **21**, 279–301.

Birukow, G. and Oberdorfer, H. (1959) Schwerkraftorientierung beim Wasserläufer *Velia currens* F. (Heteroptera) am Tage und zur Nachtzeit. *Zeits f. Tierpsychol.*, **16**, 693–705.

Bitterman, M. E. (1960) Toward a comparative psychology of learning. *Amer. Psychologist*, **15**, 704–712.

Blase, B. (1960) Die Lautäusserungen des Neuntöters (*Lanius c. collurio* L.), Freilandbeobachtungen und Kasper-Hauser-Versuche. *Zeits f. Tierpsychol.*, **17**, 293–344.

Blauvelt, H. (1956) Neonate-mother relationship in goat and man. In "Group Processes", *Trans. of 2nd Conf.* Ed. B. Schaffner, Josiah Macy Jr., New York.

Blest, A. D. (1957) The evolution of protective displays in the Saturnioidea and Sphingidae (Lepidoptera). *Behaviour*, **11**, 257–309.

Blest, A. D. (1958) Interaction between consecutive responses in a Hemileucid Moth, and the evolution of insect communication. *Nature*, **181**, 1077–1078.

Blest, A. D. (1959) Central control of interactions between behaviour patterns in a Hemileucine Moth. *Nature*, **184**, 1164–1165.

Blest, A. D. (1961) The concept of ritualisation. In "Current Problems in Animal Behaviour", Eds. W. H. Thorpe, and O. L. Zangwill, Cambridge Univ. Press.

Blodgett, H. C. and McCutchan, K. (1948) Relative strength of place and response learning in the T maze. *J. comp. physiol. Psychol.*, **41**, 17–24.

Blough, D. S. (1957) Spectral sensitivity in the pigeon. *J. Optical Soc. Amer.*, **47**, 827–833.

Blurton-Jones, N. G. (1958–9) Experiments on the causation of the threat postures of Canada Geese. *Wildfowl Trust, 11th Annual Report*, 1960, 46–52.

Bolles, R. C. (1958) A replication and further analysis of a study on position reversal learning in hungry and thirsty rats. *J. comp. physiol. Psychol.*, **51**, 349.

Bolles, R. C. (1959) Group and individual performance as a function of intensity and kind of deprivation. *J. comp. physiol. Psychol.*, **52**, 579–585.

Bolles, R. C. (1960) Grooming behavior in the rat. *J. comp. physiol. Psychol.*, **53**, 306–310.

Bolles, R. C. and Woods, P. J. (1964) The ontogeny of behaviour in the albino rat. *Anim. Behav.*, **12**, 427–441.

Boring, E. G. (1935) The relation of the attributes of sensation to the dimensions of the stimulus. *Philos. Sci.*, **2**, 236–245.

Bovet, J. (1960) Experimentelle Untersuchungen über das Heimfindevermögen von Mäusen. *Zeits f. Tierpsychol.*, **17**, 728–755.

Bovet, J. (1962) Influence d'un effet directionnel sur le retour au gîte des Mulots fauve et sylvestre (*Apodemus flavicollis* Melch. et *A. sylvaticus* L.) et du Campagnol roux (*Clethrionomys glareolus* Schr.). *Zeits f. Tierpsychol.*, **19**, 472–488.

Bower, G. H. and Miller, N. E. (1958) Rewarding and punishing effects from stimulating the same place in the rat's brain. *J. comp. physiol. Psychol.*, **51**, 669–674.

Bowlby, J. (1952) Critical phases in the development of social responses in man and other animals. In "Prospects in Psychiatric Research", Ed. J. M. Tanner, Oxford Univ. Press.

Bowlby, J. (1960) Separation anxiety. *Int. J. Psycho-anal.*, **41**, 89–113.

Brady, J. V. (1960) Emotional behavior. In "Handbook of Physiology", Section I, Vol. III, Eds. J. Field, H. W. Magoun and V. E. Hall, Amer. Physiol. Soc., Washington.

Brady, J. V. (1961) Motivational-emotional factors and intracranial self-stimulation. In Sheer, 1961.

Brady, J. V., Boren, J. J., Conrad, D. and Sidman, M. (1957) The effect of food and water deprivation upon intracranial self-stimulation. *J. comp. physiol. Psychol.*, **50**, 134–137.

Braemer, W. (1957) Verhaltensphysiologische Untersuchungen am optischen Apparat bei Fischen. *Zeits. vergl. Physiol.*, **39**, 374–398.

Braemer, W. and Braemer, H. (1958) Zur Gleichgewichtsorientierung schrägstehender Fische. *Zeits. vergl. Physiol.*, **40**, 529–542.

Brattgård, S. (1952) The importance of adequate stimulation for the chemical composition of retinal ganglion cells during early post-natal development. *Acta Radiologica, Suppl.* 96.

Braum, E. (1963) Die ersten Beutefanghandlungen junger Blaufelchen (*Coregonus wartmanni* Bloch) und Hechte (*Esox lucius* L.). *Zeits f. Tierpsychol.*, **20**, 257–266.

Breed, F. S. (1911) The development of certain instincts and habits in chicks. *Behaviour Monographs*, **1**, 1–78.

Brereton, J. le G. and Immelmann, K. (1962) Head-scratching in the Psittaciformes. *Ibis*, **104**, 169–175.

Brindley, G. S. and Merton, P. A. (1960) The absence of position sense in human eye. *J. Physiol.*, **153**, 127–130.

Broadbent, D. E. (1952) Listening to one of two synchronous messages. *J. exp. Psychol.*, **44**, 51–55.

Broadbent, D. E. (1958) Perception and Communication. Pergamon Press, London.

Broadbent, D. E. and Gregory, M. (1963a) Vigilance considered as a statistical decision. *Brit. J. Psychol.*, **54**, 309–323.

Broadbent, D. E. and Gregory, M. (1963b) Division of attention and the decision theory of signal detection. *Proc. Roy. Soc. B.*, **158**, 222–231.

Broadhurst, P. L. (1959) The interaction of task difficulty and motivation. *Acta Psychol.*, **16**, 321–338.

Broadhurst, P. L. (1961) Analysis of maternal effects in the inheritance of behaviour. *Anim. Behav.*, **9**, 129–141.

Brobeck, J. R. (1955) Energy exchange. In "Textbook of Physiology" (17th ed.), Ed. J. F. Fulton, Saunders, Philadelphia.

Brockway, B. F. (1963) Ethological studies of the Budgerigar (*Melopsittacus undulatus*): non-reproductive behavior. *Behaviour.* **22**, 193–222.

Brogden, W. J. (1939) Sensory pre-conditioning. *J. exp. Psychol.*, **25**, 323–332.

Bromley, R. B. and Bard, P. (1940) A study of the effect of estrin on the responses to genital stimulation shown by decapitate and decerebrate female cats. *Amer. J. Physiol.*, **129**, P318–P319.

Brown, F. A. (1960) Response to pervasive geophysical factors and the biological clock problem. *Cold spring Harbor Sym. on Quant. Biol.*, **25**, 57.

Brown, J. L. (1963) Ecogeographic variation and introgression in an avian visual signal: the crest of the Stellar's Jay *Cyanocitta stelleri. Evolution*, **17**, 23–39.

Brown, J. L. (1964) Goals and terminology in ethological motivation research. *Anim. Behav.*, **12**, 538–541.

Brown, J. L. and Hunsperger, R. W. (1963) Neurothology and the motivation of agonistic behaviour. *Anim. Behav.*, **11**, 439–448.

Brown, J. S. (1953) Problems presented by the concept of acquired drives. In "Current Theory and Research in Motivation", University of Nebraska Press, Lincoln, Nebraska.

Brown, J. S. (1961) The Motivation of Behavior. McGraw-Hill Book Company Inc., New York.

Brown, J. S. and Farber, I. E. (1951) Emotions conceptualised as intervening variables—with suggestions toward a theory of frustration. *Psychol. Bull.*, **48**, 465–495.

Brown, J. S. and Jacobs, A. (1949) The role of fear in the motivation and acquisition of responses. *J. exp. Psychol.*, **39**, 747–759.

Brown, T. Graham (1911) The intrinsic factors in the act of progression in the mammal. *Proc. Roy. Soc. B.*, **84**, 308–319.

Brückner, G. H. (1933) Untersuchungen zur Tiersoziologie, insbesondere zur Auflösung der Familie. *Zeits. Psychologie.*, **128**, 1–120.

Bullock, T. H. (1958) Parameters of integrative action of the nervous system at the neuronal level. *Exper. Cell. Res., Suppl.* 5, 323–337.

Bullock, T. H. (1959a) Neuron doctrine and electrophysiology. *Science*, **129**, 997–1002.

Bullock, T. H. (1959b) Initiation of nerve impulses in receptor and central neurons. *Revs. Mod. Physics*, **31**, 504–514.

Bullock, T. H. (1961) The origins of patterned nervous discharge. *Behaviour*, **17**, 48–59.

Bullock, T. H. and Terzuolo, C. A. (1957) Diverse forms of activity in the somata of spontaneous and integrating ganglion cells. *J. Physiol.*, **138**, 341–364.

Bullough, W. S. (1942) The reproductive cycles of the British and Continental races of the Starling (*Sturnus vulgaris* L.). *Phil. Trans. Roy. Soc. Lond. B.*, **231**, 165–246.

Butenandt, A. (1955) Über Wirkstoffe des Insektenreiches: II. Zur Kenntnis der Sexual-Lockstoffe. *Naturw. Rdsch.*, **12**, 457–464.

Butler, R. A. (1953) Discrimination learning by rhesus monkeys to visual-exploration motivation. *J. comp. physiol. Psychol.*, **46**, 95–98.

Butler, R. A. (1957a) Discrimination learning by rhesus monkeys to auditory incentives. *J. comp. physiol. Psychol.*, **50**, 239–241.

Butler, R. A. (1957b) The effect of deprivation of visual incentives on visual exploration motivation in monkeys. *J. comp. physiol. Psychol.*, **50**, 177–179.

Butler, R. A. and Harlow, H. F. (1954) Persistence of visual exploration in monkeys. *J. comp. physiol. Psychol.*, **47**, 257–263.

Butler, R. A. and Woolpy, J. H. (1963) Visual attention in the rhesus monkey. *J. comp. physiol. Psychol.*, **56**, 324–328.

Butz-Kuenzer, E. (1957) Optische und labyrinthäre Auslösung der Lagereaktionen bei Amphibien. *Zeits f. Tierpsychol.*, **14**, 429–447.

Caïn, J. (1959) Le Problème des Nérvoses Expérimentales. Brouwer, Bruges.

Campbell, B. A. (1960) Effects of water deprivation on random activity. *J. comp. physiol. Psychol.*, **53**, 240–241.

Campbell, B. A. and Campbell, E. H. (1962) Retention and extinction of learned fear in infant and adult rats. *J. comp. physiol. Psychol.*, **55**, 1–8.

Campbell, B. A. and Pickleman, J. R. (1961) The imprinting object as a reinforcing stimulus. *J. comp. physiol. Psychol.*, **54**, 592–596.

Campbell, B. A. and Sheffield, F. D. (1953) Relation of random activity to food deprivation. *J. comp. physiol. Psychol.*, **46**, 320–322.

Campbell, F. W. and Robson, J. G. (1961) A fresh approach to stabilized retinal images. *J. Physiol.*, **158**, 11P.

Cane, V. (1961) Some ways of describing behaviour. In "Current Problems in Animal Behaviour", Ed. W. H. Thorpe and O. L. Zangwill, Cambridge University Press, London.

Capretta, P. J. (1962) Saccharin consumption under varied conditions of hunger drive. *J. comp. physiol. Psychol.*, **55**, 656–660.

Carbaugh, B. T., Schein, M. W. and Hale, E. B. (1962) Effects of morphological variations of chicken models on sexual responses of cocks. *Anim. Behav.*, **10**, 235–238.

Carmichael, L. (1926) The development of behavior in vertebrates experimentally removed from the influence of external stimulation. *Psychol. Rev.*, **33**, 51–58.

Carmichael, L. (1927) A further study of the development of behavior in vertebrates experimentally removed from the influence of external stimulation. *Psychol. Rev.*, **34**, 34–47.

Carr, W. J. (1952) The effect of adrenalectomy upon the NaCl taste threshold in rat. *J. comp. physiol. Psychol.*, **45**, 377–380.

Carr, W. J. and Caul, W. F. (1962) The effect of castration in rat upon the discrimination of sex odours. *Anim. Behav.*, **10**, 20–27.

Carr, W. J., Solberg, B. and Pfaffmann, C. (1962) The olfactory threshold for estrous female urine in normal and castrated male rats. *J. comp. physiol. Psychol.*, **55**, 415–417.

Carthy, J. D. (1951) Instinct. *New Biology*, **10**, 95–105.

Carthy, J. D. (1961) Do animals see polarized light? *New Scientist*, **10**, 660–662.

Caspari, E. (1958) Genetic basis of behavior. In "Behavior and Evolution", Eds. A. Roe and G. G. Simpson, Yale University Press: New Haven.

Chambers, R. M. (1956) Effects of intravenous glucose injections on learning, general activity and hunger drive. *J. comp. physiol. Psychol.*, **49**, 558–564.

Chance, M. R. A. (1962) An interpretation of some agonistic postures; the role of "cut-off" acts and postures. *Sym. Zool. Soc. Lond.*, **8**, 71–89.

Chapman, R. M. and Bragdon, H. R. (1964) Evoked responses to numerical and non-numerical visual stimuli while problem solving. *Nature*, **203**, 1155–1157.

Chapman, R. M. and Levy, N. (1957) Hunger drive and reinforcing effect of novel stimuli. *J. comp. physiol. Psychol.*, **50**, 233–238.

Charlesworth, W. R. and Thompson, W. R. (1957) Effect of lack of visual stimulus variation on exploratory behavior in the adult white rat. *Psychol. Rep.*, **3**, 509–512.

Chase, R. A., Harvey, S., Standfast, S., Rapin, I. and Sutton, S. (1961) Studies on sensory feedback: I. *Quart. J. exp. Psychol.*, **13**, 141–152.

Cherry, E. C. (1953) Some experiments on the recognition of speech, with one and with two ears. *J. acoust. Soc. Amer.*, **25**, 975–979.

Chitty, D. (1957) Self-regulation of numbers through changes in viability. *Cold Spring Harbor. Sym. Quant. Biol.*, **22**, 277–280.

Chow, K. L., and Nisson, H. W. (1955) Interocular transfer of learning in visually naive and experienced infant chimpanzees. *J. comp. physiol. Psychol.*, **48**, 229–237.

Clark, R., Schuster, C. R. and Brady, J. V. (1961) Instrumental conditioning of jugular self-infusion in the rhesus monkey. *Science*, **133**, 1829–1830.

Clarke, J. R. (1953) The effect of fighting on the adrenals, thymus and spleen of the vole (*Microtus agrestis*). *J. Endocrin.*, **9**, 114–126.

Claus, H-J. and Bindra, D. (1960) Reactions to novelty and stimulus-change induced response decrement. *Canad. J. Psychol.*, **14**, 101–110.

Clayton, Frances L. (1958) Light reinforcement as a function of water deprivation. *Psych. Rep.*, **4**, 63–66.

Clayton, F. L. and Hinde, R.A. (In prep.). The habituation and recovery of aggressive displays in *Betta splendens*.

Coghill, G. E. (1929) Anatomy and the Problem of Behaviour. Cambridge University Press, London.

Cohen, H. B. (1961) The effect of contralateral visual stimulation on visibility with stabilized retinal images. *Canad. J. Psychol.*, **15**, 212–219.

Collias, N. E. (1952) The development of social behavior in birds. *Auk*, **69**, 127–159.

Collias, N. E. (1956) The analysis of socialization in sheep and goats. *Ecology*, **37**, 228–239.

Collias, N. E. and Collias, E. C. (1962) An experimental study of the mechanisms of nest building in a weaverbird. *Auk*, **79**, 568–595.

Collias, N. E. and Collias E. C. (1964) Evolution of nest-building in the weaverbirds (*Ploceidae*). *Univ. Calif. Publ. Zool.*, **73**, 1–162.

Collias, N. and Joos, M. (1953) The spectrographic analysis of sound signals of the domestic fowl. *Behaviour*, **5**, 175–188.

Collier, G. and Willis, F. N. (1961) Deprivation and Reinforcement. *J. exp. Psychol.*, **62**, 377–384.

Coppock, H. W. and Chambers, R. M. (1954) Reinforcement of position preference by automatic intravenous injections of glucose. *J. comp. physiol. Psychol.*, **47**, 355–357.

Corbit, J. D. and Stellar, E. (1964) Palatability, food intake, and obesity in normal and hyperphagic rats. *J. comp. physiol. Psychol.*, **58**, 63–67.

Cott, H. B. (1940) Adaptive Coloration in Animals. Methuen, London.

Cotton, J. W. (1953) Running time as a function of amount of food deprivation. *J. exp. Psychol.*, **46**, 188–198.

Cowles, J. T. and Nissen, H. W. (1937) Reward-expectancy in delayed responses of chimpanzees. *J. comp. Psychol.*, **24**, 345–348.

Craik, K. J. W. (1943) The Nature of Explanation. Cambridge University Press, London.

Crane, J. (1949) Comparative biology of Salticid spiders at Rancho Grande, Venezuela: IV. An analysis of display. *Zoologica*, **34**, 159–214.

Crane, J. (1952) A comparative study of innate defensive behavior in Trinidad mantids (Orthoptera, Mantoidea). *Zoologica*, **37**, 259–294.

Crane, J. (1955) Imaginal behavior of a Trinidad butterfly, *Heliconius erato hydara* Hewitson, with special reference to the social use of color. *Zoologica*, **40**, 167–196.

Crane, J. (1957) Basic patterns of display in fiddler crabs (Ocypodidae, Genus *Uca*). *Zoologica*, **42**, 69–82.

Crook, J. H. (1960a) Studies on the reproductive behaviour of the Baya Weaver (*Ploceus philippinus*). *J. Bombay Nat. Hist. Soc.*, **57**, 1–44.

Crook, J. H. (1960b) Studies on the social behaviour of *Quelea q. quelea* (Linn.) in French West Africa. *Behaviour*, **16**, 1–55.

Crook, J. H. (1960c) Nest form and construction in certain West African Weaver-Birds. *Ibis*, **102**, 1–25.

Crook, J. H. (1962) The adaptive significance of pair formation types in weaver birds. *Sym. Zool. Soc. Lond.*, **8**, 57–70.

Crook, J. H. (1963) Comparative studies on the reproductive behaviour of two closely related weaver bird species (*Ploceus cucullatus and Ploceus nigerrimus*) and their races. *Behaviour*, **21**, 177–232.

Crook, J. H. (1964a) The evolution of social organisation and visual communication in the weaver birds (Ploceinae). *Behaviour Suppl. No.* 10, 1–178.

Crook, J. H. (1964b) Field experiments on the nest construction and repair behaviour of certain weaver birds. *Proc. Zool. Soc. Lond.*, **142**, 217–255.

Cross, B. A. (1964) The hypothalamus in mammalian homeostasis. *Sym. Soc. exp. Biol.* **18**, 157–194.

Cruze, W. W. (1935) Maturation and learning in chicks. *J. comp. Psychol.* **19**, 371–409.

Cullen, E. (1957) Adaptations in the Kittiwake to cliff-nesting. *Ibis*, **99**, 275–302.

Cullen, E. (1960) Experiment on the effect of social isolation on reproductive behaviour in the three-spined stickleback. *Anim. Behav.*, **8**, 235.

Cullen, J. M. (1959) Behaviour as a help in taxonomy. *Systematics Assn. Publ. No.* 3, 131–140.

Cullen, J. M. (1960) Some adaptations in the nesting behaviour of terns. *Proc. XIIth Int. Orn. Cong. Helsinki*, 1958, 153–157.

Cullen, J. M. and Ashmole, N. P. (1963) The Black Noddy (*Anous tenuirostris*) on Ascension Island, Pt 2, Behaviour. *Ibis*, 103b, 423–446.

Curio, E. (1960) Ontogenese und Phylogenese einiger Triebäusserungen von Fliegenschnäppern. *J. f. Orn.*, 101, 291–309.

Curtius, A. (1954) Über angeborene Verhaltensweisen bei Vögeln, insbesondere bei Hühnerkücken. *Zeits f. Tierpsychol.*, 11, 94–109.

Daanje, A. (1950) On locomotory movements in birds and the intention movements derived from them. *Behaviour*, 3, 48–98.

Dachowski, L. (1964) Irrelevant thirst drive and light aversion. *Psych. Rep.*, 14, 899–904.

D'Amato, M. R. and Jagoda, H. (1962) Effect of early exposure to photic stimulation on brightness discrimination and exploratory behavior. *J. Genet. Psychol.*, 101, 267–271.

Dane, B. and van der Kloot, W. G. (1964) An analysis of the display of the Goldeneye duck (*Bucephala clangula* L.). *Behaviour*, 22, 283–328.

Dane, B., Walcott, C. and Drury, W. H. (1959) The form and duration of the display actions of the Goldeneye (*Bucephala clangula*). *Behaviour*, 14, 265–281.

Datel, W. E. and Seward, J. P. (1952) On the persistence of an ear-scratching response in the rat. *J. abnorm. soc. Psychol.*, 47, 58–61.

Davenport, D., Camougis, G. and Hickok, J. F. (1960) Analyses of the behaviour of commensals in host-factor: 1. *Anim. Behav.*, 8, 209–218.

Davies, S. J. J. F. (1961) The orientation of pecking in very young Magpie Geese *Anseranas semipalmata. Ibis*, 103a, 277–283.

Davies, S. J. J. F. (1965) The behaviour of *Streptopelia* doves and their hybrids. Ph.D. thesis, Cambridge.

Davis, J. D. (1958) The reinforcing effect of weak-light onset as a function of amount of food deprivation. *J. comp. physiol. Psychol.*, 51, 496–498.

Deese, J. (1951) The extinction of discrimination without performance of the choice response. *J. comp. physiol. Psychol.*, 44, 362–366.

Delgado, J. M. R. (1962) Brain centers and control of behavior—animals. First Hahnemann Sym. on Psychosom. Med., 221–227, Lea and Febiger.

Delgado, J. M. R. and Anand, B. K. (1953) Increase of food intake induced by electrical stimulation of the lateral hypothalamus. *Amer. J. Physiol.*, 172, 162–168.

Delius, J. D. (1963) Das Verhalten der Feldlerche. *Zeits f. Tierpsychol.*, 20, 297–348.

Dell, P. C. (1958) Some basic mechanisms of the translation of bodily needs into behaviour. In Ciba Foundation Symposium on the "Neurological Basis of Behaviour", Wolstenholme, G. E. W. and O'Connor, C. M. (Eds.), Boston.

Dember, W. N. and Fowler, H. (1958) Spontaneous alternation behavior. *Psychol. Bull.*, 55, 412–428.

Dempsey, E. W. and Rioch, D. McK. (1939) The localization in the brain stem of the oestrous responses of the female guineapig. *J. Neurophysiol.*, 2, 9–18.

Denenberg, V. H. (1962) An attempt to isolate critical periods of development in the rat. *J. comp. physiol. Psychol.*, 55, 813–815.

Denenberg, V. H. and Bell, R. W. (1960) Critical periods for the effects of infantile experience on adult learning. *Science*, 131, 227–228.

Denenberg, V. H. and Karas, G. G. (1959) Effects of differential infantile handling upon weight gain and mortality in the rat and mouse. *Science*, 130, 629–630.

Denenberg, V. H. and Kline, N. J. (1958) The relationship between age and avoidance learning in the hooded rat. *J. comp. physiol. Psychol.*, **51**, 488–491.

Denenberg, V. H. and Morton, J. R. C. (1962) Effects of preweaning and post-weaning manipulations upon problem-solving behavior. *J. comp. physiol. Psychol.*, **55**, 1096–1098.

Denenberg, V. H. and Whimbey, A. E. (1963a) Infantile stimulation and animal husbandry: a methodological study. *J. comp. physiol. Psychol.*, **56**, 877–878.

Denenberg, V. H. and Whimbey, A. E. (1963b) Behavior of adult rats is modified by the experiences their mothers had as infants. *Science*, **142**, 1192–1193.

Dennis, W. (1934) Congenital cataract and unlearned behavior. *J. Genet. Psychol.*, **44**, 340–351.

Desmedt, J. E. (1960) Neurophysiological mechanisms controlling acoustic input. In "Neural Mechanisms of the Auditory and Vestibular Systems", Rasmussen, G. L. and Windle, W. (Eds.), C. C. Thomas, Illinois.

Desmedt, J. E. (1962) Auditory-evoked potentials from cochlea to cortex as influenced by activation of the efferent olivo-cochlear bundle. *J. Acoustical Soc. Amer.*, **34**, 1478–1496.

Desmedt, J. E. and Mechelse, K. (1958) Suppression of acoustic input by thalamic stimulation. *Proc. Soc. exp. Biol. Med.*, **99**, 772–775.

Desmedt, J. E. and Monaco, P. (1961) Mode of action of the efferent olivo-cochlear bundle on the inner ear. *Nature*, **192**, 1263–1265.

Dethier, V. G. (1943) The dioptric apparatus of lateral ocelli: II. Visual capacities of the ocellus. *J. cell. comp. Physiol.*, **22**, 115–126.

Dethier, V. G. (1963) The Physiology of Insect Senses. Methuen, London.

Dethier, V. G. and Bodenstein, D. (1958) Hunger in the Blowfly. *Zeits f. Tierpsychol.*, **15**, 129–140.

Deutsch, J. A. (1960) The Structural Basis of Behavior. Cambridge University Press, London. Copyright 1960 by the University of Chicago. Published 1960 composed and printed by the University of Chicago Press, Chicago, Ill., U.S.A.

Deutsch, J. A. (1962) A system for shape recognition. *Psychol. Rev.*, **69**, 492–500.

DeVito, J. and Smith, O. A. (1959) Effects of temperature and food deprivation on the random activity of *Macaca mulatta*. *J. comp. physiol. Psychol.*, **52**, 29–32.

Dieterlen, F. (1959) Das Verhalten des syrischen Goldhamsters (*Mesocricetus auratus* Waterhouse). *Zeits f. Tierpsychol.*, **16**, 47–103.

Dieterlen, F. (1962) Geburt und Geburtshilfe bei der Stachelmaus, *Acomys cahirinus*. *Zeits f. Tierpsychol.*, **19**, 191–222.

Dilger, W. C. (1960) The comparative ethology of the African parrot genus *Agapornis*. *Zeits f. Tierpsychol.*, **17**, 649–685.

Dilger, W. C. (1962) The behavior of Lovebirds. *Sci. Amer.*, **206**, 88–98.

Doane, B. K., Mahatoo, W. Heron, W. and Scott, T. H. (1959) Changes in perceptual function after isolation. *Canad. J. Psychol.*, **13**, 210–219.

Dobzhansky, T. (1941) Genetics and the origin of species. Columbia University Press, New York.

Dodwell, P. C. (1961) Coding and learning in shape discrimination. *Psychol. Rev.*, **68**, 373–382.

Dodwell, P. C. (1962) A test of two theories of shape discrimination. *Quart. J. exp. Psychol.*, **14**, 65–70.

Dollard, J., Doob, L. W., Miller, N. E., Mowrer, O. H. and Sears, R. R. (1939) Frustration and Aggression. Yale Univ. Press, New Haven.

Dollard, J. and Miller, N. E. (1950) Personality and Psychotherapy. McGraw-Hill Book Company Inc., New York.

Dolley, W. L. and Wierda, J. L. (1929) Relative sensitivity to light of different parts of the compound eye in *Eristalis tenax. J. exp. Zool.*, **53**, 129–139.

Doty, R. W. (1951) Influence of stimulus pattern on reflex deglutition. *Amer. J. Physiol.*, **166**, 142–158.

Doty, R. W. and Bosma, J. F. (1956) An electromyographic analysis of reflex deglutition. *J. Neurophysiol.*, **19**, 44–60.

Doyle, G. and Pratt Yule, E. (1959) Grooming activities and freezing behavior in relation to emotionality in albino rats. *Anim. Behav.*, **7**, 18–22.

Drees, O. (1952) Untersuchungen über die angeborenen Verhaltensweisen bei Springspinnen (*Salticidae*). *Zeits f. Tierpsychol.*, **9**, 169–207.

Duffy, E. (1951) The concept of energy mobilization. *Psychol. Rev.*, **58**, 30–40.

Duffy, E. (1962) Activation and Behavior. Wiley, New York.

Dufort, R. H. (1964) The rat's adjustment to 23-, 47-, and 71-hour food-deprivation schedules. *Psychol. Rep.*, **14**, 663–669.

Duncan, C. P. (1949) The retroactive effect of electroshock on learning. *J. comp. physiol. Psychol.*, **42**, 32–44.

Dürrwächter, G. (1957) Untersuchungen über Phototaxis und Geotaxis einiger *Drosophila*-Mutanten nach Aufzucht in verschiedenen Lichtbedingungen. *Zeits f. Tierpsychol.*, **14**, 1–28.

Dzimirski, I. (1959) Untersuchungen über Bewegungssehen und Optomotorik bei Springspinnen (Salticidae). *Zeits f. Tierpsychol.*, **16**, 385–402.

Earl, R. W. (1957) Motivation, performance and extinction. *J. comp. physiol. Psychol.*, **50**, 248–251.

Eayrs, J. T. (1954) Spontaneous activity in the rat. *Brit. J. Anim. Behav.*, **2**, 25–30.

Egger, M. D. and Flynn, J. P. (1963) Effects of electrical stimulation of the amygdala on hypothalamically elicited attack behavior in cats. *J. Neurophysiol.*, **26**, 705–720.

Ehrlich, A. (1963) Effects of tegmental lesions on motivated behavior in rats. *J. comp. physiol. Psychol.*, **56**, 390–396.

Eibl-Eibesfeldt, I. (1951a) Beobachtungen zur Fortpflanzungsbiologie und Jungendentwicklung des Eichhörnchens. *Zeits f. Tierpsychol.*, **8**, 370–400.

Eibl-Eibesfeldt, I. (1951b) Nahrungserwerb und Beuteschema der Erdkröte (*Bufo bufo* L.). *Behaviour*, **4**, 1–35.

Eibl-Eibesfeldt, I. (1951c) Gefangenschaftsbeobachtungen an der persischen Wüstenmaus (*Meriones persicus persicus* Blanford): Ein Beitrag zur vergleichenden Ethologie der Nager. *Zeits f. Tierpsychol.*, **8**, 400–423.

Eibl-Eibesfeldt, I. (1953) Zur Ethologie des Hamsters (*Cricetus cricetus* L.). *Zeits f. Tierpsychol.*, **10**, 204–254.

Eibl-Eibesfeldt, I. (1955a) Angeborenes und Erworbenes im Nestbauverhalten der Wanderratte. *Naturwiss.*, **42**, 633–4.

Eibl-Eibesfeldt, I. (1955b) Der Kommentkampf der Meerechse (*Amblyrhynchus cristatus* Bell) nebst einigen Notizen zur Biologie dieser Art. *Zeits f. Tierpsychol.*, **12**, 49–62.

Eibl-Eibesfeldt, I. (1958) Das Verhalten des Nagetiere. Handb. Zool., Berlin, 8, 12, 10.

Eibl-Eibesfeldt, I. (1961) The interactions of unlearned behaviour patterns and learning in mammals. In "Brain Mechanisms and Learning", Ed. J. F. Delafresnaye, C.I.O.M.S. Symp., Blackwell: Oxford.

Eibl-Eibesfeldt, I. (1962) Die Verhaltensentwicklung des Krallenfrosches (*Xenopus laevis*) und des Scheibenzünglers (*Discoglossus pictus*) unter besonderer Berücksichtigung der Beutefanghandlungen. *Zeits f. Tierpsychol.*, **19**, 385–393.

Eibl-Eibesfeldt, I. (1963) Angeborenes und Erworbenes im Verhalten einiger Säuger. *Zeits f. Tierpsychol.*, **20**, 705–754.

Eibl-Eibesfeldt, I. and Kramer, S. (1958) Ethology, the comparative study of animal behavior. *Quart. Rev. Biol.*, **33**, 181–211.

Eikmanns, K-H. (1955) Verhaltensphysiologische Untersuchungen über den Beutefang und das Bewegungssehen der Erdkröte (*Bufo bufo* L.). *Zeits f. Tierpsychol.*, **12**, 229–253.

Eisner, E. (1960) The relationship of hormones to the reproductive behaviour of birds, referring especially to parental behaviour: a review. *Anim. Behav.*, **8**, 155–179.

Eisner, E. (1963) A quantitative study of parental behaviour in the Bengalese Finch. *Behaviour*, **20**, 134–206.

Ellis, P. E. (1953) Social aggregation and gregarious behaviour in hoppers of *Locusta migratoria migratorioides* (R. & F.). *Behaviour*, **5**, 225–258.

Ellis, P. E. (1963) Changes in the social aggregation of locust hoppers with changes in rearing conditions. *Anim. Behav.*, **11**, 152–160.

Engelmann, C. (1941) Versuche über den Geschmackssinn des Huhns. *Zeits f. Tierpsychol.*, **4**, 204–218.

Engen, T. and Lipsitt, L. P. (1965) Decrement and recovery of responses to olfactory stimuli in the human neonate. *J. comp. physiol. Psychol.*, **59**, 312–316.

Epstein, A. N. and Teitelbaum, P. (1962) Regulation of food intake in the absence of taste, smell, and other oropharyngeal sensations. *J. comp. physiol. Psychol.*, **55**, 753–759.

Epstein, W. (1964) Experimental investigations of the genesis of visual space perception. *Psychol. Bull.*, **61**, 115–128.

Estes, W. K. (1942) Discriminative conditioning: I A discriminative property of conditioned anticipation. *J. exp. Psychol.*, **32**, 150–155.

Estes, W. K. (1948) Discriminative conditioning: II Effects of a Pavlovian conditioned stimulus upon a subsequently established operant response. *J. exp. Psychol.*, **38**, 173–177.

Estes, W. K. (1959) The statistical approach to learning theory. In Koch (1959).

Estes, W. K., Koch, S., McCorquodale, K., Meehl, P. E., Mueller, C. G., Schoenfeld, W. N., Verplanck, W. S. (1954) Modern Learning Theory. Appleton-Century-Crofts, New York.

Evans, D. R. and Browne, L. B. (1960) The physiology of hunger in the blowfly. *Amer. Midl. Nat.*, **64**, 282–300.

Ewer, R. F. (1959) Suckling behaviour in kittens. *Behaviour*, **15**, 146–162.

Ewer, R. F. (1961) Further observations on suckling behaviour in kittens, together with some general considerations of the interrelations of innate and acquired responses. *Behaviour*, **17**, 247–260.

Faber, A. (1953) Die Lant- und Gebärdensprache bei Insekten. Orthoptera I. *Mitt. Staatl. Mus. Naturk. Stuttgart*, **287**, 1–198.

Fabricius, E. (1951) Zur Ethologie junger Anatiden. *Acta. Zool. Fenn.*, **68**, 1–178.

Fabricius, E. (1962) Some aspects of imprinting in birds. *Sym. Zool. Soc. Lond.*, **8**, 139–148.

Fabricius, E. and Boyd, H. (1954) Experiments on the following-reaction of ducklings. Wildfowl Trust Annual Report, 1952–3, 84–89.

Fabricius, E. and Gustafson, K-J. (1954) Further aquarium observations on the spawning behavior of the Char, *Salmo alpinus* L. Inst. Freshwater Res. Drottningholm, Rep. No. 35, 58–104.

Fantz, R. L. (1957) Form preferences in newly hatched chicks. *J. comp. physiol. Psychol.*, **50**, 422–430.

Fantz, R. L. (1958) Pattern vision in young infants. *Psychol. Record.*, **8**, 43–47.

Fantz, R. L. (1965) Ontogeny of Perception. In "Behavior of Nonhuman Primates", Eds. Schrier, A. M., Harlow, H. F., Stollnitz, F., Vol. II, Academic Press, New York, London.

Fantz, R. L., Ordy, J. M. and Udelf, M. S. (1962) Maturation of pattern vision in infants during the first six months. *J. comp. physiol. Psychol.*, **55**, 907–917.

Faure, J. C. (1932) The phases of locusts in South Africa. *Bull. ent. Res.*, **23**, 293–405.

Fehrer, E. (1956) The effects of hunger and familiarity of locale on exploration. *J. comp. physiol. Psychol.*, **49**, 549–552.

Feldman, S. M. and Waller, J. H. (1962) Dissociation of electro-cortical activation and behavioral arousal. *Nature*, **196**, 1320–1322.

Fentress, J. C. (1965) Aspects of arousal and control in the behaviour of voles. Ph.D. thesis, Cambridge.

Fernández-Guardiola, A., Roldán, E., Fanjal, M. L. and Castells, C. (1961) Role of the pupillary mechanism in the process of habituation of the visual pathways. *Electroenceph. clin. Neurophysiol.*, **13**, 564–576.

Ferster, C. B. and Skinner, B. F. (1957) Schedules of Reinforcement. Appleton-Century-Crofts, New York.

Ficken, M. S. and Dilger, W. C. (1960) Comments on redirection with examples of avian copulations with substitute objects. *Anim. Behav.*, **8**, 219–222.

Fiedler, K. (1954) Vergleichende Verhaltensstudien an Seeadeln, Schlangennadeln und Seepferdchen. *Zeits f. Tierpsychol.*, **11**, 358–416.

Fiedler, K. (1964) Verhaltensstudien an Lippfischen der Gattung *Crenilabrus* (Labridae, Perciformes). *Zeits f. Tierpsychol.*, **21**, 521–591.

Fischer, G. J. and Campbell, G. L. (1964) The development of passive avoidance conditioning in Leghorn chicks. *Anim Behav.*, **12**, 268–269.

Fischer, K. (1961) Untersuchungen zur Sonnenkompassorientierung und Laufaktivität von Smaragdeidechsen (*Lacerta viridis* Laur.). *Zeits f. Tierpsychol.*, **18**, 450–470.

Fisher, A. E. (1962) Effects of stimulus variation on sexual satiation in the male rat. *J. comp. physiol. Psychol.*, **55**, 614–620.

Fisher, A. E. and Hale, E. B. (1956–7) Stimulus determinants of sexual and aggressive behaviour in male domestic fowl. *Behaviour*, **10**, 309–323.

Floyd, N. F. and Welford, A. T. (1953) Ergonomics Symposium on Fatigue. H. K. Lewis, London.

Flynn, J. P. and Jerome, E. A. (1952) Learning in an automatic multiple-choice box with light as incentive. *J. comp. physiol. Psychol.*, **45**, 336–340.

Forgays, D. G. and Forgays, J. W. (1952) The nature of the effect of free-environmental experience in the rat. *J. comp. physiol. Psychol.*, **45**, 322–328.

Forgays, D. G. and Levin, H. (1958) Learning as a function of change of sensory stimulation in food-deprived and food-satiated animals. *J. comp. physiol. Psychol.*, **51**, 50–54.

Forgays, D. G. and Levin, H. (1959) Discrimination and reversal learning as a function of change of sensory stimulation. *J. comp. physiol. Psychol.*, **52**, 191–194.

Forgays, D. G. and Read, J. M. (1962) Crucial periods for free-environmental experience in the rat. *J. comp. physiol. Psychol.*, **55**, 816–818.

Forgus, R. H. (1955) Early visual and motor experience as determiners of complex maze-learning ability under rich and reduced stimulation. *J. comp. physiol. Psychol.*, **48**, 215–220.

Forgus, R. H. (1958) The interaction between form pre-exposure and test requirements in determining form discrimination. *J. comp. physiol. Psychol.*, **51**, 588–591.

Forselius, S. (1957) Studies of Anabantid fishes: I, II and III. *Zool. bidrag från Uppsala*, **32**, 97–597.

Fowler, H. (1963) Facilitation and inhibition of performance by punishment: the effects of shock intensity and distribution of trials. *J. comp. physiol. Psychol.*, **56**, 531–538.

Fowler, H. and Whalen, R. E. (1961) Variation in incentive stimulus and sexual behavior in the male rat. *J. comp. physiol. Psychol.*, **54**, 68–71.

Fox, S. S. (1962) Self-maintained sensory input and sensory deprivation in monkeys: a behavioral and neuropharmacological study. *J. comp. physiol. Psychol.*, **55**, 438–444.

Fox, W. (1952) Behavioral and evolutionary significance of the abnormal growth of beaks of birds. *Condor*, **54**, 160–162.

Fraenkel, G. S. (1931) Die Mechanik der Orientierung der Tiere im Raum. *Biol. Rev.*, **6**, 36–87, by permission of the Cambridge Philosophical Society.

Fraenkel, G. S. and Gunn, D. L. (1940) The Orientation of Animals. Clarendon Press, Oxford.

Franzisket, L. (1953) Untersuchungen zur Spezifität und Kumulierung der Erregungsfähigkeit und zur Wirkung einer Ermüdung in der Afferenz bei Wischbewegungen des Rückenmarksfrosches. *Zeits. vergl. Physiol.*, **34**, 525–538.

Franzisket, L. (1959) Zentralnervöse Steuerung des peripheren Nervenwachstums. *Verh. Deutsch. Zool. Gesell, Münster.* **8**, 139–145.

Franzisket, L. (1963) Characteristics of instinctive behaviour and learning in reflex activity of the frog. *Anim. Behav.*, **11**, 318–324.

Fredericson, E. (1951) Competition: the effects of infantile experience upon adult behavior. *J. abnorm. soc. Psychol.*, **46**, 406–409.

Fredericson, E. (1952) Perceptual homeostasis and distress vocalization in puppies. *J. Personal.*, **20**, 472–477.

Free, J. B. (1956) A study of the stimuli which release the food-begging and offering responses of worker honeybees. *Brit. J. Anim. Behav.*, **4**, 94–101.

Free, J. B. (1961) The stimuli releasing the stinging response of honeybees. *Anim. Behav.*, **9**, 193–196.

Freedman, S. J. (1961) Sensory deprivation: facts in search of a theory. *J. nerv. ment. Dis.*, **132**, 17–21.

Freud, S. (1915) Instincts and Their Vicissitudes. Coll. Papers Vol. IV, Hogarth, London.

Frisch, K. von (1950) Bees, their Vision, Chemical Senses and Language. Ithaca, New York.

Frisch, K. von (1953) Aus dem Leben der Bienen. By permission from Karl von Frisch, "The Dancing Bees," Methuen & Co. Ltd., London, 1954.

Frisch, O. von (1962) Zur Biologie des Zwergchamäleons (*Microsaurus punilus*). *Zeits f. Tierpsychol.* **19**, 276–289.

Fromme, A. (1941) An experimental study of the factors of maturation and practice in the behavioural development of the embryo of the frog, *Rana pipiens. Genet. Psychol. Monogr.*, **24**, 219–256.

Fromme, H. G. (1961) Untersuchungen über das Orientierungsvermögen nächtlich ziehender Kleinvögel (*Erithacus rubecula, Sylvia communis*). *Zeits f. Tierpsychol.*, **18**, 205–220.

Fuortes, M. G. F. (1958) Electrical activity of cells in the eye of Limulus. *Amer. J. Ophthal.*, **46**, 210.

Fuster, J. M. (1958) Effects of stimulation of brain stem on tachistoscopic perception. *Science*, **127**, 150.

Galambos, R. (1956) Suppression of auditory nerve activity by stimulation of efferent fibres to cochlea. *J. Neurophysiol.*, **19**, 424–437.

Galambos, R. (1959) Electrical correlates of conditioned learning. In the "Central Nervous System and Behaviour, I", Ed. M. A. B. Brazier, Josiah Macy, Jr. Foundation, New York.

Galambos, R. (1960) Studies of the auditory system with implanted electrodes. In "Neural Mechanisms of the Auditory and Vestibular Systems", Eds. G. L. Rasmussen and W. F. Windle, Thomas, Springfield.

Galambos, R. and Davis, H. (1944) Inhibition of activity in single auditory nerve fibers by acoustic stimulation. *J. Neurophysiol.*, **7**, 287–303.

Galambos, R., Sheatz, G. and Vernier, V. G. (1956) Electrophysiological correlates of a conditioned response in cats. *Science*, **123**, 376–377.

Gardner, B. T. (1964) Hunger and sequential responses in the hunting behavior of Salticid spiders. *J. comp. physiol. Psychol.*, **58**, 167–173.

Gastaut, H., Jus, A., Jus, C., Morrell, F., van Leeuwen, W. S., Dongier, S., Naquet, R., Regis, H., Roger, A., Bekkering, D., Kamp, A. and Werre, J. (1957) Étude topographique des reáctions électroencéphalographiques conditionnées chez l'homme. *Electroenceph. clin. Neurophysiol.*, **9**, 1–34.

Gauss, G. H. (1961) Ein Beitrag zur Kenntnis des Balzverhaltens einheimischer Molche. *Zeits f. Tierpsychol.*, **18**, 60–66.

Gauthier-Pilters, H. (1959) Einige Beobachtungen zum Droh-, Angriffs- und Kampfverhalten des Dromedarhengstes, sowie über Geburt und Verhaltensentwicklung des Jungtieres, in der nordwestlichen Sahara. *Zeits f. Tierpsychol.*, **16**, 593–604.

Geisler, M. (1961) Untersuchungen zur Tagesperiodik des Mistkäfers *Geotrupes silvaticus* Panz. *Zeits f. Tierpsychol.*, **18**, 389–420.

Geist, V. (1963) On the behaviour of the North American Moose (*Alces alces andersoni* Peterson 1950) in British Columbia. *Behaviour*, **20**, 377–416.

Gerall, A. A. (1963) An exploratory study of the effect of social isolation variables on the sexual behaviour of male guineapigs. *Anim. Behav.*, **11**, 274–282.

Gerard, R. W. (1961) The fixation of experience. In "Brain Mechanisms and Learning", Ed. J. F. Delafresnaye, C.I.O.M.S. Symposium, Oxford, Univ. Press, London.

Gerard, R. W., Marshall, W. H. and Saul, L. J. (1936) Electrical activity of the cat's brain. *A. M. A. Arch. Neurol. Psychiat.*, **36**, 675–738.

Gernandt, B. (1949) Response of mammalian vestibular neurons to horizontal rotation and caloric stimulation. *J. Neurophysiol.*, **12**, 173–184.

Gesell, A. (1954) The ontogenesis of infant behaviour. In "Manual of Child Psychology", 2nd Ed., Ed. L. Carmichael, New York.

Ghent, L. (1957) Some effects of deprivation on eating and drinking behavior. *J. comp. physiol. Psychol.*, **50**, 172–176.

Gibb, J. (1954) Feeding ecology of tits, with notes on Treecreeper and Goldcrest. *Ibis*, **96**, 513–543.

Gibb, J. A. (1962) L. Tinbergen's hypothesis of the role of specific search images. *Ibis*, **104**, 106–111.

Gibson, E. J. and Walk, R. D. (1956) The effect of prolonged exposure to visually presented patterns on learning to discriminate them. *J. comp. physiol. Psychol.*, **49**, 239–242.

Gibson, E. J. and Walk, R. D. (1960) The visual cliff. *Scien. Amer.*, **202**, 64–71.

Gibson, E. J., Walk, R. D., Pick, H. L. and Tighe, T. J. (1958) The effect of prolonged exposure to visual patterns on learning to discriminate similar and different patterns. *J. comp. physiol. Psychol.*, **51**, 584–587.

Gibson, E. J., Walk, R. D. and Tighe, T. J. (1959) Enhancement and deprivation of visual stimulation during rearing as factors in visual discrimination learning. *J. comp. physiol. Psychol.*, **52**, 74–81.

Gibson, J. J. (1950) The Perception of the Visual World. Houghton Mifflin. Cambridge, Mass.

Gibson, J. J. (1959) Perception as a function of stimulation. In "Psychology, a Study of a Science", Ed. S. Koch, McGraw-Hill Book Company Inc., New York.

Gibson, J. J. and Gibson, E. J. (1955) Perceptual learning; differentiation or enrichment? *Psychol. Rev.*, **62**, 32–41. See also *Psychol. Rev.*, **62**, 447–450.

Giebel, H-D. (1958) Visuelles Lernvermögen bei Einhufern. *Zool. Jahrb.*, **67**, 487–520.

Ginsburg, N. (1960) Conditioned vocalization in the budgerigar. *J. comp. physiol. Psychol.*, **53**, 183–186.

Girdner, J. B. (1953) An experimental analysis of the behavioural effects of a perceptual consequence unrelated to organic drive states. *Amer. Psychol.*, **8**, 354–355.

Glanzer, M. (1953a) Stimulus satiation: an explanation of spontaneous alternation and related phenomena. *Psychol. Rev.*, **60**, 257–269.

Glanzer, M. (1953b) The role of stimulus satiation in spontaneous alternation. *J. exp. Psychol.*, **45**, 387–393.

Glanzer, M. (1958) Curiosity, exploratory drive, and stimulus satiation. *Psychol. Bull.*, **55**, 302–315.

Goethe, F. (1954) Vergleichende Beobachtungen zum Verhalten der Silbermöwe (*Larus argentatus*) und der Heringsmöwe (*Larus fuscus*). *Proc. XI. Int. Orn. Congr.*, 577–582.

Goodall, J. M. (1962) Nest building behavior in the free ranging Chimpanzee. *Ann. N.Y. Acad. Sci.*, **102**, 455–467.

Goodhart, C. B. (1960) The evolutionary significance of human hair patterns and skin colouring. *Advanc. Sci.*, **17**, 53–59.

Górska, T. and Jankowska, E. (1961) The effect of deafferentation on instrumental (Type II) conditioned reflexes in dogs. *Acta Biol. Exp.*, **21**, 219–234.

Górska, T., Jankowska, E. and Kozak, W. (1961) The effect of deafferentation on instrumental (Type II) cleaning reflex in cats. *Acta Biol. Exp.*, **21**, 207–217.

Gottlieb, G. (1963) A naturalistic study of imprinting in Wood ducklings (*Aix sponsa*). *J. comp. physiol. Psychol.*, **56**, 86–91.

Gottlieb, G. (1965) Imprinting in relation to parental and species identification by avian neonates. *J. comp. physiol. Psychol.*, **59**, 345–356.

Gottlieb, G. and Klopfer, P. H. (1962) The relation of developmental age to auditory and visual imprinting. *J. comp. physiol. Psychol.*, **55**, 821–826.

Gottlieb, G. and Kuo, Z-Y. (1965) Development of behavior in the duck embryo. *J. comp. physiol. Psychol.*, **59**, 183–188.

Goy, R. W. and Young, W. C. (1956–7) Strain differences in the behavioral responses of female guineapigs to alpha-estradiol benzoate and progesterone. *Behaviour*, **10**, 340–354.

Graff, H. and Stellar, E. (1962) Hyperphagia, obesity and finickiness. *J. comp. physiol. Psychol.*, **55**, 418–424.

Graham Brown, T. (1911) The intrinsic factors in the act of progression in the mammal. *Proc. Roy. Soc. B*, **84**, 308–319.

Granit, R. (1947) The Sensory Mechanisms of the Retina. Oxford Univ. Press, London.

Granit, R. (1955a) Receptors and Sensory Perception. Yale Univ. Press, New Haven.

Granit, R. (1955b) Centrifugal and antidromic effects on ganglion cells of retina. *J. Neurophysiol.*, **18**, 388–411.

Granit, R. and Kaada, B. R. (1952) Influence of stimulation of central nervous structures on muscle spindles in cat. *Acta physiol. scand.*, **27**, 130–160.

Grant, E. C. (1963) An analysis of the social behaviour of the male laboratory rat. *Behaviour*, **21**, 260–281.

Grant, E. C. and Mackintosh, J. H. (1963) A comparison of the social postures of some common laboratory rodents. *Behaviour*, **21**, 246–259.

Gray, J. (1950) The role of peripheral sense organs during locomotion in the vertebrates. *Sym. Soc. exp. Biol.*, **4**, 112–126.

Gray, J. and Lissmann, H. W. (1946a) Further observations on the effect of deafferentation on the locomotory activity of amphibian limbs. *J. exp. Biol.*, **23**, 121–132.

Gray, J. and Lissmann, H. W. (1946b) The coordination of limb movements in the amphibia. *J. exp. Biol.*, **23**, 133–142.

Gray, J. and Lissmann, H. W. (1947) The effect of labyrinthectomy on the coordination of limb movements in the toad. *J. exp. Biol.*, **24**, 36–40.

Gray, J. and Sand, A. (1936a) The locomotory rhythm of the dogfish (*Scyllium canicula*). *J. exp. Biol.*, **13**, 200–209.

Gray, J. and Sand, A. (1936b) Spinal reflexes of the dogfish, *Scyllium canicula. J. exp. Biol.*, **13**, 210–218.

Gray, P. H. (1961) The releasers of imprinting: differential reactions to color as a function of maturation. *J. comp. physiol. Psychol.*, **54**, 597–601.

Gregory, R. L. (1958) Eye movements and the stability of the visual world. *Nature*, **182**, 1214–1216.

Gregory, R. L. and Wallace, J. G. (1963) Recovery from early blindness. *Exp. Psychol. Soc. Monogr. No. 2.*

Grey Walter, W. (1959) Intrinsic rhythms of the brain. In "Handbook of Physiology", Section 1, Neurophysiology, Vol. 1, Eds. J. Field, H. W. Magoun and V. E. Hall, American Physiol. Soc. Washington.

Grindley, G. C. (1932) The formation of a simple habit in guinea-pigs. *Brit. J. Psychol.*, **23**, 127–147.

Grohmann, J. (1939) Modifikation oder Funktionsreifung? Ein Beitrag zur Klärung der wechselseitigen Beziehungen zwischen Instinkthandlung und Erfahrung. *Zeits f. Tierpsychol.*, **2**, 132–144.

Grossman, S. P. (1960) Eating or drinking elicited by direct adrenergic or cholinergic stimulation of hypothalamus. *Science*, **132**, 301–302.

Grunt, J. A. and Young, W. C. (1952) Psychological modification of fatigue following orgasm (ejaculation) in the male guineapig. *J. comp. physiol. Psychol.*, **45**, 508–510.

Grunt, J. A. and Young, W. C. (1953) Consistency of sexual behavior patterns in individual male guineapigs following castration and androgen therapy. *J. comp. physiol. Psychol.*, **46**, 138–144.

Grüsser-Cornehls, U., Grüsser, O-J. and Bullock, T. H. (1963) Unit responses in the frog's tectum to moving and nonmoving visual stimuli. *Science*, **141**, 820–822.

Guhl, A. M. (1961) Gonadal hormones and social behavior in infrahuman vertebrates. In "Sex and Internal Secretions", Vol. II, Ed. Young, W. C., Williams & Wilkins Co., Baltimore.

Guhl, A. M. (1962) The behaviour of chickens. In "The Behaviour of Domestic Animals", Ed. E. S. E. Hafez, Baillière, Tindall and Cox, London.

Guiton, P. (1959) Socialisation and imprinting in Brown Leghorn chicks. *Anim. Behav.*, **7**, 26–34.

Guiton, P. (1961) The influence of imprinting on the agonistic and courtship responses of the Brown Leghorn cock. *Anim. Behav.*, **9**, 167–177.

Guiton, P. (1962a) The development of sexual response in domestic fowl in relation to the concept of imprinting. *Anim. Behav.*, **10**, 184.

Guiton, P. (1962b) The development of sexual responses in the domestic fowl, in relation to the concept of imprinting. *Sym. Zool. Soc. Lond.*, **8**, 227–234.

Gunther, M. (1955) Instinct and the nursing couple. *Lancet*, **1955**, 575–578.

Guthrie, E. R. (1935, 1952) The Psychology of Learning. Harper, New York.

Guttman, N. (1954) Equal-reinforcement values for sucrose and glucose solutions compared with equal-sweetness values. *J. comp. physiol. Psychol.*, **47**, 358–361.

Haartmann, L. von (1957) Adaptation in hole-nesting birds. *Evolution*, **11**, 339–347.

Haber, R. N. (1958) Discrepancy from adaptation level as a source of affect. *J. exp. Psychol.*, **56**, 370–375.

Hagamen, W. D., Zitzmann, E. K. and Reeves, A. G. (1963) Sexual mounting of diverse objects in a group of randomly selected, unoperated male cats. *J. comp. physiol. Psychol.*, **56**, 298–302.

Hagbarth, K.–E. and Fex, J. (1959) Centrifugal influences on single unit activity in spinal sensory paths. *J. Neurophysiol.*, **22**, 321–338.

Hagbarth, K.–E. and Kerr, D. I. B. (1954) Central influences on spinal afferent conduction. *J. Neurophysiol.*, **17**, 295–307.

Hagiwara, S. (1961) Nervous activities of the heart in Crustacea. *Ergebn. Biol.*, **24**, 287–311.

Hagiwara, S. and Watanabe, A. (1956) Discharges in motoneurons of cicada. *J. cell. comp. Physiol.*, **47**, 415–428.

Hailman, J. P. (1962) Pecking of Laughing Gull chicks at models of the parental head. *Auk*, **79**, 89–98.

Hall, J. F. (1956) The relationship between external stimulation, food deprivation and activity. *J. comp. physiol. Psychol.*, **49**, 339–341.

Hall-Craggs, J. (1962) The development of song in the Blackbird *Turdus merula. Ibis*, **104**, 277–300.

Hamilton, C. L. (1963) Interactions of food intake and temperature regulation in the rat. *J. comp. physiol. Psychol.*, **56**, 3, 476–488.

Hammond, P. H., Merton, P. A. and Sutton, G. G. (1956) Nervous gradation of muscular contraction. *Brit. Med. Bull.*, **12**, 214–218.

Hanson, N. R. (1955) Causal chains. *Mind*, **64**, 289–311.

Harker, J. E. (1958a) Diurnal rhythms in the animal kingdom. *Biol. Rev.* **33**, 1–52.

Harker, J. E. (1958b) Experimental production of midgut tumours in *Periplaneta americana*. L. *J. exp. Biol.*, **35**, 251–259.

Harker, J. E. (1964) The Physiology of Diurnal Rhythms. Cambridge Univ. Press, London.

Harlow, H. F. (1959a) The development of learning in the rhesus monkey. *Amer. Scientist*, **47**, 459–479.

Harlow, H. F. (1959b) Learning set and error factory theory. In "Psychology: a Study of a Science", Ed. S. Koch, McGraw-Hill Book Company Inc., New York.

Harlow, H. F. (1962) Development of the second and third affectional systems in macaque monkeys. In "Research Approaches to Psychiatric Problems", Ed. T. T. Tourlentes *et al.*, U.S.A.

Harlow, H. F. (1963) The maternal affectional system. In "Determinants of Infant Behavior, II", Ed. B. M. Foss, Methuen, London.

Harlow, H. F. and Harlow, M. K. (1962) Principles of Primate Learning. In "Little Club Clinics in Developmental Medicine", No. 7, Heinemann, London.

Harlow, H. F. and Harlow, M. K. (1965) The affectional systems. In "Behavior of Nonhuman Primates", Vol. II, Eds. Schrier, A. M., Harlow, H. F., Stollnitz, F., Academic Press, New York, London.

Harlow, H. F., Harlow, M. K. and Meyer, D. R. (1950) Learning motivated by a manipulation drive. *J. exp. Psychol.*, **40**, 228–234.

Harlow, H. F. and Zimmermann, R. R. (1959) Affectional responses in the infant monkey. *Science*, **130**, 421–432.

Harnly, M. H. (1941) Flight capacity in relation to phenotypic and genotypic variations in the wings of *Drosophila melanogaster. J. exp. Zool.*, **88**, 263–273.

Harrington, G. M. and Linder, W. K. (1962) A positive reinforcing effect of electrical stimulation. *J. comp. physiol. Psychol.*, **55**, 1014–1015.

Harris, G. W. (1955) Neural Control of the Pituitary Gland. Arnold, London.

Harris, G. W., Michael, R. P. and Scott, P. P. (1958) Neurological site of action of stilboestrol in eliciting sexual behaviour. Ciba Foundation Sym. on the "Neurological Basis of Behaviour", Churchill, London.

Harris, J. E. and Whiting, H. P. (1954) Control of rhythmical activity in the skeletal muscle of the embryonic dogfish. *J. Physiol.*, **124**, 63P.

Hartline, H. K. (1938) The response of single optic nerve fibers of the vertebrate eye to illumination of the retina. *Amer. J. Physiol.*, **121**, 400–415.

Hartline, H. K. (1949) Inhibition of activity of visual receptors by illuminating nearby retinal areas in the *Limulus* eye. *Fed. Proc.*, **8**, 69.

Hartline, H. K. and Graham, C. H. (1932) Nerve impulses from single receptors in the eye. *J. cell. comp. Physiol.*, **1**, 277–295.

Hartline, H. K. and Ratliff, F. (1956) Inhibitory interaction of receptor units in the eye of *Limulus. J. gen. Physiol.*, **40**, 357–376.

Hartline, H. K., Wagner, H. G. and Ratliff, F. (1956) Inhibition in the eye of *Limulus. J. gen. Physiol.*, **39**, 651–673.

Haskell, P. T. (1956) Hearing in certain Orthoptera: II. The nature of the response of certain receptors to natural and imitation stridulation. *J. exp. Biol.*, **33**, 767–776.

Haskell, P. T. (1957) Stridulation and associated behaviour in certain Orthoptera: 1. Analysis of the stridulation of, and behaviour between, males. *Brit. J. Anim. Behav.*, **5**, 139–148.

Haskell, P. T. (1960) Stridulation and associated behaviour in certain Orthoptera: 3. The influence of the gonads. *Anim. Behav.*, **8**, 76–81.

Hassenstein, B. (1959) Optokinetische Wirksamkeit bewegter periodischer Muster. *Zeits f. Naturforschung*, **14**, 659–674.

Hassenstein, B. (1961) Wie sehen Insekten Bewegungen? *Naturwissenschaften*, **48**, 207–214.

Hassenstein, B. and Reichardt, W. (1959) Wie sehen Insekten Bewegungen? *Umschau*, **10**, 302–305.

Head, H. (1920) Studies in Neurology. Oxford Univ. Press, London.

Hebb, D. O. (1937a) The innate organization of visual activity: I. Perception of figures by rats reared in total darkness. *J. genet. Psychol.*, **51**, 101–126.

Hebb, D. O. (1937b) The innate organization of visual activity: II. Transfer of response in the discrimination of brightness and size by rats reared in total darkness. *J. comp. Psychol.*, **24**, 277–299.

Hebb, D. O. (1946) On the nature of fear. *Psychol. Rev.*, **53**, 259–276.

Hebb, D. O. (1949) The Organization of Behaviour. Wiley, New York.

Hebb, D. O. (1953) Heredity and environment in mammalian behaviour. *Brit. J. Anim. Behav.*, **1**, 43–47.

Hebb, D. O. (1955) Drives and the C.N.S. (conceptual nervous system). *Psychol. Rev.*, **62**, 243–254.

Hebb, D. O. (1963) The semiautonomous process. *Amer. Psychol.*, **18**, 16–27.

Hebb, D. O. and Thompson, W. A. (1954) The social significance of animal studies. In "Handbook of Social Psychology", G. Lindzey (ed.). Addison-Wesley.

Hediger, H. (1950) Wild Animals in Captivity. Butterworth, London.

Hein, A. and Held, R. (1962) A neural model for labile sensori-motor coordinations. From "Biological Prototypes and Synthetic Systems", Vol. 1, Plenum Press, New York.

Heinroth, O. (1911) Beiträge zur Biologie, namentlich Ethologie und Psychologie der Anatiden. *Verh. 5 Int. Orn. Kong.*, 589–702.

Held, R. (1961) Exposure-history as a factor in maintaining stability of perception and coordination. *J. nerv. ment. Dis.* **132**, 26–32.

Held, R. and Bossom, J. (1961) Neonatal deprivation and adult rearrangement: complementary techniques for analyzing plastic sensory-motor coordinations. *J. comp. physiol. Psychol.*, **54**, 33–37.

Held, R. and Freedman, S. J. (1963) Plasticity in human sensorimotor control. *Science*, **142**, 455–462.

Held, R. and Hein, A. V. (1958) Adaptation of disarranged hand-eye coordination contingent upon re-afferent stimulation. *Percept. Motor Skills*, **8**, 87–90.

Held, R. and Hein, A. (1963) Movement-produced stimulation in the development of visually guided behavior. *J. comp. physiol. Psychol.*, **56**, 872–876.

Held, R. and Hein, A. (in press) On the modifiability of form perception. In "Symposium on Models for Perception of Speech and Visual form", Eds. J. C. Moth-Smith *et al.*

Helmholtz, H. von (1867) Handbuch der physiologischen Optik. Voss, Leipzig. English translation by Southall, J. P. C. (1925), Optical Society of America, Wisconsin.

Helson, H. (1948) Adaptation-level as a basis for a quantitative theory of frames of reference. *Psychol. Rev.*, **55**, 297–313.

Hendry, D. P. and Rasche, R. H. (1961) Analysis of a new nonnutritive positive reinforcer based on thirst. *J. comp. physiol. Psychol.*, **54**, 477–483.

Henke, K. (1930) Die Lichtorientierung und die Bedingungen der Lichtstimmung bei der Rollassel *Armadillidium* cinereum Zenker. *Z. vergl. Physiol.*, **13**, 534–625.

Hensel, H. and Zotterman, Y. (1951) The response of mechanoreceptors to thermal stimulation. *J. Physiol.*, **115**, 16–24.

Hernández-Peón, R., Guzman-Flores, C., Alcares, M. and Fernández-Guardiola, A. (1957a) Sensory transmission in the visual pathway during "attention" in unanaesthetised cats. *Acta Neur. Lat.-Amer.*, **3**, 1–8.

Hernández-Peón, R., Jouvet, M. and Scherrer, H. (1957b) Auditory potentials at cochlear nucleus during acoustic habituation. *Acta Neur. Lat.-Amer.*, **3**, 114–116.

Hernández-Peón, R., Scherrer, H. and Jouvet, M. (1956) Modification of electric activity in cochlear nucleus during "attention" in unanaesthetized cats. *Science*, **123**, 331–2.

Herren, R. Y. (1933) The effect of high and low female sex hormone concentration on the two-point threshold of pain and touch and upon tactile sensitivity. *J. exp. Psychol.*, **16**, 324–327.

Herrnstein, R. J. and Loveland, D. H. (1964) Complex visual concept in the pigeon. *Science*, **146**, 549–551.

Herrnstein, R. J. and van Sommers, P. (1962) Method for sensory scaling with animals. *Science*, **135**, 40–41.

Hersher, L., Moore, A. U. and Richmond, J. B. (1958) Effect of post partum separation of mother and kid on maternal care in the domestic goat. *Science*, **128**, 1342–1343.

Hersher, L., Richmond, J. B. and Moore, A. U. (1963) Modifiability of the critical period for the development of maternal behavior in sheep and goats *Behaviour*, **20**, 311–320.

Herter, K. (1927) Reizphysiologische Untersuchungen an der Karpfenlaus (*Argulus foliaceus* L.). *Zeits. vergl. Physiol.*, **5**, 283–370.

Hertz, M. (1929, 1930, 1931) Die Organisation des optischen Feldes bei der Biene: I, II, and III. *Zeits. vergl. Physiol.*, **8**, 693–748; **11**, 107–145; **14**, 629–674.

Hertz, M. (1933) Über figurale Intensitäten und Qualitäten in der optischen Wahrnehmung der Biene. *Biol. Zbl.*, **53**, 10–40.

Hertz, M. (1935) Die Untersuchungen über die Formensinn der Honigbiene. *Naturwissenschaften*, **23**, 618–624.

Hess, E. H. (1956a) Natural preferences of chicks and ducklings for objects of different colours. *Psych. Rep.*, **2**, 477–483.

Hess, E. H. (1956b) Space perception in the chick. *Sci. Amer.*, **195**, 71–80.

Hess, E. H. (1959a) Imprinting. *Science*, **130**, 133–141.

Hess, E. H. (1959b) Two conditions limiting critical age for imprinting. *J. comp. physiol. Psychol.*, **52**, 515–8.

Hess, W. R. (1943) Das Zwischenhirn als Koordinationsorgan. *Helv. Physiol. Acta*, **1**, 549–565.

Hess, W. R. (1954) Diencephalon: Autonomic and Extrapyramidal Functions. Grune, New York.

Heusser, H. (1958) Über die Beziehungen der Erdkröte (*Bufo bufo* L.) zu ihrem Laichplatz: I. *Behaviour*, **12**, 208–232.

Hildreth, P. E. (1962) Quantitative aspects of mating behavior in *Drosophila*. *Behaviour*, **19**, 57–73.

Hilgard, E. R. (1948, 1956) Theories of Learning. Appleton-Century-Crofts, New York.

Hilgard, E. R. and Marquis, D. G. (1961) Conditioning and Learning. Revised G. A. Kimble, Methuen, London.

Hill, W. F. (1958) The effect of varying periods of confinement on activity in tilt cages. *J. comp. physiol., Psychol.*, **51**, 570–574.

Hinde, R. A. (1952) The Behaviour of the Great Tit (*Parus major*) and some other related species. *Behaviour, Supplement No. 2*, 1–201.

Hinde, R. A. (1953a) The conflict between drives in the courtship and copulation of the Chaffinch. *Behaviour*, **5**, 1–31.

Hinde, R. A. (1953b) A possible explanation of paper-tearing behaviour in birds. *Brit. Birds*, **46**, 21–23.

Hinde, R. A. (1954a) Factors governing the changes in strength of a partially inborn response, as shown by the mobbing behaviour of the chaffinch (*Fringilla coelebs*): I. The nature of the response, and an examination of its course. *Proc. Roy. Soc. B.*, **142**, 306–331.

Hinde, R. A. (1954b) Factors governing the changes in strength of a partially inborn response, as shown by the mobbing behaviour of the chaffinch (*Fringilla coelebs*): II. The waning of the response. *Proc. Roy. Soc. B.*, **142**, 331–358.

Hinde, R. A. (1954c) The courtship and copulation of the Greenfinch (*Chloris chloris*). *Behaviour*, **7**, 207–232.

Hinde, R. A. (1954d) Changes in responsiveness to a constant stimulus. *Brit. J. Anim. Behav.*, **2**, 41–55.

Hinde, R. A. (1955) The following response of Moorhens and Coots. *Brit. J. Anim. Behav.*, **3**, 121–122.

Hinde, R. A. (1955/6) A comparative study of the courtship of certain finches (*Fringillidae*). *Ibis*, **97**, 706–745; **98**, 1–23.

Hinde, R. A. (1956a) Ethological models and the concept of drive. *Brit. J. Philos. Sci.*, **6**, 321–331.

Hinde, R. A. (1956b) The biological significance of the territories of birds. *Ibis*, **98**, 340–369.

Hinde, R. A. (1958a) The nest-building behaviour of domesticated canaries. *Proc. Zool. Soc. Lond.*, **131**, 1–48.

Hinde, R. A. (1958b) Alternative motor patterns in Chaffinch song. *Anim. Behav.*, **6**, 211–218.

Hinde, R. A. (1959a) Behaviour and speciation in birds and lower vertebrates. *Biol. Rev.*, **34**, 85–128.

Hinde, R. A. (1959b) Some recent trends in ethology. From "Psychology: a Study of a Science", Study 1, Vol. 2, Ed. S. Koch, McGraw-Hill Book Company Inc., New York.

Hinde, R. A. (1959c) Some factors influencing sexual and aggressive behaviour in male Chaffinches. *Bird Study*, **6**, 112–122.

Hinde, R. A. (1959d) Unitary drives. *Anim. Behav.*, **7**, 130–141.

Hinde, R. A. (1960) Energy models of motivation. *Sym. Soc. exp. Biol.*, **14**, 199–213.

Hinde, R. A. (1961) Factors governing the changes in strength of a partially inborn response, as shown by the mobbing behaviour of the chaffinch (*Fringilla coelebs*): III. The interaction of short-term and long-term incremental and decremental effects. *Proc. Roy. Soc., B.*, **153**, 398–420.

Hinde, R. A. (1962a) Sensitive periods and the development of behaviour. From "Lessons from Animal Behaviour for the Clinician", Little Club Clinic in Developmental Medicine, No. 7, The National Spastics Society Study Group 1962.

Hinde, R. A. (1962b) Some aspects of the imprinting problem. *Sym. Zool. Soc. Lond.*, **8**, 129–138.

Hinde, R. A. (1962c) The relevance of animal studies to human neurotic disorders. In "Aspects of Psychiatric Research", Eds. D. Richter, J. M. Tanner, Lord Taylor and O. L. Zangwill, Oxford Univ. Press, London.

Hinde, R. A. (1965) The integration of the reproductive behaviour of female canaries. In "Sex and Behavior", Ed. F. A. Beach, John Wiley, New York.

Hinde, R. A. (in press) Ritualization and social communication in Rhesus monkeys. *Proc. Roy. Soc. B.*

Hinde, R. A., Bell, R. Q. and Steel, E. A. (1963) Changes in sensitivity of the canary brood patch during the natural breeding season. *Anim. Behav.*, **11**, 553–560.

Hinde, R. A. and Rowell, T. E. (1962) Communication by postures and facial expressions in the rhesus monkey (*Macaca mulatta*). *Proc. Zool. Soc. Lond.*, **138**, 1–21.

Hinde, R. A., Rowell, T. E. and Spencer-Booth, Y. (1964) Behaviour of socially living rhesus monkeys in their first six months. *Proc. Zool. Soc. Lond.* **143**, 609–649.

Hinde, R. A. and Steel, E. A. (1962) Selection of nest material by female canaries. *Anim. Behav.*, **10**, 67–75.

Hinde, R. A. and Steel, Elizabeth (1964) Effect of exogenous hormones on the tactile sensitivity of the canary brood patch. *J. Endocrin.*, **30**, 355–359.

Hinde, R. A., Thorpe, W. H. and Vince, M. A. (1956) The following response of young Coots and Moorhens. *Behaviour*, **9**, 2–3, 214–242.

Hinde, R. A. and Tinbergen, N. (1958) The comparative study of species-specific behavior. From "Behavior and Evolution", Eds. Anne Roe and G. G. Simpson, Yale Univ. Press, New Haven.

Hinde, R. A. and Warren, Roslyn P. (1959) The effect of nest building on later reproductive behaviour in domesticated canaries. *Anim. Behav.*, 7, 35–41.

Hines, M. (1942) The development and regression of reflexes, postures and progression in the young macaque. *Contr. Embryol. Carnegie Instn.*, Wash., 30, 153–209.

Hitchcock, L., Michels, K. M. and Brown, D. R. (1963) Discrimination learning: squirrels vs. raccoons. *Perceptual and Motor Skills*, 16, 405–414.

Hoagland, H. (1933a) Electrical responses from the lateral-line nerves of catfish: I. *J. gen. Physiol.*, 16, 695–714.

Hoagland, H. (1933b) Quantitative analysis of responses from lateral-line nerves of fishes: II. *J. gen. Physiol.*, 16, 715–732.

Hockman, C. H. (1961) Prenatal maternal stress in the rat: its effects on emotional behavior in the offspring. *J. comp. physiol. Psychol.*, 54, 679–684.

Hodgson, E. S. (1957) Electrophysiological studies of arthropod chemoreception: II Responses of labellar chemoreceptors of the blowfly to stimulation by carbohydrates. *J. insect Physiol.*, 1, 240–247.

Hodgson, E. S. and Roeder, K. D. (1956) Electrophysiological studies of arthropod chemoreception: I. General properties of the labellar chemoreceptors of Diptera. *J. cell. comp. Physiol.*, 48, 51–76.

van Hof, M. W., van Hof-van Duin, J., van Der Mark, F. and Rietveld, W. J. (1962) The effect of image formation and that of flash-counting on the occipito-cortical response to lightflashes. *Acta physiol. pharm. néerl.*, 11, 485–493.

Hoffmann, K. (1953) Experimentelle Anderung des Richtungsfinden beim Star durch Beeinflussung der "innen Uhr". *Naturwissenschaften*, 40, 148.

Hogan, J. A. (1965). An experimental study of conflict and fear: an analysis of behaviour of young chicks towards a mealworm. *Behaviour*, 25, 45–97.

Holmgren, B. and Merton, P. A. (1954) Local feedback control of motoneurones. *J. Physiol.*, 123, 47P.

von Holst, E. (1935a) Erregungsbildung und Erregungsleitung im Fischrückenmark. *Pflüg. Arch. ges Physiol.*, 235, 345–359.

von Holst, E. (1935b) Über den Prozess der zentralnervösen Koordination. *Pflüg. Arch. ges. Physiol.*, 236, 149–158.

von Holst, E. (1935c) Alles oder Nichts, Block, Alternans, Bigemini und verwandte Phänomene als Eigenschaften des Ruckenmarks. *Pflüg. Arch. ges. Physiol.*, 236, 515–532.

von Holst, E. (1935d) Über den Lichtrüchenreflex bei Fischen. *Publ. Staz. Zool. Napoli*, 15, 143–158.

von Holst, E. (1936) Versuche zur Theorie der relativen Koordination. *Pflüg. arch. ges. Physiol.*, 237, 93–121.

von Holst, E. (1939) Entwurf eines Systems der Lokomotorischen Periodenbildungen bei Fischen. *Zeits. vergl. Physiol.*, 26, 481–528.

von Holst, E. (1948) Von der Mathematik der nervösen Ordnungsleistung. *Experientia*, 4, 374–381.

von Holst, E. (1950a) Quantitative Messung von Stimmungen im Verhalten der Fische. *Sym. Soc. Exp. Biol.*, IV, 143–172.

von Holst, E. (1950b) Die Arbeitsweise des Statolithenapparates bei Fischen. *Zeits. vergl. Physiol.*, 32, 60–120.

von Holst, E. (1954) Relations between the central nervous system and the peripheral organs. *Brit. J. Anim. Behav.*, 2, 89–94.

von Holst, E. und Mittelstaedt, H. (1950) Das Reafferenzprincip. *Naturwissenschaften*, **37**, 464–476.

von Holst, E. and von Saint Paul, U. (1963) On the functional organisation of drives. *Anim. Behav.*, **11**, 1–20, translated from *Naturwissenschaften*, **18**, 409–422.

von Holst, E. and Schoen, L. (1954) Der Einfluss mechanisch veränderter, Augenstellungen auf die Richtungslokalisation bei Fischen. *Zeits. vergl. Physiol.*, **36**, 433–442.

Holzapfel, M. (1939a) Über Bewegungstereotypien bei gehaltenen Säugern: III. *Der Zoologische Garten*, **10**, 184–193.

Holzapfel, M. (1939b) Analyse des Sperrens und Pickens in der Entwicklung des Stars. *J. f. Ornith.*, **87**, 525–553.

Holzapfel, M. (1949) Die Beziehungen zwischen den Trieben junger und erwachsener Tiere. *Schweiz. Zeits. Psych.*, **8**, 32–60.

Holzapfel, M. (1956a) Das Spiel bei Säugetieren. In "Handbuch der Zoologie", Vol. 8, 10 Teil., ed. Kükenthal.

Holzapfel, M. (1956b) Über die Bereitschaft zu Spiel-und Instinkthandlungen. *Zeits. f. Tierpsychol.*, **13**, 442–462.

Hooff, J. A. R. A. M. van (1962) Facial expressions in higher primates. *Sym. Zool. Soc. Lond.*, **8**, 97–125.

Hoogland, R., Morris, D. and Tinbergen, N. (1956–7) The spines of Sticklebacks (*Gasterosteus* and *Pygosteus*) as means of defence against predators (*Perca* and *Esox*). *Behaviour*, 10, 205–236.

Horn, G. (1952) The neurological basis of thought. *Mermaid*, **18**, 17–25.

Horn, G. (1960) Electrical activity of the cerebral cortex of the unanaesthetized cat during attentive behaviour. *Brain*, **83**, 57–76.

Horn, G. (1962) Some neural correlates of perception. "Viewpoints in Biology", I, Ed. J. Carthy, Butterworths, London.

Horn, G. (1963) The response of single units in the striate cortex of unrestrained cats to photic and somaesthetic stimuli. *J. Physiol.*, **165**, 80–81P.

Horn, G. (1965) Physiological and psychological aspects of selective perception. In "Advances in the Study of Behavior", Eds. D. Lehrman, R. A. Hinde and E. Shaw, Academic Press, New York.

Horn, G. and Hill, R. M. (1964) Habituation of the response to sensory stimuli of neurones in the brain stem of rabbits. *Nature*, **202**, 296–298.

Horridge, G. A. (1959a) Analysis of the rapid responses of *Nereis* and *Harmothöe* (Annelida). *Proc. Roy. Soc. B.*, **150**, 245–262.

Horridge, G. A. (1959b) The nerves and muscles of medusae: VI. The rhythm. *J. exp. Biol.*, **36**, 72–91.

Horridge, G. A. (1961) The centrally determined sequence of impulses initiated from a ganglion of the clam *Mya*. *J. Physiol.*, **155**, 320–336.

Howard, E. (1935) The Nature of a Bird's World. Cambridge Univ. Press, London.

Howarth, C. I. and Ellis, K. (1961) The relative intelligibility threshold for one's own name compared with other names. *Quart. J. exp. Psychol.*, **13**, 236–239.

Howell, T. R. and Bartholomew, G. A. (1952) Experiments on the mating behavior of the Brewer Blackbird. *Condor*, **54**, 140–151.

Hubel, D. H. and Wiesel, T. N. (1959) Receptive fields of single neurones in the cat's striate cortex. *J. Physiol.*, **148**, 574–591.

Hubel, D. H. and Wiesel, T. N. (1961) Integrative action in the cat's lateral geniculate body. *J. Physiol.*, **155**, 385–398.

Hubel, D. H. and Wiesel, T. N. (1962) Receptive fields, binocular interaction and functional architecture in the cat's visual cortex. *J. Physiol.*, **160**, 106–154.

Huber, F. (1955) Sitz und Bedeutung nervöser Zentren für Instinkthandlungen beim Männchen von *Gryllus campestris* L. *Zeits f. Tierpsychol.*, **12**, 12–48.

Huber, F. (1960) Untersuchungen über die Funktion des Zentralnervensystems und insbesondere des Gehirnes bei der Fortbewegung und der Lauterzeugung der Grillen. *Zeits. vergl. Physiol.*, **44**, 60–132.

Hughes, G. M. (1957) The coordination of insect movements: II. The effect of limb amputation and the cutting of commissures in the cockroach (*Blatta orientalis*). *J. exp. Biol.*, **34**, 306–333.

Hughes, G. M. (1958) The coordination of insect movements: III. Swimming in *Dytiscus, Hydrophilus*, and a dragonfly nymph. *J. exp. Biol.*, **35**, 567–583.

Hughes, G. M. and Kerkut, G. A. (1956) Electrical activity in a slug ganglion in relation to the concentration of Locke solution. *J. exp. Biol.*, **33**, 282–294.

Hughes, G. M. and Tauc, L. (1963) An electrophysiological study of the anatomical relations of two giant nerve cells in *Aphysia depilans*. *J. exp. Biol.*, **40**, 469–486.

Hughes, G. M. and Wiersma, C. A. G. (1960) The co-ordination of swimmeret movements in the crayfish, *Procambarus clarkii* (Girard). *J. exp. Biol.*, **37**, 657–670.

Hull, C. L. (1933) Differential habituation to internal stimuli in the albino rat. *J. comp. Psychol.*, **16**, 255–273.

Hull, C. L. (1943) Principles of Behavior. Appleton-Century-Crofts, New York.

Hull, C. L. (1952) A Behavior System. Yale Univ. Press, New Haven, Conn.

Humphrey, G. (1933) The Nature of Learning. Kegan Paul, New York.

Hunt, H. H. and Otis, L. S. (1955) Restricted experience and "timidity" in the rat. *Amer. Psychologist*, **10**, 432.

Hunt, J. McV. (1941) The effects of infant feeding-frustration upon adult hoarding in the albino rat. *J. abnorm. soc. Psychol.*, **36**, 338–360.

Hunt, J. McV., Schlosberg, H., Solomon, R. L. and Stellar, E. (1947) Studies of the effects of infantile experience on adult behavior in rats: I. *J. comp. physiol. Psychol.*, **40**, 291–304.

Hurwitz, H. M. B. (1956) Conditioned responses in rats reinforced by light. *Brit. J. Anim. Behav.*, **4**, 31–33.

Hurwitz, H. M. B. (1957) Periodicity of response in operant extinction. *Quart. J. exp. Psychol.*, **9**, 177–184.

Hurwitz, H. M. B. and De S. C. (1958) Studies in light reinforced behavior. *Psychol. Rep.*, **4**, 71–77.

Hutchings, D. E. (1963) Early "experience" and its effects on later behavioral processes in rats: III. Effects of infantile handling and body temperature reduction on later emotionality. *Trans. N. Y. Acad. Sci.*, **25**, 890–901.

Hutchison, J. B. (1964) Investigations on the neural control of clasping and feeding in *Xenopus laevis* (Daudin). *Behaviour*, **24**, 47–65.

Hutchison, J. B. and Poynton, J. C. (1963) A neurological study of the clasp reflex in *Xenopus laevis* (Daudin). *Behaviour*, **22**, 41–63.

Huxley, J. S. (1942) Evolution, the modern synthesis. Allen and Unwin, London.

Hymovitch, B. (1952) The effects of experimental variations on problem solving in the rat. *J. comp. physiol. Psychol.*, **45**, 313–321.

Iersel, J. J. A. van (1953) An analysis of the parental behaviour of the male Three-spined Stickleback (*Gasterosteus aculeatus* L.). *Behaviour*, Suppl. 3, 1–159.

Iersel, J. J. A. van. (1965) Aspects of orientation in the Diggerwasp *Bembix rostrata*. In "Learning and Associated Phenomena in Invertebrates". Anim. Behav. Sup. 1. Eds. Thorpe, W. H. and Davenport, D., Baillière, Tindall and Cassell: London.

Iersel, J. J. A. van and Bol, A. C. Angela (1958) Preening of two tern species. A study on displacement activities. *Behaviour*, **13** ,1–88.

Igel, G. J. and Calvin, A. D. (1960) The development of affectional responses in infant dogs. *J. comp. physiol. Psychol.*, **53**, 302–305.

Ikeda, K. and Wiersma, C. A. G. (1964) Autogenic rhythmicity in the abdominal ganglia of the crayfish: the control of swimmeret movements. *Comp. Biochem. Physiol.*, **12**, 107–115.

Immelmann, K. (1962) Beiträge zu einer vergleichenden Biologie australischer Prachtfinken (Spermestidae). *Zool. Jb. Syst. Bd.*, **90**, 1–196.

Inhelder, E. (1955) Zur Psychologie einiger Verhaltensweisen-besonders des Spiels-von Zootieren. *Zeits f. Tierpsychol.*, **12**, 88–144.

Isaac, D. and Marler, P. (1963) Ordering of sequences of singing behaviour of Mistle Thrushes in relation to timing. *Anim. Behav.*, **11**, 179–188.

Isaac, W. (1960) Arousal and reaction times in cats. *J. comp. physiol. Psychol.*, **53** 234–236.

Jacobs, W. (1953) Verhaltensbiologische Studien an Feldheuschrecken. *Zeits f. Tierpsychol.*, *Beit.* **1**, 1–228.

Jahn, T. (1960) Optische Gleichgewichtsregelung und zentrale Kompensation bei Amphibien, insbesondere bei der Erdkröte (*Bufo bufo* L.). *Zeits. vergl. Physiol.*, **43**, 119–140.

James, H. (1959) Flicker: an unconditioned stimulus for imprinting. *Canad. J. Psychol.*, **13**, 59–67.

James, H. (1960a) Imprinting with visual flicker: evidence for a critical period. *Canad. J. Psychol.*, **14**, 13–20.

James, H. (1960b) Social inhibition of the domestic chick's response to visual flicker. *Anim. Behav.*, **8**, 223–4.

James, W. (1892) Textbook of Psychology. MacMillan, London.

James, W. T. (1953) Social facilitation of eating behavior in puppies after satiation. *J. comp. physiol. Psychol.*, **46**, 427–428.

James, W. T. (1957) The effect of satiation on the sucking response in puppies. *J. comp. physiol. Psychol.*, **50**, 375–8.

James, W. T. (1963) Suppression of sucking by food injection in puppies. *Psychol. Rep.*, **13**, 862.

James, W. T. and Gilbert, T. F. (1956) The effect of social facilitation on food intake of puppies fed separately and together for the first 90 days of life. *Brit. J. Anim. Behav.*, **3**, 131–133.

Jander, R. (1957) Die Optische Richtungsorientierung der Roten Waldameise (*Formica rufa* L.). *Zeits. vergl. Physiol.*, **40**, 162–238.

Jander, R. and Voss, C. (1963) Die Bedeutung von Streifenmustern für das Formensehen der Roten Waldameise (*Formica rufa* L.). *Zeits f. Tierpsychol.*, **20**, 1–9.

Jander, R. and Waterman, T. H. (1960) Sensory discrimination between polarized light and light intensity patterns by arthropods. *J. cell. comp. Physiol.*, **56**, 137–159.

Janowitz, H. D. and Grossman, M. I. (1949) Some factors affecting the food intake of normal dogs and dogs with esophagostomy and gastric fistula. *Amer. J. Physiol.*, **159**, 143–148.

Jarmon, H. and Gerall, A. A. (1961) The effect of food deprivation upon the sexual performance of male guinea pigs. *J. comp. physiol. Psychol.*, **54**, 306–309.

Jasper, H. H. (1949) Diffuse projection systems: the integrative action of the thalamic system. *Electroenceph. clin. Neurophysiol.*, **1**, 405–420.

Jasper, H. H. (1961) Thalamic reticular system. In Sheer (1961).

Jasper, H. H., Proctor, L. D., Kaighton, R. S., Noshay, W. C. and Costello, R. T. (Eds.) (1958) Reticular Formation of the Brain. Little, Brown and Co., Boston.

Jaynes, J. (1956) Imprinting: the interaction of learned and innate behavior: I. Development and generalization. *J. comp. physiol. Psychol.*, **49**, 201–206.

Jaynes, J. (1957) Imprinting: the interaction of learned and innate behavior: II. The critical period. *J. comp. physiol. Psychol.*, **50**, 6–10.

Jaynes, J. (1958a) Imprinting: the interaction of learned and innate behavior: III. Practice effects on performance, retention and fear. *J. comp. physiol. Psychol.*, **51**, 234–7.

Jaynes, J. (1958b) Imprinting: the interaction of learned and innate behavior: IV. Generalization and emergent discrimination. *J. comp. physiol. Psychol.*, **51**, 238–42.

Jenkins, J. J. and Hanratty, J. A. (1949) Drive intensity discrimination in the albino rat. *J. comp. physiol. Psychol.*, **42**, 228–32.

Jennings, H. S. (1906) Behavior of the Lower Organisms. Columbia Univ. Press, New York.

Jensen, D. D. (1961) Operationism and the question "Is this behavior learned or innate?". *Behaviour*, **17**, 1–8.

Johnsgard, P. A. (1961) The taxonomy of the Anatidae—a behavioural analysis. *Ibis*, **103a**, 71–85.

Jouvet, M. and Desmedt, J. E. (1956) Contrôle central des messages acoustiques afférents. *C. R. Acad. Sci.*, **243**, 1916–1917.

Jouvet, M. and Lapras, C. (1959) Variations des résponses électriques somesthésiques au niveau du thalamus chez l'homme au cours de l'attention. *C. R. Soc. Biol.*, **153**, 98–101.

Jung, R. and Hassler, R. (1960) The extrapyramidal motor system. "Handbook of Physiology", Section 1, Vol. 2, Eds. J. Field, H. W. Magoun, and V. E. Hall, Amer. Physiol. Soc. Washington.

Kagan, J. (1955) Differential reward value of incomplete and complete sexual behavior. *J. comp. physiol. Psychol.*, **48**, 59–64.

Kagan, J. and Beach, F. A. (1953) Effects of early experience on mating behavior in male rats. *J. comp. physiol. Psychol.*, **46**, 204–8.

Kagan, J. and Berkun, M. (1954) The reward value of running activity. *J. comp. physiol. Psychol.*, **47**, 108.

Kahn, M. W. (1951) The effect of severe defeat at various age levels on the aggressive behavior of mice. *J. genet. Psychol.*, **79**, 117–130.

Kalish, H. I. (1954) Strength of fear as a function of the number of acquisition and extinction trials. *J. exp. Psychol.*, **47**, 1–9.

Kalter, J. and Warkang, J. (1959) Experimental production of congenital malformations in mammals by metabolic procedure. *Physiol. Rev.*, **39**, 69–115.

Kästle, W. (1964) Verhaltensstudien an Taggeckonen der Gattungen *Lygodactylus* und *Phelsuma. Zeits f. Tierpsychol.*, **21**, 486–507.

Katz, D. (1937) Animals and Men. Longmans Green, New York.

Kaufman, I. C. and Hinde, R. A. (1961) Factors influencing distress calling in chicks, with special reference to temperature changes and social isolation. *Anim. Behav.*, **9**, 197–204.

Kavanau, J. L. (1963) Compulsory regime and control of environment in animal behavior: I. Wheel running. *Behaviour*, **20**, 251–281.

Kear, J. (1962) Food selection in finches with special reference to interspecific differences. *Proc. Zool. Soc. Lond.*, **138**, 163–204.

Keeler, C. E. and King, H. D. (1942) Multiple effects of coat color genes in the Norway rat, with special reference to temperament and domestication. *J. comp. Psychol.*, **34**, 241–250.

Keenleyside, M. H. A. (1955) Some aspects of the schooling behaviour of fish. *Behaviour*, **8**, 183–248.

Keenleyside, M. H. A. and Yamamoto, F. T. (1962) Territorial behaviour of juvenile Atlantic salmon (*Salmo salar* L.). *Behaviour*, **19**, 139–169.

Keesey, R. E. (1964) Duration of stimulation and the reward properties of hypothalamic stimulation. *J. comp. physiol. Psychol.*, **58**, 201–207.

Keller, F. S. (1941) Light-aversion in the white rat. *Psychol. Rec.*, **4**, 235–250.

Keller, F. S. and Hill, L. M. (1936) Another "insight" experiment. *J. genet. Psychol.*, **48**, 484–489.

Kendler, H. H. (1946) The influence of simultaneous hunger and thrist drives upon the learning of two opposed spatial responses of the white rat. *J. exp. Psychol.*, **36**, 212–220.

Kendler, H. H. and Gasser, W. P. (1948) Variables in spatial learning: I. Number of reinforcements during training. *J. comp. physiol. Psychol.*, **41**, 178–187.

Kennedy, J. S. (1945) Classification and nomenclature of animal behaviour. *Nature*, **156**, 754.

Kennedy, J. S. (1954) Is modern ethology objective? *Brit. J. Anim. Behav.*, **2**, 12–19.

Kennedy, J. S. (1958) The experimental analysis of aphid behaviour and its bearing on current theories of instinct. *Proc. 10th Int. Cong. Entom., Montreal*, **2**, 397–404.

Kennedy, J. S. and Booth, C. O. (1963) Co-ordination of successive activities in an aphid. The effect of flight on the settling responses. *J. exp. Biol.*, **40**, 351–369.

Kennedy, J. and Booth, C. O. (1964) Coordination of successive activities in an aphid. Depression of settling after flight. *J. exp. Biol.*, **41**, 805–824.

Kent, G. C. and Liberman, R. J. (1949) Induction of psychicestrus in the hamster with progesterone administered via the lateral brain ventricle. *Endocrinology*, **45**, 29–32.

Kerkut, G. A. and Taylor, B. J. R. (1958) The effect of temperature changes on the activity of poikilotherms. *Behaviour*, **13**, 259–279.

Kinder, E. F. (1927) A study of the nest-building activity of the albino rat. *J. exp Zool.*, **47**, 117–161.

King, J. A. and Eleftheriou, B. E. (1959) The effects of early handling upon adult behavior in two subspieces of deermice, *Peromyscus maniculatus*. *J. comp. physiol. Psychol.*, **52**, 82–88.

King, J. A. and Gurney, N. L. (1954) Effect of early social experience on adult aggressive behavior in C57BL/10 mice. *J. comp. physiol. Psychol.*, **47**, 326–330.

Kirkman, F. B. (1937) Bird Behaviour. Nelson, London.

Kish, G. B. (1955) Learning when the onset of illumination is used as reinforcing stimulus. *J. comp. physiol. Psychol.*, **48**, 261–264.

Kish, G. B. and Barnes, G. W. (1961) Reinforcing effects of manipulation in mice. *J. comp. physiol. Psychol.*, **54**, 713–715.

Kish, G. B. and Baron, A. (1962) Satiation of sensory reinforcement. *J. comp. physiol. Psychol.*, **55**, 1007–1010.

Kislak, J. W. and Beach, F. A. (1955) Inhibition of aggressiveness by ovarian hormones. *Endocrinology*, **56**, 684–692.

Klausewitz, W. (1953) Die Korrelation von Verhaltensphysiologie und Farbphysiologie bei *Agama cyanogaster atricollis*. *Zeits f. Tierpsychol.*, **10**, 169–180.

Kling, J. W., Horowitz, L. and Delhagen, J. E. (1956) Light as a positive reinforcer for rat responding. *Psychol. Rep.*, **2**, 337–340.

Klinghammer, E. and Hess, E. H. (1964) Parental feeding in Ring Doves (*Streptopelia roseogrisea*): innate or learned? *Zeits f. Tierpsychol.*, **21**, 338–347.

Klopfer, P. H. (1959a) An analysis of learning in young Anatidae, *Ecology*, **40**, 90–102.

Klopfer, P. H. (1959b) Social interactions in discrimination learning with special reference to feeding behavior in birds. *Behaviour*, **14**, 282–299.

Klopfer, P. H. (1963) Behavioral aspects of habitat selection: the role of early experience. *Wilson Bull.*, **75**, 15–22.

Klopfer, P. H. and Hailman, J. P. (1964) Perceptual preferences and imprinting in chicks. *Science*, **145**, 1333–1334.

Knoll. M. (1953) Über das Tages—und Dämmerungssehen des Grasfrosches (*Rana temporaria* L.) nach Aufzucht in veränderten Lichtbedingungen. *Zeits. vergl. Physiol.*, **35**, 42–70.

Koch, S. (1959) Psychology, a Study of a Science: Study I, Conceptual and Systematic. Vols. 1 and 2, McGraw-Hill Book Company Inc., New York.

Koffka, K. (1935) Principles of Gestalt Psychology. Harcourt Brace, New York.

Köhler, I. (1951) Ueber Aufbau und Wandlungen der Wahrnahmungsvelt, Sitzungsber. *Oest. Akad. Wiss.*, **227**, 1–118.

Köhler, O. (1955) "Zahlende" Vogel und vergleichende Verhaltensforschung. *Acta XI Congr. Int. Orn.* 1954, 588–598.

Kohn, M. (1951) Satiation of hunger from food injected directly into the stomach versus food ingested by mouth. *J. comp. physiol. Psychol.*, **44**, 412–422.

Kolb, E. (1955) Untersuchungen über Zentrale Kompensation und Kompensationsbewegungen einseitig entstateter Frösche. *Zeits. vergl. Physiol.*, **37**, 136–160.

Konishi, M. (1963) The role of auditory feedback in the vocal behavior of the domestic fowl. *Zeits f. Tierpsychol.*, **20**, 349–367.

Konishi, M. (1964) Effects of deafening on song development in two species of Juncos. *Condor*, **66**, 85–102.

Konorski, J. (1948) Conditioned Reflexes and Neuron Organization. Cambridge Univ. Press, London.

Koronakos, C. and Arnold, W. J. (1957) The formation of learning sets in rats. *J. comp. physiol. Psychol.*, **50**, 11–14.

Kortlandt, A. (1940) Eine Übersicht der angeborenen Verhaltensweisen des Mitteleuropäischen Kormorans (*Phalacrocorax carbo sinensis*). *Arch. néerl. Zool.*, **14**, 401–442.

Kramer, G. (1952) Experiments on bird orientation. *Ibis*, **94**, 265–285.

Kramer, G. (1957) Experiments on bird orientation and their interpretation. *Ibis*, **99**, 196–227.

Kramer, G. (1959) Recent experiments on bird orientation. *Ibis*, **101**, 399–416.

Kramer, G. (1961) Long distance orientation. In "Biology and Comparative Physiology of Birds", Ed. A. J. Marshall, Academic Press, New York.

Kramer, G. and von St. Paul, U. (1951) Über angeborenes und erworbenes Feinderkennen beim Gimpel (*Pyrrhula pyrrhula* L.). *Behaviour*, **3**, 243–251.

Krech, D. (1965) Contribution to a conference on Learning, Remembering and Forgetting. In "The Anatomy of Memory". Ed. Kimble, D. P., Science and Behavior Books, Inc., Palo Alto.

Krechevsky, I. (1937) Brain mechanisms and variability I, II and III. *J. comp. Psychol.*, **23**, 121–138, 139–164, 351–364.

Kruijt, J. P. (1962) Imprinting in relation to drive interactions in Burmese Red Junglefowl. *Sym. Zool. Soc. Lond.*, **8**, 219–226.

Kruijt, J. P. (1964) Ontogeny of social behaviour in Burmese Red Junglefowl (*Gallus gallus spadiceus*) Bonnaterre. *Behaviour Suppl. No.* 12.

Kuczka, H. (1956) Verhaltensphysiologische Untersuchungen über die Wischhandlung der Erdkröte (*Bufo bufo* L.). *Zeits f. Tierpsychol.*, **13**, 185–207.

Kuehn, R. E. and Beach, F. A. (1963) Quantitative measurement of sexual receptivity in female rats. *Behaviour*, **21**, 282–299.

Kuenzer, P. (1958) Verhaltensphysiologische Untersuchungen über das Zucken des Regenwurms. *Zeits f. Tierpsychol.*, **15**, 31–49.

Kuenzer, E. and P. (1962) Untersuchungen zur Brutpflege der Zwergcichliden *Apistogramma reitzigi* und *A. borellii*. *Zeits f. Tierpsychol.*, **19**, 56–83.

Kuffler, S. W. (1953) Discharge patterns and functional organization of mammalian retina. *J. Neurophysiol.*, **16**, 37–68.

Kuffler, S. W., FitzHugh, R. and Barlow, H. B. (1957) Maintained activity in the cat's retina in light and darkness. *J. gen. Physiol.*, **40**, 683–702.

Kühme, W. (1961) Boebachtungen am afrikanischen Elefanten (*Loxodonta africana* Blumenbach) in Gefangenschaft. *Zeits f. Tierpsychol.*, **18**, 285–296.

Kühme, W. (1962) Das Schwarmverhalten elterngerführter Jungcichliden (Pisces). *Zeits f. Tierpsychol.*, **19**, 513–538.

Kühme, W. (1963) Ergänzende Beobachtungen an afrikanischen Elefanten (*Loxodonta africana* Blumenbach 1797) im Freigehege. *Zeits f. Tierpsychol.*, **20**, 66–79.

Kühn, A. (1919) Die Orientierung der Tiere im Raum. Jena.

Kunkel, P. (1959) Zum Verhalten einiger Prachtfinken (Estrilidinae). *Zeits f. Tierpsychol.*, **16**, 302–350.

Kunkel, P. (1962) Bewegungsformen, Sozialverhalten, Balz und Nestbau des Gangesbrillenvogels (*Zosterops palpebrosa* Temm.). *Zeits f. Tierpsychol.*, **19**, 559–576.

Kuo, Z-Y. (1932) Ontogeny of embryonic behavior in Aves: IV. The influence of embryonic movements upon the behavior after hatching. *J. comp. Psychol.*, **14**, 109–122.

Kuo, Z-Y. (1963) Total patterns, local reflexes or gradients of response? *Proc. 16th Int. Cong. Zool.*, **4**, 371–374.

Lacey, J. I. (1966) Somatic response patterning and stress: some revisions of activation theory. *Paper delivered at a symposium on "Issues in Stress", held at York University, Toronto, Canada, May* 10–12, 1965.

Lacey, J. I., Kagan, J., Lacey, B. C. and Moss, H. A. (1963) The visceral level: situational determinants and behavioral correlates of autonomic response patterns. In P. H. Knapp (Ed.), "Expression of the Emotions in Man", International Univ. Press, New York.

Lack, D. (1939) The behaviour of the robin: I and II. *Proc. Zool. Soc. Lond. A*, **109**, 169–178.

Lack, D. (1947) Darwin's Finches. Cambridge Univ. Press, London.

Lade, B. I. and Thorpe, W. H. (1964) Dove songs as innately coded patterns of specific behaviour. *Nature*, **202**, 366–368.

Lanyon, W. E. (1957) The comparative biology of the meadowlarks in Wisconsin. *Pub. Nuttall Ornith. Club.*, No. 1. Cambridge, Mass.

Lanyon, W. E. (1960) The ontogeny of vocalisations in birds. In "Animal Sounds and Communication", *Amer. Inst. Biol. Sciences, Publ. No. 7.*

Larsson, K. (1956) Conditioning and Sexual Behavior in the Male Albino Rat. Almquist and Wiksell, Stockholm.

Larsson, K. (1958) Aftereffects of copulatory activity of the male rat: II. *J. comp. physiol. Psychol.*, **51**, 417–420.

Larsson, K. (1959a) Experience and maturation in the development of sexual behaviour in male puberty rat. *Behaviour*, **14**, 101–107.

Larsson, K. (1959b) The effect of restraint upon copulatory behaviour in the rat. *Anim. Behav.*, **7**, 23–25.

Larsson, K. (1962) Spreading cortical depression and the mating behaviour in male and female rats. *Zeits f. Tierpsychol.*, **19**, 321–331.

Larsson, K. (1963) Non-specific stimulation and sexual behaviour in the male rat. *Behaviour*, **20**, 110–114.

Larsson, K. (1964) Mating behavior in male rats after cerebral cortex ablation. *J. exp. Zool.*, **155**, 203–213.

Larsson, S. (1954) On the hypothalamic organisation of the nervous mechanism regulating food intake. *Acta. physiol. scand.*, **32**, *Suppl.* 115, 1–40.

Lashley, K. S. (1917) The accuracy of movement in the absence of excitation from the moving organ. *Amer. J. Physiol.*, **43**, 169–194.

Lashley, K. S. (1930) The mechanism of vision: I. A method for rapid analysis of pattern-vision in the rat. *J. genet. Psychol.*, **37**, 453–460.

Lashley, K. S. (1938a) Experimental analysis of instinctive behavior. *Psychol. Rev.*, **45**, 445–471.

Lashley, K. S. (1938b) The mechanism of vision: XV. Preliminary studies of the rat's capacity for detail vision. *J. gen. Psychol.*, **18**, 123–193.

Lashley, K. S. (1952) Functional interpretation of anatomic patterns. *Proc. Ass. Res. Nerv. Ment. Dis.*, **30**, 529–547.

Lashley, K. S. and Ball, J. (1929) Spinal conduction and kinesthetic sensitivity in the maze habit. *J. comp. Psychol.*, **9**, 71–105.

Lashley, K. S. and Russell, J. T. (1934) The mechanism of vision: XI. A preliminary test of innate organisation. *J. genet. Psychol.*, **45**, 136–144.

Lashley, K. S. and Wade, M. (1946) The Pavlovian theory of generalization. *Psychol. Rev.*, **53**, 72–87.

Lassek, A. M. and Mayer, E. K. (1953) An ontogenetic study of motor deficits following dorsal brachial rhizotomy. *J. Neurophysiol.*, **16**, 247–251.

Lawrence, D. H. (1949) Acquired distinctiveness of cues: I. Transfer between discriminations on the basis of familiarity with the stimulus. *J. exp. Psychol.*, **39**, 770–784.

Lawrence, D. H. (1950) Acquired distinctiveness of cues: II. Selective association in a constant stimulus situation. *J. exp. Psychol.*, **40**, 175–188.

Lawrence, D. H. and Mason, W. A. (1955) Food intake in the rat as a function of deprivation intervals and feeding rhythms. *J. comp. physiol. Psychol.*, **48**, 267–271.

Leblond, C. P. and Nelson, W. O. (1937) Maternal behavior in hypophysectomized male and female mice. *Amer. J. Physiol.*, **120**, 167–172.

Lehrman, D. S. (1953) A critique of Konrad Lorenz's theory of instinctive behaviour. *Quart. Rev. Biol.*, **28**, 337–363.

Lehrman, D. S. (1955) The physiological basis of parental feeding behaviour in the Ring Dove (*Streptopelia risoria*). *Behaviour*, **7**, 241–286.

Lehrman, D. S. (1961) Gonadal hormones and parental behavior in birds and infrahuman mammals. In Young (1961a).

Lehrman, D. S. (1962) Interaction of hormonal and experiential influences on development of behavior. In "Roots of Behavior", Ed. Bliss, E. L., Hoeber, New York.

Lehrman, D. S. and Wortis, R. P. (1960) Previous breeding experience and hormone-induced incubation behavior in the ring dove. *Science*, **132**, 1667–1668.

Le Magnen, J. (1952) Les phénomènes olfacto-sexuels chez le rat blanc. *Arch. Sci. Physiol.*, **6**, 295–331.

Lettvin, J. Y., Maturana, H. R., McCulloch, W. S. and Pitts, W. H. (1959) What the frog's eye tells the frog's brain. *Proc. Instit. Radio Engineers,* **47**, 1940–1951.

Leuba, C. (1955) Toward some integration of learning theories: the concept of optimal stimulation. *Psychol. Rep.,* **1**, 27–33.

Levin, H. and Forgays, D. G. (1959) Learning as a function of sensory stimulation of various intensities. *J. comp. physiol. Psychol.,* **52**, 195–201.

Levine, S. (1953) The role of irrelevant drive stimuli in learning. *J. exp. Psychol.,* **45**, 410–416.

Levine, S. (1957) Infantile experience and resistance to physiological stress. *Science,* **126**, 405.

Levine, S. (1961) The psychophysiological effect of early stimulation. In "Roots of Behavior", Ed. Bliss, E. L., Hoeber, New York.

Levine, S. (1962a) The effects of infantile experience on adult behavior. In "Experimental Foundations of Clinical Psychology", Ed. A. J. Bachrach, Basic Books, New York.

Levine, S. (1962b) "Some effects of stimulation in infancy." Little Club Clinics in Developmental Medicine, No. 7, Heinemann, London.

Levine, S. (1962c) Plasma-free corticosteroid response to electric shock in rats stimulated in infancy. *Science,* **135**, 795–796.

Levine, S. and Alpert, M. (1959) Differential maturation of the central nervous system as a function of early experience. *Arch. gen. Psychiat.,* **1**, 403–405.

Levine, S., Chevalier, J. A. and Korchin, S. J. (1956) The effects of early shock and handling on later avoidance learning. *J. Pers.,* **24**, 475–493.

Levison, P. K. and Flynn, J. P. (1965) The objects attacked by cats during stimulation of the hypothalamus. *Anim. Behav.,* **13**, 217–220.

Lewis, M. M. (1963) Language, Thought and Personality. Harrap, London.

Leyhausen, P. (1956) Verhaltensstudien bei Katzen. *Zeits f. Tierpsychol., Beiheft 2.*

Liesenfeld, F. J. (1956) Untersuchungen am Netz und über den Erschütterungssinn von *Zygiella x-notata* (Cl.) (Araneidae). *Zeits. vergl. Physiol.,* **38**, 563–592.

Lind, H. (1959) The activation of an instinct caused by a "transitional action". *Behaviour,* **14**, 123–135.

Lind, H. (1961) Studies on the behaviour of the Black-tailed Godwit (*Limosa limosa* L.). *Naturfredningsrådets reservatudvalg nr 66, Copenhagen.*

Lind, H. (1962) Zur Analyse des sexuellen Verhaltens der Kolbenente, *Netta rufina* (Pallas). *Zeits f. Tierpsychol.,* **19**, 607–625.

Lindauer, M. (1961) Communication among Social Bees. Harvard Univ. Press.

Lindauer, M. (1964) Allgemeine Sinnesphysiologie Orientierung im Raum. *Fortschr. der. Zool.,* **16**, 58–140.

Lindenlaub, E. (1955) Über das Heimfindevermögen von Säugetieren: II. Versuche an Maüsen. *Zeits f. Tierpsychol.,* **12**, 452–458.

Lindenlaub, E. (1960) Neue Befunde über die Anfangsorientierung von Mäusen. *Zeits f. Tierpsychol.,* **17**, 555–578.

Lindsley, D. B. (1956) Physiological psychology. *Ann. Rev. Psychol.,* **7**, 323–348.

Lindsley, D. B. (1960) Attention, consciousness, sleep and wakefulness. In "Handbook of Physiology", Sect. 1, Vol. 111, Eds. J. Field, H. W. Magoun and V. E. Hall, Amer. Physiol. Soc. Washington.

Lindsley, D. B. (1961) The reticular activating system and perceptual integration. In Sheer (1961).

Lindzey, G., Winston, H. D. and Manosevitz, M. (1963) Early experience, genotype and temperament in *Mus musculus. J. comp. physiol. Psychol.,* **56**, 622–629.

Lipsitt, L. P. and Kaye, H. (1965) Change in neonatal response to optimizing and non-optimizing sucking stimulation. *Psychonomic Science,* **2**, 221–222.

Lisk, R. D. (1962a) Diencephalic placement of estradiol and sexual receptivity in the female rat. *Amer. J. Physiol.*, **203**, 493–496.

Lisk, R. D. (1962b) Testosterone-sensitive centers in the hypothalamus of the rat. *Acta Endocrin.*, **41**, 195–204.

Lisk, R. D. and Newlon, M. (1963) Estradiol: evidence for its direct effect on hypothalamic neurons. *Science*, **139**, 223–224.

Lissmann, H-W. (1932) Die Umwelt des Kampffisches (*Betta splendens* Regan). *Zeits. vergl. Physiol.*, **18**, 65–111.

Lissmann, H. W. (1946a) The neurological basis of the locomotory rhythm in the spinal dogfish (*Scyllium canicula, Acanthias vulgaris*): I. Reflex behaviour. *J. exp. Biol.*, **23**, 143–161.

Lissmann, H. W. (1946b) The neurological basis of the locomotory rhythm in the spinal dogfish (*Scyllium canicula, Acanthias vulgaris*): II. The effect of deafferentation. *J. exp. Biol.*, **23**, 162–176.

Lissmann, H. W. (1958) On the function and evolution of electric organs in fish. *J. exp. Biol.*, **35**, 156–191.

Lissmann, H. W. and Machin, K. E. (1958) The mechanism of object location in *Gymnarchus niloticus* and similar fish. *J. exp. Biol.*, **35**, 451–486.

Livingston, W. K., Haugen, F. P. and Brookhart, J. M. (1954) Functional organization of the central nervous system. *Neurology*, **4**, 485–496.

Livingstone, R. B. (1959) Central control of receptors and sensory transmission systems. In "Handbook of Physiology", Section 1, Vol. 1, Eds. J. Field, H. W. Magoun and V. E. Hall, Amer. Physiol. Soc., Washington.

Lockard, R. B. (1963a) Self-regulated exposure to light by albino rats as a function of rearing luminance and test luminance. *J. comp. physiol. Psychol.*, **56**, 558–564.

Lockard, R. B. (1963b) Some effects of light upon the behavior of rodents. *Psychol. Bull.*, **60**, 509–529.

Loewenstein, W. R. (1956) Modulation of cutaneous mechanoreceptors by sympathetic stimulation. *J. Physiol.*, **132**, 40–60.

London, I. D. (1954) Research on sensory interaction in the Soviet Union. *Psych. Bull.*, **51**, 531–568.

Lorber, S. H., Komarov, S. A. and Shay, H. (1950) Effect of sham feeding on gastric motor activity of the dog. *Amer. J. Physiol.*, **162**, 447–451.

Lorenz, K. (1935) Der Kumpan in der Umwelt des Vogels. *J. f. Ornith.*, **83**, 137–213, 289–413.

Lorenz, K. (1937) Über die Bildung des Instinktbegriffes. *Naturwissenschaften*, **25**, 289–300, 307–318, 324–331.

Lorenz, K. (1939) Vergleichende Verhaltensforschung. *Zool. Anz. Suppl. Bd.*, **12**, 69–102.

Lorenz, K. (1941) Vergleichende Bewegungsstudien an Anatinen. *Suppl. J. Ornith.*, **89**, 194–294.

Lorenz, K. (1950) The comparative method in studying innate behaviour patterns. *Sym. Soc. exp. Biol.*, **4**, 221–268.

Lorenz, K. (1951) Über die Entstehung auslösender "Zeremonien". *Vogelwarte*, **16**, 9–13.

Lorenz, K. (1960) Prinzipien der vergleichenden Verhaltensforschung. *Fortschritte der Zoologie*, **12**, 265–294.

Lorenz, K. (1961) Phylogenetische Anpassung und adaptive Modifikation des Verhaltens. *Zeits f. Tierpsychol.*, **18**, 139–187.

Lorenz, K. and Tinbergen, N. (1939) Taxis und Instinkthandlung in der Eirollbewegung der Graugans: I. *Zeits f. Tierpsychol.*, **2**, 1–29.

Löwenstein, O. and Sand, A. (1940) The mechanism of the semicircular canal: a study of the responses of single fibre preparations to angular accelerations and to rotation at constant speed. *Proc. Roy. Soc. B.*, **129**, 256–275.

McBride, G. (1963) The "teat order" and communication in young pigs. *Anim. Behav.*, **11**, 53–56.

McCleary, R. A. (1953) Taste and post-ingestion factors in specific-hunger behavior. *J. comp. physiol. Psychol.*, **46**, 411–421.

McClelland, D. C. and Atkinson, J. W. (1948) The projective expression of needs: I. *J. Psychol.*, **25**, 205–222.

MacCorquodale, K. and Meehl, P. E. (1954) Edward C. Tolman. In "Modern Learning Theory". Eds. Estes *et al.*, Appleton-Century-Crofts, New York.

MacDonnell, M. F. and Flynn, J. P. (1964) Attack elicited by stimulation of the thalamus of cats. *Science*, **144**, 1249–1250.

McDougall, W. (1923) An Outline of Psychology. Methuen, London.

McFarland, D. J. (1963) Some interactions of feeding and drinking behaviour in the Barbary Dove. *Anim. Behav.*, **11**, 607.

McFarland, J. H., Werner, H. and Wapner, S. (1962) The effect of postural factors on the distribution of tactual sensitivity and the organization of tactual kinaesthetic space. *J. exp. Psychol.*, **63**, 148–154.

McGaugh, J. L. (1965) Facilitation and impairment of memory storage processes. In "The Anatomy of Memory", Vol. I, Ed. Kimble, D. P., Science and Behavior Books, Inc.: Palo Alto.

McGill, T. E. (1962a) Reduction in "head-mounts" in the sexual behavior of the mouse as a function of experience. *Psych. Rep.*, **10**, 284.

McGill, T. E. (1962b) Sexual behavior in three inbred strains of mice. *Behaviour*, **19**, 341–350.

MacKay, D. M. (1962) In "Aspects of the Theory of Artificial Intelligence". Ed. C. A. Muses, Plenum Press, London.

McKelvey, R. K. and Marx, M. H. (1951) Effects of infantile food and water deprivation on adult hoarding in the rat. *J. comp. physiol. Psychol.*, **44**, 423–430.

McKinney, F. (1961) An analysis of the displays of the European Eider *Somateria mollissima mollissima* (Linnaeus) and the Pacific Eider *Somateria mollissima v. nigra* Bonaparte. *Behaviour, Supplement No.* 7.

Mackintosh, J. and Sutherland, N. S. (1963) Visual discrimination by the goldfish: the orientation of rectangles. *Anim. Behav.*, **11**, 135–141.

Mackintosh, N. J. (1963) Extinction of a discrimination habit as a function of over-training. *J. comp. physiol. Psychol.*, **56**, 842–847.

Mackintosh, N. J. (1964) Overtraining and transfer within and between dimensions in the rat. *Quart. J. exp. Psychol.*, **16**, 250–256 .

Mackintosh, N. J. and Mackintosh, J. (1964) Performance of *Octopus* over a series of reversals of a simultaneous discrimination. *Anim. Behav.*, **12**, 321–324.

Mackintosh, N. J., Mackintosh, J. and Sutherland, N. S. (1963) The relative importance of horizontal and vertical extents in shape discrimination by Octopus. *Anim. Behav.*, **11**, 355–358.

Mackworth, J. F. (1962) The visual image and the memory trace. *Canad. J. Psychol.*, **16**, 55–59.

McMichael, R. E. (1961) The effects of preweaning shock and gentling on later resistance to stress. *J. comp. physiol. Psychol.*, **54**, 416–421.

McNiven, M. A. (1960) "Social-releaser mechanisms" in birds—a controlled replication of Tinbergen's study. *Psychol. Rec.*, **10**, 259–265.

Magnus, D. (1955) "Zum Problem der uberoptimalen Schlüsselreize. (Versuche am Kaisermantel *Argynnis paphia*). *Verh. Dtsch. zool. Ges. Tubingen* 1954 (*Zool. Anz.*), *Suppl.* 18, 317–325.

Magnus, D. (1958) Experimentelle Untersuchungen zur Bionomie und Ethologie des Kaisermantels *Argynnis paphia* L. (Lep. Nymph.): I Über optische. Auslöser von Anfliegereaktionen und ihre Bedeutung für das Sichfinden der Geschlechter. *Zeits f. Tierpsychol.*, **15**, 397–426.

Maier, N. R. F. and Schneirla, T. C. (1935) Principles of Animal Psychology. New York.

Malmo, R. B. (1959) Activation: a neurophysiological dimension. *Psychol. Rev.*, **66**, 367–386.

Malmo, R. B., Shagass, C. and Davis, J. F. (1951) Electromyographic studies of muscular tension in psychiatric patients under stress. *J. clin. exp. Psychopath*, **12**, 45–66.

Mandler, J. M. (1958) Effect of early food deprivation on adult behavior in the rat. *J. comp. physiol. Psychol.*, **51**, 513–517.

Manning, A. (1956) The effect of honey-guides. *Behaviour*, **9**, 114–139.

Marler, P. (1955) Studies of fighting in Chaffinches: (2) The effect on dominance relations of disguising females as males. *Brit. J. Anim. Behav.*, **3**, 137–146.

Marler, P. (1956a) The voice of the chaffinch and its function as a language. *Ibis*, **98**, 231–261.

Marler, P. (1956b) Behaviour of the Chaffinch (*Fringilla coelebs*). *Behaviour, Supplement No. 5*, 1–184.

Marler, P. (1956c) Studies of fighting in Chaffinches: (3) Proximity as a cause of aggression. *Brit. J. Anim. Behav.*, **4**, 23–30.

Marler, P. (1957a) Studies of fighting in Chaffinches: (4) Appetitive and consummatory behaviour. *Brit. J. Anim. Behav.*, **5**, 29–37.

Marler, P. (1957b) Specific distinctiveness in the communication signals of birds. *Behaviour*, **11**, 13–39.

Marler, P. (1959) Developments in the study of animal communication. In "Darwin's Biological Work", Ed. P. R. Bell, Cambridge Univ. Press, London.

Marler, P. (1960) Bird songs and mate selection. In "Animal Sounds and Communication", *Amer. Inst. Biol. Sci.*, **7**, 348–367.

Marler, P. (1961) The filtering of external stimuli during instinctive behaviour. In "Current Problems of Animal Behaviour", Eds. W. H. Thorpe and O. L. Zangwill, Cambridge Univ. Press, London.

Marler, P., Kreith, M. and Tamura, M. (1962) Song development in hand-raised Oregon Juncos. *Auk*, **79**, 12–30.

Marshall, S. L. A. (1947) Men against Fire. Morrow, New York.

Marx, M. H. (1952) Infantile deprivation and adult behavior in the rat: retention of increased rate of eating. *J. comp. physiol. Psychol.*, **45**, 43–49.

Marx, M. H., Henderson, R. L. and Roberts, C. L. (1955) Positive reinforcement of the bar-pressing response by a light stimulus following dark operant pretests with no aftereffect. *J. comp. physiol. Psychol.*, **48**, 73–76.

Marx, M. H. and Knarr, F. A. (1963) Long-term development of reinforcing properties of a stimulus as a function of temperal relationship to food reinforcement. *J. comp. physiol. Psychol.*, **56**, 546–550.

Marzocco, F. N. (1951) Doctoral dissertation, Iowa, cited by Brown (1961).

Mason, W. A. and Berkson, G. (1962) Conditions influencing vocal responsiveness of infant chimpanzees. *Science*, **137**, 127–128.

Mason, W. A. and Harlow, H. F. (1958) Formation of conditioned responses in infant monkeys. *J. comp. physiol. Psychol.*, **51**, 68–70.

Mast, S. O. (1911) Light and the Behavior of Organisms. John Wiley & Sons: London.

Mast, S. O. (1912) Behavior of fireflies, with special reference to the problem of orientation. *J. anim. Behav.*, **2**, 256–272.

Matthews, B. H. C. (1931) The response of a single end organ. *J. Physiol.*, **71**, 64–110.

Matthews, G. V. T. (1955) Bird Navigation. Cambridge Univ. Press, London.

Matthews, G. V. T. (1961) "Nonsense" orientation in Mallard *Anas platyrhynchos* and its relation to experiments on bird navigation. *Ibis*, **103**a, 211–230.

Matthews, W. A. (1964) Shape discrimination in tropical fish. *Anim. Behav.*, **12** 111–115.

Matthews, W. A. and Hemmings, G. (1963) A theory concerning imprinting. *Nature*, **198**, 1183–1184.

Maynard, D. M. (1955) Activity in a crustacean ganglion: II. Pattern and interaction in burst formation. *Biol. Bull.*, **109**, 420–436.

Mayr, E. (1942) Systematics and the Origin of Species. Columbia Univ. Press, New York.

Mayr, E. (1963) Animal Species and Evolution. Harvard Univ. Press, Cambridge, Mass.

Mayr, E., Andrew, R. J. and Hinde, R. A. (1956) Die systematische Stellung der Gattung *Fringilla*. *J. f. Ornith.*, **97**, 258–273.

Meier, G. W. (1961) Infantile handling and development in siamese kittens. *J. comp. physiol. Psychol.*, **54**, 284–286.

Meier, G. W. and McGee, R. K. (1959) A re-evaluation of the effect of early perceptual experience on discrimination performance during adulthood. *J. comp. physiol. Psychol.*, **52**, 390–395.

Melton, A. W. (1963) Implications of short-term memory for a general theory of memory. *J. Verbal Learning and Verbal Behaviour*, **2**, 1–21.

Melzack, R. (1952) Irrational fears in the dog. *Canad. J. Psychol.*, **6**, 141–147.

Melzack, R. (1961) On the survival of mallard ducks after "habituation" to the hawk-shaped figure. *Behaviour*, **17**, 9–16.

Melzack, R., Penick, E. and Beckett, A. (1959) The problem of "innate fear" of the hawk shape: an experimental study with mallard ducks. *J. comp. physiol. Psychol.*, **52**, 694–698.

Melzack, R. and Scott, T. H. (1957) The effects of early experience on the response to pain. *J. comp. physiol. Psychol.*, **50**, 155–161.

Meng, M. (1957) Untersuchungen zum Farben- und Formensehen der Erdkröte (*Bufo bufo* L.). *Zool. Beitr.*, **3**, 313–364.

Menzel, E. W., Davenport, R. K. and Rogers, C. M. (1963) The effects of environmental restriction upon the chimpanzee's responsiveness to objects. *J. comp. physiol. Psychol.*, **56**, 78–85.

Merton, P. A. (1964) Human position sense and sense of effort. *Sym. Soc. exp. Biol.*, **18**, 387–400.

Messmer, E. and Messmer, I. (1956) Die Entwicklung der Lautäusserungen und einiger Verhaltensweisen der Amsel (*Turdus merula merula* L.) unter natürlichen Bedingungen und nach Einzelaufzucht in schalldichten Räumen. *Zeits f. Tierpsychol.*, **13**, 341–441.

Meyer, D. R. (1952) The stability of human gustatory sensitivity during changes in time of food deprivation. *J. comp. physiol., Psychol.*, **45**, 373–376.

Meyers, B. (1964) Discrimination of visual movement in perceptually deprived cats. *J. comp. physiol. Psychol.*, **57**, 152–153.

Meyers, B. and McCleary, R. (1964) Interocular transfer of a pattern discrimination in pattern deprived cats. *J. comp. physiol. Psychol.*, **57**, 16–21.

Meyers, W. J. (1962) Critical period for the facilitation of exploratory behavior by infantile experience. *J. comp. physiol. Psychol.*, **55**, 1099–1101.

Michael, R. P. (1961) Observations upon the sexual behaviour of the domestic cat (*Felis catus* L.) under laboratory conditions. *Behaviour*, **18**, 1–21.

Michael, R. P. and Herbert, J. (1963) Menstrual cycle influences grooming behavior and sexual activity in the rhesus monkey. *Science*, **140**, 500–501.

Michels, K. M., Bevan, W. and Strasel, H. C. (1958) Discrimination learning and interdimensional transfer under conditions of systematically controlled visual experience. *J. comp. physiol. Psychol.*, **51**, 778–781.

Michels, K. M., Pittman, G. G., Hitchcock, L. and Brown, D. R. (1962) *Perceptual and Motor Skills*. **15**, 443–450.

Miles, R. C. and Meyer, D. R. (1956) Learning sets in marmosets. *J. comp. physiol. Psychol.*, **49**, 219–222.

Millenson, J. R. (1962) Acquired counting behaviour in mice maintained under two reinforced procedures. *Anim. Behav.*, **10**, 171–173.

Miller, G. A. (1964) Kenneth Craik lecture delivered in Cambridge.

Miller, G. A., Galanter, E. and Pribram, K. H. (1960) Plans and the Structure of Behavior. Holt, Rinehart and Winston, Inc., New York.

Miller, N. E. (1948a) Theory and experiment relating psychoanalytic displacement to stimulus-response generalization. *J. abnorm. soc. Psychol.*, **43**, 155–178.

Miller, N. E. (1948b) Studies of fear as an acquirable drive: I Fear as motivation and fear-reduction as reinforcement in the learning of new responses. *J. exp. Psychol.*, **38**, 89–101.

Miller, N. E. (1956) Effects of drugs on motivation: the value of using a variety of measures. *Ann. N. Y. Acad. Sci.*, **65**, 318–333.

Miller, N. E. (1957) Experiments on motivation. *Science*, **126**, 1271–1278.

Miller, N. E. (1959) Liberalization of basic S-R concepts. In "Psychology: a Study of a Science", Study I, Vol. 2, Ed. S. Koch, McGraw-Hill Book Company Inc., New York.

Miller, N. E. (1960) Motivational effects of brain stimulation and drugs. *Fed. Proc.*, **19**, 846–854.

Miller, N. E. (1961a) Learning and performance motivated by direct stimulation of the brain. In Sheer (1961).

Miller, N. E. (1961b) Implications for theories of reinforcement. In Sheer (1961).

Miller, N. E. and Dollard, J. (1941) Social Learning and Imitation. Yale Univ. Press, New Haven.

Miller, N. E. and Kessen, M. L. (1952) Reward effects of food via stomach fistula compared with those of food via mouth. *J. comp. physiol. Psychol.*, **45**, 555–564.

Miller, N. E., Sampliner, R. I. and Woodrow, P. (1957) Thirst-reducing effects of water by stomach fistula vs. water by mouth measured by both a consummatory and an instrumental response. *J. comp. physiol. Psychol.*, **50**, 1–5.

Miller, N. E. and Stevenson, S. S. (1936) Agitated behavior of rats during experimental extinction and a curve of spontaneous recovery. *J. comp. Psychol.*, **21**, 205–231.

Miller, P. L. (1960) Respiration in the desert locust. *J. exp. Biol.*, **37**, 224–278.

Mittelstaedt, H. (1949) Telotaxis und Optomotorik von *Eristalis* bei Augeninversion. *Naturwissen.*, **36**, 90–91.

Mittelstaedt, H. (1960) The analysis of behavior in terms of control systems. 5th Cong. on Group Processes, Josiah Macy, New York.

Mittelstaedt, H. (1961) Die Regelungstheorie als methodisches Werkzeug der Verhaltensanalyse. *Naturwiss.*, **48**, 246–254.

Mittelstaedt, H. (1962) Control systems of orientation in insects. *Ann. Rev. Entomol.*, **7**, 177–198.

Mittelstaedt, H. (1964) Basic control patterns of orientational homeostasis. *Soc. exp. Biol. Sym.*, **18**, 365–386.

Moltz, H. (1960) Imprinting: empirical basis and theoretical significance. *Psychol. Bull.*, **57**, 291–314.

Moltz, H. (1963) Imprinting: an epigenetic approach. *Psychol. Rev.*, **70**, 123–138.

Moltz, H. and Stettner, L. J. (1961) The influence of patterned-light deprivation on the critical period for imprinting. *J. comp. physiol. Psychol.*, **54**, 279–283.

Moltz, H. and Stettner, L. J. (1962) Interocular mediation of the following-response after patterned-light deprivation. *J. comp. physiol. Psychol.*, **55**, 626–632.

Monteith, L. G. (1962) Apparent continual changes in the host preferences of *Drino bohemica* Mesn (Diptera: Tachinidae), and their relation to the concept of host-conditioning. *Anim. Behav.*, **10**, 292–299.

Montgomery, A. V. and Holmes, J. H. (1955) Gastric inhibition of the drinking response. *Amer. J. Physiol.*, **182**, 227–231.

Montgomery, K. C. (1952) A test of two explanations of spontaneous alternation. *J. comp. physiol. Psychol.*, **45**, 287–293.

Montgomery, K. C. (1954) The role of the exploratory drive in learning. *J. comp. physiol. Psychol.*, **47**, 60–64.

Montgomery, K. C. (1955) The relation between fear induced by novel stimulation and exploratory behavior. *J. comp. physiol. Psychol.*, **48**, 254–260.

Montgomery, K. C. and Segall, M. (1955) Discrimination learning based upon the exploratory drive. *J. comp. physiol. Psychol.*, **48**, 225–228.

Mook, D. G. (1963) Oral and postingestional determinants of the intake of various solutions in rats with esophageal fistulas. *J. comp. physiol. Psychol.*, **56**, 645–659.

Mook, J. H., Mook, L. J. and Heikens, H. S. (1960) Further evidence for the role of "searching images" in the hunting behaviour of titmice. *Arch. Néerl. Zool.*, **13**, 448–465.

Morgan, C. T. (1943) Physiological Psychology. McGraw-Hill Book Company, Inc., New York.

Morgan, C. T. (1959) Physiological theory of drive. In Koch (1959).

Morgan, C. T. and Morgan, J. D. (1940a, b) Studies in hunger: I and II. *J. genet. Psychol.*, **56**, 137–147, **57**, 153–163.

Morris, D. (1954a) The reproductive behaviour of the Zebra Finch (*Poephila guttata*), with special reference to pseudofemale behaviour and displacement activities. *Behaviour*, **6**, 271–322.

Morris, D. (1954b) The reproductive behaviour of the River Bullhead (*Cottus gobi* L.) with special reference to the fanning activity. *Behaviour*, **7**, 1–32.

Morris, D. (1955) The causation of pseudofemale and pseudomale behaviour: a further comment. *Behaviour*, **8**, 46–56.

Morris, D. (1956) The feather postures of birds and the problem of the origin of social signals. *Behaviour*, **9**, 75–113.

Morris, D. (1957a) "Typical intensity" and its relation to the problem of ritualisation. *Behaviour*, **11**, 1–12.

Morris, D. (1957b) The reproductive behaviour of the Bronze Mannikin (*Lonchura cucullata*). *Behaviour*, **11**, 156–201.

Morris, D. (1958a) The reproductive behaviour of the Ten-spined Stickleback (*Pygosteus pungitius* L.). *Behaviour, Suppl. No.* 6, 1–154.

Morris, D. (1958b) The function and causation of courtship ceremonies. In "L'instinct dans le Comportement des Animaux et de L'homme", Foundation Singer Polignac, Paris.

Morris, D. (1958c) The comparative ethology of grassfinches (*Erythrurae*) and Mannikins (*Amadinae*). *Proc. Zool. Soc. Lond.*, **131**, 389–439.

Morrison, S. D. and Mayer, J. (1957a) Adipsia and aphagia in rats after lateral subthalamic lesions. *Amer. J. Physiol.*, **191**, 248–254.

Morrison, S. D. and Mayer, J. (1957b) Effect of sham operations in the hypothalamus on food and water intake of the rat. *Amer. J. Physiol.*, **191**, 255–258.

Moruzzi, G. and Magoun, H. W. (1949) Brain-stem reticular formation and activation of the EEG. *Electroenceph. clin. Neurophysiol.*, **1**, 455–473.

Mote, F. A. and Finger, F. W. (1942) Exploratory drive and secondary reinforcement in the acquisition and extinction of a simple running response. *J. exp. Psychol.*, **31**, 57–68.

Mott, F. W. and Sherrington, C. S. (1895) Experiments upon the influence of sensory nerves upon movement and nutrition of the limbs. Preliminary communication. *Proc. Roy. Soc.*, **57**, 481–488.

Mountcastle, V. B. (1957) Modality and topographic properties of single neurons in the cat's somatic sensory cortex. *J. Neurophysiol.*, **20**, 408–434.

Mowrer, O. H. (1936) "Maturation" v. "Learning" in the development of vestibular and optokinetic nystagmus. *J. genet. Psychol.*, **48**, 383–404.

Mowrer, O. H. (1939) A stimulus-response analysis of anxiety and its role as a reinforcing agent. *Psychol. Rev.*, **46**, 553–565.

Moyer, K. E. (1963) Startle response: habituation over trials and days, and sex and strain differences. *J. comp. physiol. Psychol.*, **56**, 863–865.

Moyer, K. E. and Bunnell, B. N. (1962) Effect of stomach distention caused by water on food and water consumption in the rat. *J. comp. physiol. Psychol.*, **55**, 652–655.

Moynihan, M. (1955) Some aspects of reproductive behavior in the Black-headed Gull (*Larus ridibundus ridibundus* L.) and related species. *Behaviour, Suppl. No.* 4, 1–201.

Moynihan, M. (1956) Notes on the behavior of some north american gulls: I. Aerial hostile behavior. *Behaviour*, **10**, 126–178.

Moynihan, M. (1958a) Notes on the behavior of some north american gulls: II. Non-aerial hostile behavior of adults. *Behaviour*, **12**, 95–182.

Moynihan, M. (1958b) Notes on the behavior of some north american gulls: III. Pairing behavior. *Behaviour*, **13**, 112–130.

Moynihan, M. (1959) Notes on the behavior of some north american gulls: IV. The ontogeny of hostile behavior and display patterns. *Behaviour*, **14**, 214–239.

Moynihan, M. (1962) Hostile and sexual behavior patterns of South American and Pacific Laridae. *Behaviour, Suppl. No.* 8, 1–365.

Moynihan, M. and Hall, M. F. (1954) Hostile, sexual and other social behaviour patterns of the Spice Finch (*Lonchura punctulata*) in captivity. *Behaviour*, **7**, 33–76.

Mrosovsky, N. (1963) Retention and reversal of conditioned avoidance following severe hypothermia. *J. comp. physiol. Psychol.*, **56**, 811–813.

Mrosovsky, N. (1964) The performance of dormice and other hibernators on tests of hunger motivation. *Anim. Behav.*, **12**, 454–469.

Muenzinger, K. F., Brown, W. O., Crow, W. J. and Powlowski, R. F. (1952) Motivation in learning: XI. An analysis of electric shock for correct responses into its avoidance and accelerating components. *J. exp. Psychol.*, **43**, 115–119.

Müller, A. (1925) Über Lichtreaktionen von Landasseln. *Z. vergl. Physiol.*, **3**, 113–144.

Müller, D. (1961) Quantitative Luftfeind-Attrapenversuche bei Auer-und Birkhühnern. *Zeits. Naturf.*, **16**, 551–553.

Munn, N. L. (1950) Handbook of Psychological Research on the Rat. Houghton Mifflin, New York.

Munn, N. L. (1955) The Evolution and Growth of Human Behavior. Houghton Mifflin, New York.

Myers, R. D. (1964) Modification of drinking patterns by chronic intracranial chemical infusion. 1st. Int. Sym. on Thirst. Florida State Univ. 533–549, Pergamon Press, Oxford.

Myrberg, A. A. (1964) An analysis of the preferential care of eggs and young by adult Cichlid Fishes. *Zeits f. Tierpsychol.*, **21**, 53–98.

Nachman, M. and Pfaffmann, C. (1963) Gustatory nerve discharge in normal and sodium-deficient rats. *J. comp. physiol. Psychol.*, **56**, 1007–1011.

Naquet, R., Regis, H., Fischer-Williams, M. and Fernandez-Guardiola, A. (1960) Variations in the responses evoked by light along the specific pathways. *Brain*, **83**, 52–56.

Nauta, W. J. H. (1946) Hypothalamic regulation of sleep in rats: an experimental study. *J. Neurophysiol.*, **9**, 285–316.

Nebraska Symposia on motivation (1953 and subsequent years).

Nelson, K. (1964) The temporal patterning of courtship behaviour in the glandulo-caudine fishes (Ostariophysi, Characidae). *Behaviour*, **24**, 90–146.

Neumann, G-H. (1961) Die visuelle Lernfähigkeit primitiver Säugetiere. *Zeits f. Tierpsychol.*, **18**, 71–83.

Nice, M. M. (1943) Studies in the life-history of the Song Sparrow: II: *Trans. Linn. Soc. N.Y.*, **6**, 1–328.

Nicolai, J. (1956) Zur Biologie und Ethologie des Gimpels (*Pyrrhula pyrrhula* L.). *Zeits f. Tierpsychol.*, **13**, 93–132.

Nissen, H. W. (1930) A study of exploratory behaviour in the white rat by means of the obstruction method. *J. genet. Psychol.*, **37**, 361–376.

Nissen, H. W. (1954) Cited by Young, W. C. in "Sex and Internal Secretions", Ed. Young, W. C., Williams and Wilkins, Baltimore.

Nissen, H. W., Chow, K. L. and Semmes, J. (1951) Effects of restricted opportunity for tactual, kinesthetic and manipulative experience on the behavior of a chimpanzee. *Amer. J. Psychol.*, **64**, 485–507.

Noble, G. K. (1936) Courtship and sexual selection of the flicker (*Colaptes auratus luteus*). *Auk*, **53**, 269–282.

Noble, G. K. and Curtis, B. (1935–6) Sexual selection in fishes. *Anat. Rec.*, **64**, 84–5.

Noble, G. K. and Curtis, B. (1939) The social behavior of the jewel Fish, *Hemichromis bimaculatus* Gill. *Bull. Amer. Mus. Nat. Hist.*, **76**, 1–46.

Noble, G. K. and Zitrin, A. (1942) Induction of mating behaviour in male and female chicks following injections of sex hormones. *Endocrinology*, **30**, 327–334.

Noirot, E. (1964a) Changes in responsiveness to young in the adult mouse: I. The problematical effect of hormones. *Anim. Behav.*, **12**, 52–58.

Noirot, E. (1964b) Changes in responsiveness to young in the adult mouse: II. The effect of external stimuli. *J. comp. physiol. Psychol.*, **57**, 97–99.

Noirot, E. (1964c) Changes in responsiveness to young in the adult mouse: IV. The effect of an initial contact with a strong stimulus. *Anim. Behav.*, **12**, 442–445.

Noirot, E. (1965) Changes in responsiveness to young in the adult mouse: III. The effect of immediately preceding performances. *Behaviour*, **24**, 318–325.

Noirot, E. and Richards, M. (1966) Maternal behaviour in virgin female Golden Hamsters: changes consequent upon initial contact with pups. *Anim. Behav.*, in press.

Oehlert, B. (1958) Kampf und Paarbildung einiger Cichliden. *Zeits f. Tierpsychol.* **15**, 141–174.

O'Kelly, L. (1954) The effect of preloads of water and sodium chloride on voluntary water intake of thirsty rats. *J. comp. physiol. Psychol.*, **47**, 7–13.

Oldfield, R. C. and Zangwill, O. L. (1942a, b) Head's concept of the schema and its application in contemporary British psychology: I and II. *Brit. J. Psychol.*, **32**, 267–286, **33**, 58–64.

Olds, J. (1958) Selective effects of drives and drugs on "reward" systems of the brain. In "Neurological Basis of Behaviour", Eds. Wolstenholme, G. E. W. and O'Connor, C. M., Churchill, London.

Olds, J. (1961) Differential effects of drives and drugs on self stimulation at different brain sites. In Sheer (1961).

Olds, J. (1962) Hypothalmic substrates of reward. *Physiol. Rev.*, **42**, 554–604.

Olds, J. and Milner, P. (1954) Positive reinforcement produced by electrical stimulation of septal area and other regions of rat brain. *J. comp. physiol. Psychol.*, **47**, 419–427.

Osgood, C. E. (1953) Method and Theory in Experimental Psychology. Oxford Univ. Press, New York.

Ottinger, D. R. and Simmons, J. E. (1964) Behavior of human neonates and prenatal maternal anxiety. *Psychol. Rep.*, **14**, 391–394.

Overall, J. E. (1964) Note on the scientific status of factors. *Psychol. Bull.*, **61**, 270–276.

Padilla, S. G. (1935) Further studies on the delayed pecking of chicks. *J. comp. Psychol.*, **20**, 413–443.

Paillard, J. (1960) The patterning of skilled movements. In "Handbook of Physiology", Section 1, Vol. III, Eds. J. Field, H. W. Magoun and V. E. Hall, *Amer. Physiol. Soc.*, Washington.

Paré, W. P. (1964) Relationship of various behaviors in the open-field test of emotionality. *Psychol. Rep.*, **14**, 19–22.

Parriss, J. R. (1963) Retention of shape discrimination after regeneration of the optic nerves in the toad. *Quart. J. exp. Psychol.*, **15**, 22–26.

Parriss, J. R. and Young, J. Z. (1962) The limits of transfer of a learned discrimination to figures of larger and smaller sizes. *Zeits. vergl. Physiol.*, **45**, 618–635.

Pastore, N. (1958) Form perception and size constancy in the duckling. *J. Psychol.*, **45**, 259–261.

Pastore, N. (1959) Perceptual functioning in the duckling. *J. genet. Psychol.*, **95**, 157–169.

Pavlov, I. P. (1955) Selected Works. Central Books Ltd., London.

Peirce, J. T. and Nuttall, R. L. (1961a) Duration of sexual contacts in the rat. *J. comp. physiol. Psychol.*, **54**, 585–587.

Peirce, J. T. and Nuttall, R. L. (1961b) Self-paced sexual behavior in the female rat. *J. comp. physiol. Psychol.*, **54**, 310–313.

Pelkwijk, J. J. ter and Tinbergen, N. (1937) Eine reizbiologische Analyse einiger Verhaltensweisen von *Gasterosteus aculeatus* L. *Zeits f. Tierpsychol.*, **1**, 193–200.

Pennycuick, C. J. (1960) The physical basis of astro-navigation in birds; theoretical considerations. *J. exp. Biol.*, **37**, 573–593.

Perdeck, A. C. (1956) Vogel trekstation (Texel). *Jaarsverslag* 1956, 66–74.

Perdeck, A. C. (1958) The isolating value of specific song patterns in two sibling species of grasshoppers (*Chorthippus brunneus* Thunb. and *C. biguttulus* L.). *Behaviour*, **12**, 1–75.

Perdeck, A. C. (1963) Does navigation without visual clues exist in Robins? *Ardea*, **51**, 91–104.

Peters, J. J. and Isaacson, R. L. (1963) Acquisition of active and passive responses in two breeds of chickens. *J. comp. physiol. Psychol.*, **56**, 793–796.

Peters, J. J., Vonderahe, A. R. and Powers, T. H. (1958) Electrical studies of functional development of the eye and optic lobes in the chick embryo. *J. exper. Zool.*, **139**, 459–468.

Peters, R. S. (1958) The Concept of Motivation. Routledge and Kegan-Paul, London.

Petersen, B., Lundgren, L. and Wilson, L. (1956–7) The development of flight capacity in a butterfly. *Behaviour*, **10**, 324–339.

Peterson, N. (1960) Control of behaviour by presentation of an imprinted stimulus. *Science*, **132**, 1395–1396.

Pfaffmann, C. (1964) Taste, its sensory and motivating properties. *Amer. Scientist*, **52**, 187–206.

Pfaffmann, C. and Bare, J. K. (1950) Gustatory nerve discharges in normal and adrenalectomized rats. *J. comp. physiol. Psychol.*, **43**, 320–324.

Pfeiffer, W. (1960) Über die Schreckreaktion bei Fischen und die Herkunft des Schreckstoffes. *Zeits vergl. Physiol.*, **43**, 578–614.

Phoenix, C. H. (1961) Hypothalamic regulation of sexual behavior in male guinea pigs. *J. comp. physiol. Psychol.*, **54**, 72–77.

Piaget, J. (1952) The Origins of Intelligence in Children. Int. Univ. Press, New York.

Piaget, J. (1955) The Child's Construction of Reality. Routledge and Kegan-Paul, London.

Pitz, G. F. and Ross, R. B. (1961) Imprinting as a function of arousal. *J. comp. physiol. Psychol.*, **54**, 602–604.

Pollack, L. J. and Davis, L. (1931) Studies in decerebration: VI. The effect of deafferentation upon decerebrate rigidity. *Amer. J. Physiol.*, **98**, 47–49.

Pomeroy, D. E. (1962) Birds with abnormal bills. *Brit. Birds*, **55**, 49–72.

Portmann, A. (1961) Sensory organs: skin, taste and olfaction. In "Biology and Comparative Physiology of Birds", Ed. A. J. Marshall, Academic Press, New York.

Poulsen, H. (1954) On the song of the linnet (*Carduelis cannabina*). *Dansk. Ornith. For. Tidsskr.*, **48**, 32–37.

Poulsen, H. (1959) Song learning in the domestic canary. *Zeits f. Tierpsychol.*, **16**, 173–178.

Poulton, E. C. (1952) Perceptual anticipation in tracking with two-pointer and one-pointer displays. *Brit. J. Psychol.*, **43**, 222–229.

Poulton, E. C. (1956) Listening to overlapping calls. *J. exp. Psychol.*, **52**, 334–339.

Precht, H. and Freytag, G. (1958) Über Ermüdung und Hemmung angeborener Verhaltensweisen bei Springspinnen (Salticidae). Zugleich ein Beitrag zum Triebproblem. *Behaviour*, **13**, 143–211.

Prechtl, H. F. R. (1952) Angeborene Bewegungsweisen junger Katzen. *Experientia*, **8**, 220.

Prechtl, H. F. R. (1953) Zur Physiologie der angeborenen auslösenden Mechanismen: I. Quantitative Untersuchungen über die Sperrbewegung junger Singvögel. *Behaviour*, **5**, 32–50.

Prechtl, H. F. R. (1958) The directed head turning response and allied movements of the human baby. *Behaviour*, **13**, 212–242.

Prechtl, H.F.R. (1965) Problems of behavioural studies in the newborn infant. In "Advances in the Study of Behavior", Ed. Lehrman, D. S., Hinde, R. A. and Shaw, E., Academic Press, New York.

Premack, D., Collier, G. and Roberts, C. L. (1957) Frequency of light contingent bar pressing as a function of the amount of deprivation for light. *Amer. Psychol.*, **12**, 411.

Prescott, R. G. W. (1964) Brain-stem stimulation and reinforcement in the albino rat. Ph.D. thesis, Cambridge.

Pribram, K. H. (1958) Neocortical function in behaviour. In "Biological Biochemical Bases of Behavior", Ed. H. F. Harlow and C. N. Woolsey, Univ. Wisconsin Press.

Pribram, K. H. (1961) Limbic system. In Sheer (1961).

Pribram, K. H. (1963) Reinforcement revisited: a structural view. Nebraska symposia on motivation, 1963.

Pringle, J. W. S. (1951) On the parallel between learning and evolution. *Behaviour*, **3**, 174–215.

Pritchard, R. M., Heron, W. and Hebb, D. O. (1960) Visual perception approached by the method of stabilized images. *Canad. J. Psychol.*, **14**, 67–77.

Pumphrey, R. J. (1940) Hearing in insects. *Biol. Rev.*, **15**, 107–132.

Pumphrey, R. J. (1948) The sense organs of birds. *Ibis*, **90**, 171–199.

Quine, D. A. and Cullen, J. M. (1964) The pecking response of young Arctic Terns (*Sterna macrura*) and the adaptiveness of the "releasing mechanism". *Ibis*, **106**, 145–173.

Rabb, G. B. and M. S. (1963) On the behavior and breeding biology of the African pipid frog *Hymenochirus boettgeri. Zeits f. Tierpsychol.*, **20**, 215–241.

Räber, H. (1948) Analyse des Balzverhalten eines domestizierten Truthahns (*Meleagris*). *Behaviour*, **1**, 237–266.

Ranson, S. W., Fisher, C. and Ingram, W. R. (1937) Hypothalamic regulation of temperature in the monkey. *Arch. neurol. Psychiat.*, **38**, 445–466.

Rasmussen, E. W. (1939) Wildness in rats. *Acta Psychol.*, **4**, 295–304.

Ratner, S. C., Gawronski, J. J. and Rice, F. E. (1964) The variable of concurrent action in the language of children: effects of delayed speech feedback. *Psychol. Rec.*, **14**, 47–56.

Ratner, S. C. and Thompson, R. W. (1960) Immobility reactions (fear) of domestic fowl as a function of age and prior experience. *Anim. Behav.*, **8**, 186–191.

Razran, G. H. S. (1933) Conditioned responses in animals other than dogs. *Psychol. Bull.*, **30**, 261–324.

Razran, G. H. S. (1935) Conditioned responses: an experimental study and a theoretical analysis. *Arch. Psychol.*, *N. Y.*, 191.

Razran, G. (1961) The observable unconscious and the inferable conscious in current Soviet psychophysiology: interoceptive conditioning, semantic conditioning and the orienting reflex. *Psychol. Rev.*, **68**, 81–147.

Reese, E. S. (1963) The behavioral mechanisms underlying shell selection by hermit crabs. *Behaviour*, **21**, 78–126.

Reid, L. S. and Finger, F. W. (1955) The rat's adjustment to 23-hour food-deprivation cycles. *J. comp. physiol. Psychol.*, **48**, 110–113.

Rensch, B. (1961) Malversuche mit Affen. *Zeits f. Tierpsychol.*, **18**, 347–364.

Ressler, R. H. (1963) Genotype-correlated parental influences in two strains of mice. *J. comp. physiol. Psychol.*, **56**, 882–886.

Reyniers, J. A. (1953) Germfree life. *Lancet*, 933–934.

Reynolds, G. S. (1961) Contrast, generalisation and the process of discrimination. *J. exp. Anal. Behav.*, **4**, 289–294.

Reynolds, R. W. (1958) The relationship between stimulation voltage and rate of hypothalamic self-stimulation in the rat. *J. comp. physiol. Psychol.*, **51**, 193–198.

Rheingold, H. L. and Hess, E. H. (1957) The chick's "preference" for some visual properties of water. *J. comp. physiol. Psychol.*, **50**, 417–421.

Richter, C. P. (1937) Hypophyseal control of behavior. *Cold Spring Harbor Sym. Quant. Biol.*, **5**, 258–268.

Richter, C. P. and Hawkes, C. D. (1939) Increased spontaneous activity and food intake produced in rats by removal of the frontal poles of the brain. *J. Neurol. Psychiatr.*, **2**, 231–242.

Riesen, A. H. (1958) Plasticity of behavior: psychological aspects. In "Biological and Biochemical Bases of Behavior", Eds. Harlow, H. T. and Woolsey, C. N., Univ. of Wisconsin Press, Madison.

Riesen, A. H. (1961) Studying perceptual development using the technique of sensory deprivation. *J. nerv. ment. Dis.*, **132**, 21–25.

Riesen, A. H. and Aarons, L. (1959) Visual movement and intensity discrimination in cats after early deprivation of pattern vision. *J. comp. physiol. Psychol.*, **52**, 142–149.

Riesen, A. H. and Mellinger, J. C. (1956) Interocular transfer of habits in cats after alternating monocular visual experience. *J. comp. physiol. Psychol.*, **49**, 516–520.

Riess, B. F. (1950) The isolation of factors of learning and native behavior in field and laboratory studies. *Ann. N.Y. Acad. Sci.*, **51**, 1093–1102.

Rigby, W. K. (1954) Approach and avoidance gradients and conflict behavior in a predominantly temporal situation. *J. comp. physiol. Psychol.*, **47**, 83–89.

Rilling, S., Mittelstaedt, H. and Roeder, K. D. (1959) Prey recognition in the Praying Mantis. *Behaviour*, **14**, 164–184.

Riss, W., Valenstein, E. S., Sinks, J. and Young, W. C. (1955) Development of sexual behavior in male guinea pigs from genetically different stocks under controlled conditions of androgen treatment and caging. *Endocrinology*, **57**, 139–146.

Ritchie, B. F. (1948) Studies in spatial learning: VI. Place orientation and direction orientation. *J. exp. Psychol.*, **38**, 659–669.

Roberts, C. L., Marx, M. H. and Collier, G. (1958) Light onset and light offset as reinforcers for the albino rat. *J. comp. physiol. Psychol.*, **51**, 575–579.

Roberts, M. B. V. (1962) The giant fibre reflex of the earthworm, *Lumbricus terrestris* L: II. Fatigue. *J. exp. Biol.*, **39**, 229–237.

Roberts, W. W. (1958) Both rewarding and punishing effects from stimulation of posterior hypothalamus of cat with same electrode at same intensity. *J. comp. physiol. Psychol.*, **51**, 400–407.

Roberts, W. W. and Kiess, H. O. (1964) Motivational properties of hypothalamic aggression in cats. *J. comp. physiol. Psychol.*, **58**, 187–193.

Rodgers, W. L., Melzack, R. and Segal, J. R. (1963) "Tail flip response" in goldfish. *J. comp. physiol. Psychol.*, **56**, 917–923.

Roeder, K. D. (1962a) The behaviour of free-flying moths in the presence of artificial ultrasonic pulses. *Anim. Behav.*, **10**, 300–304.

Roeder, K. D. (1962b) Neural mechanisms of animal behavior. *Am. Zoologist*, **2**, 105–115.

Roeder, K. D. (1964) Aspects of the noctuid tympanic nerve response having significance in the avoidance of bats. *J. Ins. Physiol.*, **10**, 529–546.

Roeder, K. D., Tozian, L. and Weiant, E. A. (1960) Endogenous nerve activity and behaviour in the mantis and cockroach. *J. Insect Physiol.*, **4**, 45–62.

Rosen, J. and Hart, F. M. (1963) Effects of early social isolation upon adult timidity and dominance in *Peromyscus*. *Psychol. Rep.*, **13**, 47–50.

Rosenblatt, J. S. (1950) Hoarding or Hauling? M.Sc. thesis, New York Univ. Library.

Rosenblatt, J. S. and Aronson, L. R. (1958a) The influence of experience on the behavioural effects of androgen in prepuberally castrated male cats. *Anim. Behav.*, **6**, 171–182.

Rosenblatt, J. S. and Aronson, L. R. (1958b) The decline of sexual behavior in male cats after castration with special reference to the role of prior sexual experience. *Behaviour*, **12**, 285–338.

Rosenblatt, J. S. and Lehrman, D. S. (1963) Maternal behavior of the laboratory rat. In "Maternal Behavior in Mammals", Ed. H. Rheingold, Wiley, New York.

Rosenblatt, J. S., Turkewitz, G. and Schneirla, T. C. (1961) In "Determinants of Infant Behaviour", Ed. B. Foss, Methuen, London.

Rosenblueth, A., Wiener, N. and Bigelow, J. (1943) Behavior, purpose and teleology. *Philosophy of Science*, **10**, 18–24.

Rosenblum, L. A. and Cross, H. A. (1963) Performance of neonatal monkeys in the visual-cliff situation. *Amer. J. Psychol.*, **76**, 318–320.

Rosenzweig, M. R., Krech, D., Bennett, E. L. and Diamond, M. C. (1962) Effects of environmental complexity and training on brain chemistry and anatomy: a replication and extension. *J. comp. physiol. Psychol.*, **55**, 429–437.

Ross, S. (1950) Sucking behavior in neonate dogs. *J. abn. soc. Psychol.*, **46**, 142–149.

Ross, S., Goldstein, I. and Kappel, S. (1962) Perceptual factors in eating behavior in chicks. *J. comp. physiol. Psychol.*, **55**, 240–241.

Ross, S., Sawin, P. B., Zarrow, M. X. and Denenberg, V. H. (1963) Maternal behavior in the rabbit. In "Maternal Behavior in Mammals", Ed. H. Rheingold, Wiley, New York.

Roth, L. L. and Rosenblatt, J. S. (1964) Pregnancy changes in the self-licking patterns of rats. Paper presented at Amer. Psychol. Assn. Sept. 1964.

Rowell, C. H. F. (1961) Displacement grooming in the Chaffinch. *Anim. Behav.*, **9**, 38–63.

Rowell, C. H. F. (1964) Comments on a recent discussion of some ethological terms. *Anim. Behav.*, **12**, 535–537.

Rowell, T. E. (1961) Maternal behaviour in non-maternal Golden Hamsters (*Mesocricetus auratus*). *Anim. Behav.*, **9**, 11–15.

Rowell, T. E. (1962) Agonistic noises of the rhesus monkey (*Macaca mulatta*). *Sym. Zool. Soc. Lond.*, **8**, 91–96.

Rowell, T. E. (1963) Behaviour and female reproductive cycles of rhesus macaques. *J. Reprod. Fertil.*, **6**, 193–203.

Rowell, T. E. and Hinde, R. A. (1962) Vocal communication by the rhesus monkey (*Macaca mulatta*). *Proc. Zool. Soc. Lond.*, **138**, 279–294.

Rowland, V. (1957) Differential electroencephalographic response to conditioned auditory stimuli in arousal from sleep. *EEG Clin. Neurophysiol.*, **9**, 585–594.

Ruch, T. C. (1951) Motor systems. In "Handbook of Experimental Psychology", Ed. Stevens, S. S., Wiley, New York.

Rudel, R. G. and Teuber, H.-L. (1963) Discrimination of direction of line in children. *J. comp. physiol. Psychol.*, **56**, 892–898.

Ruiter, L. de (1952) Some experiments on the camouflage of stick caterpillars. *Behaviour*, **4**, 222–232.

Ruiter, L. de and Beukema, J. J. (1963) Foraging and feeding behaviour in the Three-spined Stickleback. *Anim. Behav.*, **11**, 605.

Rüppell, G. (1962) Vorläufige Beiträge zur Kenntnis des Drohverhaltens beim Rotschenkel *Tringa totanus totanus* Linné. *Zeits f. Tierpsychol.*, **19**, 465–471.

Russek, M. (1963) Participation of hepatic glucoreceptors in the control of intake of food. *Nature*, **197**, 79–80.

Russell, E. S. (1943) Perceptual and sensory signs in instinctive behaviour. *Proc. Linn. Soc. Lond.*, **154**, 195–216.

Russell, E. S. (1945) The Directiveness of Organic Activities. Cambridge Univ. Press, London.

Russell, W. M. S. (1954) Experimental studies of the reproductive behaviour of *Xenopus laevis*: I. The control mechanisms for clasping and unclasping, and the specificity of hormone action. *Behaviour*, **7**, 113–188.

Sackett, G. P. (1963) A neural mechanism underlying unlearned, critical period and developmental aspects of visually controlled behavior. *Psychol. Rec.*, **70**, 40–50.

Salzen, E. A. (1962) Imprinting and fear. *Sym. Zool. Soc. Lond.*, **8**, 199–217.

Sand, A. (1937) The mechanism of the lateral sense organs of fishes. *Proc. Roy. Soc. B.*, **123**, 472–495.

Satinoff, E. and Stanley, W. C. (1963) Effect of stomach loading on sucking behavior in neonatal puppies. *J. comp. physiol. Psychol.*, **56**, 66–68.

Sauer, F. (1954) Die Entwicklung der Lautäusserungen vom Ei ab schalldicht gehaltener Dorngrasmücken (*Sylvia c. communis*, Latham) im Vergleich mit später isolierten und mit wildlebenden Artgenossen. *Zeits f. Tierpsychol.*, **11**, 10–93.

Sauer, F. (1955) Über Variationen der Artgesänge bei Grasmücken. *J. f. Ornith.*, **96**, 129–146.

Sauer, F. (1957) Die Sternenorientierung nächtlich ziehender Grasmücken (*Sylvia atricapilla, bovin und curruca*). *Zeits f. Tierpsychol.*, **14**, 29–70.

Sauer, F. (1963) Migration habits of Golden Plovers. *Proc. XIIIth Int. Orn. Cong.*, 454–467.

Saxena, A. (1960) Lernkapazität, Gedächtnis und Transpositionsvermögen bei Forellen. *Zool. Jahrb.*, **69**, 63–94.

Schaefer, H. H. and Hess, E. H. (1959) Color preferences in imprinting objects. *Zeits f. Tierpsychol.*, **16**, 161–172.

Schaefer, T. (1963) Early "experience" and its effects on later behavioral processes in rats: II. A critical factor in the early handling phenomenon. *Trans. N. Y. Acad. Sci.*, **25**, 871–889.

Schaller, G. B. and Emlen, J. T. (1961) The development of visual discrimination patterns in the crouching reactions of nestling grackles. *Auk*, **78**, 125–137.

Schein, M. W. (1963) On the irreversibility of imprinting. *Zeits f. Tierpsychol.*, **20**, 462–467.

Schein, M. W. and Hale, E. B. (1959) The effect of early social experience on male sexual behaviour of androgen injected turkeys. *Anim. Behav.*, **7**, 189–200.

Schein, M. W. and Hale, E. B. (1965) Stimuli eliciting sexual behavior. In "Sex and Behavior", Ed. Beach, F. A., Wiley, New York.

Schiffman, H. R. and Walk, R. D. (1963) Behavior on the visual cliff of monocular as compared to binocular chicks. *J. comp. physiol. Psychol.*, **56**, 1064–1068.

Schiller, P. H. (1957) Manipulative patterns in the chimpanzee. In "Instinctive Behavior", Ed. Schiller, P. H., Methuen, London.

Schleidt, M. (1954) Untersuchungen über die Auslösung des Kollerns beim Truthahn (*Meleagris gallopavo*). *Zeits f. Tierpsychol.*, **11**, 417–435.

Schleidt, W. M. (1961) Reaktionen von Truthühnern auf fliegende Raubvögel und Versuche zur Analyse ihrer AAM's. *Zeits f. Tierpsychol.*, **18**, 534–560.

Schleidt, W. (1962) Die historische Entwicklung der Begriffe "Angeborenes auslösendes Schema" und "Angeborener Auslösemechanismus" in der Ethologie. *Zeits f. Tierpsychol.*, **19**, 697–722.

Schleidt, W. M. (1964) Über die Spontaneität von Erbkoordinationen. *Zeits f. Tierpsychol.*, **21**, 235–256.

Schlosberg, H. (1937) The relationship between success and the laws of conditioning. *Psychol. Rev.*, **44**, 379–394.

Schlosberg, H. (1954) Three dimensions of emotion. *Psychol. Rev.*, **61**, 81–88.

Schmidt, H-D. (1956) Das Verhalten von Haushunden in Konfliktsituationen. *Zeits. f. Psychol.*, **159**, 161–245.

Schmidt-Koenig, K. (1961) Die Sonne als Kompass im Heim-Orientierungssystem der Brieftauben. *Zeits f. Tierpsychol.*, **18**, 221–244.

Schneider, G. E. and Gross, C. G. (1965) Curiosity in the hamster. *J. comp. physiol. Psychol.*, **59**, 150–152.

Schneirla, T. C. (1933) Some important features of ant learning. *Zeits. vergl. Physiol.*, **19**, 439–452.

Schneirla, T. C. (1946) Problems in the biopsychology of social organisation. *J. abn. soc. Psychol.*, **41**, 385–402.

Schneirla, T. C. (1949) Levels in the psychological capacities of animals. In "Philosophy for the Future", Ed. R. W. Sellars *et al.*, Macmillan, New York.

Schneirla, T. C. (1951) A consideration of some problems in the ontogeny of family life and social adjustments in various infra-human animals. In "Problems of Infancy and Childhood", Ed. M. J. E. Senn, Macy, New York.

Schneirla, T. C. (1952) A consideration of some conceptual trends in comparative psychology. *Psych. Bull.*, **49**, 559–597.

Schneirla, T. C. (1956) Interrelationships of the "innate" and the "acquired" in instinctive behavior. In "L'Instinct dans le Comportement des Animaux et de L'homme", Foundation Singer Polignac, Paris.

Schneirla, T. C. (1959) An evolutionary and developmental theory of biphasic processes underlying approach and withdrawal. In "Nebraska Symposium on Motivation", Ed. Jones, M. R., Lincoln.

Schneirla, T. C. (1965) Aspects of stimulation and organisation in approach/withdrawal processes underlying vertebrate behavioural development. In "Advances in the Study of Behavior I," Eds. Lehrman, D., Hinde, R. A. and Shaw, E., Academic Press, New York.

Schneirla, T. C. and Rosenblatt, J. S. (1961) Behavioural organisation and genesis of the social bond in insects and mammals. *Amer. J. Orthopsych.*, **31**, 223–253.

Schneirla, T. C. and Rosenblatt, J. S. (1963) "Critical Periods" in the development of behavior. *Science*, **139**, 1110–1115.

Schneirla, T. C., Rosenblatt, J. S. and Tobach, E. (1963) Maternal behavior in the cat. In "Maternal Behavior in Mammals", Ed. Rheingold, H., Wiley, New York.

Schoen, L. (1950) Quantitative Untersuchungen über die zentrale Kompensation nach einseitiger Utriculusausschaltung bei Fischen. *Zeits. verg. Physiol.*, **32**, 121–150.

Schoen, L. (1951) Das Zusammenspiel beider Augen als Gleichgewichtsorgane der Fische. *Verh. dtsch. zool. Gesell.*, **45**, 191–195.

Schoenfeld, W. N., Antonitis, J. J. and Bersh, P. J. (1950) A preliminary study of training conditions necessary for secondary reinforcement. *J. exp. Psychol.*, **40**, 40–45.

Schöne, H. (1951) Die Lichtorientierung der Larven von *Acilius sulcatus* L. und *Dytiscus marginalis* L. *Zeits. vergl. Physiol.*, **33**, 63–98.

Schöne, H. (1962) Optisch gesteuerte Lageänderungen (Versuche an Dytiscidenlarven zur Vertikalorientierung). *Zeits. verg. Physiol.*, **45**, 590–604.

Schutz, F. (1956) Vergleichende Untersuchungen über die Schreckreaktion bei Fischen und deren Verbreitung. *Zeits. vergl. Physiol.*, **38**, 84–135.

Schutz, F. (1963a) Objektfixierung geschlechtlicher Reaktionen bei Anatiden und Hühnern. *Naturwiss.*, **50**, 624–625.

Schutz, F. (1963b) Über geschlechtlich unterschiedliche Objektfixierung sexueller

Reaktionen bei Enten im Zusammenhang mit dem Prachtkleid des Männchens. *Verh. Deutsch. Zool. Gesell. München*, 282–287.

Schutz, F. (1965) Sexuelle Prägung bei Anatiden. *Zeits. f. Tierpsychol.*, **22**, 50–103.

Schüz, E. (1949) Die Spät-Auflassung ostpreussischer Jungstörche in West-Deutschland durch die Vogelwarte Rossitten 1933. *Vogelwarte*, **15**, 63–78.

Schwartz, M. and Beach, F. A. (1954) Effects of adrenalectomy upon mating behavior in castrated male dogs. *Amer. Psychol.*, **9**, 467–468.

Scott, J. P. (1945) Social behavior, organisation and leadership in a small flock of domestic sheep. *Comp. Psychol. Monogr.*, 18, *No. 4*.

Scott, J. P. (1954) The process of socialization in higher animals. *Child Family Digest*, 1954, 69–84.

Scott, J. P. (1958) Critical periods in the development of social behavior in puppies. *Psychsom. Med.*, **20** 42–54.

Scott, J. P. and Marston, M. V. (1950) Critical periods affecting the development of normal and maladjustive social behavior of puppies. *J. genet. Psychol.*, **77**, 25–60.

Searle, L. V. (1949) The organization of hereditary maze-brightness and maze-dullness. *Genet. Psychol. Monogr.*, 39, 279–325.

Sechzer, J. A. and Brown, J. L. (1964) Color discrimination in the cat. *Science*, **144**, 427–429.

Seidel, R. J. (1959) A review of sensory preconditioning. *Psych. Bull.*, **56**, 58–73.

Seitz, A. (1940–41) Die Paarbildung bei einigen Cichliden: I. *Zeits f. Tierpsychol.*, **4** 40–84.

Seitz, A. (1943) Die Paarbildung bei einigen Cichliden: II. *Zeits f. Tierpsychol.*, **5** 74–101.

Senden, M.r. (1932) Raum- und Gestaltauffassung bei operierten Blindgeborenen vor und nach der Operation. Barth, Leipzig.

Sevenster, P. (1961) A causal analysis of a displacement activity (Fanning in *Gasterosteus aculeatus* L.). *Behav. Suppl. No. 9*, 1–170.

Sevenster-Bol, A. C. A. (1962) On the causation of drive reduction after a consummatory act. *Arch. Néerl. Zool.*, **15**, 175–236.

Sharpless, S. and Jasper, H. (1956) Habituation of the arousal reaction. *Brain*, **79**, 655–680.

Sheer, D. E. (Ed.) (1961) Electrical Stimulation of the Brain. Hogg Foundation for Mental Health: Univ. of Texas.

Sheffield, F. D. and Campbell, B. A. (1954) The role of experience in the "spontaneous" activity of hungry rats. *J. comp. physiol. Psychol.*, **47**, 97–100.

Sheffield, F. D. and Roby, T. B. (1950) Reward value of a non-nutritive sweet taste. *J. comp. physiol. Psychol.*, **43**, 471–481.

Sheffield, F. D., Wulff, J. J. and Backer, R. (1951) Reward value of copulation without sex drive reduction. *J. comp. physiol. Psychol.*, **44**, 3–8.

Sherrington, C. S. (1906) Integrative Action of the Nervous System. Cambridge Univ. Press, London.

Sherrington, C. S. (1910) Flexion-reflex of the limb, crossed extension reflex, and reflex stepping and standing. *J. Physiol.*, **40**, 28–121.

Sherrington, C. S. (1913) Further observations on the production of reflex stepping by combination of reflex excitation with reflex inhibition. *J. Physiol.*, **47**, 196–214.

Sherrington, C. S. (1917) Reflexes elicitable in the cat from pinna vibrissae and jaws. *J. Physiol.*, **51**, 404–431.

Sherrington, C. S. (1931) Quantitative management of contraction in lowest level coordination. *Brain*, **54**, 1–28.

Shinkman, P. G. (1962) Visual depth discrimination in animals. *Psychol. Bull.*, **59**, 489–501.

Shinkman, P. G. (1963) Visual depth-discrimination in day-old chicks. *J. comp. physiol. Psychol.*, **56**, 410–414.

Shipley, W. U. (1963) The demonstration in the domestic guinea pig of a process resembling classical imprinting. *Anim. Behav.*, **11**, 470–474.

Shreck, P. K., Sterritt, G. M., Smith, M. P. and Stilson, D. W. (1963) Environmental factors in the development of eating in chicks. *Anim. Behav.*, **11**, 306–309.

Siegel, A. I. (1953a) Deprivation of visual form definition in the ring dove: I Discriminatory learning. *J. comp. physiol. Psychol.*, **46**, 115–119.

Siegel, A. I. (1953b) Deprivation of visual form definition in the ring dove: II Perceptual-motor transfer. *J. comp. physiol. Psychol.*, **46**, 249–252.

Siegel, P. S. and Brantley, J. J. (1951) The relationship of emotionality to the consummatory response of eating. *J. exp. Psychol.*, **42**, 304–306.

Siegel, P. S. and Dorman, L. B. (1954) Food intake of the rat following the intragastric administration of "hungry" and "satiated" blood. *J. comp. physiol. Psychol.*, **47**, 227–229.

Siegel, P. S. and Siegel, H. S. (1949) The effect of emotionality on the water intake of the rat. *J. comp. physiol. Psychol.*, **42**, 12–16.

Simmons, K. E. L. (1955) The nature of the predator-reactions of waders towards humans; with special reference to the role of the aggressive-, escape- and brooding-drives. *Behaviour*, **8**, 130–173.

Simmons, K. E. L. (1961) Problems of head-scratching in birds. *Ibis*, **103a**, 37–49.

Simpson, G. G. (1961) Principles of animal taxonomy. Columbia Univ. Press, New York.

Skinner, B. F. (1938) The Behavior of Organisms; an Experimental Analysis. Appleton-Century-Crofts, New York.

Skinner, B. F. (1948) "Superstition" in the pigeon. *J. exp. Psychol.*, **38**, 168–172.

Sluckin, W. (1962) Perceptual and associative learning. *Sym. Zool. Soc. Lond.*, **8**, 193–198.

Sluckin, W. and Salzen, E. A. (1961) Imprinting and perceptual learning. *Quart. J. exp. Psychol.*, **13**, 65–77.

Smith, C. J. (1959) Mass action and early environment in the rat. *J. comp. physiol. Psychol.*, **52**, 154–6.

Smith, F. V. (1962) Perceptual aspects of imprinting. *Sym. Zool. Soc. Lond.*, **8**, 171–191.

Smith, F. V. and Bird, M. W. (1964a) The approach response of chicks in groups in relation to the strength of the stimulus. *Anim. Behav.*, **12**, 252–258.

Smith, F. V. and Bird, M. W. (1964b) The correlation of responsiveness to visual and auditory stimuli in the domestic chick. *Anim. Behav.*, **12**, 259–263.

Smith, K. U. (1962) Delayed Sensory Feedback and Behavior. W.B. Saunders Co., Philadelphia and London.

Smith, M. and Duffy, M. (1955) The effects of intragastric injection of various substances on subsequent bar-pressing. *J. comp. physiol. Psychol.*, **48**, 387–391.

Smith, M. and Duffy, M. (1957) Some physiological factors that regulate eating behavior. *J. comp. physiol. Psychol.*, **50**, 601–608.

Smith, M. H., Salisbury, R. and Weinberg, H. (1961) The reaction of hypothalamic-hyperphagic rats to stomach preloads. *J. comp. physiol. Psychol.*, **54**, 660–664.

Smith, O. A. (1961) Food intake and hypothalamic stimulation. In "Electrical Stimulation of the Brain", Ed. Sheer, D. E., Univ. of Texas Press.

Sokolov, E. N. (1960) Neuronal models and the orienting reflex. In "The Central Nervous System and Behavior". Ed. Brazier, M. A. B., Josiah Macy Jr. Foundation, New York.

Solomon, P. *et al.* (Ed.) (1961) Sensory Deprivation. Harvard Univ. Press.

Solomon, R. L. and Turner, L. H. (1962) Discriminative classical conditioning in dogs paralyzed by curare can later control discriminative avoidance responses in the normal state. *Psychol. Rev.*, **69**, 202–219.

Spalding, D. A. (1873) Instinct with original observations on young animals. *MacMillan's Magazine*, **27**, 282–293, reprinted *Brit. J. anim. Behav.*, **2**, 2–11.

Spence, J. T. and Maher, B. A. (1962) Handling and noxious stimulation of the albino rat: I. Effects on subsequent emotionality. *J. comp. physiol. Psychol.*, **55**, 247–251.

Spence, K. W. (1956) Behavior Theory and Conditioning. Yale Univ. Press, New Haven, Conn.

Spencer-Booth, Y., Hinde, R. A. and Bruce, M. (1965) Social companions and the mother-infant relationship in rhesus monkeys. *Nature*, **208**, 301.

Sperry, R. W. (1941) The effect of crossing nerves to antagonistic muscles in the hind limb of the rat. *J. comp. Neurol.*, **75**, 1–19.

Sperry, R. W. (1943) Effect of 180 degrees rotation of the retinal field on visuomotor coordination. *J. exp. Zool.*, **92**, 263–279.

Sperry, R. W. (1947) Effect of crossing nerves in antagonistic limb muscles in the monkey. *Arch. Neurol. Psychiatr., Lond.*, **58**, 452–473.

Sperry, R. W. (1950) Neural basis of the spontaneous optokinetic response produced by visual inversion. *J. comp. physiol. Psychol.*, **43**, 482–489.

Sperry, R. W. (1951) Mechanisms of neural maturation. In "Handbook of Experimental Psychology", Ed. Stevens, S. S., Wiley, New York.

Sperry, R. W. (1958) Physiological plasticity and brain circuit theory. In "Biological and Biochemical Bases of Behavior", Ed. Harlow, H. F. and Woolsey, C. N., Univ. Wisconsin Press.

Sperry, R. W. (1963) Chemoaffinity in the orderly growth of nerve fibre patterns and connections. *Proc. Nat. Acad. Sci.*, **50**, 703–710.

Sperry, R. W. and Deupree, N. (1956) Functional recovery following alterations in nerve-muscle connections of fishes. *J. comp. Neurol.*, **106**, 143–158.

Stamm, R. A. (1962) Aspekte des Paarverhaltens von *Agapornis personata* Reichenow (Aves, Psittacidae, Loriini). *Behaviour*, **19**, 1–56.

Stanley, W. C. and Bacon, W. E. (1963) Suppression of sucking behavior in non-deprived puppies. *Psychol. Rep.*, **13**, 175–178.

Steel, E. A. and Hinde, R. A. (1963) Hormonal control of brood patch and oviduct development in domesticated canaries. *J. Endocrin*, **26**, 11–24.

Steel, Elizabeth and Hinde, R. A. (1964) Effect of exogenous oestrogen on brood patch development of intact and ovariectomized canaries. *Nature*, **202**, 718–719.

Steinberg, J. and Bindra, D. (1962) Effects of pregnancy and salt-intake on genital licking. *J. comp. physiol. Psychol.*, **55**, 103–106.

Stellar, E. (1954) The physiology of motivation. *Psychol. Rev.*, **61**, 5–22.

Stellar, E. (1960) Drive and Motivation. In "Handbook of Physiology", Section 1, Vol. III, Eds. Field, J., Magoun, H. W. and Hall, V. E., Amer. Physiol. Soc., Washington.

Stellar, E. and Hill, J. H. (1952) The rat's rate of drinking as a function of water deprivation. *J. comp. physiol. Psychol.*, **45**, 96–102.

Stellar, E., Hyman, R. and Samet, S. (1954) Gastric factors controlling water- and salt-solution-drinking. *J. comp. physiol. Psychol.*, **47**, 220–226.

Sterritt, G. M. (1962) Inhibition and facilitation of eating by electric shock. *J. comp. physiol. Psychol.*, **55**, 226–229.

Sterritt, G. M. and Smith, M. P. (1965) Reinforcement effects of specific components of feeding in young leghorn chicks. *J. comp. physiol. Psychol.*, **59**, 171–135.

Stevens, S. S. (1951) Handbook of Experimental Psychology. Wiley, New York.

Stevens, S. S. (1958) Measurement and man. *Science*, **127**, 383–389.

Stevens, S. S. (1961) To honor Fechner and repeal his law. *Science*, **133**, 80–86.

Stevenson, J. G. (in press) Reinforcing effects of song in the male Chaffinch.

Stichmann, W. (1962) Transpositionsversuche mit Haushuhnrassen stark verscheidener Körpergrösse. *Zeits f. Tierpsychol.*, **19**, 290–320.

Stokes, A. W. (1962a) Agonistic behaviour among Blue Tits at a winter feeding station. *Behaviour*, **19**, 118–138.

Stokes, A. W. (1962b) The comparative ethology of Great, Blue, Marsh and Coal Tits at a winter feeding station. *Behaviour*, **19**, 208–218.

Stokes, A. W. (1963) Agonistic and sexual behaviour in the Chukar Partridge (*Alectoris graeca*). *Anim. Behav.*, **11**, 121–134.

Stout, J. F. (1963) The significance of sound production during the reproductive behaviour of *Notropis analostanus* (Family Cyprinidae). *Anim. Behav.*, **11**, 83–92.

Stratton, G. (1897) Vision without inversion of the retinal image. *Psychol. Rev.*, **4**, 341–360.

Stretch, R. G. A. (1960) Exploratory behaviour in the rat. *Nature*, **186**, 454–456.

Sutherland, N. S. (1957) Visual discrimination of orientation and shape by the Octopus. *Nature*, **179**, 11–13.

Sutherland, N. S. (1959) Stimulus analysing mechanisms. In Proc. sym. mechanization of thought processes. Her Majesty's Stationery Office, London, 575–609.

Sutherland, N. S. (1961) The methods and findings of experiments on the visual discrimination of shape by animals. *Exp. Psychol. Soc. Monogr. No.* 1.

Sutherland, N. S. (1962) Visual discrimination of shape by *Octopus*: squares and crosses. *J. comp. physiol. Psychol.*, **55**, 939–943.

Sutherland, N. S. (1963) Cat's ability to discriminate oblique rectangles. *Science*, **139**, 209–210.

Sutherland, N. S., Mackintosh, N. J. and Mackintosh, J. (1963) Simultaneous discrimination training of *Octopus* and transfer of discrimination along a continuum. *J. comp. physiol. Psychol.*, **56**, 150–156.

Szlep, R. (1952) On the plasticity of instinct of a garden spider (*Aranea diadema* L.) construction of a cobweb. *Acta. Biol. Exp.*, **16**, 5–22.

Tallarico, R. B. and Farrell, W. M. (1964) Studies of visual depth perception: an effect of early experience on chicks on a visual cliff. *J. comp. physiol. Psychol.*, **57**, 94–96.

Tapp, J. T. and Markowitz, H. (1963) Infant handling: effects on avoidance learning, brain weight and cholinesterase activity. *Science*, **140**, 486–487.

Teghtsoonian, R. and Campbell, B. A. (1960) Random activity of the rat during food deprivation as a function of environmental conditions. *J. comp. physiol. Psychol.*, **53**, 242–244.

Teitelbaum, P. (1955) Sensory control of hypothalamic hyperphagia. *J. comp. physiol. Psychol.*, **48**, 156–163.

Teitelbaum, P. (1957) Random and food-directed activity in hyperphagic and normal rats. *J. comp. physiol. Psychol.*, **50**, 486–490.

Tembrock, G. (1958) Spielverhalten beim Rotfuchs. *Zool. Beitr.*, **3**, 423–496.

Tembrock, G. (1962a) Versuch einer Analyse des Imponierverhaltens beim Rotfuchs. *Vulpes vulpes* (L.), *Zeits f. Tierpsychol.*, **19**, 577–585.

Tembrock, G. (1962b) Zur Strukturanalyse des Kampfverhaltens bei *Vulpes*. *Behaviour*, **19**, 261–282.

Tenen, S. S. and Miller, N. E. (1964) Strength of electrical stimulation of lateral hypothalamus, food deprivation, and tolerance for quinine in food. *J. comp. physiol. Psychol.*, **58**, 55–62.

Teuber, H-L. (1960) Perception. In "Handbook of Physiology", Section I, Vol. III, Eds. Field, J., Magoun, H. W. and Hall, V. E., Amer. Physiol. Soc., Washington.

Teuber, H-L. (1961) Sensory deprivation, sensory suppression and agnosia: notes for a neurologic theory. *J. nerv. ment. Dis.*, **132**, 32–40.

Thielcke,G. (1962) Versuche mit Klangattrapen zur Klärung der Verwandtschaft der Baumläufer *Certhia familiaris* L., *C. brachydactyla* Brehm and *C. americana* Bonaparte. *J. f. Ornith.*, **103**, 266–271.

Thielcke, G. and Linsenmaier, K. E. (1963) Zur geographischen Variation des Gesanges des Zilpzalps *Phylloscopus collybita*, in Mittel- und Südwesteuropa mit einem Vergleich des Gesanges des Fitis *Phylloscopus trochilus*. *J. f. Ornith.*, **104**, 372–402.

Thielcke-Poltz, H. and Thielcke, G. (1960) Akustisches Lernen verschieden alter schallisolierter Amseln (*Turdus merula* L.) und die Entwicklung erlernter Motive ohne und mit Künstlichen Einfluss von Testosteron. *Zeits f. Tierpsychol.*, **17**, 211–244.

Thistlethwaite, D. (1951) A critical review of latent learning and related experiments. *Psychol. Bull.*, **48**, 97–129.

Thompson, T. I. (1963) Visual reinforcement in Siamese fighting fish. *Science*. **141**, 55–57.

Thompson, W. R. (1953) The inheritance of behaviour; behavioural differences in fifteen mouse strains. *Canad. J. Psychol.*, **7**, 145–153.

Thompson, W. R. (1957) Influence of prenatal maternal anxiety on emotionality in young rats. *Science*, **125**, 698–699.

Thompson, W. R. and Heron, W. (1954) The effects of restricting early experience on the problem-solving capacity of dogs. *Canad. J. Psychol.*, **8**, 17–31.

Thompson, W. R., Watson, J. and Charlesworth, W. R. (1962) The effects of pre-natal maternal stress on offspring behavior in rats. *Psychol. Monogr.*, **76**, 1–26.

Thorpe, W. H. (1945) The evolutionary significance of habitat selection. *J. Anim. Ecol.*, **14**, 67–70.

Thorpe, W. H. (1954) The process of song-learning in the chaffinch as studied by means of the sound spectrograph. *Nature*, **173**, 465–469.

Thorpe, W. H. (1958) The learning of song patterns by birds, with especial reference to the song of the chaffinch, *Fringilla coelebs*. *Ibis*, **100**, 535–570.

Thorpe, W. H. (1961a) Sensitive periods in the learning of animals and men. In "Current Problems in the Study of Animal Behaviour", Eds. Thorpe, W. H. and Zangwill, O. L., Cambridge Univ. Press, London.

Thorpe, W. H. (1961b) Bird-song. Cambridge Univ. Press, London.

Thorpe, W. H. (1963a) Learning and Instinct in Animals. (1st Edn., 1956) Methuen, London.

Thorpe, W. H. (1963b) Ethology and the coding problem in germ cell and brain. *Zeits f. Tierpsychol.*, **20**, 529–551.

Thorpe, W. H. and Jones, F. G. W. (1937) Olfactory conditioning and its relation to the problem of host selection. *Proc. Roy. Soc. B.*, **124**, 56–81.

Tinbergen, L. (1960) The natural control of insects in pinewoods: I. Factors influencing the intensity of predation by song birds. *Arch. néerl. Zool.*, **13**, 265–343.

Tinbergen, N. (1935) Über die Orientierung des Bienenwolfes (*Philanthus triangulum* Fabr.). *Zeits. vergl. Physiol.*, **21**, 699–716.

Tinbergen, N. (1937) Über das Verhalten kämpfender Kohlmeisen (*Parus m. major* L.). *Ardea*, 26, 222–223.

Tinbergen, N. (1940–41) Die Übersprungbewegung. *Zeits f. Tierpsychol.*, 4, 1–10.

Tinbergen, N. (1942) An objectivistic study of the innate behaviour of animals. *Biblioth. Biother.*, 1, 39–98.

Tinbergen, N. (1948) Social releasers and the experimental method required for their study. *Wilson Bull.*, 60, 6–51.

Tinbergen, N. (1951) The Study of Instinct. Clarendon Press, Oxford.

Tinbergen, N. (1952) Derived activities: their causation, biological significance, origin and emancipation during evolution. *Quart. Rev. Biol.*, 27, 1–32.

Tinbergen, N. (1953) The Herring Gull's World. Collins, London.

Tinbergen, N. (1955) In "Trans. First Conf. on Group Processes (1954)", Ed. B. Schaffner, Macy Foundation, New York.

Tinbergen, N. (1959) Comparative studies of the behaviour of gulls (*Laridae*): a progress report. *Behaviour*, 15, 1–70.

Tinbergen, N. (1962) The evolution of animal communication—a critical examination of methods. *Sym. Zool. Soc. Lond.*, 8, 1–6.

Tinbergen, N. (1963) On aims and methods of ethology. *Zeits f. Tierpsychol.*, 20, 410–433.

Tinbergen, N., Broekhuysen, G. J., Feekes, F., Houghton, J. C. W., Kruuk, H. and Szulc, E. (1962) Egg shell removal by the Black-headed Gull, *Larus ridibundus*, L.; a behaviour component of camouflage. *Behaviour*, 19, 74–117.

Tinbergen, N., Kruuk, H. and Paillette, M. (1962) Egg shell removal by the Black-headed Gull, *Larus r. ridibundus:* II. *Bird Study*, 9, 123–131.

Tinbergen, N. and Kruyt, W. (1938) Über die Orientierung des Bienenwolfes (*Philanthus triangulum* Fabr.): III. Die Bevorzugung bestimmter Wegmarken. *Zeits. vergl. Physiol.*, 25, 292–334.

Tinbergen, N. and Kuenen, D. J. (1939) Über die auslösenden und die richtunggebenden Reizsituationen der Sperrbewegung von jungen Drosseln (*Turdus m. merula* L. und *T. e. ericetorum* Turton). *Zeits f. Tierpsychol.*, 3, 37–60.

Tinbergen, N., Meeuse, B. J. D., Boerema, L. K. and Varossieau, W. W. (1943) Die Balz des Samtfalters, *Eumenis* (= *Satyrus*) *semele* (L.). *Zeits f. Tierpsychol.*, 5, 182–226.

Tinbergen, N. and Perdeck, A. C. (1950) On the stimulus situation releasing the begging response in the newly hatched Herring Gull chick (*Larus argentatus argentatus* Pont.). *Behaviour*, 3, 1–39.

Tinkelpaugh, O. L. (1928) An experimental study of representative factors in monkeys. *J. comp. Psychol.*, 8, 197–236.

Tirala, L. G. (1923) Die Form als Reiz. *Zool. Jarhb. Allg. Zool. Physiol.*, 39, 395–442.

Tobach, E. and Schneirla, T. C. (1962) Eliminative responses in mice and rats and the problem of "emotionality". In "Roots of Behavior", Ed. E. L. Bliss, Hoeber, New York.

Tolman, C. W. (1964) Social facilitation of feeding behaviour in the domestic chick. *Anim. Behav.*, 12, 245–251.

Tolman, E. C. (1932) Purposive Behavior in Animals and Men. Century, New York.

Tolman, E. C. (1959) Principles of purposive behavior. In Koch (1959).

Tolman, E. C., Ritchie, B. F. and Kalish, D. (1946–7) Studies in spatial learning: I and V. *J. exp. Psychol.*, 36, 221–229, 37, 285–292.

Toulmin, S. E. (1953) The Philosophy of Science. Hutchinson, London.

Towbin, E. J. (1949) Gastric distension as a factor in the satiation of thirst in esophagostomized dogs. *Amer. J. Physiol.*, **159**, 533–541.

Trumler, E. (1959) Das "Rossigkeitsgesicht" und ännliches Ausdrucksverhalten bei Einhufern. *Zeits f. Tierpsychol.*, **16**, 478–488.

Tsang, Y-C. (1938) Hunger motivation in gastrectomized rats. *J. comp. Psychol.*, **26**, 1–17.

Tschanz, B. (1959) Zur Brutbiologie der Trottellumme (*Uria aalge aalge* Pont.). *Behaviour*, **14**, 1–100.

Tugendhat, B. (1960a) The normal feeding behavior of the Three-spined Stickleback (*Gasterosteus aculeatus*). *Behaviour*, **15**, 284–318.

Tugendhat, B. (1960b) The disturbed feeding behavior of the Three-spined Stickleback: I. Electric shock is administered in the food area. *Behaviour*, **16**, 159–187.

Tugendhat Gardner, B. (1964) Hunger and sequential responses in the hunting behavior of Salticid spiders. *J. comp. physiol. Psychol.*, **58**, 167–173.

Tyhurst, J. S. (1951) Individual reactions to community disaster. *Amer. J. Psychiat.*, **107**, 764–769.

Uexküll, J. von, (1934) Streifzüge durch die Umwelten von Tieren und Menschen. Springer, Berlin. Translated in "Instinctive Behaviour" (1957), Ed. Schiller, C. H., Methuen, London.

Ullyott, P. (1936) The behaviour of *Dendrocoelum lacteum:* I and II. *J. exp. Biol.*, **13**, 253–264, 265–278.

Ulrich, R. E., Wolff, P. C. and Azrin, N. H. (1964) Shock as an elicitor of intra- and inter-species fighting behaviour. *Anim. Behav.*, **12**, 14–15.

Uttley, A. M. (1954) The classification of signals in the nervous system. *EEG. clin. Neurophysiol.*, **6**, 479–494.

Valenstein, E. S. and Goy, R. W. (1957) Further studies of the organization and display of sexual behavior in male guinea pigs. *J. comp. physiol. Psychol.*, **50**, 115–119.

Valenstein, E. S., Riss, W. and Young, W. C. (1955) Experiential and genetic factors in the organization of sexual behavior in male guinea pigs. *J. comp. physiol. Psychol.*, **48**, 397–403.

Verney, E. B. (1947) The antidiuretic hormone and the factors which determine its release. *Proc. Roy. Soc. B.*, **135**, 25–106.

Vernon, M. D. (1952) A further Study of Visual Perception. Cambridge Univ. Press, London.

Verplanck, W. S. (1954) Birrkus F. Skinner. In "Modern Learning Theory", ed Estes *et al.*, Appleton-Century-Crofts, New York.

Verplanck, W. S. and Hayes, J. R. (1953) Eating and drinking as a function of maintenance schedule. *J. comp. physiol. Psychol.*, **46**, 327–333.

Verwey, J. (1930) Die Paarungsbiologie des Fischreihers. *Zool. Jahrb.*, *Abt. f. allg. Zool. Physiol.*, **48**, 1–120.

Vince, M. A. (1960) Developmental changes in responsiveness in the great tit (*Parus major*). *Behaviour*, **15**, 219–243.

Vince, M. A. (1961a) Developmental changes in learning capacity. In "Current Problems in Animal Behaviour", Ed. Thorpe, W. H. and Zangwill, O. L., Cambridge Univ. Press, London.

Vince, M. A. (1961b) "String-pulling" in birds: III. The successful response in greenfinches and canaries. *Behaviour*, **17**, 103–129.

Vince, M. A. (1964a) Use of the feet in feeding by the Great Tit *Parus major*. *Ibis*, **106**, 508–529.

Vince, M. A. (1964b) Social facilitation of hatching in the Bobwhite Quail. *Anim. Behav.*, **12**, 531–534.

Vince, M. A. and Warren, R. P. (1963) Individual differences in taste discrimination in the Great Tit (*Parus major*). *Anim. Behav.*, **11**, 548–552.

Vogel, G. (1957) Verhaltensphysiologische Untersuchungen über die den Weibchenbesprung des Stubenfliegen-Männchens (*Musca domestica*) auslösenden optischen Faktoren. *Zeits f. Tierpsychol.*, **14**, 309–323.

Volkonsky, M. (1939) Sur la photo-akinèse des acridiens. *Arch. Inst. Pasteur Algér.*, **17**, 194–220.

von Buddenbrock, W. (1922) Mechanisms der phototropen Bewegungen? *Wiss. Meeresuntersuch. N. F. Abt. Helgoland*, **15**, 1–10.

Voronin, L. G. (1962) Some results of comparative-physiological investigations of higher nervous activity. *Psychol. Bull.*, **59**, 161–195.

Vowles, D. M. (1954a) The orientation of ants: I. The substitution of stimuli. *J. exp. Biol.*, **31**, 341–355.

Vowles, D. M. (1954b) The orientation of ants: II. Orientation to light, gravity and polarized light. *J. exp. Biol.*, **31**, 356–375.

Walk, R. D. (1958) "Visual" and "visual-motor" experience: a replication. *J. comp. physiol. Psychol.*, **51**, 785–787.

Walk, R. D. (1965) The study of visual depth and distance perception in animals. In "Advances in the Study of Behavior", Eds. Lehrman, D. S., Hinde, R. A. and Shaw, E., Academic Press, New York and London.

Walk, R. D. and Gibson, E. J. (1961) A comparative and analytical study of visual depth perception. *Psychol. Monogr.*, 75, 44pp.

Walk, R. D., Gibson, E. J. and Tighe, T. J. (1957) Behavior of light- and dark-reared rats on a visual cliff. *Science*, **126**, 80–81.

Walker, E. L., Dember, W. N., Earl, R. W., Fawl, C. L. and Karoly, A. J. (1955) Choice alternation: III. Response intensity vs. response discriminability. *J. comp. physiol. Psychol.*, **48**, 80–85.

Walker, K. C. (1942) Effect of a discriminative stimulus transferred to a previously unassociated response. *J. exp. Psychol.*, **31**, 312–321.

Wallace, G. K. (1962) Experiments on visually controlled orientation in the Desert Locust, *Schistocerca gregaria* (Forskål). *Anim. Behav.*, **10**, 361–369.

Wallis, D. I. (1962) Aggressive behaviour in the ant, *Formica fusca*. *Anim. Behav.*, **10**, 267–274.

Wallraff, H. G. (1960) Können Grasmücken mit Hilfe des Sternenhimmels navigieren? *Zeits f. Tierpsychol.*, **17**, 165–177.

Walther, F. (1958) Zum Kampf- und Paarungsverhalten einiger Antilopen. *Zeits f. Tierpsychol.*, **15**, 340–380.

Walther, F. (1960) "Antilopenhafte" Verhaltensweisen im Paarungszeremoniell des Okapi (*Okapia johnstoni* Sclater, 1901). *Zeits f. Tierpsychol.*, **17**, 188–210.

Warden, C. J. (1931) Animal Motivation: Experimental Studies on the Albino Rat. Columbia Univ. Press, New York.

Warren, J. M. (1957) The phylogeny of maze learning: (i) Theoretical orientation. *Brit. J. Anim. Behav.*, **5**, 90–93.

Warren, J. M. (1965) Primate learning in comparative perspective. In "Behavior of Nonhuman Primates", Vol. I, Eds. Schrier, A. M., Harlow, H. F. and Stollnitz, F., Academic Press, New York, London.

Warren, R. P. (1963) Preference aversion in mice to bitter substance. *Science*, **140**, 808–809.

Warren, R. P. and Aronson, L. R. (1957) Sexual behavior in adult male hamsters castrated-adrenalectomized prior to puberty. *J. comp. physiol. Psychol.*, **50**, 475–480.

Warren, R. P. and Hinde, R. A. (1959) The effect of oestrogen and progesterone on the nest-building of domesticated canaries. *Anim. Behav.*, **7**, 209–213.

Warren, R. P. and Hinde, R. A. (1961a) Roles of the male and the nest-cup in controlling the reproduction of female canaries. *Anim. Behav.*, **9**, 64–67.

Warren, R. P. and Hinde, R. A. (1961b) Does the male stimulate oestrogen secretion in female canaries? *Science*, **133**, 1354–1355.

Warriner, C. C., Lemmon, W. B. and Ray, T. S. (1963) Early experience as a variable in mate selection. *Anim. Behav.*, **11**, 221–224.

Wasman, M. and Flynn, J. P. (1962) Directed attack elicited from hypothalamus. *Arch Neurol.*, **6**, 220–227.

Watson, A. J. (1955) Perception. In "Experimental Psychology", Ed. Farrell, B. A., Blackwell, Oxford.

Watson, A. J. (1961) The place of reinforcement in the explanation of behaviour. In "Current Problems in Animal Behaviour", Ed. W. H. Thorpe and O. L. Zangwill, Cambridge Univ. Press, London.

Watson, J. B. (1919) Psychology from the Standpoint of a Behaviorist. Lippincott, Philadelphia.

Weasner, M. H., Finger, F. W. and Reid, L. S. (1960) Activity changes under food deprivation as a function of recording device. *J. comp. physiol. Psychol.*, **53**, 470–474.

Webb, W. B. (1949) The motivational aspect of an irrelevant drive in the behavior of the white rat. *J. exp. Psychol.*, **39**, 1–14.

Weddell, G. (1955) Somesthesis and the chemical senses. *Ann. Rev. Psychol.*, **6**, 119–136.

Weddell, G., Taylor, D. A. and Williams, C. M. (1955) Studies on the innervation of skin: III. The patterned arrangement of the spinal sensory nerves to the rabbit ear. *J. Anat. Lond.*, **89**, 317–342.

Weidmann, R. and Weidmann, U. (1958) An analysis of the stimulus situation releasing food-begging in the Black-headed Gull. *Anim. Behav.*, **6**, 114.

Weidmann, U. (1958) Verhaltensstudien an der Stockente (*Anas platyrhynchos* L.): II. *Zeits f. Tierpsychol.*, **15**, 277–300.

Weiner, I. H. and Stellar, E. (1951) Salt preference of the rat determined by a single-stimulus method. *J. comp. physiol. Psychol.*, **44**, 394–401.

Weis-Fogh, T. (1956) Biology and physics of locust flight: II. Flight performance of the desert locust (*Schistocerca gregaria*). *Phil. Trans. Roy. Soc. B.*, **239**, 459–510.

Weis-Fogh, T. (1964) Control of basic movements in flying insects. *Sym. Soc. exp. Biol.*, **18**, 343–361.

Weiskrantz, L. (1958) Sensory deprivation and the cat's optic nervous system. *Nature*, **181**, 1047–1050.

Weiskrantz, L. (1964) Neurological studies and animal behaviour. *Brit. Med. Bull.*, **20**, 49–53.

Weiskrantz, L. and Cowey, A. (1963) The aetiology of food reward in monkeys. *Anim. Behav.*, **11**, 225–234.

Weiss, P. (1941a) Does sensory control play a constructive role in the development of motor coordination? *Schweiz. Med. Wochenschr.*, **71**, 591–595.

Weiss, P. (1941b) Self-differentiation of the basic patterns of coordination. *Comp. Psychol. Monogr.*, **17**.

Weiss, P. (1950) Experimental analysis of coordination by the disarrangement of central-peripheral relations. *Sym. Soc. exp. Biol.*, **4**, 92–111.

Welford, A. T. (1962) Experimental psychology and the study of social behaviour. In

"Society: Problems and Methods of Study", Ed. Welford, A. T. *et al.*, Routledge and Kegan-Paul, London.

Welford, A. T., Brown, R. A. and Gabb, J. E. (1950) Two experiments on fatigue as affecting skilled performance in civilian air crew. *Brit. J. Psychol.*, **40**, 195–211.

Welker, W. I. (1956) Effects of age and experience on play and exploration of young chimpanzees. *J. comp. physiol. Psychol.*, **49**, 223–226.

Welker, W. I. (1964) Analysis of sniffing of the albino rat. *Behaviour*, **22**, 223–244.

Welker, W. I. and King, W. A. (1962) Effects of stimulus novelty on gnawing and eating by rats. *J. comp. physiol. Psychol.*, **55**, 838–842.

Wells, G. P. (1950) Spontaneous activity cycles in polychaete worms. *Sym. Soc. exp. Biol.*, **4**, 127–142.

Wells, G. P. (1955) The sources of animal behaviour. Inaugural lecture, Univ. Coll. Lond.

Wells, M. J. (1958) Factors affecting reactions to *Mysis* by newly hatched *Sepia*. *Behaviour*, **13**, 96–111.

Wells, M. J. (1959) Functional evidence for neurone fields representing the individual arms within the central nervous system of *Octopus*. *J. exp. Biol.*, **36**, 501–511.

Wells, M. J. (1961) Weight discrimination by *Octopus*. *J. exp. Biol.*, **38**, 127–133.

Wells, M. J. (1962a) Early learning in Sepia. *Sym. Zool. Soc. Lond.*, **8**, 149–169.

Wells, M. J. (1962b) Brain and Behaviour in Cephalopods. Heinemann, London: Stanford University Press, Stanford.

Wells, M. J. (1964a) Tactile discrimination of shape by *Octopus*. *Quart. J. exp. Psychol.*, **16**, 156–162.

Wells, M. J. (1964b) Tactile discrimination of surface curvature and shape by the Octopus. *J. exp. Biol.*, **41**, 433–445.

Wells, M. J. and Wells, J. (1957) The function of the brain of *Octopus* in tactile discrimination. *J. exp. Biol.*, **34**, 131–142.

Wendler, G. (1964) Relative Koordination erläutert an Beispielen *v.* Holst's und einem neuen Lokomotionstyp. *Biol. Jahresheft*, **4**, 157–166.

Wenner, A. M. (1962) Sound production during the waggle dance of the honey bee. *Anim. Behav.*, **10**, 79–95.

Werner, G. and Mountcastle, V. B. (1963) The variability of central nervous activity in a sensory system, and its implications for the central reflection of sensory events. *J. Neurophysiol.*, **26**, 958–977.

Whalen, R. E. (1961) Effects of mounting without intromission and intromission without ejaculation on sexual behaviour and maze learning. *J. comp. physiol. Psychol.*, **54**, 409–415.

Whalen, R. E. (1963a) The initiation of mating in naive female cats. *Anim. Behav.*, **11**, 461–463.

Whalen, R. E. (1963b) Sexual behavior of cats. *Behaviour*, **20**, 321–342.

Whalen, R. E., Beach, F. A. and Kuehn, R. E. (1961) Effects of exogenous androgen on sexually responsive and unresponsive male rats. *Endocrinology*, **69**, 373–380.

White, B. L. (1963) Plasticity in perceptual development during the first six months of life. Oral presentation to the American Association for the Advancement of Science, Cleveland, Ohio.

Whitman, C. O. (1919) The behavior of pigeons. *Publ. Carneg. Inst.*, **257**, 1–161.

Wickens, D. D., Hall, J. and Reid, L. S. (1949) Associative and retro-active inhibition as a function of the drive stimulus. *J. comp. physiol. Psychol.*, **42**, 398–403.

Wickler, W. (1958) Vergleichende Verhaltensstudien an Grundfischen: II. *Zeits f. Tierpsychol.*, **15**, 427–446.

Wickler, W. (1960) Die Stammesgeschichte typischer Bewegungsformen der Fisch-Brustflosse. *Zeits f. Tierpsychol.*, **17**, 31–66.

Wickler, W. (1961a) Ökologie und Stammesgeschichte von Verhaltensweisen. *Fortschr. der Zool.*, **13**, 303–365.

Wickler, W. (1961b) Über die Stammesgeschichte und den taxonomischen Wert einiger Verhaltensweisen der Vögel. *Zeits f. Tierpsychol.*, **18**, 320–342.

Wickler, W. (1962) Ei-Attrappen und Maulbrüten bei afrikanischen Cichliden. *Zeits f. Tierpsychol.*, **19**, 129–164.

Wiemer, F-K. (1955) Mittelhirnfunktion bei Urodelen nach Regeneration und Transplantation. *Roux' Arch. Entwicklungs-mechanik.*, **147**, 560–633.

Wiepkema, P. R. (1961) An ethological analysis of the reproductive behaviour of the bitterling. *Arch. néerl. Zool.*, **14**, 103–199.

Wiersma, C. A. G. (1931) An experiment on the "Resonance theory" of muscular activity. *Arch. néerl. Physiol.*, **16**, 337–345.

Wiersma, C. A. G., Waterman, T. H. and Bush, B. M. H. (1961) Impulse traffic in the optic nerve of decapod Crustacea. *Science*, **134**, 1435.

Wiesel, T. N. (1960) Receptive fields of ganglion cells in the cat's retina. *J. Physiol.*, **153**, 583–594.

Wiesner, B. P. and Sheard, N. M. (1933) Maternal Behaviour in the Rat. Oliver and Boyd, Edinburgh.

Wigglesworth, V. B. (1941) The sensory physiology of the human louse *Pediculus humanus corporis* de Geer (Anoplyra). *Parasitology*, **33**, 67–109.

Wigglesworth, V. B. (1949) The utilisation of reserve substances in *Drosophila* during flight. *J. exp. Biol.*, **28**, 150–163.

Wikler, A. (1952) Pharmacologic dissociation of behavior and EEG "sleep patterns' in dogs: Morphine, N-allylnormorphine, and atropine. *Proc. Soc. Exp. Biol. Med.*, **79**, 261–265.

Williams, E. and Scott, J. P. (1953) The development of social behavior patterns in the mouse, in relation to natural periods. *Behaviour*, **6**, 35–65.

Wilson, D. M. (1961) The central nervous control of flight in a locust. *J. exp. Biol.*, **38**, 471–490.

Wilson, D. M. (1964) Relative refractoriness and patterned discharge of locust flight motor neurones. *J. exp. Biol.*, **41**, 191–205.

Wilson, D. M. (in press, 1966) Insect Walking. *Ann. Rev. Ent.*

Wilson, D. M. and Gettrup, E. (1963) A stretch reflex controlling wingbeat frequency in grasshoppers. *J. exp. Biol.*, **40**, 171–185.

Wilson, D. M. and Weis-Fogh, T. (1963) Patterned activity of coordinated motor units, studied in flying locusts. *J. exp. Biol.*, **39**, 643–667.

Wilson, E. O. (1962) Chemical communication among workers of the fire ant *Solenopsis saevissima* (Fr. Smith): 3. The experimental induction of social responses. *Anim. Behav.*, **10**, 159–164.

Wilson, J. R., Kuehn, R. E. and Beach, F. A. (1963) Modification in the sexual behavior of male rats produced by changing the stimulus female. *J. comp. physiol. Psychol.*, **56**, 636–644.

Windle, W. F. (1944) Genesis of somatic motor function in mammalian embryos: a synthesizing article. *Physiol. Zool.*, **17**, 247–260.

Winn, H. E. (1957) Egg site selection by three species of darters (*Pisces, percidae*). *Brit. J. Anim. Behav.*, **5**, 25–28.

Wolda, H. (1961) Response decrement in the prey-catching activity of *Notonecta glauca* L. (Hemiptera). *Arch. néerl. Zool.*, **14**, 61–89.

Wolf, E. and Zerrahn-Wolf, G. (1937) Flicker and the reactions of bees to flowers. *J. gen. Physiol.*, **20**, 511–518.

Wolfe, J. B. (1936) Effectiveness of token-records for chimpanzees. *Comp. Psychol. Monogr.*, **12**, *No. 5.*

Wolfe, J. B. (1939) An exploratory study of food-storing in rats. *J. comp. Psychol.*, **28**, 97–108.

Wood-Gush, D. G. M. (1956) The agonistic and courtship behaviour of the Brown Leghorn Cock. *Brit. J. Anim. Behav.*, **4**, 133–142.

Woods, P. J. (1959) The effects of free and restricted environmental experience on problem-solving behavior in the rat. *J. comp. physiol. Psychol.*, **52**, 399–402.

Woodworth, R. S. (1918) Dynamic Psychology. Columbia Univ. Press, New York.

Worden, F. G. and Livingston, R. B. (1961) Brain-stem reticular formation. In Sheer (1961).

Worden, F. G. and Marsh, J. T. (1963) Amplitude changes of auditory potentials evoked at cochlear nucleus during acoustic habituation. *Electroenceph. clin. Neurophysiol.*, **15**, 866–881.

Wünschmann, A. (1963) Quantitative Untersuchungen zum Neugierverhalten von Wirbeltieren. *Zeits f. Tierpsychol.*, **20**, 80–109.

Wüstehube, C. (1960) Beiträge zur Kenntnis besonders des Spiel- und Beuteverhaltens einheimischer Musteliden. *Zeits f. Tierpsychol.*, **17**, 579–613.

Wynne, L. C. and Solomon, R. L. (1955) Traumatic avoidance learning: acquisition and extinction in dogs deprived of normal peripheral autonomic function. *Genetic Psychol. Monogr.*, **52**, 241–284.

Wyrwicka, W. and Dobrzecka, C. (1960) Relationship between feeding and satiation centers of the hypothalamus. *Science*, **132**, 805–806.

Wyrwicka, W., Dobrzecka, C. and Tarnocki, R. (1960) The effect of electrical stimulation of the hypothalamic feeding centre in satiated goats on alimentary conditioned reflexes, Type II. *Acta Biol. Exp.*, **20**, 121–136.

Yates, A. J. (1963) Delayed auditory feedback. *Psychol. Bull.*, **60**, 213–232.

Young, F. A. (1954) An attempt to obtain pupillary conditioning with infrared photography. *J. exp. Psychol.*, **48**, 62–68.

Young, J. Z. (1960) Regularities in the retina and optic lobes of *Octopus* in relation to form discrimination. *Nature*, **186**, 836–839.

Young, J. Z. (1961) Learning and discrimination in the octopus. *Biol. Rev.*, **36**, 32–96.

Young, J. Z. (1964) Paired centres for the control of attack by *Octopus. Proc. Roy. Soc. B.*, **159**, 565–588.

Young, P. T. (1949) Food-seeking drive, affective process and learning. *Psychol. Rev.*, **56**, 98–121.

Young, W. C. (1961a) Ed. "Sex and Internal Secretions". Williams & Wilkins, Baltimore.

Young, W. C. (1961b) The hormones and mating behavior. In "Sex and Internal Secretions", Ed. W. C. Young, Williams & Wilkins, Baltimore.

Young, W. C. (1965) The organization of sexual behaviour by hormonal action during the prenatal and larval periods in vertebrates. In "Sex and Behavior", Ed. F. A. Beach, Wiley, New York.

Young, W. C., Goy, R. W. and Phoenix, C. H. (1964) Hormones and sexual behavior. *Science*, **143**, 212–218.

Zeigler, H. P. (1961) Learning-set formation in pigeons. *J. comp. physiol. Psychol.*, **54**, 252–254.

Zener, K. (1937) The significance of behavior accompanying conditioned salivary secretion for theories of the conditioned response. *Amer. J. Psychol.*, **50**, 384–403.

Zerrahn, G. (1933) Formdressur und Formunterscheidung bei der Honigbiene. *Zeits. vergl. Physiol.*, **20**, 117–161.

Zimbardo, P. G. (1958) The effects of early avoidance training and rearing conditions upon the sexual behavior of the male rat. *J. comp. physiol. Psychol.*, **51**, 764–769.

Author Index

Subject and Species Index